77-2065-500M-12-62 82

## PROPERTY OF THE BOARD OF EDUCATION
CITY OF NEW YORK

Name of School ..................................................................................

Keep this book covered at all times; if any pages become loose or torn, repair them at once.

A fine will be imposed if this book is misused or if the pages on which the serial number appears is missing.

When you return the book be sure to get your original receipt or you may be called upon to pay for it. Fill out in ink, on first unoccupied line, the information called for.

| NAME FAMILY | GIVEN | OFFICIAL CLASS | DATE ISSUED | CONDITION WHEN RETURNED |
|---|---|---|---|---|
| Burgos | Miriam | E7 | 1/8/77 | |
| | | | | |
| | | | | |
| | | | | |
| | | | | |
| | | | | |
| | | | | |

# SHORT STORIES

*Edited by*
H. C. SCHWEIKERT
*Central High School, St. Louis, Missouri*

ENLARGED EDITION

HARCOURT, BRACE & WORLD, INC.
*New York Chicago Atlanta Dallas Burlingame*

COPYRIGHT, 1925, 1934, BY
HARCOURT, BRACE & WORLD, INC.

All rights reserved. No part of this book may be reproduced in any form, by mimeograph or any other means, without permission in writing from the publisher.

PRINTED IN THE U.S.A.

# ACKNOWLEDGMENTS

To the Houghton Mifflin Company for " The Postmistress of Laurel Run " and " The Father."

To Charles Scribner's Sons for " The Remarkable Wreck of the *Thomas Hyke*," " Zenobia's Infidelity," " Will o' the Mill," and Galsworthy's " Quality."

To Mr. Sinclair Lewis and the *Century Magazine* for " Young Man Axelbrod."

To Alfred A. Knopf, Inc., for " The Token " and for " A Cup of Tea," reprinted from THE DOVE'S NEST, by Katherine Mansfield.

To Miss Fannie Hurst and Harper & Brothers for " Ice Water, Pl—— ! "

To Harper & Brothers for " The Third Ingredient " and " Happiness."

To Miss Anzia Yezierska for " Hunger."

To Mrs. Frances Gilchrist Wood and the *Pictorial Review* for " Turkey Red."

To Mrs. Dorothy Canfield Fisher and Henry Holt & Company for " The Heyday of the Blood."

To Mr. Edison Marshall and *Everybody's Magazine* for " The Elephant Remembers."

To James B. Pinker & Son, of London, and Doubleday, Doran & Company for " The Inn of the Two Witches."

To Doubleday, Doran & Company, Inc., for " Penrod's Busy Day "; " Meadow Lark," from THEY BROUGHT THEIR WOMEN, copyright 1933, by Edna Ferber; and for " The Silver Mine," from THE GIRL FROM MARSHCROFT, by Selma Lagerlöf, copyright, 1910, by Doubleday, Doran & Co., Inc.

To Sir Arthur Conan Doyle and Harper & Brothers for " The Speckled Band."

To Dodd, Mead & Company for " The Monkey's Paw."

To Hodder & Stoughton, of Toronto, for " The Stove."

To E. P. Dutton & Co., Inc., for " They Grind Exceeding Small," taken from THRIFTY STOCK by Ben Ames Williams.

## Acknowledgments

To Mr. I. V. Morris and *The Story Magazine* for "The Sampler."

To the Paget Literary Agency, Inc., for "The Frill," copyright, 1933, by Pearl S. Buck, first published in the March, 1933 issue of *The Woman's Home Companion* and included in THE FIRST WIFE AND OTHER STORIES, published by the John Day Company.

# CONTENTS

|  | PAGE |
|---|---|
| ACKNOWLEDGMENTS | iii |
| CHRONOLOGICAL ORDER | vii |
| PREFACE | ix |
| HINTS TO FELLOW-WORKERS | xi |
| A WORD TO THE STUDENT | xiii |
| INTRODUCTION | xvii |
|     I. The Short Story Defined | xvii |
|     II. The Ingredients of the Short Story | xix |
|     III. Types of the Short Story | xxii |
|     IV. Historical Sketch of the Short Story | xxiv |
| THE TOKEN ........................ *Joseph Hergesheimer* | 3 |
| THE THIRD INGREDIENT ............ *O. Henry* | 32 |
| TURKEY RED ...................... *Frances Gilchrist Wood* | 47 |
| THE ELEPHANT REMEMBERS ...... *Edison Marshall* | 63 |
| THE FALL OF THE HOUSE OF USHER *Edgar Allan Poe* | 90 |
| THE POSTMISTRESS OF LAUREL RUN *Bret Harte* | 112 |
| THE AMBITIOUS GUEST ........... *Nathaniel Hawthorne* | 131 |
| PENROD'S BUSY DAY .............. *Booth Tarkington* | 142 |
| YOUNG MAN AXELBROD ........... *Sinclair Lewis* | 158 |
| ICE WATER, PL——! .............. *Fannie Hurst* | 175 |
| THE HEYDAY OF THE BLOOD ....... *Dorothy Canfield* | 205 |
| HUNGER .......................... *Anzia Yezierska* | 216 |
| THE REMARKABLE WRECK OF THE THOMAS HYKE ................. *Frank R. Stockton* | 233 |
| ZENOBIA'S INFIDELITY ........... *H. C. Bunner* | 254 |
| THE LEGEND OF SLEEPY HOLLOW ... *Washington Irving* | 266 |
| MEADOW LARK .................... *Edna Ferber* | 299 |
| THE FRILL ....................... *Pearl S. Buck* | 320 |
| THEY GRIND EXCEEDING SMALL ... *Ben Ames Williams* | 334 |
| THE SAMPLER (a short short) ...... *I. V. Morris* | 348 |
| THE SPECKLED BAND ............. *Arthur Conan Doyle* | 351 |
| THAT BRUTE SIMMONS ........... *Arthur Morrison* | 378 |
| THE MONKEY'S PAW .............. *W. W. Jacobs* | 387 |
| THE THREE STRANGERS ........... *Thomas Hardy* | 400 |

## Contents

| | PAGE |
|---|---|
| THE INN OF THE TWO WITCHES ...*Joseph Conrad* | 424 |
| THE STOVE ...*Marjorie L. C. Pickthall* | 453 |
| IN THE MATTER OF A PRIVATE ...*Rudyard Kipling* | 466 |
| A LETTER HOME ...*Arnold Bennett* | 477 |
| WILL O' THE MILL ...*Robert Louis Stevenson* | 486 |
| HOW GAVIN BIRSE PUT IT TO MAG LOWNIE ...*James Matthew Barrie* | 514 |
| QUALITY ...*John Galsworthy* | 521 |
| A CUP OF TEA ...*Katherine Mansfield* | 531 |
| HAPPINESS ...*Guy de Maupassant* | 544 |
| THE BET ...*Anton Pavlovich Chekhov* | 552 |
| THE FATHER ...*Björnstjerne Björnson* | 561 |
| ZODOMIRSKY'S DUEL ...*Alexandre Dumas* | 566 |
| THE SILVER MINE ...*Selma Lagerlöf* | 581 |
| READING LISTS ACCORDING TO TYPES | 597 |
| A LIST OF SHORT STORIES | 602 |
| BIBLIOGRAPHY | 609 |
| a. Historical and Critical | 609 |
| b. Collections of Short Stories | 610 |
| c. Books on Short Story Writing | 611 |

# CHRONOLOGICAL ORDER

For teachers who prefer to teach the stories chronologically, the following order is suggested:

## AMERICAN

| | | PAGE |
|---|---|---|
| THE LEGEND OF SLEEPY HOLLOW | Washington Irving (1783–1859) | 268 |
| THE AMBITIOUS GUEST | Nathaniel Hawthorne (1804–1864) | 132 |
| THE FALL OF THE HOUSE OF USHER | Edgar Allan Poe (1809–1849) | 92 |
| THE REMARKABLE WRECK OF THE THOMAS HYKE | Frank R. Stockton (1834–1902) | 234 |
| THE POSTMISTRESS OF LAUREL RUN | Bret Harte (1839–1902) | 113 |
| ZENOBIA'S INFIDELITY | H. C. Bunner (1855–1896) | 254 |
| THE THIRD INGREDIENT | O. Henry (1862–1910) | 33 |
| PENROD'S BUSY DAY | Booth Tarkington (1869– ) | 143 |
| TURKEY RED | Mrs. Frances Gilchrist Wood | 48 |
| THE HEYDAY OF THE BLOOD | Dorothy Canfield (1879– ) | 206 |
| THE TOKEN | Joseph Hergesheimer (1880– ) | 4 |
| YOUNG MAN AXELBROD | Sinclair Lewis (1885– ) | 159 |
| HUNGER | Anzia Yezierska (1885– ) | 217 |
| MEADOW LARK | Edna Ferber (1887– ) | 300 |
| THEY GRIND EXCEEDING SMALL | Ben Ames Williams (1889– ) | 335 |
| ICE WATER, PL——! | Fannie Hurst (1889– ) | 176 |
| THE FRILL | Pearl S. Buck (1892– ) | 322 |
| THE ELEPHANT REMEMBERS | Edison Marshall (1894– ) | 64 |
| THE SAMPLER | I. V. Morris (1903– ) | 348 |

## BRITISH

| | | |
|---|---|---|
| THE THREE STRANGERS | Thomas Hardy (1840–1929) | 401 |
| WILL O' THE MILL | Robert Louis Stevenson (1850–1894) | 488 |

## Chronological Order

|  | PAGE |
|---|---|
| THE INN OF THE TWO WITCHES ..*Joseph Conrad* (1857–1924).. | 425 |
| THE SPECKLED BAND ............*Arthur Conan Doyle* (1859–1929) ..................... | 352 |
| HOW GAVIN BIRSE PUT IT TO MAG LOWNIE ......................*James M. Barrie* (1860–  ) | 515 |
| THE MONKEY'S PAW .............*W. W. Jacobs* (1863–  )... | 388 |
| THAT BRUTE SIMMONS ...........*Arthur Morrison* (1863–  ) | 379 |
| IN THE MATTER OF A PRIVATE .....*Rudyard Kipling* (1865–  ) | 467 |
| A LETTER HOME .................*Arnold Bennett* (1867–1931).. | 478 |
| QUALITY .......................*John Galsworthy* (1867–1933) | 523 |
| THE STOVE ....................*Marjorie L. C. Pickthall* (Canadian; 1883–1922) .... | 453 |
| A CUP OF TEA ..................*Katherine Mansfield* (1888–1923) ..................... | 534 |

## CONTINENTAL

|  |  |
|---|---|
| ZODOMIRSKY'S DUEL .............*Alexandre Dumas* (1802–1870) | 567 |
| THE FATHER ...................*Björnstjerne Björnson* (1832–1910) ..................... | 562 |
| HAPPINESS .....................*Guy de Maupassant* (1850–1893) ..................... | 545 |
| THE SILVER MINE ...............*Selma Lagerlöf* (1858–  ).. | 582 |
| THE BET ......................*Anton Chekhov* (1860–1904).. | 553 |

# PREFACE

UNDOUBTEDLY the first question a reader will ask about the revised edition of SHORT STORIES is how it differs from the original edition. Seven new stories by modern writers — Selma Lagerlöf, Katherine Mansfield, Ben Ames Williams, Edna Ferber, I. V. Morris, Pearl Buck, and John Galsworthy — have been added and minor revisions in the Introduction, the notes, the questions, and the bibliographies have been made.

The next logical question is upon what basis were these particular seven stories selected. As with the original twenty-nine, they were chosen because they are more than interesting — each bears the touch of imagination which lifts it above the commonplace. The literary quality of these contributions is markedly high. Three of the authors, for example, have been awarded the Nobel Prize for Literature.

A second reason for the choices was to give greater representation to women. Since in the short story form the ratio of significant women writers is increasing, this is as it should be. " Elizabethans," it has been said, " looked through a man's eyes." We moderns can see ourselves at least half of the time as women perceive us. Among the scenes that flash in front of us when we take up these new binoculars, everyday familiar incidents are becoming more and more numerous. " A Cup of Tea " will illustrate how apt was Galsworthy's appraisal when he attributed to Katherine Mansfield " mastership of significant insignificances." An incident which would be only trivial in the hands of a lesser artist becomes in hers the revelation of a woman's entire nature. Tracing the consequences of the ordinary act of the ordering of a dress Pearl Buck's " The Frill " contrasts the startling poverty and hopelessness of the Chinese workman with the arrogant and selfish materialism of one class of Westerner.

A third reason for the choices is that the addition of four American, two English, and one European story maintains the balance of the original collection. The editor's experience that it is a happy one from the teaching standpoint has been confirmed by other teachers using the first edition.

Wider in scope and thoroughly representative, this group of thirty-six stories will be adaptable to many purposes. It can be used (*a*) to encourage and develop a pleasant reading habit, (*b*) to trace the development of story-writing during the last 130 years, (*c*) to examine the characteristics of the story as a literary form, and (*d*) perhaps to stimulate embryo writers to interpret their own experiences in short story form.

The editor of an anthology for classroom use gathers not only for those who by capacity or training recognize literary excellence but also for those who have yet to develop that taste and appreciation. This book aims to nourish both. It is hoped that students who intuitively love the best in literature will find this anthology a joy to use. For the other members of the class the editor has tried to choose examples and suggestions which will lead them to the selection of stories that do more than entertain — that stretch the boundaries of the reader's experience. That the thirty-six stories in this book intensify living in varying degrees of effectiveness constitutes part of the usefulness of the volume as a tool in the literature classroom.

But we cannot command taste. What instructor has not been irritated and what student not antagonized by the frequent claim: this book of stories and its equipment " will sharpen the critical taste." This editor promises no sure-fire reactions but humbly hopes that this book will enrich the imagination and deepen the sympathy so that reading will become a pursuit that is good in itself.

# HINTS TO FELLOW-WORKERS

THE grouping of the stories in this volume makes it convenient for classes that are studying American short stories only; otherwise there is nothing sacred about the arrangement. For the sake of those who wish to follow a strictly chronological approach a table in chronological order is included.

The compiler of this book has found that at the beginning of the study of short stories it is best to confine discussion to general values. This procedure generally leads at once to stimulating argument based on the individual preferences of the students. But from the first, every opinion should be defended with a reason. The student will find it easier to express his reasons as he progresses through the course and becomes familiar with technique and technical terms. With the awareness of a genuine sense of literary values the student will find his pleasure in reading increasing.

It has been the editor's personal experience that calling for written answers to specific questions is an effective way to combat vagueness. Blurred reactions tend to disappear in a written answer. A suggested list of questions is printed after each story.

Frankness begets frankness. The tables are often turned, and students ask the instructor his opinion. There are two missteps to avoid in such a situation: sarcasm and irony and belittling the opinions of the class. Enthusiasm, on the other hand, is contagious if it is genuine. The voluntary reading that students will do under the deft sympathy of an enthusiastic teacher is astounding.

It is the hope of the editor that teachers and students will find this book an enjoyable as well as practical manual for studying the most delightful form of prose literature.

# A WORD TO THE STUDENT

STORIES are written to entertain, to show the reader a "good time." When you pick up this book, forget that it is a textbook, prepared by an instructor, for study. Think of it rather as an agreeable companion to whom you can turn when everything else bores you.

The first thing to do with a story is to read it through at a single sitting. Forget that there are such encumbrances as dictionaries and cyclopedias and English classes. If you read a story and find it interesting, the rest will be easy.

After you have read a story, turn to the prefatory sketch of the author to find out what is said about him and his work. Compare your own general impression of the story with the opinions expressed in the sketch. When the story is discussed in class you will have opportunity to air your views, but at all times make sure that your ideas are borne out by the story. If you like the story, be able to say why. If you do not like it, why not? You will gain no credit for saying, "I don't like the story, but I can't just say why not " — or the contrary. Definite ideas can always be put into words.

After you have formed a general impression you are ready to turn to the questions. These are designed not to "catch" you but to help your understanding of the material and technique of the story. At this point you will no doubt want to read the story again, either to confirm or to attack what is suggested by the questions. Fortified by the knowledge obtained in this way, you are prepared for class discussion. Your classmates will be equally fortified, and under the guidance of the teacher you will find plenty of chance to combat one another's views, to the final benefit of everyone, especially those who are fully prepared to take active part in the discussion.

With the story now stowed away as a permanent addition to your knowledge of literature, you can turn to its more mechanical side as mere English. Ignore the words you know, but look up in the dictionary and encyclopedia those you do not know. In that way you not only will catch some of the finer shades of meaning in the story, but also will add many of these words to your own working vocabulary. It is no sin to be able to use rich and varied English. And your pronunciation! After you have learned the correct way to pronounce *inquiry* note how many of your friends say it incorrectly.

In a short story course you are going to read many stories in a comparatively short time, and no matter how vivid may be your impressions while studying a particular story, these impressions may become confused with others as you continue the course. It is an excellent mechanical device to make notes on each story as you read and study it. Such notes will be a great convenience in preparing for examinations, a real short cut, because usually they save you from re-reading the story. Scanning the notes made while the story was still fresh in your mind will readily bring back the details.

The following list of general questions will facilitate such notebook work. Not all the questions will apply equally to every story, but you will easily select the significant ones. Follow the hints of your instructor in this work, for he will be sure to have his own favorite questions. These you can add to the list.

## SUGGESTIONS FOR NOTEBOOK WORK
### GENERAL QUESTIONS

1. What type of story is this?
2. Is the title clear, inviting, short, attractive, fitting?
3. Do the characters have reality or are they only types?
4. What is the theme?
5. Is it symbolic of a greater truth or an interesting anecdote affecting only the actors?
6. State the plot in not more than two sentences.
7. Is the setting predominant?
8. Does it have any effect upon plot or characters?
9. Write down the series of incidents that create a complication.
10. Explain the complication in one sentence.
11. Is it brought about by direct action, or by some other factor?
12. Is there an element of suspense? If so, where?
13. What is the climax? Is it foreshadowed? Are there any other crises?
14. Who is the main character?
15. Is the main character introduced by description? conversation? action?
16. Is there any humor? If so, where?
17. Is there any dialect? State your opinion of its use.
18. What is the "single effect" obtained from the story?

## A Word to the Student

19. Which character stays longest in your mind? Why?
20. Is he clearly individualized?
21. Analyze the story for its fulfilment of the technical requirements.
22. Does the significance lie in factual exactness or mood?
23. Does the story end satisfactorily? Explain.
24. To make sure, try to devise a different ending.
25. Does the story contain a " surprise " element? Did it surprise you?
26. Does the author use coincidence? If so, where?
27. Is the presentation matter-of-fact, idealistic, ironic?
28. Does it persuade you of its truth while you are reading it?
29. Write down other impressions not suggested by these questions.
30. Briefly, clearly, and truthfully, did you or did you not like the story? Why?

# INTRODUCTION

## I. THE SHORT STORY DEFINED

ALL theoretical discussion of the modern short story begins with Edgar Allan Poe. In his review of Hawthorne's *Twice Told Tales,* in 1842, Poe asserts that an author must strive for a single effect to which everything else is subordinate. This effect is possible only if the story can be read at a single sitting of not more than three hours. Subsequent definitions have either retained these ideas or taken them for granted, with certain variations made necessary by the development of the art of the short story. In *A Handbook on Story Writing* Dr. Blanche Colton Williams crisply sums up the demands of the modern short story: " The short-story is a narrative artistically presenting characters in a struggle or complication which has a definite outcome."

Note the emphasis on *struggle* and *complication.* These words in their literal sense have become technical terms in the discussion of story-writing. *Struggle* implies that a character is trying to overcome some obstacle; the *complication* is the entangling circumstance; and the story consists of the manner in which all of this finally comes out. A girl has two suitors; that already suggests struggle. She loves one, but her parents want her to take the other. That complication intensifies the struggle, and the *outcome* depends upon what effect the writer intends to create. The stories " Hunger," " The Token," and " Meadow Lark " in this volume illustrate three of the infinite possibilities of the love story. A *struggle* does not necessarily have to involve more than one character; it may be an inner struggle produced by conflicting traits of character, as in " The Father " and " The Bet."

All definitions carry the implication that there must be a story, an absorbing one interestingly told, from which the reader receives artistic satisfaction. To put it colloquially, he should be able to say, " That's a good story! " If he cannot say that, there is something wrong somewhere, either in the writer and his story, or in the reader, or in all three. Only too often it is in the reader, whose tastes have become vulgarly standardized through reading one-track popular magazines and watching sentimental moving pictures. The chief note in these standards is " success." As you read this paragraph, ask yourself frankly why you like your favorite magazine. Does it feature stories in which the office boy becomes head of the company at twenty-five? or stories in which a ten-dollar-a-week salesgirl supports a family of six, and is rewarded by a mansion on upper Fifth Avenue? or stories in which an apparent numskull saves the firm a million dollars? You know the type. Now there is nothing wrong about *success*. Far from it. The trouble is that these " success " stories give a lopsided presentation of life. Where one person succeeds, in the modern sense of that term, a thousand do not. Furthermore, the stories of those who do not succeed are likely to be intrinsically more entertaining.

The " success " idea unfortunately also carries with it that other bugaboo of the modern story, the " happy ending." Librarians and clerks in bookstores tell a sad tale of the many prospective customers who look at the ending of a book before they decide to read or buy. Writers who know better, and who would prefer to do better, must cater to prevailing tastes if they hope to sell their wares. Of course there are honorable exceptions, but their works appear less often in the " popular " magazines.

In itself there is nothing wrong with a happy ending, but it should not be made the ultimate test of a story. A reader should not ask, " Does it end happily? " but, " Does it end right? " From the circumstances of the story, is the conclusion inevitable? Examine the work of Mr. Hergesheimer, for instance. " The Token " ends both happily and right. His novel *Balisand* (1924) ends right, but far from happily. The heroine falls downstairs and breaks her neck early in the story, while the hero is killed in a duel on the last page. It was inevitable that he should be killed. Similarly, Hazen Kinch's character makes his son's death inevitable in " They Grind Exceeding Small."

Again, what story would there have been in " The Ambitious Guest " if the young stranger had lived to achieve his ambitions and returned to marry the daughter? Yet today many a magazine editor would demand just that. It would then be a typical "success" story. Apply the idea to "Zodomirsky's Duel," in which a clever French author has captured the very spirit and atmosphere of his Russian setting. A possible happy ending hangs by a thread. Does the author end the story right? An easy way of turning "The Sampler" into a "success" story will occur to the reader.

In reading the stories presented in this book the student should pause a moment to reflect on the artistic phase of fiction-writing and fiction-reading. It is only by conscious study of the art of fiction that he will form what every intelligent reader at heart desires — a really keen sense of literary appreciation. And that is one of the best ways to get close to the writer's intention. After reading a number of these stories, after having studied them through the suggestive questions and the directions of the instructor, after having discussed them in class, the student can readily test himself and his powers of appreciation by applying what he has learned to the stories in his favorite magazine.

II. THE INGREDIENTS OF THE SHORT STORY

The fundamental essentials of all stories are *characters, setting,* and *plot.*

*Characters* are the persons of the story. They may be described by the author, as in "The Legend of Sleepy Hollow"; indirectly, as in "The Monkey's Paw" or "The Silver Mine," mainly through conversation; or indirectly by action, as in "Turkey Red." By whatever method they are introduced, characters must at once be convincing to the reader.

*Setting* furnishes the background, including *place where, time when,* and *conditions under which* a story is laid. On the stage this background is usually supplied by what is called a stage "set," which consists of the scenery and all stage "properties," including costumes. By these mechanical means it becomes easy to provide atmosphere in a play. If the curtain goes up on the battlements of a medieval castle, patrolled by knights in clanking armor, the audience adapts its mood to the atmosphere of the age of chivalry. The action and the dialogue must be consistent with this atmosphere. In a story, the author has to create similar effects through words, either direct description, as in "The Third Ingredient," or subtle suggestion as in

"The Father," or conversation, as in "Ice Water, Pl —— !" Seldom is one method used to the exclusion of the others, and at all times the details of the setting must be so commingled with the action that the movement of the story is not impeded. To appreciate a story fully the reader must accept the conditions of time, place, and circumstances, and the writer himself must not transgress the limits he has set. "The Fall of the House of Usher" is a remarkable example of how this harmony can be effected.

The *plot* consists of a carefully chosen series of incidents so contrived as to create a complication in the lives of the characters. Usually all these incidents lead up to what develops into the turning-point of the story, the *climax*. This may be at the end of the story, as in "The Token" or "They Grind Exceeding Small," or it may be some distance from the end, as in "The Inn of the Two Witches." The action up to the turning-point is called the involution of the plot; from that point on it becomes the evolution. Someone has said more simply that plot is nothing more than getting characters into trouble, and then getting them out again. To refer to Poe again, the "single effect" may be gained through plot, through character, through setting, or through a combination of all of them.

In order to facilitate analytic discussion of stories the student should familiarize himself with certain other terms in common use.

*Action* consists of the series of incidents that make up the story. The movement depends upon how swiftly or slowly things happen. Compare "The Speckled Band" with "The Frill."

An *incident* is anything that happens. Ichabod Crane receives an invitation to the party; again, he encounters the Headless Horseman. These are incidents. Theoretically, everything we do, or anything we have done to us, is an incident. A student's coming to class is an incident in his daily life; being called on and making a perfect recitation, or a flat failure, is another. Having a hand crushed in a street-car crash on his way to school is an incident to which we ordinarily refer as an *accident*. Receiving his diploma at commencement is the culminating incident of school or college life. It is obvious that these incidents vary in intensity, and they do not necessarily suggest a story.

A *crisis* is an incident that causes a permanent change in the life of one or more of the characters. Ichabod Crane's conversation with Katrina, for instance, and, in " Young Man Axelbrod," the hero's determination to go to college, are crises.

A *climax* is an intensified crisis, an event that makes the greatest change in the life or destiny of a person or character. When the Headless Horseman pitches his " head " at Ichabod the ignominy of that pedagogue is complete. Axelbrod's night out with the young poet is another excellent example of climax.

The *theme* is the idea behind the story, the idea that the author intends to develop through the telling of his tale. This idea the writer draws from the material out of which he makes his story. In a newspaper Hawthorne saw an account of a mountain slide which, by a peculiar freak of circumstance, killed a family. Had the family remained in the house they would have been safe. That constitutes the material of " The Ambitious Guest." In this material, besides its dramatic possibilities, the author saw an idea to be developed. To make the idea more interesting he introduced the young ambitious stranger into the family group. He too is enveloped in the tragedy. Ambition, however noble, is of no avail against Fate. That is the theme. An author has his theme in mind, consciously or subconsciously, before he begins to write; the reader deduces it from the finished story. In well-constructed stories the theme pervades the whole; it is not obvious nor obtrusive; it harmonizes with the characters, setting, and incidents so as not to destroy the unified impression.

Great skill is needed to integrate the theme with the story. Even artists of first rank at times become mere propagandists. A skillful handling of one of the important themes of this century can be studied in " Quality." Galsworthy gives poignant expression to the impact of the machine age upon the individual craftsman.

The *moral* is the meaning or lesson that the reader draws from the story. Note carefully the distinction between moral and theme. Students often confuse the two, a confusion that is natural because after all the only difference is that of point of view. The *theme* presents the viewpoint of the author; the *moral* is the final reaction of the reader. The author was able to develop his theme through observation and experience in life; the reader accepts the moral because it means something to him, or gives him a new angle on life's complexities. In short, the moral enriches his own philosophy of life.

The theme and the moral are not always so obvious as in Hawthorne's story used for illustration, and there are many good stories in which either one or the other appears but faintly, if at all. A writer's intention may be nothing more than to amuse the reader, as in " Zenobia's Infidelity." But the world's greatest stories, both long and short, base their themes on the most significant of human traits and emotions and conflicts — love, jealousy, hate, pride, humility, anger, fear, courage, ambition, terror, and the infinite variations of all of these.

Students should not get the idea that a story, to be considered good, must bristle with a brave array of all the technical elements discussed in the preceding paragraphs. Some stories may have them all, but most do not. Furthermore, this study of technical terms is merely one of the steps in the direction of short story appreciation. Nor must students be deceived into believing that a given formula will produce willy-nilly a story. This is frequent bait used by correspondence courses in writing. A short story should be " experience transmuted " so as to give " proportion and meaning to life." Far more helpful advice is that of the artist skeptic who said, " You should learn technique only to forget it."

Some modern writers have ignored conventional form and have been, nevertheless, so persuasive in suggesting the four dimensions of life that we are willing to agree that with these particular artists that substance is all-important. Compare, for instance, " A Cup of Tea " with " The Third Ingredient " or " The Matter of a Private." What makes " The Sampler " a short story?

### III. TYPES OF THE SHORT STORY

For the sake of convenience in this study, stories are grouped into certain *types,* depending upon the sort of thing emphasized in the particular story. After having mastered the technical terms the student will find nearly all of the following typenames self-explanatory, but a dictionary will be useful.

1. Tale
2. Fable
3. Legend
4. Plot
5. Setting
6. Dramatic Incident
7. Mystery
8. Supernatural

## Introduction

9. Ghost
10. Detective-Ingenuity
11. Humor
12. Psychological
13. Problem
14. Local Color — Regional
15. Atmosphere
16. Theme
17. Love
18. Animal
19. Terror
20. Adventure
21. Dialect
22. Character
23. Fantasy
24. Cross-section

In classifying stories as to type two important facts should be borne in mind. First, that such classifying is a valuable mental gymnastic. It develops the student's analytic powers; it makes him pay close attention to the mechanics of literary form; it stimulates critical judgment; and all this not only fixes the story in his mind, but also helps him toward an appreciation of literary values. In the second place, students will find that but few stories even approach the single type effect. No story can be all plot, for instance. In fixing the type to which a story belongs it is customary to do so through the predominant emphasis. There can be no doubt about " Zenobia's Infidelity." It is a humorous story, an animal story, and is set within a love story. But it is primarily humorous. " The Heyday of the Blood " is a character story with a strong tinge of local color. If more than one feature stands out prominently a type may be hyphenated. " The Fall of the House of Usher " may be classified as atmosphere-terror; " The Inn of the Two Witches," as dramatic incident-mystery-terror. On the whole, however, it is best to avoid being unduly minute in classifying; otherwise the process may become as ridiculous as that of Polonius in *Hamlet* where he winds up his classification of plays as " tragical-comical-historical-pastoral."

Finally, it should be remembered that all study and discussion of technical details is only a means to an end — that of developing a healthy literary sense. Stories are written to be enjoyed. They must *entertain*, in the best sense of that term. If they fail in that, they just *fail*. Not all stories will entertain all persons in the same degree. Tastes differ here, as in everything else. One person likes oranges; another prefers bananas. One person likes a plot story; another a character story; and still another finds his greatest enjoyment in stories of setting. An ideal story would be one in which all three basic elements would be equally stressed. Of these there are not many. Perhaps " The Token," in this volume, comes close to this ideal.

The final test of a story should be the answer to this query: Has the author taken an interesting idea, and has he developed it logically, convincingly, and artistically, so that when the reader comes to the end he can say, "That's a good story"? A student should be able to carry the test further by being able to say why it is good.

### IV. HISTORICAL SKETCH OF THE SHORT STORY

Among the English-speaking peoples the short story is the most popular of all literary forms. It has also the added distinction of being the oldest. In tracing its history the term "short story" is used in the widest and most literal sense, to distinguish a brief narrative from a long one. The highly technical product described in previous paragraphs represents the culminating point in a history of story-telling that reaches back to primitive man. About him little enough is known. Doubtless, however, his fundamental human instincts were not unlike our own. Of these none is more universal than the delight everyone takes in talking about himself. In such talk there is always a bit of fiction, and undoubtedly the caveman embellished the tales of his battles with giant rhinoceros much as men do today when they tell about their hunting and fishing adventures. The story material was there, though limitations of language made the stories simple. In a way, the history of the short story becomes a study of the manner in which succeeding ages handled narrative material, how the hoarse guttural grunts of the savage developed into the literary art demanded today.

The first advance was the growth of spoken language as a medium for story-telling. Many famous stories in literature originated as tales told by wandering minstrels. Blind Homer chanted his stories of Troy to street-corner audiences in ancient Athens; troubadours and Minnesingers of the Middle Ages roamed from castle to castle to sing the great deeds of heroes. Stories of gods and heroes, adventure and great deeds, and the wonders of a universe far more mysterious to them than to us moderns — such was the material used by the early storytellers. With the invention of writing, stories of these types were the first to be written. The oldest known today were deciphered from the crumbling papyri of ancient Egypt, supposedly 6000 years old. Adventure in war or in the hunt constitutes the chief note in these tales — anecdotes or episodes loosely strung out — which, however, always contain a generous admixture of the fabulous and the marvelous. *Tales of the Magicians* is the title given to this collection of the oldest known short stories. In them there is no effort at characterization, no coherence. Irrelevant details are as common as in the gossipy yarns told over the back fence — or in the school yard.

Not unsimilar to these tales of old is the folklore of today. Contributions to our American literature have been made by Negroes, lumberjacks, cowboys, sailors, and others. A good example of the incredulous yarns which circulate about the fire in loggers' camps is the Paul Bunyan Saga. Many of these tall stories have been gathered and written down by James Stevens. Students will enjoy looking up his collection.

The *Iliad* and the *Odyssey*, written nearly 3000 years ago, show an almost unbelievable advance in the art of story-telling, but fundamentally the material remains the same — great deeds in war, adventures of favorite heroes, and struggle with Fate thinly disguised under the names of deities. In the *Odyssey* the incidents cohere, though somewhat indifferently, around a central figure. There is a theme, but no plot; struggle without a complication. After an adventurous twenty years the long-wandering Odysseus is safe at last in the arms of his faithful wife Penelope. Many of the individual episodes come near being short stories, as the adventure with the Cyclops, or the trick by which Odysseus escaped the artful wiles of Circe. Knowing nothing about plot, the Greeks desired one thing above all else — a glorified hero whose deeds were told in beautiful poetry.

It is interesting to note that the short story in prose is found more frequently in Greek literature than is commonly supposed, especially when Greek literature is understood to include everything written in the Greek language. The historians Xenophon and Herodotus often introduce stories into their works. Herodotus was a born story-teller, and at least two of the episodes in his *History* (fifth century B.C.) are still enjoyable, " Polycrates and His Ring " and " Arion and the Dolphin." The *Dialogues* of Plato, although primarily intended for instruction, are nevertheless cast in story form. What story could be more simple and more touchingly direct than the series of episodes that reach their tragic climax in the death of Socrates?

Simpler in form are the *Fables* of Aesop, originating perhaps as early as the sixth century B.C. In their present form they are attributed to the third century of our era. Their popularity has continued down to the present day. As a form of literature, the fable was destined to have important bearing on the short story of a later day, and will be referred to again.

Among the many Greek writers whose work was done in Rome at least two may be mentioned: Dion Chrysostom, an orator of the first century, who illumined his discourses with stories, the best known being that charming tale, "The Hunters of Euboea," extolling the serenity of life in the country; and the poet Lucian of the second century, whose *Dialogues* are satires, more or less genial, sometimes witty, and often humorous.

The Golden Age of Roman Literature was in the main a conscious echo or imitation of the Greek. Virgil's *Aeneid* at once suggests Homer. It contains a number of detached episodes, the best of which is the tragic story of Dido, the lovelorn queen of Carthage. But much more impressive from the short story point of view is the work of the poet Ovid (first century), who tells many lively tales in his *Metamorphoses*. Turning to prose we find that the Roman historians, unlike the Greek, rarely introduced into their work anything resembling the short story. A possible exception is the story of "Romulus and Remus" as told by Livy (first century). But there were a number of minor writers in the first and second centuries who wrote prose short stories. Petronius Arbiter is known for his "Matron of Ephesus" and "Trimalchio's Dinner"; Aulus Gellius for "Androcles and the Lion"; Pliny the Younger for his *Letters,* in which he often tells stories; and Apuleius for "Cupid and Psyche," by all odds the best short story of classical antiquity.

But classical antiquity is not the whole of antiquity. In ancient Hebrew literature the "Book of Ruth" (fifth century B.C.) and the "Book of Esther" (second century B.C.) approach the short story form. The "Book of Jonah" (third century B.C.) also makes an excellent story when shorn of some of its extraneous matter. In the *New Testament* the story of "The Prodigal Son" is a remarkable example of the effect on Hebrew literature of a touch of the art of the Greeks.

In the literature of the Middle Ages there is a bewildering mass of stories that are short. These are of all kinds — stories of the old hero type, (in fact, many of the classical heroes were revived), stories told for entertainment, and, more important, stories told to teach a lesson. The last are usually called *didactic,* and were the result of the impress of the medieval church upon a vast population as yet ignorant. The drama had been suppressed, but stories were told and written down by men who either felt their value as part of social history, or who wished simply to make more permanent such stories as served for entertainment or instruction. Characterization became more lifelike through the use of human beings instead of haloed heroes who hobnobbed familiarly with gods. But these medieval tales were dominated by the marvelous, and superimposed upon the story of an otherwise normal man the framework of the supernatural. Not all stories were of that type, but writers never hesitated to employ dragons, witches, or fairies to get the desired results. Love for the marvelous is an inherent human trait, and readers of today still enjoy ghost and mystery stories, the modern survivals of the ancient type.

During the Middle Ages, that is, between the fifth and the fifteenth centuries, the history of continental Europe was turned topsy-turvy by certain great movements more or less closely allied, and all of tremendous import in the history of storytelling. There were the barbarian invasions which produced the so-called Dark Ages; there was the spread of Christianity; the Feudal Age with its accompanying Age of Chivalry; the Revival of Learning; and the Age of Romance. There were also changes in language as the various national groups began to form. The classical Latin of what had once been the Roman Empire definitely evolved into the French, Italian, Spanish, and the other Romance languages as they are known today.

The earliest prose stories in Italian date back to the middle of the thirteenth century, when some unknown Florentine made a collection of one hundred old stories (*Il Cento Novelle Antiche*), gathered from classical, oriental, and medieval sources. About the middle of the following century Boccaccio (1313-1375) wrote the *Decameron*, another collection of one hundred tales. The *Decameron* deservedly stands out as a landmark in the history of the short story because of the literary skill with which the stories are constructed, and the excellent prose style in which they are written. Boccaccio was a Humanist; that is, he believed that literature should have a direct relation to life as it has to be lived here and now. He therefore made his stories deal with the life of his own day. Moreover, he contrived a scheme which bound these hundred stories together. Seven women and three men take refuge from the plague in a villa outside of Florence. In order to while away the tedium of their enforced stay they plan that each one in the party tell a story every day, for ten days.

The framework idea won immediate and lasting popularity. It has been frequently imitated both in Italy and in other countries. Boccaccio's countrymen Straparola, Cinthio, and Bandello made collections similar to the *Decameron*. In France, Margaret of Navarre issued the *Heptameron*. In England Chaucer modified the framework to support his *Canterbury Tales;* Gower his *Confessio Amantis*. In America, centuries later, Longfellow used it for *Tales of a Wayside Inn*. Not only has the framework of the early Italian collections been used repeatedly, but many of the actual stories as well. Writers of nearly all countries have searched these collections for story hints. For instance, Shakespeare took the plot of *Cymbeline* from one of Boccaccio's stories; Longfellow paraphrased another in *Ser Federigo's Falcon*.

In France there was great literary activity prior to the fifteenth century. From the short story point of view, the earliest development was in the *chansons de gestes* and the *contes dévots*, the function of the one being to entertain, of the other to instruct. The *chansons de gestes*, songs of great deeds, eventually flowered into the metrical romance, which many writers believe to be the richest literary achievement of the Middle Ages. The most famous metrical romance of France is the *Roman de la Rose;* the best in English is *Sir Gawain and the Green Knight*. Religious allegory was often foisted upon the metrical romance, probably because of the popularity of the *contes dévots*. By a judicious admixture of this kind of allegory, stories of love and adventure could be embodied in the metrical romances without encountering the censure of the church.

## Introduction

As already indicated, the grouping of stories remained in vogue. Sometimes they were grouped intentionally, sometimes not. There may be a central character, as in the Charlemagne cycle; a scheme of narration, as in the *Decameron;* a definite purpose, as in the *Gesta Romanorum;* or the appearance of some character or characters in successive independent stories, as in the *Morte d'Arthur.* Writers of today by no means despise the last method; Conan Doyle, for instance, with his Sherlock Holmes. In the Middle Ages the *contes dévots* tended to group themselves around the Virgin Mary, the best example in English being "The Prioress's Tale" by Chaucer. In France the *chansons de gestes* flourished enormously, the most important group being that which developed into *The Song of Roland.*

But other types of stories began to find favor early in the Middle Ages, and by the fifteenth century some of them had grown into a highly finished product, especially in France, and to a less extent in England after the Norman Conquest. One form that achieved early popularity was the *fabliau,* which, as the name indicates, was closely related to the fable. The *fabliaux* were stories told frankly to entertain. There was humor of a kind, and, in accordance with the spirit of the times, some sort of moral tacked on. This was especially true of the beast-*fabliau,* in which the characters were animals endowed with human traits — really long drawn out fables. In both varieties of the *fabliau* a definite attempt was made to represent the life of the day. Satiric or ironic reflections on that life were not uncommon in these stories. In English an early example of the *fabliau* is "Dame Siriz," of the thirteenth century, and the best beast-*fabliaux* are the "Vox and the Wolf" of the same century, and Chaucer's "Nun's Priest's Tale" of the following century. The last two make interesting reading today.

A less known story form was the *lai,* a sort of fairy tale made popular in the twelfth century by a Frenchwoman, Marie de France, who lived for a time in England but wrote in French. The best example of the *lai* in English is the tale of "Orfeo and Heurodis," a medieval variation of the old story of Orpheus and Eurydice. These stories are in verse, but there is a fine prose translation of some of the *lais* of Marie de France. Practically all the types so far discussed are represented in the two great

English collections of the fourteenth century, *The Canterbury Tales* of Chaucer (1340–1400), and *The Confessio Amantis* of Gower (1325–1408).

There remain two great medieval prose collections, the *Gesta Romanorum* and *The Thousand and One Nights*. Neither can be dated accurately or placed definitely. The *Gesta Romanorum*, or *Deeds of the Romans*, may go back as far as the thirteenth century. The stories were written in Latin; they have little to do with the Romans; the collection was made in England; and when printed in 1471 there were 181 stories — those are the known facts. The nature of the stories and the way they are told indicate that they were at least nominally made for the use of priests. The facts of each story are quickly disposed of, and the moral, or *exemplum*, as it was called, often takes up by far the longer part of the story. The *Gesta Romanorum* was tremendously popular throughout the medieval Christian world, and many a later writer has turned to it for story material and themes. The curious reader will find it not uninteresting to read the English translation. Crude as the stories are, devoid of literary form, they nevertheless contain the germ of the modern short story.

Utterly different is the content of *The Thousand and One Nights*, better known as *The Arabian Nights' Entertainments*. The last word in the second title adequately states their purpose. When they were collected, and by whom, is not known. They probably originated in Persia and were translated, paraphrased, and enlarged in the Arabic version made in Egypt. The oldest manuscript is dated 1548, but not until the beginning of the eighteenth century were these spicy tales given wide circulation in a French translation. It is rather disconcerting to learn that the original Arabic manuscript does not contain either the story of "Ali Baba" or that of "Aladdin and His Lamp." These two favorites of English readers were added after the collection became popular on the Continent. "Ali Baba" may be the creation of the Frenchman who made the first translation, based perhaps on a story he had heard somewhere in the Orient. The origin of Aladdin is totally unknown. The first English translations were made in the nineteenth century.

The sixteenth, seventeenth, and eighteenth centuries offer little that is important for a condensed sketch of the short story.

All countries were frequently in the throes of political readjustments, and conditions were such that conscious literary art was content to follow set lines. In England the drama overshadowed everything else. Even so, some of the Elizabethan dramatists, notably Greene and Dekker, found time to write short stories. In Spain, Cervantes introduced a number of short tales into *Don Quixote*, and wrote a series of *Exemplary Novels* that may be classed as long short stories. But the Spanish short story before the middle of the nineteenth century offers little of interest to the modern reader. In the Teutonic countries early traditions and myths had been gathered into cycles somewhat like those in France. In Scandinavia the *Volsunga Saga* and the *Eddas* contain stories resembling the *chansons de gestes* in so far as they have to do with heroes and their exploits, but the style and spirit of these stories is much more rugged than the French. The *Nibelungen Lied* of Germany may be considered as a compound of the *chansons de gestes* and the wonder element of the metrical romance. The *fabliau* was also very popular. But German literature is not important in the history of the modern short story, with the single exception presently to be noted.

In England the rise and growth of the periodical essay in the eighteenth century strikes the one progressive note. The essays of Addison, Steele, Defoe, and Johnson contain a number of stories. Addison's "Vision of Mirza" is an interesting combination of the Oriental tale and the *exemplum* type. Contemporary with this English group was the Frenchman Voltaire, who wrote a number of stories that are fairly short, especially "Candide" and "Zadig."

As we look back to see in perspective what has so far been said of the development of the short story, two things stand out: one, that there have always been stories that are short; the other that the universal popular interest was gradually demanding and receiving better stories from the literary artists who practiced in the form. The eighteenth century writers enriched their stories by character analysis and lively incidents. Plot only was needed to perfect stories both long and short, and this final touch was given by Samuel Richardson's *Pamela*, a long novel written in the form of letters.

The real dawn of the short story appeared with the nineteenth century and, strangely enough, it was from Germany that one of the important immediate influences came. Incidentally, this is the only contribution that German literature has made to the advancement of the modern short story. Even this contribution was in material and theme only, not in construction. In Germany mystic tales of horror and the supernatural were written in abundance by such writers as Tieck, Zschokke, and E. T. W. Hoffmann. There were similar stories in England, *The Mysteries of Udolpho* and *The Castle of Otranto*, and these, while they are not to be classed as short stories, indicate an important tendency of the times when the short story was about to be born. Hoffmann especially influenced Irving and Poe, and to a less extent Hawthorne in America, and Scott in England.

The immediate popularity of Irving's stories in England and America, and Scott's novels everywhere, indicated a rapidly growing fondness for all sorts of fiction. The time was ripe for some story-telling genius to develop the new type by stories of his own, or to define that type accurately. It happened that an American did both, first by stories of his own, and then by an essay which remains a criterion. This American, of course, was Edgar Allan Poe, and the essay was his review of Hawthorne's *Twice Told Tales*, to which reference was made earlier in this Introduction.

From this point on, that is to say, from about the middle of the nineteenth century, a brief sketch can do little more than list names and cite tendencies. For more elaborate treatment the student is referred to works listed in the bibliography. In America the traditions of Irving, Poe, and Hawthorne have been carried on by a brilliant group of writers, many of whom became known almost entirely for their work in the short story. Old types of stories were adapted to more modern conditions — the detective story, for instance. The weird horrors of "The Murders in the Rue Morgue" have been supplanted by the sheer cleverness of *The Adventures of Sherlock Holmes*. New types of stories sprang into being. In the late '60's and early '70's Bret Harte and Mark Twain were the first to write "local color" stories, now sometimes called "regional"; Thomas Bailey Aldrich wrote "Marjorie Daw," still one of the most remarkable "surprise" stories; then in the '80's came a new variety of local color stories which achieved their effect mainly through dialect, such as the Uncle Remus tales of Joel Chandler Harris, and the stories of old Virginia by Thomas Nelson Page.

The local colorists have been both numerous and prolific. George W. Cable wrote of the old Creole days in New Orleans; Hamlin Garland chose the Middle West; James Lane Allen's best tales have their setting in the Bluegrass region of Kentucky; Mary E. Wilkins Freeman and Alice Brown portray life in New England; and Ambrose Bierce revived the sordid horrors of the Civil War. Among the early humorous writers were Mark Twain, Frank R. Stockton, and H. C. Bunner. Ring Lardner and George Ade are considered by many to be their successors in the field today. Henry James and Edith Wharton gave a limited vogue to the sophisticated international story as well as the psychological, while Jack London flashed out the story of adventure. O. Henry, Jack-of-all-trades that he was, wrote all kinds.

Hundreds of other names clamor for mention. For the moment the important fact is that writers are constantly endeavoring to improve the technique of their stories without sacrificing the elements that interest the reader. Characterization, plot, and style all have their advocates. The lesson of Poe has been well learned.

Of other countries France alone approaches America in the quantity and quality of its short stories, with Russia a close third. In France the theories of Poe found ready adoption because the French are an artistic people, and because the writers of that country have always emphasized style as the prime essential of any art. That is all that need be said here, aside from the mere mention of names, such as Théophile Gautier, Prosper Mérimée, Gustave Flaubert, François Coppée, Guy de Maupassant, Alphonse Daudet, Emile Zola, and Anatole France.

The Russians also acknowledge their debt to Poe, although the work of Pushkin, Russia's first short story writer, resembles the loosely strung tale of Irving. In the Russian short story the chief note is what may be called "local color pessimism," a constant recital of the hard knocks the middle and lower classes receive. Besides Alexander Pushkin, the following are noted for their short stories: Feodor Dostoevski, Nikolai Gogol, Ivan Turgenev, Leo Tolstoi, Anton Chekhov, Leonid Andreev, Vladimir Korolenko, Alexander Kuprin, and Maxim Gorki.

In England the short story has developed more slowly than elsewhere, and only in the first quarter of the twentieth century has the abundance of production been what might be expected of a nation that has so many excellent novelists. Nor has the English short story achieved the distinction of the American, French, or Russian. English critics reluctantly admit this, but they can proudly add, " Well, at least we have Stevenson and Kipling! " Those two take rank with the best of all time. It is no discredit to either to add that Stevenson was influenced by the high moral tone of Hawthorne, and that Kipling's regional stories were made possible by Bret Harte.

One reason for the tardy growth of the short story in England may be that fiction writers prefer the novel to the shorter form. That preference also accounts for the fact that the English write the best novels. Scott, Dickens, Thackeray, Eliot, Trollope, Hardy, and Conrad, to name only a few, are all at their best in the novel. Doyle, Morrison, Barrie, and Jacobs have written novels, although their short work ranks higher. Stevenson and Kipling stand out preëminently as short story writers, yet even they have written novels. Writers of today show a tendency to practice the shorter form, and already an improvement in quality is noticeable. Some excellent stories have been written by James Barrie, Arnold Bennett, and John Galsworthy, while Katherine Mansfield has probably achieved a uniform perfection in story-writing equalled by few other authors.

Translation has made it possible for English readers to enjoy the best modern stories from all languages. French and Russian have been mentioned in previous paragraphs. Many striking stories, two of which appear in this volume, have been written in the Scandinavian countries. In modern Italian literature are such names as D'Annunzio, Papini, and Pirandello, all three better known for other forms; and Giovanni Verga, Mathilde Serao, and Grazia Deledda, favorably known for their short stories. Spain offers a good list of short story writers, most of them but little known in America: Becquer, Valera, Palacio Valdés, Alarcón, Pardo Bazán, Baroja, Valle-Inclan, and Blasco Ibañez. Some stories of all these authors are available for the English reader. It is regrettable that the same cannot be said for the Spanish-American countries. Recent years have seen the appearance in English of volumes of Roumanian, Greek, Czecho-Slovakian, and Polish stories. A compilation published in 1924 contains translations from twenty-two Continental countries.

Finally, a word should be said about the American magazine. Ever since the days of Poe it has flourished, and never more than now. The short story is its chief offering, with few exceptions. Many of these magazines blatantly announce themselves as exploiting single types — *detective, love, mystery, sea, western, adventure,* and *true* stories. The worst feature of several that boast extraordinary circulation is the " business success " story, a type that overpraises one of the thinnest of American virtues — the breakneck pursuit of the Almighty Dollar.

But in spite of everything that can be said negatively of the modern magazine, it remains true that in those vast colorful ever-changing piles on nearly every street corner there are many excellent stories, well constructed and well written. Better still, many of them find their way into book form, and thus gain greater permanency. A successful author has little difficulty in getting his short stories published in individual volumes, but many stories make their first book appearance in anthologies. These are of two kinds, those made for class use, such as this book, and those that make a serious attempt to evaluate the annual output of short stories, like the yearly volumes under the supervision of Mr. Edward J. O'Brien and Dr. Blanche Colton Williams, listed in the bibliography.

We of the twentieth century live in the Age of the Short Story!

# SHORT STORIES

# JOSEPH HERGESHEIMER
## (1880–    )

Mr. Joseph Hergesheimer is today primarily known as a novelist, but in recent years he seems to have found increasingly more time for the short story. For many years he wrote before he scored what we call a "popular hit," but his earlier stories were favorably received by the critics, and it is still the opinion of many that *The Three Black Pennys* (1917) is the best thing he ever did. This book really consists of three novelettes loosely connected, representing three generations of the same family, pioneers in the iron industry of Pennsylvania.

That his writing career was not an easy one is proved by his own assertion that he wrote steadily for fourteen years before he was able to market any of his work. What he means by "steadily" we are not quite sure. From his own account of his earlier life we may draw the hint that during those fourteen years he did a good many other things besides writing, as one would expect in a young man much interested in life.

Born in Philadelphia in 1880, Mr. Hergesheimer was brought up in a family plentiful in striking personalities — a grandfather, several great-aunts, an aunt, besides his parents. He was not strong physically, so he was allowed to idle away his boyhood almost at will. Books there were, and these he read, many of the kind that we now rather belittle because of their exaggerated sentiment. His formal schooling was limited to a few years in a Quaker institution in his native city, and again we have his own word that his career there was undistinguished.

At seventeen he determined to be an artist; at least he became an art student in the Philadelphia Academy of Fine Arts. How "steadily" he pursued art may be gleaned from the fact that he worked in the Academy two whole days per month! Then followed a number of vagabonding years, including a visit to Venice, made possible by a legacy from his grandfather. When his money was gone he returned to America, with more time spent in roaming, until he at last decided to be a novelist. That was about the year 1900; fourteen years later his first novel was published, *The Lay Anthony*.

Since then he has written steadily enough; nearly every year a new novel appears from his pen. Many of his short stories have been put between covers, but many still await that distinction.

The qualities that make for success in his novels repeat themselves in his shorter tales. He likes to throw his story against a background of tradition or history, or both, which invariably helps to intensify the effect he tries to create. *The Three Black Pennys* has already been cited. In *Balisand* (novel, 1924) he uses the years immediately following the Revolution, and in addition, the long Virginia tradition of the Bale family from which he takes his hero. Similarly, in *Java Head*, an earlier novel, he places his story in the days when Salem, Massachusetts, was still an important seaport.

"The Token," printed here, might easily have been made into a novel like *Java Head*. The material is similar, illustrating the point just made — a background of family and long custom, the story consisting of what happens when something or someone threatens a break.

Mr. Hergesheimer has consciously cultivated certain mannerisms of style, of phraseology, and even of punctuation that some readers find aggravating. On the other hand, it is equally true that when you have read that paragraph, or story, you have no doubt as to what the author was trying to say. Moreover, the scenes and characters fix themselves definitely and lastingly in the mind. There is nothing "thin" about the work of this writer.

What he has tried to do in his stories Mr. Hergesheimer states thus: "Looking back over the field of my work a very few things are evident, and principally that I always write about people, men usually nearly forty, who are not happy. The story at bottom is nearly always the same — a struggle between what is called the spirit and what is called the flesh — the spirit is victorious — that is why, it seems to me, my books are happy books."

With the exception of the age of the hero, "The Token" aptly illustrates Mr. Hergesheimer's theory. From his statement, too, it would seem that the author considers women unimportant in his stories, but that is far from the actual fact. For proof, consider how deftly but unforgettably he draws the three women in "The Token," even though he leaves it a men's story. This holds true of all his stories. But mere characters and interesting background do not make a story. There must be plot. "The Token," like all his stories, is definitely a story of plot.

# THE TOKEN

WHAT Epes Calef principally thought, walking sharply away from his discharged responsibility at the Custom House, through the thin icy light of late afternoon, was that he was glad that was finally done with. It was, he assured himself again, with articulating lips. The next time he went to sea, to the East, to Patagonia and Canton and the Falklands, or lay in the Macao Roads with the Brahminy kites perched high on the rigging, he would be first mate, perhaps even master, of the *Triton*, and no longer a mere supercargo. No words could adequately express how much he hated that position of barterer. Very privately — in view of his father's special characteristic — he hadn't considered it at all a necessary part of his training for the commanding of Calef ships;

others of his acquaintance, making like him toward such a superlative destiny, had worked their way progressively aft with no pause over kegs of Spanish dollars and the ridiculous merchants of Co-Hongs and counting-houses. They had always, from the first, been seamen, while he —— But he need bother no longer, his seemingly endless wearisome apprenticeship, the tiresome dickering, was over; and in the coming spring, before the lilacs had bloomed in Salem, he would personally, individually, order the last fast holding the *Triton* to earth cast off.

He swore a little, in a manner at once of the sea and of vainglorious youth. Epes Calef was not yet twenty, and his breath congealed in a sparkling mist. He was, he reminded himself with a lifting pleasure, home; the *Triton* had docked at noon, but he had been so busy with the infernal accounts and manifest, the wharfinger and harbor master, that he had hardly dwelt upon his safe and happy return. Neither, he suddenly realized, had he yet seen any member of his family; even Snelling Pingre, their head clerk, had been able only to wave briefly from a distance. His, Epes', father was more often than not at Derby Wharf on the return of one of his ships; either Ira Calef, or Bartlett, the elder son. Now Bartlett, his thoughts ran on, had always been splendidly suited to his appointed activity — an application to the purely financial side of the Calefs' wide trading voyages.

With Bartlett in Salem gradually taking the place of their father, and Epes a master on the sea, the fortunes and prestige of the family would increase in the next generation and the next. But this reflection, or rather its implication, suddenly changed the substance of his thoughts. They settled on Annice Balavan — with an unaccountable, an unreasonable sensation of amazement. Epes recognized that he was about to marry her. He had made this a possibility, no, inevitable, just before he had left on this last voyage. He was in for it, he told himself, in a phrase not wholly gracious, since he had given her the Calef token.

It was remarkable about that — it was an obang, really; a thin gold coin of the East, almost as broad as his palm and stamped with angular signs — because there could be no doubt that when a Calef gave it to a woman, no matter who she was or what the circumstances, he married her. It had come to

Salem in the reticule of a ridiculous Dutch girl to whom the obang had been given in the hotel of the Dutch East India Company at Batavia by the first adventurous Calef. And after that its tradition, its power, had fast animated it. Epes' attitude toward this, and to Annice Balavan, was consequently fatalistic. Now, after nearly two years on the islands and continents and wide waters of the world, he didn't see how he had come to give the token to Annice. He had, all at once, no great desire for marriage, except to the *Triton;* but with a youthfully philosophical sigh he accepted the impending consequences of his gift as inevitable to life.

There was some consolation in the reflection that Annice was, it was practically admitted, the prettiest girl in Salem, and there was a permissible question if there were any better looking in Boston. Her considerable part of the Balavan money, too, would be a material assistance to the not inconsiderable Calef funds and ambitions. It was, after all, Epes decided, a very sensible and advantageous arrangement; the more so because he knew beforehand that Annice would not insist on going to sea with him; everyone, in fact, connected with a ship hated a woman, the master's wife, on board. She didn't like the sea, and made no secret of her feeling; the air from it, drawing in through Salem Harbor, took the crispness out of her muslins and made her hair, she declared, look like strings. But that was nonsense; her ashen-gold hair, even in its net, had the softest and most delicate beauty imaginable. Very different it was from Sumatra's; but then, everything about Sumatra, the younger sister, was unlike Annice; particularly the former's exaggerated — Epes called it that — passion for ships and the sea. She carried this to a most unbecoming extent; positively her questions were a nuisance.

He passed the Essex House on the right, and then the Marine Store. The light faded rapidly and it was growing noticeably colder, frigid and still; the sky was a clear pale yellow that flickered in the patches of metallic ice along the gutters, and footfalls, voices, carried surprisingly. Unaccustomed, for a comparatively long period, to winter, he was at once aware of its sting and yet found a gratification, without specially heavy clothes, in disregarding it. He had been hardened to both danger and exposure, and he accepted them with a sense of challenge and victory. How little Salem, the land, compared with the shifting sea, changed; here there was no making or taking in of sail; it didn't matter what happened in the way of weather, the houses, the stone-laid streets, even commonly the trees, were always placidly, monotonously the same. The life in them, as well, went always over the old charted and recharted courses, every morning resembled every other morning, each night all the others. Why, take this latter voyage, twenty-five days from Bombay to Liverpool ——

He had reached Summer Street, and turned again, past Mechanics Hall; soon he would be on Chestnut, and then wholly home. Where, he wondered, after he was married to Annice, would he live? Maybe on Bath Street, overlooking Washington Square, or close to the Ammidons. Annice, he thought, would rather prefer that; there was at last a movement away from Chestnut Street toward the square. It made no difference to him; his home primarily — yes, his heart — would be on the quarter-deck of his ship. His wife might arrange all the details on shore. She would do it very well, too; Annice, in addition to her beauty, was capable; she had a direct, positive mind.

He would get the preliminaries of that business over with as soon as possible, and then, late in April, or in May — Where, he speculated already, would he set sail for? There were so many alternatives, so many diverse cargoes to load and progressively discharge. Abruptly he was swinging in between the hand-wrought iron fencing across the Calef dwelling. It was an imposing square house of brick with a square-looking classic portico, a tall elaborate Palladian window above, and four great chimneys at the corners of the white-railed captain's walk that crowned the flattened roof. Epes found the front door unsecured, and entered, calling in a voice that echoed in the bare, dignified hall.

Instantly, from the floor above, his mother replied, but in a voice strangely, almost unrecognizably emotional, and he heard her equally disturbed and hurried approach. The darkly paneled and carved stairway, bending above his head at the tall window over the portico, hid her until she had almost reached him; and then with an involuntary painful contraction of his heart he saw that she was in deep mourning, and that her face was heavy, sodden with tears. Before he could question her, her arms were about his shoulders and she was sobbing again.

"Epes, Epes, I was afraid you weren't coming back either."

"What is it?" he stammered. "Is father ———"

She drew slightly away from him, gazing with streaming eyes into his questioning face. "Why, haven't you—— But that is incredible!" She was close to him again. "Bartlett is dead. It — it happened in New York, from a torn finger and blood poisoning. In two days, Epes; we hardly got there, saw him. Your father had to go to Boston, and is just back; but he'll see you almost at once, in the music room, he said."

How like his father that insistent formality was, Epes thought; nothing, it seemed, was to shake the dignity, the aloofness of Ira Calef. His manner positively carried with it a chill as palpable as that now in the streets. He was, of course, both to the world at large and to his family, the perfect shape of integrity; but that, with his rigidly correct deportment, appeared to be his only conception of what was owing, through him, to exterior circumstance and people. All people — Clia, his wife, his two sons — had been exterior to Ira Calef; it was always evident that he viewed, weighed every possible development of living solely in the light of his own unalterable convictions and wishes. They were, it was true, always carefully studied, logical; nor were his decisions quickly formed, in any heat, generous or bitter; it was the inflexible manner, the finality and detachment of their announcement which made them appear so unbearably arbitrary.

The music room, like the stair well, was entirely paneled, walls and ceiling in dark wood, and the mahogany in it, the waxed floor, even the windows with their multiplicity of small panes, held in replica the withdrawn, almost morose effect given by Ira Calef himself. He came presently, in a gait neither slow nor fast, into the music room, where, without his mother, Epes was waiting. The other's show of welcome was, for him, unusual; he held Epes' hand for more than the strictly necessary moment, and at once indicated a chair and the fact that Epes might sit. He was a big man, past sixty, handsomely proportioned, with a handsome face evenly pallid except for the discolorations hanging under eyes themselves almost without a perceptible shading. They were, of course, gray, yet they were so pale that but for their domineering focus they rather resembled clear water slightly crystallized with ice. He made an adequate but brief reference to Bartlett's death, dwelling for a little on the collapse of the boy's mother; and then leaning back and deliberately, for the time, shifting the conversation, asked Epes Calef for a detailed account of what on his voyage as supercargo he had accomplished.

This Epes, to his considerable relief of mind, was able to explain satisfactorily. The master of the *Triton*, Whalen Dove, had come on board the ship at Gravesend, twenty miles down river from London, and after they had been wind-bound for two weeks at Ramsgate they had proceeded to Madeira for wine, put into Colombo after twenty days, and had gone on almost immediately to the Coromandel Coast, Pondicherry and Madras, where the cargo had been disposed of through Lyss, Saturi & Demonte. Yes, the ship had come home by way of Rotterdam. Lost Teneriffe above the clouds five degrees west. They had made seventeen knots with the main skysail set, when a British ship was under double-reefed topsails. But in a three-quarters gale, west southwest, they carried away a mizzen topsail and the foresail burst.

Ira Calef listened to this in an admirable silence that at the same time conveyed the impression that he was exercising an unnecessary amount of patience in the waiting for details of more importance. Epes quickly recalled himself from his enthusiasm in the mere fact of seamanship. There were close to two hundred cases of indigo in the *Triton's* hold — 186, to be precise; about a million pounds of Madras sugar; 460 pieces of redwood; 709 bags of ginger; 830 bags of pepper; 22 chests of tea — The duty, the elder decided, would be over twenty thousand dollars.

"You didn't like this," he said unexpectedly to his son.

Epes met his cold gaze fairly. "No, sir," he replied.

"Always the taste for mere ships."

To this there was no permissible answer.

"I am sorry for that," the other proceeded, "for, now that Bartlett is dead, it will be needful for you to give up the sea as a career; I shall require you to stay in Salem. There are plenty of good, even faithful masters of ships; but after me you are the only remaining Calef; and it won't do for you to be knocking around the windy reaches of the globe." He stopped, entirely inattentive of Epes' strained lips, his half lifted hand.

A choking emotion, partly made up of incredulity and in part a burning resentment, fast-rising rebellion, filled Epes Calef. This — this wasn't right, it wasn't fair, it wasn't possible. They couldn't take and, for all his past life, fix his every ambition and hope and standard on the sea, and then in a sentence or two destroy him, ruin everything he was and might be; for what his father had just said amounted to no less. It was inhuman. It couldn't be! Evidently Ira Calef expected him to speak, to acquiesce, for his regular eyebrows mounted ever so slightly. But the thing, the only safety, for Epes now was to remain silent.

"I am not even, completely, certain of Salem," the elder went on in his level voice, after what had almost become an unbearable pause. "I personally shall never live anywhere else; but it may be necessary for you to move into Boston — for a number of years anyhow. I am getting more and more absorbed in marine insurance; and the opportunities for the study of that are moving away from us here. I have spoken to Annice about all this, and since she is a sensible girl with no fancy for a husband eternally below the horizon she is delighted."

"I see," Epes said uncertainly.

Annice Balavan would be delighted with all that his father had just said, especially with the Boston part, the larger society there. She was a natural part of this new, incredibly horrible plan; instantly he identified her with it, saw her moving radiant and content over its monotonous bricks and floors and earth. Something within him, automatic, brought him to his feet. The other glanced up, once.

"You are, of course, upset by the suddenness of the news of your brother's death," he conceded. "If you like you may go to your room with no further discussion at present. There isn't a great deal left to be said — more movements than words. The most advantageous arrangements will be made for Annice and you; her mother has already promised to furnish a Boston house for her in the new style. I am pleased with the manner in which you appear to have accomplished your duties on the *Triton*."

In his room a fire of coals was burning in the grate, with a faintly audible spitting and small rushes of gaseous flame. It cast a perceptible ruddiness on the immediate oak flooring, while the rest of the room was rapidly dimming; the windows, beyond which the familiar limbs of the elms on the street were sharp and black, showed only rectangles of cold gray; the yellow light had faded from the sky. Epes stood irresolutely, with his gaze lowered, his brow drawn with lines. He could just see his blue sea chest, sent up from the ship earlier in the afternoon; and the brass disks of a nocturnal, his chiefest treasure, hung, he knew, above the chest on the wall. That old instrument of navigation, for finding at night, through the North Star, the hour, seemed to challenge and mock his wretchedness and impotence. That latter word most perfectly held the essence of his tragic situation.

He could do nothing!

Epes slipped into a chair and attempted to combat this. A daring resolution hovered about him, reckless, and yet, he told himself fiercely, entirely justified; he might run away to sea; the sea, the service, he loved. He could ship any day, from any port, as third, probably second mate, and after a single voyage become first officer. That was the reasonable thing to do. He understood that an appeal to his father was worse than useless; the opening of any protest, a difference of opinion, determination, would close Ira Calef to both sympathy and attention. He would be simply, remotely unbending — the eyebrows would climb, his mouth harden, a cutting phrase end the conversation. His father, Epes had realized, was different from the other pleasant fathers he knew; he had always been, well — inhuman. That term in such a connection was new, presumptuous, but Epes in his present mood defiantly allowed it. However, not until now had he acutely suffered from the elder Calef's disposition. Outside he had heard the words "an India liver" applied to his father; yet even Salem was cautious, deferential in its attitude there; Epes could never remember an occasion when his father had been balked in a decision, or even seriously contradicted.

He felt actually as though he hated that frozen parental figure; and he almost blamed Bartlett for dying. That recalled the fact that his brother was dead, that his emotion was neither appropriate nor decent; but the threatened, overpowering wrong to him persisted in dominating every other response. Yes, Epes repeated, he would run away; that — very successfully — had been done before. He'd leave everything, go with only the clothes in which he stood, leaving, out of the sum due him from the *Triton*, payment for them. That act, he recognized, must take him forever from his family, from, as long as Ira Calef lived, his home, Salem. The other would never relent. He thought for a moment of his mother's helpless position; never had he heard her raise her voice, oppose in any particular her husband. He was not, it was true, unkind or discourteous to her, he merely ignored the possibility of her having a single independent desire, a fraction of personality or will. And during Epes' life she had shown no indication that he was wrong. What, Epes now wondered, was the actuality beneath her calm demeanor; maybe she hated, detested Ira Calef. This amazing speculation redirected his thoughts to Annice Balavan.

Or rather, it drew his mind back to the token, the gage of the Calef men. Its reputed, its proved force exerted a species of numbing magic on him; his superstitious regard for it held his imagination as though in chains. Epes had given the obang to Annice, and therefore he was going to marry her; there was no escape from the girl who possessed it. This instinct was so strong that it struck at all his vague planning — Annice, if he knew her, would never consent to marry a runaway sailor, third mate or first or master. No matter what he might project, an unforeseen circumstance, accident, would betray him and marry him to Annice Balavan.

He tried to throw this conviction off, to laugh it away for nonsense; he derided himself unsparingly; rising, he told himself that he would tramp down through the house and out at once; but instead he sank back into his chair. Yet it might be that he could get away, come back successful, rich, in a very few years — one good voyage would secure that — and find Annice waiting for him. This seemed to him an inspiration, and a hard, active spirit welled up within him. After no more than one voyage to China. But again a disability, as gray as the dusk without, flooded him; he couldn't, when the moment came, walk away in that manner from responsibility. No matter what his father was like, he was incontrovertibly his father; already Epes Calef saw his world as the deck of a ship, and the high order, the discipline of that plane was the base of his being. There was, of course, injustice on the sea; tyrannical captains; but the injustice and tyranny could not be met with mutiny. For example, if as a subordinate he were directed to take his ship onto rocks that he could clearly see, what was there for him to do but that? How could he question or penetrate the superior, the totally responsible position?

There had been cases when a master, obviously insane or incapacitated, had been restrained, held in his cabin against the next port inquiry, by his principal officers; but even at the height of his desire Epes couldn't call his father insane. Still seeing his fate as a part of the obsessing sea he told himself that figuratively he had been set ashore on a sterile and deserted beach while his ship, having swung about with her sails filling gloriously, left him for the rush of free water. Accustomed to the open, to hour after hour, day after day, month on month, on deck, he felt all at once that he couldn't breathe in his closed room the confined heat of the coals. Epes, for a little, suffered acutely, in a constriction of nerves. His whole life was to be like this!

A knock sounded at the door, and a servant entered with fresh candles, which he proceeded to fix on the dressing stand, the overmantel, and light. The illumination, at first uncertain, wan, gained in steady brightness. It was time to dress for dinner. There had been no opportunity for him to procure mourning, but he put on his darkest, most formal clothes, and tied a severe black neckcloth.

The candelabra on the dining table showed his mother's place to be empty — she was not yet able to manage the casual — and the chair that had been Bartlett's was pushed against the wall. Ira Calef, seen to extreme advantage at the ceremony of dinner, hardly spoke; he was intent upon his codfish, with a green sauce; and he tasted critically the brown sherry before him in a large goblet of fragile glass flecked with gold. With this, it developed, he was dissatisfied; the wine had, he said curtly, withered; sherry, upon opening, could not withstand delay. He sent out the entire decanter with the order to replace it with another bottling — the Tio Pepe of the *Saragon*. He listed his cellar by the names of the vessels in which the various importations had been made. During this process he maintained an inflexible silence colored with his familiar suggestion of a restraint that no immoderate cause could break. To Epes the sherry, when it arrived, had no more warmth or flavor than was probable in the celebrated muddiness of the Hugli River.

Selecting a cheroot blindly from the box held at his elbow, and lighting it at the tendered spill, he retired mentally in the thin veil of smoke that rose across his face.

"You will, of course, stop in at the Balavans' this evening," his father said presently. Everything he uttered, Epes thought, took subconsciously the form of a direction. Still he must, he supposed, see Annice, if only for the announcement of his return.

The Balavans lived on the north edge of town, their terraced lawn descended to navigable water — to the anchorage, in fact, of the now vanished Balavan merchant fleet, and a deserted warehouse. And, shown through the hall to a drawing-room against the dark, bare garden, Epes found not Annice, as he had expected, but Sumatra. She was glad to see him. She was an indifferent girl, and this was specially noticeable; but he returned, inwardly and visibly, little if any of her pleasure.

"Tell me every shift of the wheel," she demanded, facing him from the long stool of the spinet. "Be a human log."

"I thought Annice was here," he replied.

"She will be soon enough. Did the *Triton* do anything really stirring, outsail seven ships or part both chains in Table Bay? I hope you came into Derby Wharf with the sheer poles coach-whipped and cross-pointed Turks'-heads with double-rose props."

"I assure you, Sumatra," he told her stiffly, "that I haven't any idea of what you are talking about. And, what is more, I don't think you have." With this he half turned from her.

He could still see her, though, a thickly set girl — was she sixteen yet? — with a rosy, impertinent face and hair loosely confined in a ribbon. Her name had been given her from the fact that a Balavan, a master of ships, had in the eighteenth century discovered pepper growing wild on the coast of Sumatra. But there was now, Epes told himself, a far better reason — Heaven knew she was peppery. Rather a detestable child.

Far from being disconcerted by the brevity of his retort she replied that she had heard it didn't matter what he understood or didn't understand about the sea — " Now that you are to be a clerk."

After the stress, the difficulty of his homecoming, and from Sumatra, this was positively too much; and all the bitterness banked up by his father's unassailable situation fell upon her.

" All your life," he asserted, " you have been a joke, with your language like a crazy ship chandler. You have never been in the least feminine or attractive, and you never can be, not by the width of a finger nail. Part of it — being built like a sampan — you can't help; but that won't help you, will it? But you might, at least, get a vocabulary that ought to suit you better. All I say is, you'll notice, that it ought to. What suits you I shouldn't try to guess. That's mostly what I think about you; but on this other subject, where my private affairs, perhaps sorrows, are concerned, shut up."

This ill-tempered, rasped conclusion came so abruptly that it surprised even him. He glanced at her a shade regretfully, and saw with a feeling of satisfaction that once, anyhow, he had impressed, silenced her. Her head was bent, her face obscured by her forward-swung hair; her slippers were very rigidly together.

" I suppose you are right," she admitted after a long breath. " Probably you won't believe it, but I have never thought much about myself or how I affected people. Yes, a lot of them — and you, too — must think I am a joke. So few care for anything as I do for the sea. It used to seem to me that perhaps you did; I was wrong though."

" Didn't I tell you to let me alone? " he cried, again furious. " How do you know what I care for? What do you mean by daring to judge me, you — you —— "

" Aren't you leaving the sea for your father's counting-house? " Sumatra calmly demanded of him.

" If I am it's because my duty is there," he replied miserably.

" You are the hell of a sailor," she commented.

Ever since she could walk Sumatra had, on occasion, sworn; at times it had amused Epes Calef, but now it only added to his dislike, his condemnation of her. She should not, he told her severely, have been encouraged to continue it. Her answer was the expressed reflection that he might do better on shore; his delicacy was much too great for salt water.

"Do you honestly hate me?" she asked unaccountably. "I mean, when you are not in a rage."

"No, I don't hate you, in a rage or out of it," he said coldly. "Often you go beyond your years, and you presume a good deal; but after a while you'll make a good wife for the captain of a West India lugger or some fellow trading with Bermuda Hundred."

This was an adroit insult, and pleasurably he watched her flush. She became so unhappy that he was magnanimously touched with remorse, and said with a kindly condescension that it was too bad she hadn't been born a boy.

At that he had it swiftly proven to him that attitudes, interests, vocabularies were misleading, for logical and wholly feminine tears actually streamed over her healthy cheeks. It grew worse, for she rose and came close to him, with clasped desperate hands.

"Don't listen to him!" she begged. "He's a horrid man of snow, even if he is your father; and if you let him he'll spoil your life. Tell him that you have made up your mind to go to sea, and that nothing can change it. You won't be struck dead. He isn't God with a stick of lightning."

"You don't understand," he stammered, backing away from her, intolerably embarrassed. "I am not, as you seem to think, afraid of my father. I have been over and over it all in my head. No, it's something different. You couldn't understand," he repeated. "No girl could."

"You are wrong," she replied slowly. "I see all that you mean, and — yes — I suppose I admire you for it. You can't mutiny" — she echoed his own phrase — "others could, but not a Calef. Yet you make me furious, you are so helpless, so stupid. You will marry Annice and grow fat and nearsighted, that's what'll happen to you."

Annice, in the doorway, asked: "Well, why not?"

Disregarding Sumatra, Epes went forward to meet the girl who possessed the Calef token. He had, in spite of his assertions, forgotten how lovely she was, slender and palely gold; her gray-gold hair was like a cloud in sifted sunlight, her skin had an even, warm pallor that remotely suggested oranges, and her eyes were a cool autumnal brown.

"Epes," she continued, "how burned and well you look."

She took his vigorous hands in hers, held them lightly for a second, and then relinquished him.

"There is an ocean of things for us to talk about and arrange," she proceeded, from a divan; and her glance at Sumatra was a dismissal.

The younger girl made a profound curtsy to them both, surprisingly graceful for her solidity of waist, and disappeared. Epes realized that he ought to kiss Annice, but he felt awkward in the extreme. She held her face delicately to him; it was like a tea rose. He was, he supposed, fortunate; but no sensation of gladness accompanied that supposition. It was so sad about Bartlett, she went on; and how enormously his death had affected them. Wasn't it unexpectedly sweet of her mother to furnish their house — "in miraculous brocades and hangings, with a French boudoir?"

Walking slowly home, the stars, very high above him, were like a powdering of dry, luminous snow on the polished night. The cold was so intense that his exposed face ached. What an odorous heat there would be over the mooring at the Prince's Ghat in Calcutta! He remembered the firm, light pressure of the northeast trades, the perpetual fleecy trades clouds about the horizon, the bonitos and albacore in the deeply blue, sunny water. Lovely sailing.

Was it true that all that, for him, was already a thing of the past? Epes couldn't believe it, and yet — what other conclusion was possible? Turning his thoughts to the past hour with Annice he tried, in her, to find a recompense for what he was losing, but without success. He was proud of her; in her way she was fine and beautiful. Perhaps what he understood love to be came later; it might be unreasonable to expect the whole measure of joy at once. Annice was cool enough; indeed they had acted as though they had been married for a year or more, as though they had been continuously together instead of having been so lately separated by the diameter of the world.

There was a light in the small room at the rear of the hall, used by his father as an office; and as he laid aside his wraps the elder appeared in the doorway, obviously desiring speech.

"I have seen Mr. Dove," Ira Calef told his son; "and he corroborates your report, with some added praise. I am very well pleased, Epes. Your conduct this evening, too, was admirable. I did not quite expect, at once, such a full comprehension of my intentions. The fact is," he proceeded in a general discursive manner, " that the country is changing very rapidly. A great many men are blind to this, and as a result they will have to suffer. It is not so with me. The days of the colony are at last definitely at an end; from now on not adventure but finance will be the ruling spirit. That is one of the reasons why I am withdrawing you from the sea. Let other paid men — good men, but essentially subordinate — undertake the gales and half gales; it is important for you, a Calef, to be at the center of affairs and safe."

Epes' expression was dull, unrevealing; everything that was being said contradicted and outraged his every fiber. Safe! Good men, but subordinate! He longed to shout — for all sailors, before and aft the mast — a contradiction of his father's cold patronizing periods. He loathed the money sharks who on land, in houses, traded on the courage and endurance and fidelity of ships' masters and crews. If Ira Calef was right, and they had grown unimportant, if their greatness was doomed to vanish — why, then he wanted to go too.

All this filled his brain and throat, clamored for expression; but not a word, not a protesting sound came from him. Suddenly he was tired; Epes felt as though the leaden weight of his future already rested on him. The other made an approving reference to Annice Balavan; and perversely, for no discoverable reason, in place of the golden vision of Annice he saw Sumatra, square, like a sampan — and defiant.

When, for the time, Ira Calef had quite finished the expression of his balanced judgments Epes rose with the shadow of an instinctive bow.

" Very good, sir." The sea phrase was spoken in a voice without animation.

Above, close by his room, he was mildly surprised to find his mother. It was evident that she had been waiting for him, and followed, carefully closing the door behind them.

" How did you find Annice? " she asked.

But to his reply that Annice had seemed well enough she paid no attention. With a quick, nervous gesture she pressed her handkerchief against her eyes.

" And your father —— "

Epes said nothing.

"Epes," she cried, in a sudden realization of all that, it was now clear, she wanted to say to him, " no matter how hard and unreasonable he may seem, you mustn't contradict him. It isn't as though he were going to do you harm. What he plans is right; he can see so much farther than we can. And you will be very happy, I am sure, with Annice. You'll forget the sea? " her voice rose in inquiry.

"Never," Epes answered.

Clia Calef shivered momentarily. "I was afraid of something like that," she admitted. "And that is why it is necessary for me to speak to you. You must do what your father wants."

This was, he thought, in view of his restraint, all unnecessary. He regarded his mother, seated with her head blurred against the candlelight, with a mature, unsympathetic attention. Women — the characteristic feminine world — were very far outside the scope of his interests and being. Even to his mother he could not explain, seek to justify himself; his inner being had grown obdurate, solitary; life, which had once, in the form of blue water, everywhere surrounded and touched him, had retreated, flowed away, leaving him on that sandy, meaningless beach. Why did she talk and talk?

"You have been wonderfully quiet," she still went emotionally on; " I could tell that from Ira's manner. But I wasn't sure. I'm not yet; and for that reason, to save hideous trouble, I made up my mind to tell you. There is a little strangeness about your father, and it comes out when he is contradicted. Except for that he is splendid. I don't just know what it is, but contradiction makes him wretched; he — he loses control of himself." She was speaking faster, with an obvious increasing difficulty. " I did it, once. We hadn't been married long, and it was in the garden. He had just come back from the counting-house, and he was carrying a light cane, a wanghee. And, Epes, he struck me with it. Oh, not very hard; not, really, too hard. I didn't say a word. I stood for a second, quite frozen, and then I turned to walk out of the garden, to leave him, forever. I intended to go, but it did hurt. I was confused, and instead of finding the gate I walked into the geraniums and fainted. So, you see, I stayed."

Epes Calef drew in an audible harsh breath.

"You mustn't judge him!" she exclaimed eagerly. "I am sure it spoiled a large part of his life. He carried me into the house, and neither of us has referred to it since. Yes, it hurt him beyond speech; for weeks he slept hardly at all. Epes, Epes, I can't have it happen to him again. He is your father and you must help. You love him, too, I am certain; and what he arranges is always, always best."

She was so tremulous, so self-effacing, that he felt he couldn't bear to hear another word. It was terrible, and as wrong as possible.

"He ought to be denied," Epes said in a strong voice. "Now that you have told me this I think it might be what he, what we all need; perhaps I shall have to."

"That is not for you to judge," Clia Calef told him with a resumption of dignity. "You would be very wicked indeed; and not only, perhaps, harm Ira permanently, but me as well. I have to live with him, and not you. Epes, you have the ignorance of youth; but if I can help it I won't have you upsetting our life."

He was, he saw, literally nothing before her love for the man who had struck her with his wanghee.

"It would spoil everything," she half whispered to herself. "I have tried hard, so long."

Epes rose sharply. "You must go to bed," he directed. "If you are not careful you will be sick." He was deathly sick. She clung to him.

"Promise me, promise you will do as he says."

"I have already decided that," he answered in his weary, dead voice.

Epes, with his hand under her arm, conducted her to her room. A wave of warmth flowed into the hall as the door opened and shut, like the soiled enervating breath of a hidden corruption.

It was a physical impossibility, in the temporarily empty days following immediately Epes' arrival home, for his spiritual darkness to stay at its intensest; at least his state of mourning made it unnecessary for him to go to the meaningless parties being then crowded into the heart of the winter season. It was uncomfortable for him at home, and he fell into the habit of lounging through the afternoons in the more informal of the Balavans' drawing-rooms. There, in his special position and license, he was permitted to smoke his cheroots and listen to the light easy run of Annice's voice, so much like the easy light tripping of her fingers over the keyboard of the spinet. He was engaged in exactly this manner an hour or so before Annice's departure for one of the principal cotillons of the year, at Hamilton Hall; and Annice, who had dressed early so that she could be with him, was sitting erectly by an opposite wall. Sumatra was present, too; a fact to which her elder sister repeatedly called attention by urging the necessity of Sumatra's changing for the ball. Sumatra, Epes had learned, had been half permitted and half coerced into going.

"I can get ready in twelve minutes," she announced.

"I don't doubt that," Annice retorted; "but what will you look like when it is done? In the first place your hair is like wire and takes the longest while to be really possible ——"

"It won't matter," said Sumatra; "Epes told me I couldn't make myself attractive, no matter how much we all tried."

"Did you say that, Epes?" Annice asked. "It was rather tactless of you, because, though you'd never guess it, Sumatra is crazy about you. It might even be more than I am."

Epes Calef gazed at Sumatra with a brutal indifference. She met his eyes courageously, and in an even voice replied to her sister.

"I was once," she corrected the other, "when I thought that Epes belonged to the sea. But now he's on land —" She made a gesture of dismissal. "Epes, while I suspect he's very good, is my great disappointment. I don't like good people."

"What experience have you had with bad?" he asked cuttingly. "As usual, you are just talking words. You are a regular sea lawyer."

"Do get dressed, Sumatra," Annice said.

"Something light and feminine," Epes added; "with wreaths of flowers for you to put your feet through."

He couldn't understand why, whenever he talked to Sumatra, he became so vindictive. He had no particular desire to be nasty; it came up in spite of him.

"Perhaps no one will ask me to dance."

"If they do," he advised her, "and it is near supper, don't let go or you'll get no oysters."

"Sumatra, get dressed," Annice commanded.

"Maybe I won't at all."

"Do you mean you'll go like you are?"

"It wouldn't kill anyone, would it? I shouldn't come home and cry if I didn't get an armful of favors; I can get along, for a few minutes anyhow, by myself."

This, Epes thought, promised to be amusing. Peppery Sumatra! Annice glanced at him hastily.

"Please, Sumatra," she entreated; "we simply can't be late. I'll give you my white-ribbed Spanish stockings."

The other serenely answered, "The feet would be too big."

He had never noticed her feet, and to his considerable surprise they were smaller, narrower than Annice's.

"You are a lumpish, impossible child," the elder said acrimoniously. "Why I begged mother to let you start the cotillons I can't imagine. And when we get there you are not to hang about me."

"I won't; you're not seaworthy. You are cut away too much through the middle; you would go over in a good blow."

Epes incautiously laughed.

"Be still," Annice directed him; "she must not be encouraged in such conduct."

"Well," he said pacifically, "you wouldn't, Trinidad." He often substituted the West India island for that from which she was named, reminding her of his matrimonial prediction.

"Yes, sampan," Annice echoed him. "Will you or will you not get dressed?"

"I will, when I have twelve minutes. It doesn't, you know, take me three hours." Nevertheless, she rose. "You haven't been specially nice to me, have you?" she said slowly, carefully avoiding Epes Calef. "You made pretty clear all you thought. I don't believe I could be like that."

Suddenly she gazed full at Epes. "It might be your father in you," she concluded; "if I were you I shouldn't encourage that — for Annice's sake. It would be so hard on her."

"Thank you, but I can take care of myself," Annice assured her brightly; "and it would be nicer to omit the personal history."

"All I say is wrong!" Sumatra declared.

"All," Epes echoed her.

"I must be a sampan."

"Must."

"Square bowed, and only fit for rivers."

"For rivers."

"But even that is better than a desk," she reminded him. She was beside the door, and paused with a hand upon the frame, looking over her shoulder. "What Annice told you was true," she reiterated. "I had a little picture hidden in a drawer, which I am now going up to tear into bits."

When she had gone Annice turned to him in a conciliatory manner.

"There is something I meant to tell you at once, this afternoon, but it slipped from my mind. I hope you won't be angry and I can't imagine how it happened. But the whole thing, of course, is exaggerated; it must be all nonsense at bottom. Still I am sorrier than words can say. Epes, somehow I've lost the token."

He gazed, startled at her, with a stirring of the old Calef superstition within him. However, he concealed it.

"That is too bad. We think it's rather valuable, you know. Perhaps it will turn up; there are so many places you might have left it."

No, she replied; she knew how they felt about it, and she had left it, she was certain, in the lacquer box on her dressing-case. It was very mysterious and uncertain.

"Now," she said with a smile, "you won't have to marry me. The spell, the charm is broken."

This he repudiated in a form correct and stiff. The influence that absurd East Indian coin exerted upon his thoughts was amazing. He repeated, silently, her words — "Now you won't have to marry me." But certainly they had no force, no reality. He was bound to her not by an obang, but by honor. At the same time his feeling was undeniably different; he regarded her from a more detached position. What was that Sumatra had hinted — about crying over a scarcity of favors, and taking three hours to dress? It didn't matter to him, nothing did; it only added to the general weariness, waste of existence. Epes recalled the promised French boudoir in the threatened Boston house. That was it — his life hereafter was to be passed in a little scented room choked with brocade and hangings.

A maid appeared, enveloped Annice in a long cloak luxuriously lined with sables, twisted a silvery veiling over her netted hair, over her lovely regular features, her face with its indefinite suggestion of golden oranges.

"I thought Sumatra would be late," she declared in an abstracted exasperation. Then through the veiling she gave him a metallic and masked kiss. From the hall her voice sounded, fretful about her carriage boots.

The carriage with Annice and Sumatra departed; he must go, too; where, he didn't know, it no longer mattered; home, he supposed. There was a second stamping of hoofs before the Balavan dwelling, and Mrs. Balavan, in street wraps, passed the drawing-room door. Epes remembered that he had heard his mother speak of going to a ballad soirée with her. Still he remained seated, after the hour of dinner, and it was nearly nine before he left.

The light in his father's office was, as usual, turned up, a thin haze of tobacco smoke perceptible. Without the desire to go up to his room Epes sat in a lower chamber. Snatches of the conversation — the quarrel, really — between Sumatra and Annice returned to him. How essentially different they were. Annice was far, far the lovelier. She made a business of being beautiful. But at least that, in a wife, was something; the majority of wives had far less. What a curious double life it would be — two separate people with one name, in one house. She could never, he was sure, mean more to him than she did now. And it was clear that for her part her demand was no greater.

Sumatra would be the opposite — there was no end to what she expected, fought for, insisted upon. Strangely enough, he couldn't see her as a wife — even for that coastwise figure he had so often pictured — at all. He was unable to discover what sort of man would suit her, but certainly one armed with a belaying pin. He became conscious of a clamor faintly heard from another part of Salem; it grew more distinct, and he recognized that it was the confused alarms and uproar of a fire. The fire evidently lay in the direction of Marlboro Street; the noise increased rather than subsided; but even this didn't stir him until his father appeared.

"I shall have to neglect my duty this evening," he explained; "there are some questions of foreign exchange. But perhaps you will take my place."

Epes went silently out to the hall, where two leather buckets, painted with the name Active Fire Club, were hanging. He secured them, and a wool scarf, and went unexcitedly in search of the fire. It was, as he had thought, in the vicinity of Marlboro Street, the Baptist Church. The Fire Engine Exchange, he saw, to which generally the men of the Calef family belonged, had secured the place of honor, directly at the conflagration. Its reservoir was connected by hose to another engine, and that latter to a third, which drew from the source of their water. A pandemonium rose about Epes — the hoarse, jeering shouts of the competing companies, authoritative voices magnified by trumpets, the clatter of the hand pump, and the dull roar of the unconquerable flames. A curtain of black smoke, ruddy at its base and, above, poured with live cinders, rolled up across the immaculate green sky and frosty stars.

The members of the Active Fire Club had formed their line for the rapid orderly passing of buckets, and Epes had taken his place at the end, when he saw a short, familiar feminine shape standing alone. It was Sumatra, and it was extremely wrong of her to be there, like that, so late.

He left his position hurriedly and laid a hand on her arm. How, he demanded, had she got there, and why was she by herself?

"Oh, Epes!" she exclaimed with pleasure. "The cotillon nearly killed me, it was so stupid; and then I heard the alarms, and James Saltonstall wanted to come; and so, you see, here we — here I am."

"Where is he? Why did he leave you?"

Before she could answer there was a louder opposed shouting of voices:

"Suck him dry, Exchange!"

"Overwash them, Adams. Drown the damned silk stockings!"

Sumatra clutched his hand excitedly. "Don't you see — they are trying to burst the Exchange engine; we haven't enough men to pump, because some didn't leave Hamilton Hall, and James is at the sweep. You must go, too, Epes. Quick, quick, or it will be too late!"

His negative attitude settled into an active perversity; Epes Calef made up his mind that he wouldn't pump; they could knock the silly engines into painted fragments for all him. Sumatra gave him a strong impatient shove forward, but he resisted her.

"The fire will be over in a few more minutes," he observed.

She damned the fire excitedly; it was the engine she cared about. "I'll pump, myself!" Sumatra cried.

He turned to her with a smile, but that was immediately lost as he saw that she had every intention of fulfilling her threat. Sumatra had started toward the profane companies of men when he caught her by the shoulder.

He said coldly, "You're crazy. Nobody ever heard of such a thing — a girl pumping at a fire! You'd be talked about, insulted in songs all over the country. Come home at once."

She wrenched herself from his hold, and Epes was obliged to stand in front of her with his arms outspread. Sumatra's face grew crimson with rage.

"Get out of my way!" she commanded him. "Do you think everyone is a coward and a ninny like you? I'll pump if I want to, and it doesn't matter who sings about it. I don't care what the other fools of women do."

"No, you won't," he told her grimly.

She gave him a shove, and she was so strong that, unprepared, he staggered. She nearly succeeded in evading him, but he caught her with an arm around her vigorous waist. In an instant they were fighting. Braced, with her hand crushing into his face, she tried to break his hold; then Sumatra struck him in the eye. Infuriated, he wanted to knock her head off, but he had to restrain himself to a negative attack.

"I'll throw you down and sit on you," he gasped; "here, on the street."

By way of reply she kicked his shins until, through the hurt, he could feel the blood sliding into his shoes. Shouts, which now, in his rage, he heard but dimly, derisive and encouraging calls, surrounded him. The girl, the little Amazon, was implored to crack his coco; there were protesting cries of shame, but these were lost in the larger approval and entertainment. By Jupiter, but she was finishing him! This, Epes desperately told himself, was horrible beyond words.

"Stop it!" he said savagely, again and again.

But through set teeth Sumatra replied that she'd pump if she chose, and no — no l-l-land shark could stop her. At this there was a hurrah. Her strength was amazing, and entirely wrong; she was like a maniac. Then with a free arm he punched her directly and rudely in the stomach. Sumatra settled against him limply; and holding her up, dragging her with him past threatening faces wavering in the dark, he succeeded in getting her around a corner to a deserted street.

She was still limp, struggling for breath; her face was pale and her hair in torn disorder. Sumatra slowly recovered, and — amazingly — she smiled. Epes' anger, too, fled; he gazed at her, examining in dismay her clothes with a feeling which might almost have been called admiration. Yet he spoke severely.

"You ought to be in a cage," he told her; "you're just wild."

However was she to fix her clothes, she replied; where could she go? "I ought to go back to Hamilton Hall."

To this he agreed, the Balavan house was far, inconveniently situated; and they decided, since the Calefs and Balavans were now practically one family, to stop at his dwelling for the repairing of her clothes and spirit. He secured his buckets and they hurried back, through a serene air like liquid ice, over Summer Street to Chestnut. The light was still burning in Ira Calef's office, and noiselessly they turned into an opposite room.

Epes went on into the dining-room, opening darkly beyond, leaving Sumatra with candles on the floor before a tall mirror. There, bearing a high silver candlestick and a following indeterminate illumination, he discovered a bottle of champagne, tagged the ship *Nautilus* and the year, and gathered two high glasses and some ice. He was tingling with excitement, a disturbance deeper than physical. He felt oddly detached from his late life, the commonplace and irresponsible; his mind was without images, thought — it was like a whirling of crackling colored lights. He found his situation — the uncorked champagne, the two glasses, the unsuspecting near presence of his father, Sumatra, rearranged, entering the dining-room — extraordinary and invigorating. The wine foamed whitely through the ice, turning into a silky clear amber that stung his lips. Sumatra observed, sitting down, that she ought to go on to the cotillon at once.

"What," she demanded, "will James Saltonstall think?"

That, Epes replied, was of singularly small importance.

The rose flush had returned to her cheeks, her eyes were shining; she was decidedly more attractive than he had admitted. But that, he made up his mind, he'd never tell her. She sipped and sipped from her glass; that in itself was unusual, startling. No, he corrected his impression, it would have been in any other girl of Sumatra's age, but not in her. The most unexpected, inappropriate things seemed to become her perfectly.

"I don't want to go," she added, so long after her other phrase that he almost lost the connection. "We are so different," Sumatra pointed out; "I hardly ever do what I don't want to. It's a good thing for your father I'm not you."

"It wouldn't make any difference," he said, listlessness again falling over him; "in the end it would be the same; you'd stay or go as he said."

"I would not."

"Oh, yes, but you would."

"He couldn't make me," she insisted; "not about that. It's too terribly important."

Epes became annoyed. "Can't you understand that, to my father, nothing is important except what he wants?"

"Why argue?" she decided. "After all, I am not you. And yet, even as it is, I believe if I were concerned, which I'm not, I could do what I decided with him."

He laughed. "Try, and if you are successful, why — why, I'd marry you instead of Annice."

The flush deepened painfully in her countenance; she regarded him with startled eyes. For a moment there was a ridiculously tense silence; and then, relaxing, she shook her head negatively.

"It wouldn't be any good; you'd have no regard for me."

"Regard for you!" he exclaimed. "If you did that I'd think more of you than anything else on earth; more than I did of — of the *Triton*." His voice, his manner darkened. "But you mustn't; there's a lot you don't understand — my father, first of all. He can be very nasty."

"I've told you before, he's only a man," she reminded him. "I shouldn't be afraid." Her direct gaze again challenged him, but Epes shook his head dejectedly. Suddenly she laid a hand over his. "I didn't tear that picture up," she whispered. Then with a sweep of her arm she finished what had been in her glass, and rose. " Come on, he's still in the office."

Epes Calef urged her in careful tones not to be a donkey; he tried, here discreetly, to restrain her; but she went resolutely on, through the front room into the hall. There would be a frightful row, but he couldn't desert Sumatra. However, in the passage she paused, with her lips against his ear.

" Remember, better than the *Triton*, or it would kill me."

Ira Calef looked up from his table, frowning slightly as she entered the office, followed by Epes. The elder's face was as white as marble under the artificial light.

" Why, Sumatra," he greeted her easily.

Epes tried to step between her and his father — disaster — but she held him back, speaking immediately in a voice as level as, but a little faster than, Ira Calef's.

" I suppose you think it's strange to see me here, so late, with Epes; but it is stranger even than you imagine." She put a hand over Epes Calef's mouth. " No," she protested, " you promised to let me speak. Mr. Calef," said the incredible Sumatra, " perhaps I ought to apologize to Mrs. Calef and you — Epes and I are married."

Epes' amazement, which he barely restrained, was no greater than his father's, but the latter's was given, for him, full expression.

" Married! " he repeated in a voice slightly and significantly louder than usual. " Why, that is outrageous! Nothing, nothing at all was said to me. My plan was wholly different."

He rose, beyond the table, with one hand resting beside a paper weight of greenish glass. Epes' eyes fastened upon this.

" It was, as you might guess, in a hurry," Sumatra went on; " we decided only today. You must remember that I am as much a Balavan as Annice, and I suit Epes far better; I understand and agree with his ambition."

The man's manner was colder than the night.

" What ambition? " he demanded.

" To go to sea, of course."

" Epes isn't going to sea," he instructed her.

" He wasn't, as your son," she corrected him; " but married to me, yes."

" No," Ira Calef answered in a restrained, bitter temper that yet had the effect of a shout.

"But he is," Sumatra Balavan retorted. "He is, and now you can't stop him. It doesn't matter what you want, I won't have a husband fastened like a sponge to the earth, and as soft as a sponge." Her anger, equal with Ira Calef's, rose.

The room grew quiet. Epes' attention was still concentrated on the heavy rectangle of glass close by his father's hand. With a sensation like an enveloping breath of winter air he saw the other's fingers reach out and close about the paper weight. He hadn't a second to spare; but Sumatra, too, had seen the instinctive movement on the table.

"I wish you would," she told the man facing her with a set, icy glare. "I'd have you dropped off the end of Derby Wharf. I'm not your wife or son; there would be no reason for my protecting you, hiding your beastliness from the world. Nothing could be better than having you throw a paper weight at me."

The shadows under Ira Calef's eyes, on the deathly pallor of his face, were like black smudges; a shiver passed over his rigidity. His hand drooped; both hands held the edge of the table before him. Epes, in a swift insight brushed with compassion, saw what was in his father's mind — the huddled light figure crushing the geranium border.

"Get out of here," the elder said to Sumatra in strained, dry tones. "Go, and take him with you."

"To sea?" she insisted.

"If there is any salt water in hell."

But, once more in the hall, she was pitiably shaken.

"What can we do?" she implored Epes, against him.

He reassured her that that was easy enough; a far different, apparently trivial and ill-timed question occupied him.

"Sumatra," he proceeded, "tonight Annice told me that she had lost the obang, the Calef token. Did you find it?"

"No, Epes," she replied, "I didn't find it." Her voice sank, died. "I didn't find it, Epes," she repeated with difficulty. "I couldn't, very well, could I, when I had stolen it?"

## QUESTIONS

1. In the first few pages note peculiarities of style.
2. Also note how clearly the author lays the foundation of his plot.
3. What is the first complicating fact?
4. Sum up briefly the character of the older Calef.
5. What is your feeling about the names of the characters?
6. Would Sumatra have been at once interesting with a commoner name?
7. What makes her an immediate possible complication?
8. What did Annice and Epes talk about in their first interview?
9. What can you say about Epes' mother?
10. Was Epes' nastiness toward Sumatra real? Explain.
11. Where exactly does the plot shift its direction?
12. Were you prepared for it? Explain.
13. Have you ever seen an old-fashioned fire engine? If so, tell the class about it.
14. Is the episode of the fire overdone, do you think? Explain.
15. Why did Sumatra smile after her recovery?
16. Bearing in mind her character, were you prepared for what she said to Epes' father?
17. What is the final surprise in the story? Were you expecting that?
18. Is the story well named? Explain.
19. Does it end " right "?
20. Should there have been a final scene with Annice? Explain.
21. Is it your understanding that the father relents?

## SUBJECTS FOR COMPOSITION

1. Sumatra Steals the Token.
2. Annice Visits Sumatra Five Years Later.
3. Every family has its traditions or superstitions. Write a story involving one with which you are familiar.
4. Tell orally the plot of " The Token."

## OTHER STORIES BY JOSEPH HERGESHEIMER

Tol'able David
Black Key
The Meeker Ritual

Blue Ice
Read Them and Weep

## VOLUMES OF STORIES BY JOSEPH HERGESHEIMER

*Gold and Iron*
*Dark Fleece*
*Tubal Cain*

*The Happy End*
*The Limestone Tree*
*The Presbyterian Child*

## O. HENRY
### (1862–1910)

THE most important single event in the literary life of William Sydney Porter, " O. Henry," was his apprenticeship in a drug store in Greensboro, N. C., the town where he was born in 1862. Ordinarily the profession of druggist is not known to be conducive to that of writer, but later circumstances in the life of Will Porter made it so. Work in a country drug store has few thrills, but the sixteen-year-old boy relieved the monotony by drawing caricatures of local celebrities. After three years the close confinement broke down a physique that had always been frail, and he gladly accepted the invitation of a doctor friend to go with him to Texas.

Will Porter's life in the Southwest may be summed up: he built up his health as an amateur ranchman; he studied languages and read much, one of his favorite books being Webster's *Unabridged Dictionary;* he earned a living by clerking, editing, cartooning, and as teller in a bank; married in 1887; more editing and some publishing; charged with irregularities in the bank, he avoided trial by fleeing to Central America; stopped over in New Orleans, where he adopted the name " O. Henry " for his writings; lost his wife before his trial; was convicted of embezzlement and sentenced to five years in the Federal Penitentiary at Columbus, Ohio.

It is only fair to add that subsequent analysis of the facts clearly proved that Will Porter's worst crime was carelessness in a bank that was exceedingly loose in its business methods. He certainly never took any money for himself. During this period he had written much, but nothing of distinction. He had been a " rolling stone " — little more. To crystallize his genius he needed concentrated leisure, and that was now forced on him for a little more than three years.

But leisure is not the convict's usual lot, and here is where his drugstore experience becomes of importance in his life. He became one of the prison druggists and a doctor's assistant. This responsible work carried with it the privilege of a room instead of a cell, and freedom from most of the galling horrors of prison life.

He now turned seriously to writing with a view to earning money to help support his little daughter, who lived with her grandmother and was kept ignorant of her father's imprisonment. His cheerful letters to her often became pathetic, especially around Christmas when he had to tell her that once again he would not be able to come home and " help light up the candles on the Christmas tree like we used to."

During these prison years O. Henry marketed his stories through a friend, and by the time he left in 1901 they had already begun to attract attention. At the suggestion of a New York editor, who was buying his stories at $100 apiece, O. Henry came to " Little Old

Bagdad-on-the-Subway" in 1902, where for the eight remaining years of his life he enjoyed unprecedented success.

This success was at first due to his material. He wrote about the things he knew best — the Southwest and Central America. Usually he depicted hoboes, fugitives from justice, crooks, cowboys, adventurers, and down-and-outers generally. Always he found in them some redeeming trait, and by exploiting that he made his characters likable. This interesting material he decked out in fascinating style, one of its elements being the racy dialogue.

When he began to pick up his characters on park benches, in saloons, in department stores, in soup lines, and in cheap boarding-houses, this interest of strange background was missing, and he whole-heartedly developed his gift for spinning a yarn entertainingly. Beginning in 1903, he wrote a story a week for the Sunday edition of the *World*. For two years and a half he kept that up. Space conditions kept his stories down to about 2500 words, but that was easy for O. Henry, because he had learned the art of packing much into a few words from Maupassant, who had written under similar restrictions.

The particular trick used by O. Henry was to take an incident or an anecdote, present it tersely in his inimitable style, with a humorous slant, unexpected turns of phrase, and odd twists of words, and then finish it off breathlessly with a "surprise" ending.

"The Third Ingredient" has all the characteristic earmarks of O. Henry — shopgirl, artist, both down and nearly out, racy, slangy dialogue, and unlooked-for coincidences that in a lesser artist would have been mere bunk. In this story, for good measure, we have a "movie" hero. Yet we forgive the author all his literary sins for the entertaining story he has told.

## THE THIRD INGREDIENT

THE (so-called) Vallambrosa Apartment-House is not an apartment-house. It is composed of two old-fashioned, brownstone-front residences welded into one. The parlor floor of one side is gay with the wraps and headgear of a modiste; the other is lugubrious with the sophistical promises and grisly display of a painless dentist. You may have a room there for two dollars a week or you may have one for twenty dollars. Among the Vallambrosa's roomers are stenographers, musicians, brokers, shop-girls, space-rate writers, art students, wire-tappers, and other people who lean far over the banister-rail when the door-bell rings.

This treatise shall have to do with but two of the Vallambrosians — though meaning no disrespect to the others.

At six o'clock one afternoon Hetty Pepper came back to her third-floor rear $3.50 room in the Vallambrosa with her nose and chin more sharply pointed than usual. To be discharged from the department store where you have been working four years and with only fifteen cents in your purse, does have a tendency to make your features appear more finely chiseled.

And now for Hetty's thumb-nail biography while she climbs the two flights of stairs.

She walked into the Biggest Store one morning four years before with seventy-five other girls, applying for a job behind the waist department counter. The phalanx of wage-earners formed a bewildering scene of beauty, carrying a total mass of blond hair sufficient to have justified the horseback gallops of a hundred Lady Godivas.

The capable, cool-eyed, impersonal, young, bald-headed man whose task it was to engage six of the contestants, was aware of a feeling of suffocation as if he were drowning in a sea of frangipanni, while white clouds, hand-embroidered, floated about him. And then a sail hove in sight. Hetty Pepper, homely of countenance, with small, contemptuous, green eyes and chocolate-colored hair, dressed in a suit of plain burlap and a common-sense hat, stood before him with every one of her twenty-nine years of life unmistakably in sight.

"You're on!" shouted the bald-headed young man, and was saved. And that is how Hetty came to be employed in the Biggest Store. The story of her rise to an eight-dollar-a-week salary is the combined stories of Hercules, Joan of Arc, Una, Job, and Little-Red-Riding-Hood. You shall not learn from me the salary that was paid her as a beginner. There is a sentiment growing about such things, and I want no millionaire store-proprietors climbing the fire-escape of my tenement-house to throw dynamite bombs into my skylight boudoir.

The story of Hetty's discharge from the Biggest Store is so nearly a repetition of her engagement as to be monotonous.

In each department of the store there is an omniscient, omnipresent, and omnivorous person carrying always a mileage book and a red necktie, and referred to as a "buyer."

## The Third Ingredient

The destinies of the girls in his department who live on (see Bureau of Victual Statistics) — so much per week are in his hands.

This particular buyer was a capable, cool-eyed, impersonal, young, bald-headed man. As he walked along the aisles of his department he seemed to be sailing on a sea of frangipanni, while white clouds, machine-embroidered, floated around him. Too many sweets bring surfeit. He looked upon Hetty Pepper's homely countenance, emerald eyes, and chocolate-colored hair as a welcome oasis of green in a desert of cloying beauty. In a quiet angle of a counter he pinched her arm kindly, three inches above the elbow. She slapped him three feet away with one good blow of her muscular and not especially lily-white right. So, now you know why Hetty Pepper came to leave the Biggest Store at thirty minutes' notice, with one dime and a nickel in her purse.

This morning's quotations list the price of rib beef at six cents per (butcher's) pound. But on the day that Hetty was "released" by the B. S. the price was seven and one-half cents. That fact is what makes this story possible. Otherwise, the extra four cents would have ——

But the plot of nearly all the good stories in the world is concerned with shorts who were unable to cover; so you can find no fault with this one.

Hetty mounted with her rib beef to her $3.50 third-floor back. One hot, savory beef-stew for supper, a night's good sleep, and she would be fit in the morning to apply again for the tasks of Hercules, Joan of Arc, Una, Job, and Little-Red-Riding-Hood.

In her room she got the granite-ware stew-pan out of the 2 x 4-foot china — er — I mean earthenware closet, and began to dig down in a rat's-nest of paper bags for the potatoes and onions. She came out with her nose and chin just a little sharper pointed.

There was neither a potato nor an onion. Now, what kind of a beef-stew can you make out of simply beef? You can make oyster-soup without oysters, turtle-soup without turtles, coffee-cake without coffee, but you can't make beef-stew without potatoes and onions.

But rib beef alone, in an emergency, can make an ordinary pine door look like a wrought-iron gambling-house portal to the wolf. With salt and pepper and a tablespoonful of flour (first well stirred in a little cold water) 'twill serve — 'tis not so deep as a lobster à la Newburg nor so wide as a church festival doughnut; but 'twill serve.

Hetty took her stew-pan to the rear of the third-floor hall. According to the advertisements of the Vallambrosa there was running water to be found there. Between you and me and the water-meter, it only ambled or walked through the faucets; but technicalities have no place here. There was also a sink where housekeeping roomers often met to dump their coffee grounds and glare at one another's kimonos.

At this sink Hetty found a girl with heavy, gold-brown, artistic hair and plaintive eyes, washing two large "Irish" potatoes. Hetty knew the Vallambrosa as well as any one not owning "double hextra-magnifying eyes" could compass its mysteries. The kimonos were her encyclopedia, her "Who's What?" her clearing-house of news, of goers and comers. From a rose-pink kimono edged with Nile green she had learned that the girl with the potatoes was a miniature-painter living in a kind of attic — or "studio," as they prefer to call it — on the top floor. Hetty was not certain in her mind what a miniature was; but it certainly wasn't a house; because house-painters, although they wear splashy overalls and poke ladders in your face on the street, are known to indulge in a riotous profusion of food at home.

The potato girl was quite slim and small, and handled her potatoes as an old bachelor uncle handles a baby who is cutting teeth. She had a dull shoemaker's knife in her right hand, and she had begun to peel one of the potatoes with it.

Hetty addressed her in the punctiliously formal tone of one who intends to be cheerfully familiar with you in the second round.

"Beg pardon," she said, "for butting into what's not my business, but if you peel them potatoes you lose out. They're new Bermudas. You want to scrape 'em. Lemme show you."

She took a potato and the knife, and began to demonstrate.

"Oh, thank you," breathed the artist. "I didn't know. And I *did* hate to see the thick peeling go; it seemed such a waste. But I thought they always had to be peeled. When you've got only potatoes to eat, the peelings count, you know."

## The Third Ingredient

"Say, kid," said Hetty, staying her knife, "you ain't up against it, too, are you?"

The miniature artist smiled starvedly.

"I suppose I am. Art — or, at least, the way I interpret it — doesn't seem to be much in demand. I have only these potatoes for my dinner. But they aren't so bad boiled and hot, with a little butter and salt."

"Child," said Hetty, letting a brief smile soften her rigid features, "Fate has sent me and you together. I've had it handed to me in the neck, too; but I've got a chunk of meat in my room as big as a lap-dog. And I've done everything to get potatoes except pray for 'em. Let's me and you bunch our commissary departments and make a stew of 'em. We'll cook it in my room. If we only had an onion to go in it! Say, kid, you haven't got a couple of pennies that've slipped down into the lining of your last winter's sealskin, have you? I could step down to the corner and get one at old Giuseppe's stand. A stew without an onion is worse'n a matinée without candy."

"You may call me Cecilia," said the artist. "No; I spent my last penny three days ago."

"Then we'll have to cut the onion out instead of slicing it in," said Hetty. "I'd ask the janitress for one, but I don't want 'em hep just yet to the fact that I'm pounding the asphalt for another job. But I wish we did have an onion."

In the shop-girl's room the two began to prepare their supper. Cecilia's part was to sit on the couch helplessly and beg to be allowed to do something, in the voice of a cooing ring-dove. Hetty prepared the rib beef, putting it in cold salted water in the stew-pan and setting it on the one-burner gas-stove.

"I wish we had an onion," said Hetty, as she scraped the two potatoes.

On the wall opposite the couch was pinned a flaming, gorgeous advertising picture of one of the new ferry-boats of the P. U. F. F. Railroad that had been built to cut down the time between Los Angeles and New York City one-eighth of a minute.

Hetty, turning her head during her continuous monologue, saw tears running from her guest's eyes as she gazed on the idealized presentment of the speeding, foam-girdled transport.

"Why, say, Cecilia, kid," said Hetty, poising her knife, "is it as bad art as that? I ain't a critic; but I thought it kind of brightened up the room. Of course, a manicure-painter could tell it was a bum picture in a minute. I'll take it down if you say so. I wish to the holy Saint Potluck we had an onion."

But the miniature miniature-painter had tumbled down, sobbing, with her nose indenting the hard-woven drapery of the couch. Something was here deeper than the artistic temperament offended at crude lithography.

Hetty knew. She had accepted her rôle long ago. How scant the words with which we try to describe a single quality of a human being! When we reach the abstract we are lost. The nearer to Nature that the babbling of our lips comes, the better do we understand. Figuratively (let us say), some people are Bosoms, some are Hands, some are Heads, some are Muscles, some are Feet, some are Backs for burdens.

Hetty was a Shoulder. Hers was a sharp, sinewy shoulder; but all her life people had laid their heads upon it, metaphorically or actually, and had left there all or half their troubles. Looking at Life anatomically, which is as good a way as any, she was preordained to be a Shoulder. There were few truer collar-bones anywhere than hers.

Hetty was only thirty-three, and she had not yet outlived the little pang that visited her whenever the head of youth and beauty leaned upon her for consolation. But one glance in her mirror always served as an instantaneous pain-killer. So she gave one pale look into the crinkly old looking-glass on the wall above the gas-stove, turned down the flame a little lower from the bubbling beef and potatoes, went over to the couch, and lifted Cecilia's head to its confessional.

"Go on and tell me, honey," she said. "I know now that it ain't art that's worrying you. You met him on a ferry-boat, didn't you? Go on, Cecilia, kid, and tell your — your Aunt Hetty about it."

But youth and melancholy must first spend the surplus of sighs and tears that waft and float the barque of romance to its harbor in the delectable isles. Presently, through the stringy tendons that formed the bars of the confessional, the penitent — or was it the glorified communicant of the sacred flame? — told her story without art or illumination.

## The Third Ingredient

"It was only three days ago. I was coming back on the ferry from Jersey City. Old Mr. Schrum, an art dealer, told me of a rich man in Newark who wanted a miniature of his daughter painted. I went to see him and showed him some of my work. When I told him the price would be fifty dollars he laughed at me like a hyena. He said an enlarged crayon twenty times the size would cost him only eight dollars.

"I had just enough money to buy my ferry ticket back to New York. I felt as if I didn't want to live another day. I must have looked as I felt, for I saw *him* on the row of seats opposite me, looking at me as if he understood. He was nice-looking, but oh, above everything else, he looked kind. When one is tired or unhappy or hopeless, kindness counts more than anything else.

"When I got so miserable that I couldn't fight against it any longer, I got up and walked slowly out the rear door of the ferry-boat cabin. No one was there, and I slipped quickly over the rail and dropped into the water. Oh, friend Hetty, it was cold, cold!

"For just one moment I wished I was back in the old Vallambrosa, starving and hoping. And then I got numb, and didn't care. And then I felt that somebody else was in the water close by me, holding me up. *He* had followed me, and jumped in to save me.

"Somebody threw a thing like a big, white doughnut at us, and he made me put my arms through the hole. Then the ferry-boat backed, and they pulled us on board. Oh, Hetty, I was so ashamed of my wickedness in trying to drown myself; and, besides, my hair had all tumbled down and was sopping wet, and I was such a sight.

"And then some men in blue clothes came around; and *he* gave them his card, and I heard him tell them he had seen me drop my purse on the edge of the boat outside the rail, and in leaning over to get it I had fallen overboard. And then I remembered having read in the papers that people who try to kill themselves are locked up in cells with people who try to kill other people, and I was afraid.

"But some ladies on the boat took me downstairs to the furnace-room and got me nearly dry and did up my hair. When the boat landed, *he* came and put me in a cab. He was all dripping himself, but laughed as if he thought it was all a joke. He begged me, but I wouldn't tell him my name nor where I lived, I was so ashamed."

"You were a fool, child," said Hetty, kindly. "Wait till I turn the light up a bit. I wish to Heaven we had an onion."

"Then he raised his hat," went on Cecilia, "and said: 'Very well. But I'll find you, anyhow. I'm going to claim my rights of salvage.' Then he gave money to the cab-driver and told him to take me where I wanted to go, and walked away. What is 'salvage,' Hetty?"

"The edge of a piece of goods that ain't hemmed," said the shop-girl. "You must have looked pretty well frazzled out to the little hero boy."

"It's been three days," moaned the miniature-painter, "and he hasn't found me yet."

"Extend the time," said Hetty. "This is a big town. Think of how many girls he might have to see soaked in water with their hair down before he would recognize you. The stew's getting on fine — but oh, for an onion! I'd even use a piece of garlic if I had it."

The beef and potatoes bubbled merrily, exhaling a mouth-watering savor that yet lacked something, leaving a hunger on the palate, a haunting, wistful desire for some lost and needful ingredient.

"I came near drowning in that awful river," said Cecilia, shuddering.

"It ought to have more water in it," said Hetty; "the stew, I mean. I'll go get some at the sink."

"It smells good," said the artist.

"That nasty old North River?" objected Hetty. "It smells to me like soap factories and wet setter-dogs — oh, you mean the stew. Well, I wish we had an onion for it. Did he look like he had money?"

"First, he looked kind," said Cecilia. "I'm sure he was rich; but that matters so little. When he drew out his billfolder to pay the cabman you couldn't help seeing hundreds and thousands of dollars in it. And I looked over the cab doors and saw him leave the ferry station in a motor-car; and the chauffeur gave him his bearskin to put on, for he was sopping wet. And it was only three days ago."

"What a fool!" said Hetty, shortly.

## The Third Ingredient

"Oh, the chauffeur wasn't wet," breathed Cecilia. "And he drove the car away very nicely."

"I mean *you*," said Hetty. "For not giving him your address."

"I never give my address to chauffeurs," said Cecilia, haughtily.

"I wish we had one," said Hetty, disconsolately.

"What for?"

"For the stew, of course — oh, I mean an onion."

Hetty took a pitcher and started to the sink at the end of the hall.

A young man come down the stairs from above just as she was opposite the lower step. He was decently dressed, but pale and haggard. His eyes were dull with the stress of some burden of physical or mental woe. In his hand he bore an onion — a pink, smooth, solid, shining onion as large around as a ninety-eight-cent alarm-clock.

Hetty stopped. So did the young man. There was something Joan of Arc-ish, Herculean, and Una-ish in the look and pose of the shop-lady — she had cast off the rôles of Job and Little-Red-Riding-Hood. The young man stopped at the foot of the stairs and coughed distractedly. He felt marooned, held up, attacked, assailed, levied upon, sacked, assessed, panhandled, browbeaten, though he knew not why. It was the look in Hetty's eyes that did it. In them he saw the Jolly Roger fly to the masthead and an able seaman with a dirk between his teeth scurry up the ratlines and nail it there. But as yet he did not know that the cargo he carried was the thing that had caused him to be so nearly blown out of the water without even a parley.

"*Beg* your pardon," said Hetty, as sweetly as her dilute acetic acid tones permitted, "but did you find that onion on the stairs? There was a hole in the paper bag; and I've just come out to look for it."

The young man coughed for half a minute. The interval may have given him the courage to defend his own property. Also, he clutched his pungent prize greedily, and, with a show of spirit, faced his grim waylayer.

"No," he said huskily, "I didn't find it on the stairs. It was given to me by Jack Bevens, on the top floor. If you don't believe it, ask him. I'll wait until you do."

"I know about Bevens," said Hetty, sourly. "He writes books and things up there for the paper-and-rags man. We can hear the postman guy him all over the house when he brings them thick envelopes back. Say — do you live in the Vallambrosa?"

"I do not," said the young man. "I come to see Bevens sometimes. He's my friend. I live two blocks west."

"What are you going to do with the onion? — *begging* your pardon," said Hetty.

"I'm going to eat it."

"Raw?"

"Yes: as soon as I get home."

"Haven't you got anything else to eat with it?"

The young man considered briefly.

"No," he confessed; "there's not another scrap of anything in my diggings to eat. I think old Jack is pretty hard up for grub in his shack, too. He hated to give up the onion, but I worried him into parting with it."

"Man," said Hetty, fixing him with her world-sapient eyes, and laying a bony but impressive finger on his sleeve, "you've known trouble, too, haven't you?"

"Lots," said the onion owner, promptly. "But this onion is my own property, honestly come by. If you will excuse me, I must be going."

"Listen," said Hetty, paling a little with anxiety. "Raw onion is a mighty poor diet. And so is a beef-stew without one. Now, if you're Jack Bevens' friend, I guess you're nearly right. There's a little lady — a friend of mine — in my room there at the end of the hall. Both of us are out of luck; and we had just potatoes and meat between us. They're stewing now. But it ain't got any soul. There's something lacking to it. There's certain things in life that are naturally intended to fit and belong together. One is pink cheesecloth and green roses, and one is ham and eggs, and one is Irish and trouble. And the other one is beef and potatoes *with* onions. And still another one is people who are up against it and other people in the same fix."

The young man went into a protracted paroxysm of coughing. With one hand he hugged his onion to his bosom.

"No doubt; no doubt," said he, at length. "But, as I said, I must be going, because ——"

Hetty clutched his sleeve firmly.

"Don't be a Dago, Little Brother. Don't eat raw onions. Chip it in toward the dinner and line yourself inside with the best stew you ever licked a spoon over. Must two ladies knock a young gentleman down and drag him inside for the honor of dining with 'em? No harm shall befall you, Little Brother. Loosen up and fall into line."

The young man's pale face relaxed into a grin.

"Believe I'll go you," he said, brightening. "If my onion is good as a credential, I'll accept the invitation gladly."

"It's good as that, but better as seasoning," said Hetty. "You come and stand outside the door till I ask my lady friend if she has any objections. And don't run away with that letter of recommendation before I come out."

Hetty went into her room and closed the door. The young man waited outside.

"Cecilia, kid," said the shop-girl, oiling the sharp saw of her voice as well as she could, "there's an onion outside. With a young man attached. I've asked him in to dinner. You ain't going to kick, are you?"

"Oh, dear!" said Cecilia, sitting up and patting her artistic hair. She cast a mournful glance at the ferry-boat poster on the wall.

"Nit," said Hetty. "It ain't him. You're up against real life now. I believe you said your hero friend had money and automobiles. This is a poor skeezicks that's got nothing to eat but an onion. But he's easy-spoken and not a freshy. I imagine he's been a gentleman, he's so low down now. And we need the onion. Shall I bring him in? I'll guarantee his behavior."

"Hetty, dear," sighed Cecilia, "I'm so hungry. What difference does it make whether he's a prince or a burglar? I don't care. Bring him in if he's got anything to eat with him."

Hetty went back into the hall. The onion man was gone. Her heart missed a beat, and a gray look settled over her face except on her nose and cheek-bones. And then the tides of life flowed in again, for she saw him leaning out of the front window at the other end of the hall. She hurried there. He was shouting to some one below. The noise of the street overpowered the sound of her footsteps. She looked down over his shoulder, saw whom he was speaking to, and heard his words. He pulled himself in from the window-sill and saw her standing over him.

Hetty's eyes bored into him like two steel gimlets.

"Don't lie to me," she said, calmly. "What were you going to do with that onion?"

The young man suppressed a cough and faced her resolutely. His manner was that of one who had been bearded sufficiently.

"I was going to eat it," said he, with emphatic slowness; "just as I told you before."

"And you have nothing else to eat at home?"

"Not a thing."

"What kind of work do you do?"

"I am not working at anything just now."

"Then why," said Hetty, with her voice set on its sharpest edge, "do you lean out of windows and give orders to chauffeurs in green automobiles in the street below?"

The young man flushed, and his dull eyes began to sparkle.

"Because, madam," said he, in *accelerando* tones, "I pay the chauffeur's wages and I own the automobile — and also this onion — this onion, madam."

He flourished the onion within an inch of Hetty's nose. The shop-lady did not retreat a hair's-breadth.

"Then why do you eat onions," she said, with biting contempt, "and nothing else?"

"I never said I did," retorted the young man, heatedly. "I said I had nothing else to eat where I live. I am not a delicatessen storekeeper."

"Then why," pursued Hetty, inflexibly, "were you going to eat a raw onion?"

"My mother," said the young man, "always made me eat one for a cold. Pardon my referring to a physical infirmity; but you may have noticed that I have a very, very severe cold. I was going to eat the onion and go to bed. I wonder why I am standing here and apologizing to you for it."

"How did you catch this cold?" went on Hetty, suspiciously.

The young man seemed to have arrived at some extreme height of feeling. There were two modes of descent open to him — a burst of rage or a surrender to the ridiculous. He chose wisely; and the empty hall echoed his hoarse laughter.

"You're a dandy," said he. "And I don't blame you for being careful. I don't mind telling you. I got wet. I was on a North River ferry a few days ago when a girl jumped overboard. Of course, I——"

Hetty extended her hand, interrupting his story.

"Give me the onion," she said.

The young man set his jaw a trifle harder.

"Give me the onion," she repeated.

He grinned, and laid it in her hand.

Then Hetty's infrequent, grim, melancholy smile showed itself. She took the young man's arm and pointed with her other hand to the door of her room.

"Little Brother," she said, "go in there. The little fool you fished out of the river is there waiting for you. Go on in. I'll give you three minutes before I come. Potatoes is in there, waiting. Go on in, Onions."

After he had tapped at the door and entered, Hetty began to peel and wash the onion at the sink. She gave a gray look at the gray roofs outside, and the smile on her face vanished by little jerks and twitches.

"But it's us," she said, grimly, to herself, "it's *us* that furnishes the beef."

## QUESTIONS

1. From the first pages select words and phrases giving a humorous touch.
2. What types of humor do you find throughout the story?
3. Is it grotesque, exaggeration, satire, mere words, or the situation?
4. In a short paragraph write a sketch of Hetty.
5. Make a list of repetitions. What is gained by them?
6. How does the author prepare for the "third ingredient" as part of the complication?
7. Why did Hetty say, "You met him on the ferry-boat, didn't you?"
8. How does the contrast between Hetty and Cecilia affect the story?
9. In Cecilia's story, what was to her the most "tragic" part?
10. What is *coincidence*? Where used in the story?
11. Does it improve or spoil the story? Explain.
12. What do "them thick envelopes" tell about the author upstairs?
13. Why doesn't the author tell what Hetty heard at the window-sill?

14. Had you guessed the identity of the young man? How?
15. Should the story tell what happened when the young man entered the room? Explain.
16. What does Hetty mean by her last speech? Who is "us"?
17. Is the end of the story satisfying? Explain.
18. Would you call this a "typical" O. Henry story? See sketch.

## SUBJECTS FOR COMPOSITION

1. Write an episode of Hetty's life before she entered the store.
2. A possible different ending.
3. Hetty gets a new job.
4. Cecilia ten years later.

## VOLUMES OF STORIES BY O. HENRY

*The Four Million*
*The Trimmed Lamp*
*Heart of the West*
*The Voice of the City*
*The Gentle Grafter*
*Roads of Destiny*
*Options*
*Whirligigs*
*Selected Stories from O. Henry*
*Complete Works* (one volume)

## ABOUT O. HENRY

***O. Henry Biography***, C. Alphonso Smith
***Through the Depths with O. Henry***, Al. Jennings

## FRANCES GILCHRIST WOOD

SINCE the days of James Fenimore Cooper there have been many writers who have told of the white man's adventures among the Indians and the almost unbelievable hardships of the pioneers' struggles in developing the lands west of the Alleghenies. There have been western stories of all kinds, but chiefly of the flamboyant type that had little basis in reality. It is only recently that a few writers have tried to show the spirit and courage of the pioneers in wrestling with the problems of mere survival amid the primitively hostile forces of nature, and the equally hostile, selfish rivalries among men.

Among the writers of the short story in this field no one has struck so deep a note of truth and sincerity as Mrs. Frances Gilchrist Wood. In reply to the editor's request that she tell something about herself Mrs. Wood summarized her life as follows:

"A descendant of pioneers who were in the first boatload of Roundheads landing at Plymouth Rock; and the Cavaliers settling in the state of Virginia. In the second great trek in the United States by the first All-American team of pioneers, my grandparents came respectively from New England and Virginia to the Mississippi Valley in western Illinois. There as a girl just through college I followed the family tradition and pioneered to the land of the Dakotas on the border just east of the Missouri. Those experiences were burned in deep at an impressionable age. Perhaps it was that life, plus the trend of inherited tradition, that makes me always 'see stories' in a country and people in the making, more perhaps than anywhere else.

"I was too active a tomboy to spend my early years mooning over any type of writing except the most dynamic of plays. I was one of a large family of children who squandered all our small allowance on tin footlights and candles, gilt paper and paints; when the adult audience refused to leave comfortable fireside chairs, we promptly picked up Mahomet and transported the stage to a convenient bay window in the sitting-room where the immovable Mountains had merely to lift their eyes.

"My first recorded play runs: 'She *thrushl* into the room! He clung her to his heart! She fainted! They are married!'

"The required composition work at school was my only other early effort. Given a list of possible subjects, I always chose 'Adrift on an Iceberg,' 'Under the Sea,' and such wildly adventurous titles. I remember always insisting to myself that the experience must be actually mine, and *in propria persona* of the small schoolgirl I somehow wriggled through within the bounds of imaginative credibility. Of course I was as devoted to all the English courses from primary to final college year as I bitterly hated all mathematics."

As to "Turkey Red," she says elsewhere: "The blizzards were of common occurrence, our daily life, in fact. Strangers like Smith coming into the country were contemptuous and condescending because so painfully ignorant. The isolated shacks grappling with death in far separated shacks during impassable storms was one of the terrors of life. The child with the croup was my own. That life burned in deep in the impressionable years of youth, never to be erased. Ask any pioneer the significance of our cheap turkey-red calico that covered some of the ugliness of a sod shack. They'll laugh, catch their breath, maybe, but they'll know! The thing that made me write 'Turkey Red' was the undying courage of the pioneer."

Mrs. Wood was born in Carthage, Illinois, went through college there, travels a great deal, and has her home in New York.

## TURKEY RED

THE old mail-sled running between Haney and Le Beau, in the days when Dakota was still a Territory, was nearing the end of its hundred-mile route.

It was a desolate country in those days; geographers still described it as The Great American Desert, and in looks it deserved the title. Never was there anything so lonesome as that endless stretch of snow reaching across the world until it cut into a cold gray sky, excepting the same desert burned to a brown tinder by the hot wind of summer.

Nothing but sky and plain and its voice, the wind, unless you might count a lonely sod shack blocked against the horizon, miles away from a neighbor, miles from anywhere, its red-curtained square of window glowing through the early twilight.

There were three men in the sled: Dan, the mail-carrier, crusty, belligerently western, the self-selected guardian of every one on his route; Hillas, a younger man, hardly more than a boy, living on his pre-emption claim near the upper reaches of the stage line; the third a stranger from that part of the country vaguely defined as "the East." He was traveling, had given his name as Smith, and was as inquisitive about the country as he was reticent about his business there. Dan plainly disapproved of him.

They had driven the last cold miles in silence when the stage-driver turned to his neighbor. "Letter didn't say anything about coming out in the spring to look over the country, did it?"

Hillas shook his head. "It was like all the rest, Dan. Don't want to build a railroad at all until the country's settled."

"God! Can't they see the other side of it? What it means to the folks already here to wait for it?"

The stranger thrust a suddenly interested profile above the handsome collar of his fur coat. He looked out over the waste of snow.

"You say there's no timber here?"

Dan maintained unfriendly silence and Hillas answered: "Nothing but scrub on the banks of the creeks. Years of prairie fires have burned out the trees, we think."

"Any ores — mines?"

The boy shook his head as he slid farther down in his worn buffalo coat of the plains.

"We're too busy rustling for something to eat first. And you can't develop mines without tools."

"Tools?"

"Yes, a railroad first of all."

Dan shifted the lines from one fur-mittened hand to the other, swinging the freed numbed arm in rhythmic beating against his body as he looked along the horizon a bit anxiously. The stranger shivered visibly.

"It's a God-forsaken country. Why don't you get out?"

Hillas, following Dan's glance around the blurred sky line, answered absently, "Usual answer is 'Leave? It's all I can do to stay here.'"

Smith regarded him irritably. "Why should any sane man ever have chosen this frozen wilderness?"

Hillas closed his eyes wearily. "We came in the spring."

"I see!" The edged voice snapped, "Visionaries!"

Hillas's eyes opened again, wide, and then the boy was looking beyond the man with the far-seeing eyes of the plainsman. He spoke under his breath as if he were alone.

"Visionary, pioneer, American. That was the evolution in the beginning. Perhaps that is what we are." Suddenly the endurance in his voice went down before a wave of bitterness. "The first pioneers had to wait, too. How could they stand it so long!"

The young shoulders drooped as he thrust stiff fingers deep within the shapeless coat pockets. He slowly withdrew his right hand holding a parcel wrapped in brown paper. He tore a three-cornered flap in the cover, looked at the brightly colored contents, replaced the flap and returned the parcel, his chin a little higher.

Dan watched the northern sky line restlessly. "It won't be snow. Look like a blizzard to you, Hillas?"

The traveler sat up. "Blizzard?"

"Yes," Dan drawled in willing contribution to his uneasiness, "the real Dakota article where blizzards are made. None of your eastern imitations, but a ninety-mile wind that whets slivers of ice off the frozen drifts all the way down from the North Pole. Only one good thing about a blizzard — it's over in a hurry. You get to shelter or you freeze to death."

A gust of wind flung a powder of snow stingingly against their faces. The traveler withdrew his head turtlewise within the handsome collar in final condemnation. "No man in his senses would ever have deliberately come here to live."

Dan turned. "Wouldn't, eh?"

"No."

"You're American?"

"Yes."

"Why?"

"I was born here. It's my country."

"Ever read about your Pilgrim Fathers?"

"Why, of course."

"Frontiersmen, same as us. You're living on what they did. We're getting this frontier ready for those who come after. Want our children to have a better chance than we had. Our reason's same as theirs. Hillas told you the truth. Country's all right if we had a railroad."

"Humph!" With a contemptuous look across the desert. "Where's your freight, your grain, cattle ——"

"*West*-bound freight, coal, feed, seed-grain, work, and more neighbors."

"One-sided bargain. Road that hauls empties one way doesn't pay. No company would risk a line through here."

The angles of Dan's jaw showed white. "Maybe. Ever get a chance to pay your debt to those Pilgrim pioneers? Ever take it? Think the stock was worth saving?"

## Turkey Red

He lifted his whip-handle toward a pin-point of light across the stretch of snow. " Donovan lives over there and Mis' Donovan. We call them ' old folks ' now; their hair has turned white as these drifts in two years. All they've got is here. He's a real farmer and a lot of help to the country, but they won't last long like this."

Dan swung his arm toward a glimmer nor' by nor'east. " Mis' Clark lives there, a mile back from the stage road. Clark's down in Yankton earning money to keep them going. She's alone with her baby holding down the claim." Dan's arm sagged. " We've had women go crazy out here."

The whip-stock followed the empty horizon half round the compass to a lighted red square not more than two miles away. " Mis' Carson died in the spring. Carson stayed until he was too poor to get away. There's three children — oldest's Katy, just eleven." Dan's words failed, but his eyes told. " Somebody will brag of them as ancestors some day. They'll deserve it if they live through this."

Dan's jaw squared as he leveled his whip-handle straight at the traveler. " I've answered your questions, now you answer mine! We know your opinion of the country — you're not traveling for pleasure or your health. What are you here for? "

" Business. My own! "

" There's two kinds of business out here this time of year. 'Tain't healthy for either of them." Dan's words were measured and clipped. " You've damned the West and all that's in it good and plenty. Now I say, damn the people anywhere in the whole country that won't pay their debts from pioneer to pioneer; that lets us fight the wilderness barehanded and die fighting; that won't risk —— "

A gray film dropped down over the world, a leaden shroud that was not the coming of twilight. Dan jerked about, his whip cracked out over the heads of the leaders and they broke into a quick trot. The shriek of the runners along the frozen snow cut through the ominous darkness.

" Hillas," Dan's voice came sharply, " stand up and look for the light on Clark's guide-pole about a mile to the right. God help us if it ain't burning."

Hillas struggled up, one clumsy mitten thatching his eyes from the blinding needles. " I don't see it, Dan. We can't be more than a mile away. Hadn't you better break toward it?"

"Got to keep the track till we — see — light!"

The wind tore the words from his mouth as it struck them in lashing fury. The leaders had disappeared in a wall of snow, but Dan's lash whistled forward in reminding authority. There was a moment's lull.

"See it, Hillas?"

"No, Dan."

Tiger-like the storm leaped again, bandying them about in its paws like captive mice. The horses swerved before the punishing blows, bunched, backed, tangled. Dan stood up shouting his orders of menacing appeal above the storm.

Again a breathing space before the next deadly impact. As it came Hillas shouted, "I see it — there, Dan! It's a red light. She's in trouble."

Through the whirling smother and chaos of Dan's cries and the struggling horses the sled lunged out of the road into unbroken drifts. Again the leaders swung sidewise before the lashing of a thousand lariats of ice and bunched against the wheel-horses. Dan swore, prayed, mastered them with far-reaching lash, then the off leader went down. Dan felt behind him for Hillas and shoved the reins against his arm.

"I'll get him up — or cut leaders — loose! If I don't — come back — drive to light. *Don't — get — out!*"

Dan disappeared in the white fury. There were sounds of a struggle; the sled jerked sharply and stood still. Slowly it strained forward.

Hillas was standing, one foot outside on the runner, as they traveled a team's length ahead. He gave a cry — "Dan! Dan!" and gripped a furry bulk that lumbered up out of the drift.

"All — right — son." Dan reached for the reins.

Frantically they fought their slow way toward the blurred light, staggering on in a fight with the odds too savage to last. They stopped abruptly as the winded leaders leaned against a wall interposed between themselves and insatiable fury.

Dan stepped over the dashboard, groped his way along the tongue between the wheel-horses and reached the leeway of a shadowy square. "It's the shed, Hillas. Help get the team in." The exhausted animals crowded into the narrow space without protest.

"Find the guide-rope to the house, Dan?"

"On the other side, toward the shack. Where's — Smith?"

"Here, by the shed."

Dan turned toward the stranger's voice.

"We're going 'round to the blizzard-line tied from shed to shack. Take hold of it and don't let go. If you do you'll freeze before we can find you. When the wind comes, turn your back and wait. Go on when it dies down and never let go the rope. Ready? The wind's dropped. Here, Hillas, next to me."

Three blurs hugged the sod walls around to the northeast corner. The forward shadow reached upward to a swaying rope, lifted the hand of the second who guided the third.

"Hang on to my belt, too, Hillas. Ready — Smith? Got the rope?"

They crawled forward, three barely visible figures, six, eight, ten steps. With a shriek the wind tore at them, beat the breath from their bodies, cut them with stinging needle-points and threw them aside. Dan reached back to make sure of Hillas, who fumbled through the darkness for the stranger.

Slowly they struggled ahead, the cold growing more intense; two steps, four, and the mounting fury of the blizzard reached its zenith. The blurs swayed like battered leaves on a vine that the wind tore in two at last and flung the living beings wide. Dan, clinging to the broken rope, rolled over and found Hillas with the frayed end of the line in his hand, reaching about through the black drifts for the stranger. Dan crept closer, his mouth at Hillas's ear, shouting, "Quick! Right behind me if we're to live through it!"

The next moment Hillas let go the rope. Dan reached madly. "Boy, you can't find him — it'll only be two instead of one! Hillas! Hillas!"

The storm screamed louder than the plainsman and began heaping the snow over three obstructions in its path, two that groped slowly and one that lay still. Dan fumbled at his belt, unfastened it, slipped the rope through the buckle, knotted it and crept its full length back toward the boy. A snow-covered something moved forward guiding another, one arm groping in blind search, reached and touched the man clinging to the belt.

Beaten and buffeted by the ceaseless fury that no longer gave quarter, they slowly fought their way hand-over-hand along the rope, Dan now crawling last. After a frozen eternity they reached the end of the line fastened man-high against a second haven of wall. Hillas pushed open the unlocked door, the three men staggered in and fell panting against the side of the room.

The stage-driver recovered first, pulled off his mittens, examined his fingers and felt quickly of nose, ears, and chin. He looked sharply at Hillas and nodded. Unceremoniously they stripped off the stranger's gloves, reached for a pan, opened the door, dipped it into the drift and plunged Smith's fingers down in the snow.

"Your nose is white, too. Thaw it out."

Abruptly Dan indicated a bench against the wall where the two men seated would take up less space.

" I'm —— " The stranger's voice was unsteady. " I —— " But Dan had turned his back and his attention to the homesteader.

The eight by ten room constituted the entire home. A shed roof slanted from eight feet high on the door and window side to a bit more than five on the other. A bed in one corner took up most of the space, and the remaining necessities were bestowed with the compactness of a ship's cabin. The rough boards of the roof and walls had been hidden by a covering of newspapers, with a row of illustrations pasted picture height. Cushions and curtains of turkey-red calico brightened the homely shack.

The driver had slipped off his buffalo coat and was bending over a baby exhaustedly fighting for breath that whistled shrilly through a closing throat. The mother, scarcely more than a girl, held her in tensely extended arms.

"How long's she been this way?"

"She began to choke up day before yesterday, just after you passed on the down trip."

The driver laid his finger tips on the restless wrist.

"She always has the croup when she cuts a tooth, Dan, but this is different. I've used all the medicines I have — nothing relieves the choking."

The girl lifted heavy eyelids above blue semicircles of fatigue and the compelling terror back of her eyes forced a question through dry lips.

"Dan, do you know what membranous croup is like? Is this it?"

The stage-driver picked up the lamp and held it close to the child's face, bringing out with distressing clearness the blue-veined pallor, sunken eyes, and effort of impeded breathing. He frowned, putting the lamp back quickly.

"Mebbe it is, Mis' Clark, but don't you be scared. We'll help you a spell."

Dan lifted the red curtain from the cupboard, found an emptied lard-pail, half filled it with water and placed it on an oil-stove that stood in the center of the room. He looked questioningly about the four walls, discovered a cleverly contrived tool-box beneath the cupboard shelves, sorted out a pair of pincers and bits of iron, laying the latter in a row over the oil blaze. He took down a can of condensed milk, poured a spoonful of the thick stuff into a cup of water and made room for it near the bits of heating iron.

He turned to the girl, opened his lips as if to speak, and stood with a face full of pity.

Along the four-foot space between the end of the bed and the opposite wall the girl walked, crooning to the sick child she carried. As they watched, the low song died away, her shoulder rubbed heavily against the boarding, her eyelids dropped, and she stood sound asleep. The next hard-drawn breath of the baby roused her and she stumbled on, crooning a lullaby.

Smith clutched the younger man's shoulder. "God, Hillas, look where she's marked the wall rubbing against it! Do you suppose she's been walking that way for three days and nights? Why, she's only a child — no older than my own daughter!"

Hillas nodded.

"Where are her people? Where's her husband?"

"Down in Yankton, Dan told you, working for the winter. Got to have the money to live."

"Where's the doctor?"

"Nearest one's in Haney — four days' trip away by stage."

The traveler stared, frowningly.

Dan was looking about the room again and after prodding the gay seat in the corner, lifted the cover and picked up a folded blanket, shaking out the erstwhile padded cushion. He hung the blanket over the back of a chair.

"Mis' Clark, there's nothing but steam will touch membreenous croup. We saved my baby that way last year. Set here and I'll fix things."

He put the steaming lard-pail on the floor beside the mother and lifted the blanket over the baby's head. She put up her hand.

"She's so little, Dan, and weak. How am I going to know if she — if she ——"

Dan rearranged the blanket tent. "Jest get under with her yourself, Mis' Clark, then you'll know all that's happening."

With the pincers he picked up a bit of hot iron and dropped it hissing into the pail, which he pushed beneath the tent. The room was oppressively quiet, walled in by the thick sod from the storm. The blanket muffled the sound of the child's breathing and the girl no longer stumbled against the wall.

Dan lifted the corner of the blanket and another bit of iron hissed as it struck the water. The older man leaned toward the younger.

"Stove — fire?" with a gesture of protest against the inadequate oil blaze.

Hillas whispered, "Can't afford it. Coal is $9.00 in Haney, $18.00 here."

They sat with heads thrust forward, listening in the intolerable silence. Dan lifted the blanket, hearkened a moment, then — "pst!" another bit of iron fell into the pail. Dan stooped to the tool-chest for a reserve supply when a strangling cough made him spring to his feet and hurriedly lift the blanket.

The child was beating the air with tiny fists fighting for breath. The mother stood rigid, arms out.

"Turn her this way!" Dan shifted the struggling child, face out. "Now watch out for the ——"

The strangling cough broke and a horrible something — "It's the membrane! She's too weak — let me have her!"

Dan snatched the child and turned it face downward. The blue-faced baby fought in a supreme effort — again the horrible something — then Dan laid the child, white and motionless, in her mother's arms. She held the limp body close, her eyes wide with fear.

"Dan, is — is she ——"

A faint sobbing breath of relief fluttered the pale lips that moved in the merest ghost of a smile. The heavy eyelids half-lifted and the child nestled against its mother's breast. The girl swayed, shaking with sobs, "Baby — baby!"

She struggled for self-control and stood up straight and pale. "Dan, I ought to tell you. When it began to get dark with the storm and time to put up the lantern, I was afraid to leave the baby. If she strangled when I was gone — with no one to help her — she would die!"

Her lips quivered as she drew the child closer. "I didn't go right away but — I did — at last. I propped her up in bed and ran. If I hadn't" — her eyes were wide with the shadowy edge of horror — "if I hadn't — you'd have been lost in the blizzard and — my baby would have died!"

She stood before the men as if for judgment, her face wet with unchecked tears. Dan patted her shoulder dumbly and touched a fresh, livid bruise that ran from the curling hair on her temple down across cheek and chin.

"Did you get this then?'"

She nodded. "The storm threw me against the pole when I hoisted the lantern. I thought I'd — never — get back!"

It was Smith who translated Dan's look of appeal for the cup of warm milk and held it to the girl's lips.

"Drink it, Mis' Clark, you need it."

She made heroic attempts to swallow, her head drooped lower over the cup and fell against the driver's rough sleeve. "Poor kid, dead asleep!"

Dan guided her stumbling feet toward the bed that the traveler sprang to open. She guarded the baby in the protecting angle of her arm into safety upon the pillow, then fell like a log beside her. Dan slipped off the felt boots, lifted her feet to the bed and softly drew covers over mother and child.

"Poor kid, but she's grit, clear through!"

Dan walked to the window, looked out at the lessening storm, then at the tiny alarm-clock on the cupboard. "Be over pretty soon now!" He seated himself by the table, dropped his head wearily forward on folded arms and was asleep.

The traveler's face had lost some of its shrewdness. It was as if the white frontier had seized and shaken him into a new conception of life. He moved restlessly along the bench, then stepped softly to the side of the bed and straightened the coverlet into greater nicety while his lips twitched.

With consuming care he folded the blanket and restored the corner seat to its accustomed appearance of luxury. He looked about the room, picked up the gray kitten sleeping contentedly on the floor and settled it on the red cushion with anxious attention to comfort.

He examined with curiosity the few books carefully covered on a corner shelf, took down an old hand-tooled volume and lifted his eyebrows at the ancient coat of arms on the book plate. He tiptoed across to the bench and pointed to the script beneath the plate. "Edward Winslow (7) to his dear daughter, Alice (8)."

He motioned toward the bed. "Her name?"

Hillas nodded, Smith grinned. "Dan's right. Blood will tell, even to damning the rest of us."

He sat down on the bench. "I understand more than I did, Hillas, since — you crawled back after me — out there. But how can you stand it here? I know you and the Clarks are people of education and, oh, all the rest; you could make your way anywhere."

Hillas spoke slowly. "I think you have to live here to know. It means something to be a pioneer. You can't be one if you've got it in you to be a quitter. The country will be all right some day." He reached for his greatcoat, bringing out a brown-paper parcel. He smiled at it oddly and went on as if talking to himself.

"When the drought and the hot winds come in the summer and burn the buffalo grass to a tinder and the monotony of the plains weighs on you as it does now, there's a common, low-growing cactus scattered over the prairie that blooms into the gayest red flower you ever saw.

"It wouldn't count for much anywhere else, but the pluck of it, without rain for months, dew even. It's the 'colors of courage.'"

## Turkey Red

He turned the torn parcel, showing the bright red within, and looked at the cupboard and window with shining, tired eyes.

"Up and down the frontier in these shacks, homes, you'll find things made of turkey-red calico, cheap, common elsewhere ——" He fingered the three-cornered flap. "It's our 'colors.'" He put the parcel back in his pocket. "I bought two yards yesterday after — I got a letter at Haney."

Smith sat looking at the gay curtains before him. The fury of the storm was dying down into fitful gusts. Dan stirred, looked quickly toward the bed, then the window, and got up quietly.

"I'll hitch up. We'll stop at Peterson's and tell her to come over." He closed the door noiselessly.

The traveler was frowning intently. Finally he turned toward the boy who sat with his head leaning back against the wall, eyes closed.

"Hillas," his very tones were awkward, "they call me a shrewd business man. I am, it's a selfish job and I'm not reforming now. But twice tonight you — children have risked your lives, without thought, for a stranger. I've been thinking about that railroad. Haven't you raised any grain or cattle that could be used for freight?"

The low answer was toneless. "Drought killed the crops, prairie fires burned the hay, of course the cattle starved."

"There's no timber, ore, nothing that could be used for east-bound shipment?"

The plainsman looked searchingly into the face of the older man. "There's no timber this side the Missouri. Across the river it's reservation — Sioux. We ——" He frowned and stopped.

Smith stood up, his hands thrust deep in his pockets. "I admitted I was shrewd, Hillas, but I'm not yellow clear through, not enough to betray this part of the frontier anyhow. I had a man along here last fall spying for minerals. That's why I'm out here now. If you know the location, and we both think you do, I'll put capital in your way to develop the mines and use what pull I have to get the road in."

He looked down at the boy and thrust out a masterful jaw.

There was a ring of sincerity no one could mistake when he spoke again.

"This country's a desert now, but I'd back the Sahara peopled with your kind. This is on the square, Hillas, don't tell me you won't believe I'm — American enough to trust?"

The boy tried to speak. With stiffened body and clenched hands he struggled for self-control. Finally in a ragged whisper, "If I try to tell you what — it means — I can't talk! Dan and I know of outcropping coal over in the Buttes." He nodded in the direction of the Missouri. "But we haven't had enough money to file mining claims."

"Know where to dig for samples under this snow?"

The boy nodded. "Some in my shack too. I ——" His head went down upon the crossed arms. Smith laid an awkward hand on the heaving shoulders, then rose and crossed the room to where the girl had stumbled in her vigil. Gently he touched the darkened streak where her shoulders had rubbed and blurred the newspaper print. He looked from the relentless white desert outside to the gay bravery within and bent his head. "Turkey-red — calico!"

There was the sound of jingling harness and the crunch of runners. The men bundled into fur coats.

"Hillas, the draw right by the house here ——" Smith stopped and looked sharply at the plainsman, then went on with firm carelessness, "This draw ought to strike a low grade that would come out near the river level. Does Dan know Clark's address?" Hillas nodded.

They tiptoed out and closed the door behind them softly. The wind had swept every cloud from the sky and the light of the northern stars etched a dazzling world. Dan was checking up the leaders as Hillas caught him by the shoulder and shook him like a clumsy bear.

"Dan, you blind old mole, can you see the headlight of the Overland Freight blazing and thundering down that draw over the Great Missouri and Eastern?"

Dan stared.

"I knew you couldn't!" Hillas thumped him with furry fist. "Dan" — the wind might easily have drowned the unsteady voice — "I've told Mr. Smith about the coal — for freight. He's going to help us get capital for mining and after that the road."

"Smith! Smith! Well, I'll be — aren't you a claim spotter?"

He turned abruptly and crunched toward the stage. His passengers followed. Dan paused with his foot on the runner and looked steadily at the traveler from under lowered, shaggy brows.

"You're going to get a road out here?"

"I've told Hillas I'll put money in your way to mine the coal. Then the railroad will come."

Dan's voice rasped with tension. "We'll get out the coal. Are you going to see that the road is built?"

Unconsciously the traveler held up his right hand. "I am!"

Dan searched his face sharply. Smith nodded. "I'm making my bet on the people — friend!"

It was a new Dan who lifted his bronzed face to a white world. His voice was low and very gentle. "To bring a road here" — he swung his whip-handle from Donovan's light around to Carson's square, sweeping in all that lay behind — "out here to them" — the pioneer faced the wide desert that reached into a misty space ablaze with stars — "would be like — playing God!"

The whip thudded softly into the socket and Dan rolled up on the driver's seat. Two men climbed in behind him. The long lash swung out over the leaders as Dan headed the old mail-sled across the drifted right-of-way of the Great Missouri and Eastern.

## QUESTIONS

1. How is the setting at once indicated?
2. What in the characters prepares for a complication?
3. Is the blizzard effectively introduced? Explain.
4. What are your first impressions of Dan? Be definite.
5. Just where do you find the beginning of the complication?
6. Find examples of striking figures of speech, like "hugged the sod."
7. What effect do these have on the style? Be explicit.
8. What are the first things that stir Smith?
9. What does he mean by "blood will tell"? Be sure to catch the point.
10. Why has Hillas bought the turkey-red calico?
11. Do you begin to see the significance of the title?
12. State the theme.

13. How is it advanced by the scene inside the cottage?
14. What finally caused the change in Smith?
15. Should the story tell more about " Mis' Clark " ? **Explain.**
16. Would you call this story " dramatic " ? Explain.
17. Would the story gain by a touch of humor? Or not?

## SUBJECTS FOR COMPOSITION

1. Describe an incident involving a snowstorm.
2. Tell an incident involving a drought, or a forest fire, or a flood. Be sure to have human figures struggling against elemental forces.

### OTHER STORIES BY FRANCES G. WOOD

The White Battalion
Shoes

### VOLUMES OF STORIES BY FRANCES G. WOOD

*Gospel Corners*              *Turkey Red*

# EDISON MARSHALL
(1894–    )

(Asked for a few facts on his life, Mr. Marshall replied in this letter, which is reprinted verbatim.)

MEDFORD, OREGON
December 1, 1924

DEAR MR. SCHWEIKERT: —

I am convinced that yours is going to be a good book. I should have hated to have had it go to press without the Elephant. I feel honored to be included.

I am sorry that you had to wire. This is my hunting season, you know, and I am not here much of the time. I don't kill much because I don't care to; but the days are delightful. My correspondence suffers.

My biography shall be brief. I was born in Rensselaer, Indiana, and am now thirty years old. As a boy I fished for mudcat in the Iroquois River and hunted cotton-tails with an air-gun, but caught few cat and shot no rabbits. I dreamed about them a great deal, however, like the little boy in my " Voice of the Pack." I came out here in 1907, and have been having rather a sensational time ever since.

A few little adventures, really, and the best part about them is that they get better the oftener I tell about them. I was carried in a runaway boat down a mountain river, once. Another time I was rescued from the quagmire when the last tule root I was clinging to was breaking. I was lost in a blizzard and took a nap, which is an unhealthy practice; and have been charged twice by grizzly bears. I have been in a few valleys which were unknown to white men.

I have never been to India. This will disappoint the boys, I fear. I wasn't very bad in school, and that will disappoint them even further. I began to write stories when I was a Freshman in college (up to that time I wrote only such easy things as whole dramas in blank verse, and verse), and actually sold a story when I was nineteen. I began to write as a profession in 1916. I served as a lieutenant in the war.

I like most outdoor sports, but (don't tell the boys) with the exception of shooting, I am surprisingly poor at all of them. I like golf, and play it horribly; as a boy, tennis was too civilized for me. I have hunted all kinds of American big game, including the great kadiak bear, but as I say, I don't care to kill much of it. Being fond of animals, I like to write about them. Elephants particularly appeal to me, and once, at a circus, when I had an old fellow with his trunk up, thrusting peanuts down his throat, an Alabama Hindu mahout yelled at me and almost started a riot. I think the Elephant and " The Heart of the Little Shikara " (O. Henry first prize winner for 1921) the best stories I ever wrote, and I hope you include the latter in the next book you get out.

I live a simple and pleasant life, and sometime will engender the necessary courage to visit New York. I write about four months of the year, day-dream and play about four months, and travel, usually in the far North about the same length of time. I am married, and have a small boy. I read a great deal, with Kipling foremost on my bookshelf, this man being my literary god.

It might be of interest that the Marshalls were a Colonial family, and managed to get in on all the early wars of the country. They followed the frontiers, having some kind of queer toxin in their blood; some died in the great rush of '49, and many more in the Civil War; and some managed to survive to be good Republicans. My own grandfather was a forty-niner and died in California a year later; my own father went West for the first time in 1870.

I hope some of this is interesting to you. On second thought, I believe you had better write what you want yourself.

Cordially yours,
(*Signed*) EDISON MARSHALL

# THE ELEPHANT REMEMBERS

AN ELEPHANT is old on the day he is born, say the natives of Burma, and no white man is ever quite sure just what they mean. Perhaps they refer to his pink, old-gentleman's skin and his droll, fumbling, old-man ways and his squeaking treble voice. And maybe they mean he is born with a wisdom such as usually belongs only to age. And it is true that if any animal in the world has had a chance to acquire knowledge it is the elephant, for his breed are the oldest residents of this old world.

They are so old that they don't seem to belong to the twentieth century at all. Their long trunks, their huge shapes, all seem part of the remote past. They are just the remnants of a breed that once was great.

Long and long ago, when the world was very young indeed, when the mountains were new, and before the descent of the great glaciers taught the meaning of cold, they were the rulers of the earth, but they have been conquered in the struggle for existence. Their great cousins, the mastodon and the mammoth, are completely gone, and their own tribe can now be numbered by thousands.

But because they have been so long upon the earth, because

they have wealth of experience beyond all other creatures, they seem like venerable sages in a world of children. They are like the last veterans of an old war, who can remember scenes and faces that all others have forgotten.

Far in a remote section of British India, in a strange, wild province called Burma, Muztagh was born. And although he was born in captivity, the property of a mahout, in his first hour he heard the far-off call of the wild elephants in the jungle.

The Burmans, just like the other people of India, always watch the first hour of a baby's life very closely. They know that always some incident will occur that will point, as a weather-vane points in the wind, to the baby's future. Often they have to call a man versed in magic to interpret, but sometimes the prophecy is quite self-evident. No one knows whether or not it works the same with baby elephants, but certainly this wild, far-carrying call, not to be imitated by any living voice, did seem a token and an omen in the life of Muztagh. And it is a curious fact that the little baby lifted his ears at the sound and rocked back and forth on his pillar legs.

Of all the places in the great world, only a few remain wherein a captive elephant hears the call of his wild brethren at birth. Muztagh's birthplace lies around the corner of the Bay of Bengal, not far from the watershed of the Irawadi, almost north of Java. It is strange and wild and dark beyond the power of words to tell. There are great dark forests, unknown, slow-moving rivers, and jungles silent and dark and impenetrable.

Little Muztagh weighed a flat two hundred pounds at birth. But this was not the queerest thing about him. Elephant babies, although usually weighing not more than one hundred and eighty, often touch two hundred. The queerest thing was a peculiarity that probably was completely overlooked by his mother. If she saw it out of her dull eyes, she took no notice of it. It was not definitely discovered until the mahout came out of his hut with a lighted fagot for a first inspection.

He had been wakened by the sound of the mother's pain. "*Hai!*" he had exclaimed to his wife. "Who has ever heard a cow bawl so loud in labor? The little one that tomorrow you will see beneath her belly must weigh more than you!"

This was rather a compliment to his plump wife. She was

not offended at all. Burman women love to be well-rounded. But the mahout was not weighing the effect of his words. He was busy lighting his fire-brand, and his features seemed sharp and intent when the beams came out. Rather he was already weighing the profits of little Muztagh. He was an elephant-catcher by trade, in the employ of the great white Dugan Sahib, and the cow that was at this moment bringing a son into the world was his own property. If the baby should be of the Kumiria ——

The mahout knew elephants from head to tail, and he was very well acquainted with the three grades that composed that breed. The least valuable of all are the Mierga — a light, small-headed, thin-skinned, weak-trunked and unintelligent variety that are often found in the best elephant herds. They are often born of the most noble parents, and they are as big a problem to elephant men as razor-backs to hog-breeders. Then there is a second variety, the Dwasala, that compose the great bulk of the herd — a good, substantial, strong, intelligent grade of elephant. But the Kumiria is the best of all; and when one is born in a captive herd it is a time for rejoicing. He is the perfect elephant — heavy, symmetrical, trustworthy and fearless — fitted for the pageantry of kings.

He hurried out to the lines, for now he knew that the baby was born. The mother's cries had ceased. The jungle, dark and savage beyond even the power of man to tame, lay just beyond. He could feel its heavy air; its smells; its silence was an essence. And as he stood, lifting the fagot high, he heard the wild elephants trumpeting from the hills.

He turned his head in amazement. A Burman, and particularly one who chases the wild elephants in their jungles, is intensely superstitious, and for an instant it seemed to him that the wild trumpeting must have some secret meaning, it was so loud and triumphant and prolonged. It was greatly like the far-famed elephant salute — ever one of the mysteries of these most mysterious of animals — that the great creatures utter at certain occasions and times.

"Are you saluting this little one?" he cried. "He is not a wild tusker like you. He is not a wild pig of the jungle. He is born in bonds, such as you will wear too, after the next drive!"

They trumpeted again, as if in scorn of his words. Their

## The Elephant Remembers 67

great strength was given them to rule the jungle, not to haul logs and pull chains! The man turned back to the lines and lifted higher his light.

Yes — the little elephant in the light-glow was of the Kumiria. Never had there been a more perfect calf. The light of greed sprang again in his eyes. And as he held the fagot nearer so that the beams played in the elephant's eyes and on his coat, the mahout sat down and was still, lest the gods observe his good luck, and, being jealous, turn it into evil.

The coat was not pinky dark, as is usual in baby elephants. It was distinctly light-colored — only a few degrees darker than white.

The man understood at once. In the elephants, as well as in all other breeds, an albino is sometimes born. A perfectly white elephant, up to a few years ago, had never been seen, but on rare occasions elephants are born with light-colored or clouded hides. Such creatures are bought at fabulous prices by the Malay and Siamese princes, to whom a white elephant is the greatest treasure that a king can possess.

Muztagh was a long way from being an albino, yet a tendency in that direction had bleached his hide. And the man knew that on the morrow Dugan Sahib would pay him a lifetime's earnings for the little wabbly calf, whose welcome had been the wild cries of the tuskers in the jungle.

II

Little Muztagh (which means White Mountain in an ancient tongue) did not enjoy his babyhood at all. He was born with the memory of jungle kingdoms, and the life in the elephant lines almost killed him with dullness.

There was never anything to do but nurse of the strong elephant milk and roam about in the *keddah* or along the lines. He had been bought the second day of his life by Dugan Sahib, and the great white heaven-born saw to it that he underwent none of the risks that are the happy fate of most baby elephants. His mother was not taken on the elephant drives into the jungles, so he never got a taste of this exciting sport. Mostly she was kept chained in the lines, and every day Langur Dass, the low-caste hillman in Dugan's employ, grubbed grass for her in the valleys. All night long, except the regular four hours of sleep, he would hear her grumble and rumble and mutter discontent that her little son shared with her.

Muztagh's second year was little better. Of course he had reached the age where he could eat such dainties as grass and young sugar-cane, but these things could not make up for the fun he was missing in the hills. He would stand long hours watching their purple tops against the skies, and his little dark eyes would glow. He would see the storms break and flash above them, behold the rains lash down through the jungles, and he was always filled with strange longings and desires that he was too young to understand or to follow. He would see the white haze steam up from the labyrinth of wet vines, and he would tingle and scratch for the feel of its wetness on his skin. And often, when the mysterious Burman night came down, it seemed to him that he would go mad. He would hear the wild tuskers trumpeting in the jungles a very long way off, and all the myriad noises of the mysterious night, and at times even his mother looked at him with wonder.

"Oh, little restless one," Langur Dass would say, "thou and that old cow thy mother and I have one heart between us. We know the burning — we understand, we three!"

It was true that Langur Dass understood more of the ways of the forest people than any other hillman in the encampment. But his caste was low, and he was drunken and careless and lazy beyond words, and the hunters had mostly only scorn for him. They called him Langur after a gray-bearded breed of monkeys along the slopes of the Himalayas, rather suspecting he was cursed with evil spirits, for why should any sane man have such mad ideas as to the rights of elephants? He never wanted to join in the drives — which was a strange thing indeed for a man raised in the hills. Perhaps he was afraid — but yet they could remember a certain day in the bamboo thickets, when a great, wild buffalo had charged their camp and Langur Dass acted as if fear were something he had never heard of and knew nothing whatever about.

One day they asked him about it. "Tell us, Langur Dass," they asked, mocking the ragged, dejected-looking creature, "if thy name speaks truth, thou art brother to many monkey-folk, and who knows the jungle better than thou or they? None but the monkey-folk and thou canst talk with my lord the elephant. *Hai!* We have seen thee do it, Langur Dass. How is it that when we go hunting, thou art afraid to come?"

Langur looked at them out of his dull eyes, and evaded their questions just as long as he could. "Have you forgotten the tales you heard on your mothers' breasts?" he asked at last. "Elephants are of the jungle. You are of the cooking-pots and thatch! How should such folk as ye are understand?"

This was flat heresy from their viewpoint. There is an old legend among the elephant-catchers to the effect that at one time men were subject to the elephants.

Yet mostly the elephants that these men knew were patient and contented in their bonds. Mostly they loved their mahouts, gave their strong backs willingly to toil, and were always glad and ready to join in the chase after others of their breed. Only on certain nights of the year, when the tuskers called from the jungles, and the spirit of the wild was abroad, would their love of liberty return to them. But to all this little Muztagh was distinctly an exception. Even though he had been born in captivity, his desire for liberty was with him just as constantly as his trunk or his ears.

He had no love for the mahout that rode his mother. He took little interest in the little brown boys and girls that played before his stall. He would stand and look over their heads into the wild, dark heart of the jungle that no man can ever quite understand. And being only a beast, he did not know anything about the caste and prejudices of the men he saw, but he did know that one of them, the low-caste Langur Dass, ragged and dirty and despised, wakened a responsive chord in his lonely heart.

They would have long talks together, that is, Langur would talk and Muztagh would mumble. "Little calf, little fat one," the man would say, "can great rocks stop a tree from growing? Shall iron shackles stop a prince from being king? Muztagh — jewel among jewels! Thy heart speaks through those sleepless eyes of thine! Have patience — what thou knowest, who shall take away from thee?"

But most of the mahouts and catchers noticed the rapidity with which the little Muztagh acquired weight and strength. He outweighed, at the age of three, any calf of his season in the encampment by a full two hundred pounds. And of course three in an elephant is no older than three in a human child. He was still just a baby, even if he did have the wild tuskers' love of liberty.

"Shalt thou never lie the day long in the cool mud, little one? Never see a storm break on the hills? Nor feel a warm rain dripping through the branches? Or are these matters part of thee that none may steal?" Langur Dass would ask him, contented to wait a very long time for his answer. "I think already that thou knowest how the tiger steals away at thy shrill note; how thickets feel that crash beneath thy hurrying weight! A little I think thou knowest how the madness comes with the changing seasons. How knowest thou these things? Not as I know them, who have seen — nay, but as a king knows conquering; it's in thy blood! Is a bundle of sugar-cane tribute enough for thee, Kumiria? Shall purple trappings please thee? Shall some fat rajah of the plains make a beast of burden of thee? Answer, lord of mighty memories!"

And Muztagh answered in his own way, without sound or emphasis, but giving his love to Langur Dass, a love as large as the big elephant heart from which it had sprung. No other man could even win his friendship. The smell of the jungle was on Langur Dass. The mahouts and hunters smelt more or less of civilization and were convinced for their part that the disposition of the little light-colored elephant was beyond redemption.

"He is a born rogue," was their verdict, and they meant by that, a particular kind of elephant, sometimes a young male, more often an old and savage tusker, alone in the jungle — apart from the herd. Solitariness doesn't improve their dispositions, and they were generally expelled from a herd for ill-temper to begin with. "Woe to the fool prince who buys this one!" said the graybeard catchers. "There is murder in his eyes."

But Langur Dass would only look wise when he heard these remarks. He knew elephants. The gleam in the dark eyes of Muztagh was not viciousness, but simply inheritance, a love of the wide wild spaces that left no room for ordinary friendships.

But calf-love and mother-love bind other animals as well as men, and possibly he might have perfectly fulfilled the plans

## The Elephant Remembers

Dugan had made for him but for a mistake the sahib made in the little calf's ninth year.

He sold Muztagh's mother to an elephant-breeder from a distant province. Little Muztagh saw her march away between two tuskers — down the long elephant trail into the valley and the shadow.

"Watch the little one closely tonight," Dugan Sahib said to his mahout. So when they had led him back and forth along the lines, they saw that the ends of his ropes were pegged down tightly. They were horse-hair ropes, far beyond the strength of any normal nine-year-old elephant to break. Then they went to the huts and to their women and left him to shift restlessly from foot to foot, and think.

Probably he would have been satisfied with thinking, for Muztagh did not know his strength, and thought he was securely tied. The incident that upset the mahout's plans was simply that the wild elephants trumpeted again from the hills.

Muztagh heard the sound, long drawn and strange from the silence of the jungle. He grew motionless. The great ears pricked forward, the whipping tail stood still. It was a call never to be denied. The blood was leaping in his great veins.

He suddenly rocked forward with all his strength. The rope spun tight, hummed, and snapped — very softly indeed. Then he padded in silence out among the huts, and nobody who had not seen him do it would believe how silently an elephant can move when he sees fit.

There was no thick jungle here — just soft grass, huts, approaching dark fringe that was the jungle. None of the mahouts was awake to see him. No voice called him back. The grass gave way to bamboo thickets, the smell of the huts to the wild, bewitching perfumes of the jungle.

Then, still in silence, because there are decencies to be observed by animals no less than men, he walked forward with his trunk outstretched into the primordial jungle and was born again.

### III

Muztagh's reception was cordial from the very first. The great bulls of the herd stood still and lifted their ears when they heard him grunting up the hill. But he slipped among

them and was forgotten at once. They had no dealings with
the princes of Malay and Siam, and his light-colored coat
meant nothing whatever to them. If they did any thinking
about him at all, it was just to wonder why a calf with all the
evident marks of a nine-year-old should be so tall and weigh
so much.

One can fancy that the great old wrinkled tusker that led
the herd peered at him now and then out of his little red eyes,
and wondered. A herd-leader begins to think about future
contestants for his place as soon as he acquires the leadership.
But *Hai!* This little one would not have his greatest strength
for fifteen years.

It was a compact, medium-sized herd — vast males, mothers,
old-maid elephants, long-legged and ungainly, young males
just learning their strength and proud of it beyond words, and
many calves. They ranged all the way in size from the great
leader, who stood ten feet and weighed nearly nine thousand
pounds, to little two-hundred-and-fifty-pound babies that had
been born that season. And before long the entire herd began
its cautious advance into the deeper hills.

The first night in the jungle — and Muztagh found it wonderful past all dreams. The mist on his skin was the same cool
joy he had expected. There were sounds, too, that set his
great muscles aquiver. He heard the sound that the bamboos
make — the little click-click of the stems in the wind — the
soft rustle and stir of many leafy tendrils entwining and touching together, and the whisper of the wind over the jungle grass.
And he knew, because it was his heritage, what every single
one of these sounds meant.

The herd threaded through the dark jungle, and now they
descended into a cool river. A herd of deer — either the dark
sambur or black buck — sprang from the misty shore-line and
leaped away into the bamboos. Farther down, he could hear
the grunt of buffalo.

It was simply a caress — the touch of the soft, cool water
on his flanks. Then they reared out, like great sea-gods rising
from the deep, and grunted and squealed their way up the
banks into the jungle again.

But the smells were the book that he read best; he understood them even better than the sounds of green things growing. Flowers that he could not see hung like bells from the

## The Elephant Remembers

arching branches. Every fern and every seeding grass had its own scent that told sweet tales. The very mud that his four feet sank into emitted scent that told the history of jungle-life from the world's beginnings. When dawn burst over the eastern hills, he was weary in every muscle of his young body, but much too happy to admit it.

This day was just the first of three thousand joyous days. The jungle, old as the world itself, is ever new. Not even the wisest elephant, who, after all, is king of the jungle, knows what will turn up at the next bend in the elephant trail. It may be a native woodcutter, whose long hair is stirred with fright. It may easily be one of the great breed of bears, large as the American grizzly, that some naturalists believe are to be found in the Siamese and Burman jungles. It may be a herd of wild buffalo, always looking for a fight, or simply some absurd armadillo-like thing, to make him shake his vast sides with mirth.

The herd was never still. They ranged from one mysterious hill to another, to the ranges of the Himalayas and back again. There were no rivers that they did not swim, no jungles that they did not penetrate, no elephant trails that they did not follow, in the whole northeastern corner of British India. And all the time Muztagh's strength grew upon him until it became too vast a thing to measure or control.

Whether or not he kept with the herd was by now a matter of supreme indifference to him. He no longer needed its protection. Except for the men who came with the ropes and guns and shoutings, there was nothing in the jungle for him to fear. He was twenty years old, and he stood nearly eleven feet to the top of his shoulders. He would have broken any scales in the Indian Empire that tried to weigh him.

He had had his share of adventures, yet he knew that life in reality had just begun. The time would come when he would want to fight the great arrogant bull for the leadership of the herd. He was tired of fighting the young bulls of his own age. He always won, and to an elephant constant winning is almost as dull as constant losing. He was a great deal like a youth of twenty in any breed of any land — light-hearted, self-confident, enjoying every minute of wakefulness between one midnight and another. He loved the jungle smells and the jungle sounds, and he could even tolerate the horrible laughter of the hyenas that sometimes tore to shreds the silence of the grassy plains below.

But India is too thickly populated by human beings for a wild elephant to escape observation entirely. Many natives had caught sight of him, and at last the tales reached a little circle of trackers and hunters in camp on a distant range of hills. They did not work for Dugan Sahib, for Dugan Sahib was dead long since. They were a determined little group, and one night they sat and talked softly over their fire. If Muztagh's ears had been sharp enough to hear their words across the space of hills, he wouldn't have gone to his mud-baths with such complacency the next day. But the space between them was fifty miles of sweating jungle, and of course he did not hear.

"You will go, Khusru," said the leader, "for there are none here half so skilful with horsehair rope as you. If you do not come back within twelve months, we shall know you have failed."

Of course all of them knew what he meant. If a man failed in the effort to capture a wild elephant by the hair-rope method, he very rarely lived to tell of it.

"In that case," Ahmad Din went on, "there will be a great drive after the monsoon of next year. Picked men will be chosen. No detail will be overlooked. It will cost more, but it will be sure. And our purses will be fat from the selling-price of this king of elephants with a white coat!"

IV

There is no need to follow Khusru on his long pursuit through the elephant trails. He was an able hunter and, after the manner of the elephant-trackers, the scared little man followed Muztagh through jungle and river, over hill and into dale, for countless days, and at last, as Muztagh slept, he crept up within a half-dozen feet of him. He intended to loop a horsehair rope about his great feet — one of the oldest and most hazardous methods of elephant-catching. But Muztagh wakened just in time.

And then a curious thing happened. The native could never entirely believe it, and it was one of his best stories to the day he died. Any other wild tusker would have charged in furious wrath, and there would have been a quick and certain death beneath his great knees. Muztagh started out as if he had intended to charge. He lifted his trunk out of the way — the elephant trunk is for a thousand uses, but fighting is not one of them — and sprang forward. He went just two paces. Then his little eyes caught sight of the brown figure fleeing through the bamboos. And at once the elephant set his great feet to brake himself, and drew to a sliding halt six feet beyond.

He did not know why. He was perfectly aware that this man was an enemy, jealous of his most-loved liberty. He knew perfectly it was the man's intention to put him back into his bonds. He did not feel fear, either — because an elephant's anger is too tremendous an emotion to leave room for any other impulse such as fear. It seemed to him that memories came thronging from long ago, so real and insistent that he could not think of charging.

He remembered his days in the elephant lines. These brown creatures had been his masters then. They had cut his grass for him in the jungle, and brought him bundles of sugar-cane. The hill people say that the elephant memory is the greatest single marvel in the jungle, and it was that memory that saved Khusru then. It wasn't deliberate gratitude for the grass-cutting of long ago. It wasn't any particular emotion that he could reach out his trunk and touch. It was simply an impulse — another one of the thousand mysteries that envelop, like a cloud, the mental processes of these largest of forest creatures.

These were the days when he lived apart from the herd. He did it from choice. He liked the silence, the solitary mud-baths, the constant watchfulness against danger.

One day a rhino charged him — without warning or reason. This is quite a common thing for a rhino to do. They have the worst tempers in the jungle, and they would just as soon charge a mountain if they didn't like the look of it. Muztagh had awakened the great creature from his sleep, and he came bearing down like a tank over "no man's land."

Muztagh met him squarely, with the full shock of his tusks, and the battle ended promptly. Muztagh's tusk, driven by five tons of might behind it, would have pierced a ship's side, and the rhino limped away to let his hurt grow well and meditate revenge. Thereafter, for a full year, he looked carefully out of his bleary, drunken eyes and chose a smaller objective before he charged.

Month after month Muztagh wended alone through the elephant trails, and now and then rooted up great trees just to try his strength. Sometimes he went silently, and sometimes like an avalanche. He swam alone in the deep holes, and sometimes shut his eyes and stood on the bottom, just keeping the end of his trunk out of the water. One day he was obliged to kneel on the broad back of an alligator who tried to bite off his foot. He drove the long body down into the muddy bottom, and no living creature, except possibly the catfish that burrow in the mud, ever saw it again.

He loved the rains that flashed through the jungles, the swift-climbing dawns in the east, the strange, tense, breathless nights. And at midnight he loved to trumpet to the herd on some far-away hill, and hear, fainter than the death-cry of a beetle, its answer come back to him. At twenty-five he had reached full maturity; and no more magnificent specimen of the elephant could be found in all of British India. At last he had begun to learn his strength.

Of course he had known for years his mastery over the inanimate things of the world. He knew how easy it was to tear a tree from its roots, to jerk a great tree-limb from its socket. He knew that under most conditions he had nothing to fear from the great tigers, although a fight with a tiger is a painful thing and well to avoid. But he did not know that he had developed a craft and skill that would avail him in battle against the greatest of his own kind. He made the discovery one sunlit day beside the Manipur River.

He was in the mud-bath, grunting and bubbling with content. It was a bath with just room enough for one. And seeing that he was young, and perhaps failing to measure his size, obscured as it was in the mud, a great "rogue" bull came out of the jungles to take the bath for himself.

He was a huge creature — wrinkled and yellow-tusked and scarred from the wounds of a thousand fights. His little red eyes looked out malignantly, and he grunted all the insults the elephant tongue can compass to the youngster that lolled in the bath. He confidently expected that Muztagh would yield at once, because as a rule young twenty-five-year-olds do not care to mix in battle with the scarred and crafty veterans of sixty years. But he did not know Muztagh.

The latter had been enjoying the bath to the limit, and he had no desire whatever to give it up. Something hot and raging seemed to explode in his brain and it was as if a red glare, such as sometimes comes in the sunset, had fallen over all the stretch of river and jungle before his eyes. He squealed once, reared up with one lunge out of the bath — and charged. They met with a shock.

Of all the expressions of power in the animal world, the elephant fight is the most terrible to see. It is as if two mountains rose up from their roots of strata and went to war. It is terrible to hear, too. The jungle had been still before. The river glided softly, the wind was dead, the mid-afternoon silence was over the thickets.

The jungle people were asleep. A thunder-storm would not have broken more quickly, or could not have created a wilder pandemonium. The jungle seemed to shiver with the sound.

They squealed and bellowed and trumpeted and grunted and charged. Their tusks clicked like the noise of a giant's game of billiards. The thickets cracked and broke beneath their great feet.

It lasted only a moment. It was so easy, after all. In a very few seconds indeed, the old rogue became aware that he had made a very dangerous and disagreeable mistake. There were better mud-baths on the river, anyway.

He had not been able to land a single blow. And his wrath gave way to startled amazement when Muztagh sent home his third. The rogue did not wait for the fourth.

Muztagh chased him into the thickets. But he was too proud to chase a beaten elephant for long. He halted, trumpeting, and swung back to his mud-bath.

But he did not enter the mud again. All at once he remembered the herd and the fights of his calfhood. All at once he knew that his craft and strength and power were beyond that of any elephant in all the jungle. Who was the great, arrogant herd-leader to stand against him? What yellow tusks were to meet his and come away unbroken?

His little eyes grew ever more red as he stood rocking back and forth, his trunk lifted to catch the sounds and smells of the distant jungle. Why should he abide alone, when he could be the ruler of the herd and the jungle king? Then he grunted softly and started away down the river. Far away, beyond the mountains and rivers and the villages of the hillfolk, the herd of his youth roamed in joyous freedom. He would find them and assert his mastery.

V

The night fire of a little band of elephant-catchers burned fitfully at the edge of the jungle. They were silent men — for they had lived long on the elephant trails — and curiously scarred and somber. They smoked their cheroots, and waited for Ahmad Din to speak.

"You have all heard?" he asked at last.

All but one of them nodded. Of course this did not count the most despised one of them all — old Langur Dass — who sat at the very edge of the shadow. His long hair was gray, and his youth had gone where the sun goes at evening. They scarcely addressed a word to him, or he to them. True, he knew the elephants, but was he not possessed of evil spirits? He was always without rupees, too, a creature of the wild that could not seem to understand the gathering of money. As a man, according to the standards of men, he was an abject failure.

"Khusru has failed to catch White-Skin, but he has lived to tell many lies about it. He comes tonight."

It was noticeable that Langur Dass, at the edge of the circle, pricked up his ears.

"Do you mean the white elephant of which the Manipur people tell so many lies?" he asked. "Do you, skilled catchers that you are, believe that such an elephant is still wild in the jungle?"

Ahmad Din scowled. "The Manipur people tell of him, but for once they tell the truth," was the reply. "He is the greatest elephant, the richest prize, in all of Burma. Too many people have seen him to doubt. I add my word to theirs, thou son of immorality!"

Ahmad Din hesitated a moment before he continued. Perhaps it was a mistake to tell of the great, light-colored elephant until this man should have gone away. But what harm could this wanderer do them? All men knew that the jungle had maddened him.

Langur Dass's face lit suddenly. "Then it could be none but Muztagh, escaped from Dugan Sahib fifteen years ago.

That calf was also white. He was also overgrown for his years."

One of the trackers suddenly gasped. "Then that is why he spared Khusru!" he cried. "He remembered men."

The others nodded gravely. "They never forget," said Langur Dass.

"You will be silent while I speak," Ahmad Din went on. Langur grew silent as commanded, but his thoughts were flowing backward twenty years, to days at the elephant lines in distant hills. Muztagh was the one living creature that in all his days had loved Langur Dass. The man shut his eyes, and his limbs seemed to relax as if he had lost all interest in the talk. The evil one took hold of him at such times, the people said, letting understanding follow his thoughts back into the purple hills and the far-off spaces of the jungle. But tonight he was only pretending. He meant to hear every word of the talk before he left the circle.

"He tells a mad story, as you know, of the elephant sparing him when he was beneath his feet," Ahmad Din went on; "that part of his story does not matter to us. *Hai!* He might have been frightened enough to say that the sun set at noon. But what matters to us more is that he knows where the herd is — but a day's journey beyond the river. And there is no time to be lost."

His fellows nodded in agreement.

"So tomorrow we will break camp. There can be no mistake this time. There must be no points overlooked. The chase will cost much, but it will return a hundredfold. Khusru says that at last the white one has started back toward his herd, so that all can be taken in the same *keddah*. And the white sahib that holds the license is not to know that White-Coat is in the herd at all."

The circle nodded again, and contracted toward the speaker.

"We will hire beaters and drivers, the best that can be found. Tomorrow we will take the elephants and go."

Langur Dass pretended to waken. "I have gone hungry many days," he said. "If the drive is on, perhaps you will give your servant a place among the beaters."

The circle turned and stared at him. It was one of the stories of Langur Dass that he never partook in the elephant hunts. Evidently poor living had broken his resolutions.

"You shall have your wish, if you know how to keep a closed mouth," Ahmad Din replied. "There are other hunting parties in the hills."

Langur nodded. He was very adept indeed at keeping a closed mouth. It is one of the first lessons of the jungle.

For another long hour they sat and perfected their plans. Then they lay down by the fire together, and sleep dropped over them one by one. At last Langur sat by the fire alone.

"You will watch the flame tonight," Ahmad Din ordered. "We did not feed you tonight for pity on your gray hairs. And remember — a gypsy died in a tiger's claws on this very slope — not six months past."

Langur Dass was left alone with his thoughts. Soon he got up and stole out into the velvet darkness. The mists were over the hills as always.

"Have I followed the tales of your greatness all these years for this?" he muttered. "It is right for pigs with the hearts of pigs to break their backs in labor. But you, my Muztagh! Jewel among elephants! King of the jungle! Thou art of the true breed! Moreover I am minded that thy heart and mine are one!

"Thou art born ten thousand years after thy time, Muztagh," he went on. "Thou art of the breed of masters, not of slaves! We are of the same womb, thou and I. Can I not understand? These are not my people — these brown men about the fire. I have not thy strength, Muztagh, or I would be out there with thee! Yet is not the saying that brother shall serve brother?"

He turned slowly back to the circle of the firelight. Then his brown, scrawny fingers clenched.

"Am I to desert my brother in his hour of need? Am I to see these brown pigs put chains around him, in the moment of his power? A king, falling to the place of a slave? Muztagh, we will see what can be done! Muztagh, my king, my pearl, my pink baby, for whom I dug grass in the long ago! Thy Langur Dass is old, and his whole strength is not that of thy trunk, and men look at him as a worm in the grass. But *hai!* perhaps thou wilt find him an ally not to be despised!"

## VI

The night had just fallen, moist and heavy over the jungle, when Muztagh caught up with his herd. He found them in an open grassy glade, encircled by hills, and they were all waiting, silent, as he sped down the hills toward them. They had heard him coming a long way. He was not attempting silence. The jungle people had not got out of his way.

The old bull that led the herd, seventy years of age and at the pride of his wisdom and strength, scarred, yellow-tusked and noble past any elephant patriarch in the jungle, curled up his trunk when he saw him come. He knew very well what would happen. And because no one knows better than the jungle people what a good thing it is to take the offensive in all battles, and because it was fitting his place and dignity, he uttered the challenge himself.

The silence dropped as something from the sky. The little pink calves who had never seen the herd grow still in this same way before, felt the dawn of the storm that they could not understand, and took shelter beneath their mothers' bellies. But they did not squeal. The silence was too deep for them to dare to break.

It is always an epoch in the life of the herd when a young bull contests for leadership. It is a much more serious thing than in the herds of deer and buffalo. The latter only live a handful of years, then grow weak and die. A great bull who has attained strength and wisdom enough to obtain the leadership of an elephant herd may often keep it for forty years. Kings do not rise and fall half so often as in the kingdoms of Europe. For, as most men know, an elephant is not really old until he has seen a hundred summers come and go. Then he will linger fifty years more, wise and gray and wrinkled and strange and full of memories of a time no man can possibly remember.

Long years had passed since the leader's place had been questioned. The aristocracy of strength is drawn on quite inflexible lines. It would have been simply absurd for an elephant of the Dwasila or Mierga grades to covet the leadership. They had grown old without making the attempt. Only the great Kumiria, the grand dukes in the aristocracy, had ever made the trial at all. And besides, the bull was a better fighter after thirty years of leadership than on the day he had gained the honor.

The herd stood like heroic figures in stone for a long moment — until Muztagh had replied to the challenge. He was so surprised that he couldn't make any sound at all at first. He had expected to do the challenging himself. The fact that the leader had done it shook his self-confidence to some slight degree. Evidently the old leader still felt able to handle any young and arrogant bulls that desired his place.

Then the herd began to shift. The cows drew back with their calves, the bulls surged forward, and slowly they made a hollow ring, not greatly different from the pugilistic ring known to fight-fans. The calves began to squeal, but their mothers silenced them. Very slowly and grandly, with infinite dignity, Muztagh stamped into the circle. His tusks gleamed. His eyes glowed red. And those appraising old bulls in the ring knew that such an elephant had not been born since the time of their grandfathers.

They looked him over from tail to trunk. They marked the symmetrical form, the legs like mighty pillars, the sloping back, the wide-apart, intelligent eyes. His shoulders were an expression of latent might — power to break a tree-trunk at its base; by the conformity of his muscles he was agile and quick as a tiger. And knowing these things, and recognizing them, and honoring them, devotees of strength that they were, they threw their trunks in the air till they touched their foreheads and blared their full-voiced salute.

They gave it the same instant — as musicians strike the same note at their leader's signal. It was a perfect explosion of sound, a terrible blare, that crashed out through the jungles and wakened every sleeping thing. The dew fell from the trees. A great tawny tiger, lingering in hope of an elephant calf, slipped silently away. The sound rang true and loud to the surrounding hills and echoed and re-echoed softer and softer, until it was just a tiny tremor in the air.

Not only the jungle folk marveled at the sound. At an encampment three miles distant Ahmad Din and his men heard the wild call, and looked with wondering eyes upon each other. Then out of the silence spoke Langur Dass.

" My lord Muztagh has come back to his herd — that is his salute," he said.

Ahmad Din looked darkly about the circle. "And how long shall he stay?" he asked.

The trap was almost ready. The hour to strike had almost come.

Meanwhile the grand old leader stamped into the circle, seeming unconscious of the eyes upon him, battle-scarred and old. Even if this fight were his last, he meant to preserve his dignity.

Again the salute sounded — shattering out like a thunderclap over the jungle. Then challenger and challenged closed.

At first the watchers were silent. Then as the battle grew ever fiercer and more terrible, they began to grunt and squeal, surging back and forth, stamping the earth and crashing the underbrush. All the jungle-folk for miles about knew what was occurring. And Ahmad Din wished his *keddah* were completed, for never could there be a better opportunity to surround the herd than at the present moment, when they had forgotten all things except the battling monsters in the center of the ring.

The two bulls were quite evenly matched. The patriarch knew more of fighting, had learned more wiles, but he had neither the strength nor the agility of Muztagh. The late twilight deepened into the intense dark, and the stars of midnight rose above the eastern hills.

All at once, Muztagh went to his knees. But as might a tiger, he sprang aside in time to avoid a terrible tusk blow to his shoulder. And his counter-blow, a lashing cut with the head, shattered the great leader to the earth. The elephants bounded forward, but the old leader had a trick left in his trunk. As Muztagh bore down upon him he reared up beneath, and almost turned the tables. Only the youngster's superior strength saved him from immediate defeat.

But as the night drew to morning, the bulls began to see that the tide of the battle had turned. Youth was conquering — too mighty and agile to resist. The rushes of the patriarch were ever weaker. He still could inflict punishment, and the hides of both of them were terrible to see, but he was no longer able to take advantage of his openings. Then Muztagh did a thing that reassured the old bulls as to his craft and wisdom. Just as a pugilist will invite a blow to draw his opponent within range, Muztagh pretended to leave his great shoulder exposed. The old bull failed to see the plot. He bore down, and Muztagh was ready with flashing tusk.

What happened thereafter occurred too quickly for the eyes of the elephants to follow. They saw the great bull go down and Muztagh stand lunging above him. And the battle was over.

The great leader, seriously hurt, backed away into the shadowed jungle. His trunk was lowered in token of defeat. Then the ring was empty except for a great red-eyed elephant, whose hide was no longer white, standing blaring his triumph to the stars.

Three times the elephant salute crashed out into the jungle silence — the full-voiced salaam to a new king. Muztagh had come into his birthright.

## VII

The *keddah* was built at last. It was a strong stockade, opening with great wings spreading out one hundred yards, and equipped with the great gate that lowered like a portcullis at the funnel end of the wings. The herd had been surrounded by the drivers and beaters, and slowly they had been driven, for long days, toward the *keddah* mouth. They had guns loaded with blank cartridges, and firebrands ready to light. At a given signal they would close down quickly about the herd, and stampede it into the yawning mouth of the stockade.

No detail had been overlooked. No expense had been spared. The profit was assured in advance, not only from the matchless Muztagh, but from the herd as well. The king of the jungle, free now as the winds or the waters, was about to go back to his chains. These had been such days! He had led the herd through the hills, and had known the rapture of living as never before. It had been his work to clear the trail of all dangers for the herd. It was his pride to find them the coolest watering-places, the greenest hills. One night a tiger had tried to kill a calf that had wandered from its mother's side. Muztagh lifted his trunk high and charged down with great, driving strides — four tons and over of majestic wrath. The tiger leaped to meet him, but the elephant was ready. He had met tigers before. He avoided the terrible stroke of outstretched claws, and his tusks lashed to one side as the tiger was in midspring. Then he lunged out, and the great knees descended slowly, as a hydraulic press descends on yellow apples. And soon after that the kites were dropping out of the sky for a feast.

His word was law in the herd. And slowly he began to overcome the doubt that the great bulls had of him — doubt of his youth and experience. If he had had three months more of leadership, their trust would have been absolute. But in the meantime, the slow herding toward the *keddah* had begun.

"We will need brave men to stand at the end of the wings of the *keddah*," said Ahmad Din. He spoke no less than truth. The man who stands at the end of the wings, or wide-stretching gates, of the *keddah* is of course in the greatest danger of being charged and killed. The herd, mad with fright, is only slightly less afraid of the spreading wings of the stockade than of the yelling, whooping beaters behind. Often they will try to break through the circle rather than enter the wings.

"For two rupees additional I will hold one of the wings," replied old Langur Dass. Ahmad Din glanced at him — at his hard, bright eyes and determined face. Then he peered hard, and tried in vain to read the thoughts behind the eyes. "You are a madman, Langur Dass," he said wonderingly. "But thou shalt lie behind the right-wing men to pass them torches. I have spoken."

"And the two extra rupees?" Langur asked cunningly.

"Maybe." One does not throw away rupees in Upper Burma.

Within the hour the signal of "*Maîl, maîl!*" (Go on, go on!) was given, and the final laps of the drive began.

The hills grew full of sound. The beaters sprang up with firebrand and rifle, and closed swiftly about the herd. The animals moved slowly at first. The time was not quite ripe to throw them into a panic. Many times the herd would leave their trail and start to dip into a valley or a creek-bed, but always there was a new crowd of beaters to block their path. But presently the beaters closed in on them. Then the animals began a wild descent squarely toward the mouth of the *keddah*.

"*Hai!*" the wild men cried. "Oh, you forest pigs! On, on! Block the way through that valley, you brainless sons of jackals! Are you afraid? *Ai!* Stand close! Watch,

Puran! Guard your post, Khusru! Now on, on — do not let them halt! *Arre! Aihai!*"

Firebrands waved, rifles cracked, the wild shout of beaters increased in volume. The men closed in, driving the beasts before them.

But there was one man that did not raise his voice. Through all the turmoil and pandemonium he crouched at the end of the stockade wing, tense and silent and alone. To one that could have looked into his eyes, it would have seemed that his thoughts were far and far away. It was just old Langur Dass, named for a monkey and despised of men.

He was waiting for the instant that the herd would come thundering down the hill, in order to pass lighted firebrands to the bold men who held that corner. He was not certain that he could do the thing he had set out to do. Perhaps the herd would sweep past him, through the gates. If he did win, he would have to face alone the screaming, infuriated hillmen, whose knives were always ready to draw. But knives did not matter now. Langur Dass had only his own faith and his own creed, and no fear could make him betray them.

Muztagh had lost control of his herd. At their head ran the old leader that he had worsted. In their hour of fear they had turned back to him. What did this youngster know of elephant-drivers? Ever the waving firebrands drew nearer, the beaters lessened their circle, the avenues of escape became more narrow. The yawning arms of the stockade stretched just beyond.

"Will I win, jungle gods?" a little gray man at the *keddah* wing was whispering to the forests. "Will I save you, great one that I knew in babyhood? Will you go down into chains before the night is done? *Ai!* I hear the thunder of your feet! The moment is almost here. And now — your last chance, Muztagh!"

"Close down, close down!" Ahmad Din was shouting to his beaters. "The thing is done in another moment. Hasten, pigs of the hills! Raise your voice! Now! *Aihai!*"

The herd was at the very wings of the stockade. They had halted an instant, milling, and the beaters increased their shouts. Only one of all the herd seemed to know the danger — Muztagh himself, and he had dropped from the front rank to the very rear. He stood with uplifted trunk, facing the

## The Elephant Remembers 87

approaching rows of beaters. And there seemed to be no break in the whole line.

The herd started to move on, into the wings of captivity; and they did not heed his warning squeals to turn. The circle of fire drew nearer. Then his trunk seemed to droop, and he turned, too. He could not break the line. He turned, too, toward the mouth of the *keddah*.

But even as he turned, a brown figure darted toward him from the end of the wing. A voice known long ago was calling to him — a voice that penetrated high and clear above the babble of the beaters. "Muztagh!" it was crying. "Muztagh!"

But it was not the words that turned Muztagh. An elephant cannot understand words, except a few elemental sounds such as a horse or dog can learn. Rather it was the smell of the man, remembered from long ago, and the sound of his voice, never quite forgotten. For an elephant never forgets.

"Muztagh! Muztagh!"

The elephant knew him now. He remembered his one friend among all the human beings that he knew in his calf-hood; the one mortal from whom he had received love and given love in exchange.

"More firebrands!" yelled the men who held that corner of the wing. "Firebrands! Where is Langur Dass?" but instead of firebrands that would have frightened beast and aided men, Langur Dass stepped out from behind a tree and beat at the heads of the right-wing guards with a bamboo cane that whistled and whacked and scattered them into panic — yelling all the while — "Muztagh! O my Muztagh! Here is an opening! Muztagh, come!"

And Muztagh did come — trumpeting — crashing like an avalanche, with Langur Dass hard after him, afraid, now that he had done the trick. And hot on the trail of Langur Dass ran Ahmad Din, with his knife drawn, not meaning to let that prize be lost to him at less than the cost of the trickster's life.

But it was not written that the knife should ever enter the flesh of Langur Dass.

The elephant never forgets, and Muztagh was monarch of his breed. He turned back two paces, and struck with his trunk. Ahmad Din was knocked aside as the wind whips a straw.

For an instant elephant and man stood front to front. To the left of them the gates of the stockade dropped shut behind the herd. The elephant stood with trunk slightly lifted, for the moment motionless. The long-haired man who had saved him stood lifting upstretched arms.

It was such a scene as one might remember in an old legend, wherein beasts and men were brothers, or such as sometimes might steal, like something remembered from another age, into a man's dreams. Nowhere but in India, where men have a little knowledge of the mystery of the elephant, could it have taken place at all.

For Langur Dass was speaking to my lord the elephant:

"Take me with thee, Muztagh! Monarch of the hills! Thou and I are not of the world of men, but of the jungle and the rain, the silence, and the cold touch of rivers. We are brothers, Muztagh. O beloved, wilt thou leave me here to die!"

The elephant slowly turned his head and looked scornfully at the group of beaters bearing down on Langur Dass, murder shining no less from their knives than from their lighted eyes.

"Take me," the old man pleaded; "thy herd is gone."

The elephant seemed to know what he was asking. He had lifted him to his great shoulders many times, in the last days of his captivity. And besides, his old love for Langur Dass had never been forgotten. It all returned, full and strong as ever. For an elephant never can forget.

It was not one of the man-herd that stood pleading before him. It was one of his own jungle people, just as, deep in his heart, he had always known. So with one motion light as air, he swung him gently to his shoulder.

The jungle, vast and mysterious and still, closed its gates behind them.

## QUESTIONS

1. Does an animal born in captivity retain its primitive instincts?
2. How did Muztagh differ from the other captive elephants?
3. Is the relationship between Langur Dass and Muztagh exaggerated?
4. Where does the story really begin?
5. Is the part preceding necessary as a foundation for the story?
6. Describe Muztagh's escape and his enjoyment of liberty.
7. What saved the life of Khusru?

## The Elephant Remembers 89

8. Sum up Muztagh's life in the wilds to the end of section four.
9. Try to visualize the fight between the two giants, and describe it.
10. Do wild herds have leaders, as described in the story?
11. Do elephants have mental qualities like those of Muztagh in the story?
12. Are your sympathies with Langur Dass and Muztagh? Why?
13. What is the climax? Explain.
14. Do you like animal stories? This particular one? Why?
15. What animals usually appear in stories? Do you like them better?
16. Are you familiar with Kipling's stories of animals?

### SUBJECTS FOR COMPOSITION

1. Orally, contrast this story with " Zenobia's Infidelity."
2. Write an episode, from your own knowledge, about animal intelligence.
3. From a visit to a zoo or a circus, write out your observations of elephants.

### OTHER STORIES BY EDISON MARSHALL

The Man That Was in Him
The Voice of the Pack
Vagabond or Gentleman

Furs
The Heart of the Little Shikara

## EDGAR ALLAN POE
### (1809-1849)

IN THE field of the American short story Poe shares pre-eminence with Hawthorne. In addition to the mere fact that they were contemporaries, there are striking parallels and contrasts in their work. Both were representative of their day in so far as they wrote stories of the type then fashionable — stories of romantic horror, of extravagant fantasy, of the weird and the supernatural, and of death. Of the two, Hawthorne was the more restrained. He reveled less in grim detail, but secured the desired effect through suggestion, and never failed to suffuse his story with the moral atmosphere of Puritan New England. Poe, on the other hand, created his effects by relentlessly massing his facts in the manner of Defoe to make them seem real. The individual mannerisms of the two authors are clearly shown in the stories printed in this book.

By 1840 Poe had written twenty-six short tales, all except one being included in the volume published at that time, *Tales of the Grotesque and the Arabesque*. After reading " The Fall of the House of Usher " the meaning of that title will be understood. It is Poe's best story in every way, not only because it is so thoroughly characteristic of his manner, but also because it is in accord with his own theory of the short story, a theory almost universally accepted today. And it must not be forgotten that this theory was evolved in a critical review of Hawthorne's *Twice Told Tales*.

Nothing could have been more dissimilar than the lives of these two men, with one important exception — that of seclusiveness. Both lived much within their own minds and shunned publicity, a trait common to those endowed with a powerful imagination. The story of Poe's life is not unlike that of one of his own tales. His parents were members of a troupe of wandering actors that happened to be in Boston when Poe was born. But Poe rightly considered himself a Southerner. The parents died before he was three years old, and the boy was adopted by John Allan, a wealthy Richmond tobacco merchant. Mr. Allan's business took him to England, where Poe went to school between the ages of six and eleven. His preparation for college was completed in Virginia, and he entered the university in 1826.

After ten months he left college. The records show that he was a brilliant student, especially in languages, but already the erratic tendencies in his nature were clearly evident. Gaming and drink were immediately responsible, Mr. Allan refusing to recognize the young man's gambling debts as legitimate expenses. They quarreled, but a temporary adjustment was made, Poe taking a position in Mr. Allan's business. But he was not interested, and went North, where he enlisted in the army. Two years later he was once more reconciled to

Mr. Allan, an honorable discharge from the army was obtained, and Poe received an appointment to West Point. When Mr. Allan married a second time — his first wife having died in 1829 — Poe once more became discontented. He felt that now he might be cut off from all financial expectations, and such eventually proved to be the case. He deliberately violated the rules and was court-martialed out of the Academy in 1831.

Up to that time Poe had published a slim volume of poetry which created no stir. During the next two years he kept in seclusion and must have written a great deal. In 1833 *The Baltimore Visitor* offered a $100 prize in a short story contest to which Poe submitted six stories, one of which, " A Manuscript Found in a Bottle," received the prize.

Like Hawthorne, Poe had definitely decided upon a literary career, and every cent he ever earned from this time on came through his pen. It was little enough, and the story of the rest of Poe's life is a record of struggle and poverty, both aggravated by peculiarities of temperament and genius. He was eternally restless; always when he seemed anchored to a post for which he seemed ideally fitted he broke loose and was again on the uncharted seas of authorship.

Matters were further complicated by his marriage to Virginia Clemm, a cousin, only thirteen years old. She was a beautiful and intelligent girl, and may have been the inspiration of " Annabel Lee." He now worked with some regularity in various editorial offices, writing many critical articles and stories that invariably increased the circulation of the journals on which he worked. But he never stayed long in one place. First Richmond, then Philadelphia, and by 1845 New York, where he became contributing editor of *The Evening Mirror,* and later of *The Broadway Journal* — that summarizes his journalistic career. Always there was ultimate failure.

In 1847 his wife died. So acute was his agony that a complete breakdown was feared by his friends, but he recovered and resumed writing. In about a year or so he became engaged to a woman who had been one of his early attachments. To complete the arrangements for the marriage Poe took a trip to Virginia, and, on the way back to New York, stopped over in Baltimore. It happened to be election day. In those times corrupt practices were at least as common as they are now, a particular trick being to get hold of strangers, either drug them or make them drunk, and then " vote them " all over the city. This happened to Poe, it is thought; at any rate, he was found unconscious and died October 7, 1849.

# THE FALL OF THE HOUSE OF USHER

Son cœur est un luth suspendu;
Sitôt qu'on le touche il résonne.
— DE BÉRANGER.

DURING the whole of a dull, dark, and soundless day in the autumn of the year, when the clouds hung oppressively low in the heavens, I had been passing alone, on horseback, through a singularly dreary tract of country; and at length found myself, as the shades of the evening drew on, within view of the melancholy House of Usher. I know not how it was; but, with the first glimpse of the building, a sense of insufferable gloom pervaded my spirit. I say insufferable; for the feeling was unrelieved by any of that half-pleasurable, because poetic, sentiment, with which the mind usually receives even the sternest natural images of the desolate or terrible. I looked upon the scene before me — upon the mere house, and the simple landscape features of the domain — upon the bleak walls — upon the vacant eye-like windows — upon a few rank sedges — and upon a few white trunks of decayed trees — with an utter depression of soul which I can compare to no earthly sensation more properly than to the after-dream of the reveler upon opium — the bitter lapse into every-day life — the hideous dropping off of the veil. There was an iciness, a sinking, a sickening of the heart — an unredeemed dreariness of thought which no goading of the imagination could torture into aught of the sublime. What was it — I paused to think — what was it that so unnerved me in the contemplation of the House of Usher? It was a mystery all insoluble; nor could I grapple with the shadowy fancies that crowded upon me as I pondered. I was forced to fall back upon the unsatisfactory conclusion that while, beyond doubt, there *are* combinations of very simple natural objects which have the power of thus affecting us, still the analysis of this power lies among considerations beyond our depth. It was impossible, I reflected, that a mere different arrangement of the particulars of the scene, of the details of the picture, would be sufficient to modify, or perhaps to annihilate its capacity for sorrowful impression; and, acting upon this idea, I reined my horse to the precipitous brink of a black and lurid tarn that lay in unruffled luster by the dwelling, and gazed down — but with a shudder even more thrilling than before — upon the remodeled and inverted images of the gray sedge, and the ghastly tree stems, and the vacant and eye-like windows.

Nevertheless, in this mansion of gloom I now proposed to myself a sojourn of some weeks. Its proprietor, Roderick Usher, had been one of my boon companions in boyhood; but many years had elapsed since our last meeting. A letter, however, had lately reached me in a distant part of the country — a letter from him — which, in its wildly importunate nature, had admitted of no other than a personal reply. The MS. gave evidence of nervous agitation. The writer spoke of acute bodily illness, of a mental disorder which oppressed him, and of an earnest desire to see me, as his best, and indeed his only, personal friend, with a view of attempting, by the cheerfulness of my society, some alleviation of his malady. It was the manner in which all this, and much more, was said — it was the apparent *heart* that went with his request — which allowed me no room for hesitation; and I accordingly obeyed forthwith what I still considered a very singular summons.

Although, as boys, we had been even intimate associates, yet I really knew little of my friend. His reserve had been always excessive and habitual. I was aware, however, that his very ancient family had been noted, time out of mind, for a peculiar sensibility of temperament, displaying itself, through long ages, in many works of exalted art, and manifested, of late, in repeated deeds of munificent, yet unobtrusive, charity, as well as in a passionate devotion to the intricacies, perhaps even more than to the orthodox and easily recognizable beauties, of musical science. I had learned, too, the very remarkable fact that the stem of the Usher race, all time-honored as it was, had put forth, at no period, any enduring branch; in other words, that the entire family lay in the direct line of descent, and had always, with very trifling and very temporary variation, so lain. It was this deficiency, I considered, while running over in thought the perfect keeping of the character of the premises with the accredited character of the people, and while speculating upon the possible influence which the one, in the long lapse of centuries, might have exercised upon the other — it was this deficiency, perhaps, of collateral issue, and the consequent undeviating transmission, from sire to son, of the patrimony with the name, which had, at length, so identified the two as to merge the original title of the estate in the quaint and equivocal appellation of the *House of Usher* — an appellation which seemed to include, in the minds of the peasantry who used it, both the family and the family mansion.

I have said that the sole effect of my somewhat childish experiment of looking down within the tarn had been to deepen the first singular impression. There can be no doubt that the consciousness of the rapid increase of my superstition — for why should I not so term it? — served mainly to accelerate the increase itself. Such, I have long known, is the paradoxical law of all sentiments having terror as a basis. And it might have been for this reason only, that, when I again uplifted my eyes to the house itself, from its image in the pool, there grew in my mind a strange fancy — a fancy so ridiculous, indeed, that I but mention it to show the vivid force of the sensations which oppressed me. I had so worked upon my imagination as really to believe that about the whole mansion and domain there hung an atmosphere peculiar to themselves and their immediate vicinity — an atmosphere which had no affinity with the air of heaven, but which had reeked up from the decayed trees, and the gray wall, and the silent tarn — a pestilent and mystic vapor, dull, sluggish, faintly discernible, and leaden-hued.

Shaking off from my spirit what *must* have been a dream, I scanned more narrowly the real aspect of the building. Its principal feature seemed to be that of an excessive antiquity. The discoloration of ages had been great. Minute fungi overspread the whole exterior, hanging in a fine, tangled web-work from the eaves. Yet all this was apart from any extraordinary dilapidation. No portion of the masonry had fallen; and there appeared to be a wild inconsistency between its still perfect adaptation of parts, and the crumbling condition of the individual stones. In this there was much that reminded me of the specious totality of old woodwork which has rotted for years in some neglected vault, with no disturbance from the breath of the external air. Beyond this indication of extensive decay, however, the fabric gave little token of instability. Perhaps the eye of a scrutinizing observer might have discovered a barely perceptible fissure, which, extending from the roof of the building in front, made its way down the wall in a zigzag direction, until it became lost in the sullen waters of the tarn.

Noticing these things, I rode over a short causeway to the house. A servant in waiting took my horse, and I entered the Gothic archway of the hall. A valet, of stealthy step, thence conducted me, in silence, through many dark and intricate passages in my progress to the *studio* of his master. Much that I encountered on the way contributed, I know not how, to heighten the vague sentiments of which I have already spoken. While the objects around me — while the carvings of the ceilings, the somber tapestries of the walls, the ebon blackness of the floors, and the phantasmagoric armorial trophies which rattled as I strode, were but **matters** to which, or to such as which, I had been accustomed from my infancy — while I hesitated not to acknowledge how familiar was all this — I still wondered to find how unfamiliar were the fancies which ordinary images were stirring up. On one of the staircases I met the physician of the family. His countenance, I thought, wore a mingled expression of low cunning and perplexity. He accosted me with trepidation and passed on. The valet now threw open a door and ushered me into the presence of his master.

The room in which I found myself was very large and lofty. The windows were long, narrow, and pointed, and at so vast a distance from the black oaken floor as to be altogether inaccessible from within. Feeble gleams of encrimsoned light made their way through the trellised panes, and served to render sufficiently distinct the more prominent objects around; the eye, however, struggled in vain to reach the remoter angles of the chamber, or the recesses of the vaulted and fretted ceiling. Dark draperies hung upon the walls. The general furniture was profuse, comfortless, antique, and tattered. Many books and musical instruments lay scattered about, but failed to give any vitality to the scene. I felt that I breathed an atmosphere of sorrow. An air of stern, deep, and irredeemable gloom hung over and pervaded all.

Upon my entrance, Usher arose from a sofa on which he

had been lying at full length, and greeted me with a vivacious warmth which had much in it, I at first thought, of an overdone cordiality — of the constrained effort of the *ennuyé* man of the world. A glance, however, at his countenance convinced me of his perfect sincerity. We sat down; and for some moments, while he spoke not, I gazed upon him with a feeling half of pity, half of awe. Surely, man had never before so terribly altered, in so brief a period, as had Roderick Usher! It was with difficulty that I could bring myself to admit the identity of the wan being before me with the companion of my early boyhood. Yet the character of his face had been at all times remarkable. A cadaverousness of complexion; an eye large, liquid, and luminous beyond comparison; lips somewhat thin and very pallid, but of a surpassingly beautiful curve; a nose of a delicate Hebrew model, but with a breadth of nostril unusual in similar formations; a finely molded chin, speaking, in its want of prominence, of a want of moral energy; hair of a more than web-like softness and tenuity; these features, with an inordinate expansion above the regions of the temple, made up altogether a countenance not easily to be forgotten. And now in the mere exaggeration of the prevailing character of these features, and of the expression they were wont to convey, lay so much of change that I doubted to whom I spoke. The now ghastly pallor of the skin, and the now miraculous luster of the eye, above all things startled, and even awed me. The silken hair, too, had been suffered to grow all unheeded, and as, in its wild gossamer texture, it floated rather than fell about the face, I could not, even with effort, connect its arabesque expression with any idea of simple humanity.

In the manner of my friend I was at once struck with an incoherence — an inconsistency; and I soon found this to arise from a series of feeble and futile struggles to overcome an habitual trepidancy, an excessive nervous agitation. For something of this nature I had indeed been prepared, no less by his letter than by reminiscences of certain boyish traits, and by conclusions deduced from his peculiar physical conformation and temperament. His action was alternately vivacious and sullen. His voice varied rapidly from a tremulous indecision (when the animal spirit seemed utterly in abeyance) to that species of energetic concision — that abrupt, weighty unhurried, and hollow-sounding enunciation — that leaden, self-balanced, and perfectly modulated guttural utterance, which may be observed in the lost drunkard, or the irreclaimable eater of opium, during the periods of his most intense excitement.

It was thus that he spoke of the object of my visit, of his earnest desire to see me, and of the solace he expected me to afford him. He entered, at some length, into what he conceived to be the nature of his malady. It was, he said, a constitutional and a family evil, and one for which he despaired to find a remedy — a mere nervous affection, he immediately added, which would undoubtedly soon pass off. It displayed itself in a host of unnatural sensations. Some of these, as he detailed them, interested and bewildered me; although, perhaps, the terms and the general manner of the narration had their weight. He suffered much from a morbid acuteness of the senses. The most insipid food was alone endurable; he could wear only garments of certain texture; the odors of all flowers were oppressive; his eyes were tortured by even a faint light; and there were but peculiar sounds, and these from stringed instruments, which did not inspire him with horror.

To an anomalous species of terror I found him a bounden slave. "I shall perish," said he, "I *must* perish in this deplorable folly. Thus, thus, and not otherwise, shall I be lost. I dread the events of the future, not in themselves, but in their results. I shudder at the thought of any, even the most trivial, incident, which may operate upon this intolerable agitation of soul. I have, indeed, no abhorrence of danger, except in its absolute effect — in terror. In this unnerved — in this pitiable condition — I feel that the period will sooner or later arrive when I must abandon life and reason together in some struggle with the grim phantasm, FEAR."

I learned, moreover, at intervals, and through broken and equivocal hints, another singular feature of his mental condition. He was enchained by certain superstitious impressions in regard to the dwelling which he tenanted, and whence, for many years, he had never ventured forth — in regard to an influence whose supposititious force was conveyed in terms too shadowy here to be restated — an influence which some peculiarities in the mere form and substance of his family mansion, had, by dint of long sufferance, he said, obtained over his spirit — an effect which the *physique* of the gray walls and turrets, and of the dim tarn into which they all looked down, had, at length, brought upon the *morale* of his existence.

He admitted, however, although with hesitation, that much of the peculiar gloom which thus afflicted him could be traced to a more natural and far more palpable origin — to the severe and long-continued illness — indeed to the evidently approaching dissolution — of a tenderly beloved sister, his sole companion for long years, his last and only relative on earth. "Her decease," he said, with a bitterness which I can never forget, "would leave him (him the hopeless and the frail) the last of the ancient race of the Ushers." While he spoke, the lady Madeline (for so was she called) passed slowly through a remote portion of the apartment, and, without having noticed my presence, disappeared. I regarded her with an utter astonishment not unmingled with dread; and yet I found it impossible to account for such feelings. A sensation of stupor oppressed me, as my eyes followed her retreating steps. When a door, at length, closed upon her, my glance sought instinctively and eagerly the countenance of the brother; but he had buried his face in his hands, and I could only perceive that a far more than ordinary wanness had overspread the emaciated fingers through which trickled many passionate tears.

The disease of the lady Madeline had long baffled the skill of her physicians. A settled apathy, a gradual wasting away of the person, and frequent although transient affections of a partially cataleptical character, were the unusual diagnosis. Hitherto she had steadily borne up against the pressure of her malady, and had not betaken herself finally to bed; but on the closing in of the evening of my arrival at the house, she succumbed (as her brother told me at night with inexpressible agitation) to the prostrating power of the destroyer; and I learned that the glimpse I had obtained of her person would thus probably be the last I should obtain — that the lady, at least while living, would be seen by me no more.

For several days ensuing her name was unmentioned by either Usher or myself; and during this period I was busied in earnest endeavors to alleviate the melancholy of my friend. We painted and read together; or I listened, as if in a dream, to the wild improvisations of his speaking guitar. And thus, as a closer and still closer intimacy admitted me more unreservedly into the recesses of his spirit, the more bitterly did I perceive the futility of all attempt at cheering a mind from which darkness, as if an inherent positive quality, poured forth upon all objects of the moral and physical universe, in one unceasing radiation of gloom.

I shall ever bear about me the memory of the many solemn hours I thus spent alone with the master of the House of Usher. Yet I should fail in any attempt to convey an idea of the exact character of the studies, or of the occupations in which he involved me, or led me the way. An excited and highly distempered ideality threw a sulphurous luster over all. His long, improvised dirges will ring forever in my ears. Among other things, I hold painfully in mind a certain singular perversion and amplification of the wild air of the last waltz of von Weber. From the paintings over which his elaborate fancy brooded, and which grew, touch by touch, into vaguenesses at which I shuddered the more thrillingly because I shuddered knowing not why, — from these paintings (vivid as their images now are before me) I would in vain endeavor to educe more than a small portion which should lie within the compass of merely written words. By the utter simplicity, by the nakedness of his designs, he arrested and overawed attention. If ever mortal painted an idea, that mortal was Roderick Usher. For me, at least, in the circumstances then surrounding me, there arose out of the pure abstractions which the hypochondriac contrived to throw upon his canvas, an intensity of intolerable awe, no shadow of which felt I ever yet in the contemplation of the certainly glowing yet too concrete reveries of Fuseli.

One of the phantasmagoric conceptions of my friend, partaking not so rigidly of the spirit of abstraction, may be shadowed forth, although feebly, in words. A small picture presented the interior of an immensely long and rectangular vault or tunnel, with low walls, smooth, white, and without interruption or device. Certain accessory points of the design served well to convey the idea that this excavation lay at an exceeding depth below the surface of the earth. No outlet was observed in any portion of its vast extent, and no torch or other artificial source of light was discernible; yet a flood of intense rays rolled throughout, and bathed the whole in a ghastly and inappropriate splendor.

I have just spoken of that morbid condition of the auditory nerve which rendered all music intolerable to the sufferer, with the exception of certain effects of stringed instruments. It was, perhaps, the narrow limits to which he thus confined himself upon the guitar, which gave birth, in great measure, to the fantastic character of his performances. But the fervid *facility* of his *impromptus* could not be so accounted for. They must have been, and were, in the notes, as well as in the words of his wild fantasias (for he not unfrequently accompanied himself with rimed verbal improvisations), the result of that intense mental collectedness and concentration to which I have previously alluded as observable only in particular moments of the highest artificial excitement. The words of one of these rhapsodies I have easily remembered. I was, perhaps, the more forcibly impressed with it, as he gave it, because, in the under or mystic current of its meaning, I fancied that I perceived, and for the first time, a full consciousness on the part of Usher, of the tottering of his lofty reason upon her throne. The verses, which were entitled "The Haunted Palace," ran very nearly, if not accurately, thus: —

I

In the greenest of our valleys,
  By good angels tenanted,
Once a fair and stately palace —
  Radiant palace — reared its head.
In the monarch Thought's dominion —
  It stood there!
Never seraph spread a pinion
  Over fabric half so fair.

II

Banners yellow, glorious, golden,
  On its roof did float and flow;
(This — all this — was in the olden
  Time long ago)

And every gentle air that dallied,
  In that sweet day,
Along the ramparts plumed and pallid,
  A wingèd odor went away.

### III

Wanderers in that happy valley
  Through two luminous windows saw
Spirits moving musically
  To a lute's well-tunèd law,
Round about a throne, where sitting
  (Porphyrogene!)
In state his glory well befitting,
  The ruler of the realm was seen.

### IV

And all with pearl and ruby glowing
  Was the fair palace door,
Through which came flowing, flowing, flowing,
  And sparkling evermore,
A troop of Echoes whose sweet duty
  Was but to sing,
In voices of surpassing beauty,
  The wit and wisdom of their king.

### V

But evil things, in robes of sorrow,
  Assailed the monarch's high estate
(Ah, let us mourn, for never morrow
  Shall dawn upon him, desolate!);
And, round about his home, the glory
  That blushed and bloomed
Is but a dim-remembered story
  Of the old time entombed.

### VI

And travelers now within that valley,
  Through the red-litten windows, see
Vast forms that move fantastically
  To a discordant melody;

> While, like a rapid ghastly river,
> Through the pale door,
> A hideous throng rush out forever,
> And laugh — but smile no more.

I well remember that suggestions arising from this ballad led us into a train of thought wherein there became manifest an opinion of Usher's which I mention not so much on account of its novelty (for other men have thought thus) as on account of the pertinacity with which he maintained it. This opinion, in its general form, was that of the sentience of all vegetable things. But, in his disordered fancy, the idea had assumed a more daring character, and trespassed, under certain conditions, upon the kingdom of inorganization. I lack words to express the full extent or the earnest abandon of his persuasion. The belief, however, was connected (as I have previously hinted) with the gray stones of the home of his forefathers. The conditions of the sentience had been here, he imagined, fulfilled in the method of collocation of these stones — in the order of their arrangement, as well as in that of the many fungi which overspread them, and of the decayed trees which stood around — above all, in the long-undisturbed endurance of this arrangement, and in its reduplication in the still waters of the tarn. Its evidence — the evidence of the sentience — was to be seen, he said (and I here started as he spoke), in the gradual yet certain condensation of an atmosphere of their own about the waters and the walls. The result was discoverable, he added, in that silent, yet importunate and terrible influence which for centuries had molded the destinies of his family, and which made *him* what I now saw him — what he was. Such opinions need no comment, and I will make none.

Our books — the books which, for years, had formed no small portion of the mental existence of the invalid — were, as might be supposed, in strict keeping with this character of phantasm. We pored together over such works as the *Ververt et Chartreuse* of Gresset; the *Belphegor* of Machiavelli; the *Heaven and Hell* of Swedenborg; the *Subterranean Voyage of Nicholas Klimm* by Holberg; the *Chiromancy* of Robert Flud, of Jean d'Indaginé, and of De la Chambre; the *Journey into the Blue Distance* of Tieck; and the *City of the Sun* of Campanella. One favorite volume was a small octavo edition of the *Directorium Inquisitorium* by the Dominican Eymeric de Cironne; and there were passages in *Pomponius Mela*, about the old African Satyrs and Œgipans, over which Usher would sit dreaming for hours. His chief delight, however, was found in the perusal of an exceedingly rare and curious book in quarto Gothic — the manual of a forgotten church — the *Vigiliæ Mortuorum secundum Chorum Ecclesiæ Maguntinæ*.

I could not help thinking of the wild ritual of this work, and of its probable influence upon the hypochondriac, when, one evening, having informed me abruptly that the lady Madeline was no more, he stated his intention of preserving her corpse for a fortnight (previously to its final interment) in one of the numerous vaults within the main walls of the building. The worldly reason, however, assigned for this singular proceeding, was one which I did not feel at liberty to dispute. The brother had been led to his resolution, so he told me, by consideration of the unusual character of the malady of the deceased, of certain obtrusive and eager inquiries on the part of her medical men, and of the remote and exposed situation of the burial ground of the family. I will not deny that when I called to mind the sinister countenance of the person whom I met upon the staircase, on the day of my arrival at the house, I had no desire to oppose what I regarded as at best but a harmless, and by no means an unnatural precaution.

At the request of Usher, I personally aided him in the arrangements for the temporary entombment. The body having been encoffined, we two alone bore it to its rest. The vault in which we placed it (and which had been so long unopened that our torches, half smothered in its oppressive atmosphere, gave us little opportunity for investigation) was small, damp, and entirely without means of admission for light; lying, at great depth, immediately beneath that portion of the building in which was my own sleeping apartment. It had been used, apparently, in remote feudal times, for the worst purposes of a donjon-keep, and in later days, as a place of deposit for powder, or some other highly combustible substance, as a portion of its floor, and the whole interior of a long archway through which we reached it, were carefully sheathed with copper. The door, of massive iron, had been also similarly protected. Its immense weight caused an unusually sharp grating sound as it moved upon its hinges.

Having deposited our mournful burden upon tressels within this region of horror, we partially turned aside the yet unscrewed lid of the coffin, and looked upon the face of the tenant. A striking similitude between the brother and sister now first arrested my attention; and Usher, divining, perhaps, my thoughts, murmured out some few words from which I learned that the deceased and himself had been twins, and that sympathies of a scarcely intelligible nature had always existed between them. Our glances, however, rested not long upon the dead — for we could not regard her unawed. The disease which had thus entombed the lady in the maturity of youth, had left, as usual in all maladies of a strictly cataleptical character, the mockery of a faint blush upon the bosom and the face, and that suspiciously lingering smile upon the lip which is so terrible in death. We replaced and screwed down the lid, and having secured the door of iron, made our way, with toil, into the scarcely less gloomy apartments of the upper portion of the house.

And now, some days of bitter grief having elapsed, an observable change came over the features of the mental disorder of my friend. His ordinary manner had vanished. His ordinary occupations were neglected or forgotten. He roamed from chamber to chamber with hurried, unequal, and objectless step. The pallor of his countenance had assumed, if possible, a more ghastly hue — but the luminousness of his eye had utterly gone out. The once occasional huskiness of his tone was heard no more; and a tremulous quaver, as if of extreme terror, habitually characterized his utterance. There were times, indeed, when I thought his unceasingly agitated mind was laboring with some oppressive secret, to divulge which he struggled for the necessary courage. At times, again, I was obliged to resolve all into the mere inexplicable vagaries of madness; for I beheld him gazing upon vacancy for long hours, in an attitude of the profoundest attention, as if listening to some imaginary sound. It was no wonder that his condition terrified — that it infected me. I felt creeping upon me, by slow yet certain degrees, the wild influence of his own fantastic yet impressive superstitions.

It was, especially, upon retiring to bed late in the night of the seventh or eighth day after the placing of the lady Madeline within the donjon, that I experienced the full power of such feelings. Sleep came not near my couch, while the hours waned and waned away. I struggled to reason off the nervousness which had dominion over me. I endeavored to believe that much, if not all of what I felt, was due to the bewildering influence of the gloomy furniture of the room — of the dark and tattered draperies, which, tortured into emotion by the breath of a rising tempest, swayed fitfully to and fro upon the walls, and rustled uneasily about the decorations of the bed. But my efforts were fruitless. An irrepressible tremor gradually pervaded my frame; and, at length, there sat upon my very heart an incubus of utterly causeless alarm. Shaking this off with a gasp and a struggle, I uplifted myself upon the pillows, and peering earnestly within the intense darkness of the chamber, hearkened — I knew not why, except that an instinctive spirit prompted me — to certain low and indefinite sounds which came, through the pauses of the storm, at long intervals, I knew not whence. Overpowered by an intense sentiment of horror, unaccountable yet unendurable, I threw on my clothes with haste (for I felt that I should sleep no more during the night), and endeavored to arouse myself from the pitiable condition into which I had fallen, by pacing rapidly to and fro through the apartment.

I had taken but few turns in this manner, when a light step on an adjoining staircase arrested my attention. I presently recognized it as that of Usher. In an instant afterwards he rapped, with a gentle touch, at my door, and entered, bearing a lamp. His countenance was, as usual, cadaverously wan — but, moreover, there was a species of mad hilarity in his eyes — and evidently restrained hysteria in his whole demeanor. His air appalled me — but anything was preferable to the solitude which I had so long endured, and I even welcomed his presence as a relief.

"And you have not seen it?" he said abruptly, after having stared about him for some moments in silence — "you have not then seen it? — but stay! you shall." Thus speaking, and having carefully shaded his lamp, he hurried to one of the casements, and threw it freely open to the storm.

The impetuous fury of the entering gust nearly lifted us

from our feet. It was, indeed, a tempestuous yet sternly beautiful night, and one wildly singular in its terror and its beauty. A whirlwind had apparently collected its force in our vicinity; for there were frequent and violent alterations in the direction of the wind; and the exceeding density of the clouds (which hung so low as to press upon the turrets of the house) did not prevent our perceiving the lifelike velocity with which they flew careering from all points against each other, without passing away into the distance. I say that even their exceeding density did not prevent our perceiving this — yet we had no glimpse of the moon or stars — nor was there any flashing forth of the lightning. But the under surfaces of the huge masses of agitated vapor, as well as all terrestrial objects immediately around us, were glowing in the unnatural light of a faintly luminous and distinctly visible gaseous exhalation which hung about and enshrouded the mansion.

"You must not — you shall not behold this!" said I, shudderingly, to Usher, as I led him, with a gentle violence, from the window to a seat. "These appearances, which bewilder you, are merely electrical phenomena not uncommon — or it may be that they have their ghastly origin in the rank miasma of the tarn. Let us close this casement — the air is chilling and dangerous to your frame. Here is one of your favorite romances. I will read and you shall listen; and so we will pass away this terrible night together."

The antique volume which I had taken up was the *Mad Trist* of Sir Launcelot Canning; but I had called it a favorite of Usher's more in sad jest than in earnest; for, in truth, there is little in its uncouth and unimaginative prolixity which could have had interest for the lofty and spiritual ideality of my friend. It was, however, the only book immediately at hand; and I indulged a vague hope that the excitement which now agitated the hypochondriac, might find relief (for the history of mental disorder is full of similar anomalies) even in the extremeness of the folly which I should read. Could I have judged, indeed, by the wild, overstrained air of vivacity with which he hearkened, or apparently hearkened, to the words of the tale, I might well have congratulated myself upon the success of my design.

I had arrived at that well-known portion of the story where

Ethelred, the hero of the *Trist,* having sought in vain for peaceable admission into the dwelling of the hermit, proceeds to make good an entrance by force. Here, it will be remembered, the words of the narrative run thus: —

" And Ethelred, who was by nature of a doughty heart, and who was now mighty withal, on account of the powerfulness of the wine which he had drunken, waited no longer to hold parley with the hermit, who, in sooth, was of an obstinate and maliceful turn; but, feeling the rain upon his shoulders, and fearing the rising of the tempest, uplifted his mace outright, and, with blows, made quickly room in the plankings of the door for his gauntleted hand; and now pulling therewith sturdily, he so cracked, and ripped, and tore all asunder, that the noise of the dry and hollow-sounding wood alarumed and reverberated throughout the forest."

At the termination of this sentence I started, and for a moment paused; for it appeared to me (although I at once concluded that my excited fancy had deceived me) — it appeared to me that, from some very remote portion of the mansion, there came, indistinctly, to my ears what might have been, in its exact similarity of character, the echo (but a stifled and dull one certainly) of the very cracking and ripping sound which Sir Launcelot had so particularly described. It was, beyond doubt, the coincidence alone which had arrested my attention; for, amid the rattling of the sashes of the casements, and the ordinary commingled noises of the still increasing storm, the sound, in itself, had nothing, surely, which should have interested or disturbed me. I continued the story: —

" But the good champion Ethelred, now entering within the door, was sore enraged and amazed to perceive no signal of the maliceful hermit; but, in the stead thereof, a dragon of a scaly and prodigious demeanor, and of a fiery tongue, which sate in guard before a palace of gold, with a floor of silver; and upon the wall there hung a shield of shining brass with this legend enwritten: —

> Who entereth herein, a conqueror hath been;
> Who slayeth the dragon, the shield he shall win.

And Ethelred uplifted his mace, and struck upon the head of the dragon, which fell before him, and gave up his pesty breath, with a shriek so horrid and harsh, and withal so piercing, that Ethelred had fain to close his ears with his hands against the dreadful noise of it, the like whereof was never before heard."

Here again I paused abruptly, and now with a feeling of wild amazement — for there could be no doubt whatever that, in this instance, I did actually hear (although from what direction it proceeded I found it impossible to say) a low and apparently distant, but harsh, protracted, and most unusual screaming or grating sound — the exact counterpart of what my fancy had already conjured up for the dragon's unnatural shriek as described by the romancer.

Oppressed, as I certainly was, upon the occurrence of this second and most extraordinary coincidence, by a thousand conflicting sensations, in which wonder and extreme terror were predominant, I still retained sufficient presence of mind to avoid exciting, by any observation, the sensitive nervousness of my companion. I was by no means certain that he had noticed the sounds in question; although, assuredly, a strange alteration had, during the last few minutes, taken place in his demeanor. From a position fronting my own, he had gradually brought round his chair, so as to sit with his face to the door of the chamber; and thus I could but partially perceive his features, although I saw that his lips trembled as if he were murmuring inaudibly. His head had dropped upon his breast — yet I knew that he was not asleep, from the wide and rigid opening of the eye as I caught a glance of it in profile. The motion of his body, too, was at variance with this idea — for he rocked from side to side with a gentle yet constant and uniform sway. Having rapidly taken notice of all this, I resumed the narrative of Sir Launcelot, which thus proceeded: —

"And now the champion, having escaped from the terrible fury of the dragon, bethinking himself of the brazen shield, and of the breaking up of the enchantment which was upon it, removed the carcass from out of the way before him, and approached valorously over the silver pavement of the castle to where the shield was upon the wall; which in sooth tarried not for his full coming, but fell down at his feet upon the silver floor, with a mighty, great and terrible ringing sound."

No sooner had these syllables passed my lips, than — as if a shield of brass had indeed, at the moment, fallen heavily upon a floor of silver — I became aware of a distinct, hollow, metallic and clangorous, yet apparently muffled reverberation. Completely unnerved, I leaped to my feet; but the measured rocking movement of Usher was undisturbed. I rushed to the chair in which he sat. His eyes were bent fixedly before him, and throughout his whole countenance there reigned a stony rigidity. But, as I placed my hand upon his shoulder, there came a strong shudder over his whole person; a sickly smile quivered about his lips; and I saw that he spoke in a low, hurried, and gibbering murmur, as if unconscious of my presence. Bending closely over him, I at length drank in the hideous import of his words.

"Not hear it? — yes, I hear it, and *have* heard it. Long — long — long — many minutes, many hours, many days, have I heard it — yet I dared not — oh, pity me, miserable wretch that I am! — I dared not — I *dared* not speak! *We have put her living in the tomb!* Said I not that my senses were acute? I *now* tell you that I heard her first feeble movements in the hollow coffin. I heard them — many, many days ago — yet I dared not — *I dared not speak!* And now — to-night — Ethelred — ha! ha! — the breaking of the hermit's door, and the death-cry of the dragon, and the clangor of the shield! — say, rather, the rending of her coffin, and the grating of the iron hinges of her prison, and her struggles within the coppered archway of the vault! Oh, whither shall I fly? Will she not be here anon? Is she not hurrying to upbraid me for my haste? Have I not heard her footstep on the stair? Do I not distinguish that heavy and horrible beating of her heart? Madman!" — here he sprang furiously to his feet, and shrieked out his syllables, as if in the effort he were giving up his soul — "*Madman! I tell you that she now stands without the door!*"

As if in the superhuman energy of his utterance there had been found the potency of a spell — the huge antique panels to which the speaker pointed threw slowly back, upon the instant, their ponderous and ebony jaws. It was the work of the rushing gust — but then without those doors there *did* stand the lofty and enshrouded figure of the lady Madeline of Usher. There was blood upon her white robes, and the evidence of some bitter struggle upon every portion of her emaciated frame. For a moment she remained trembling and reeling to and fro upon the threshold — then, with a low, moaning cry, fell heavily inward upon the person of her brother, and in her violent and now final death-agonies, bore him to the floor a corpse, and a victim to the terrors he had anticipated.

From that chamber, and from that mansion, I fled aghast. The storm was still abroad in all its wrath as I found myself crossing the old causeway. Suddenly there shot along the path a wild light, and I turned to see whence a gleam so unusual could have issued; for the vast house and its shadows were alone behind me. The radiance was that of the full, setting, and blood-red moon, which now shone vividly through that once barely discernible fissure, of which I have before spoken as extending from the roof of the building, in a zigzag direction, to the base. While I gazed, this fissure rapidly widened — there came a fierce breath of the whirlwind — the entire orb of the satellite burst at once upon my sight — my brain reeled as I saw the mighty walls rushing asunder — there was a long tumultuous shouting sound like the voice of a thousand waters — and the deep and dank tarn at my feet closed sullenly and silently over the fragments of the "*House of Usher.*"

## QUESTIONS

1. Is this a story of "atmosphere"? See Introduction.
2. Note how by words and phrases Poe creates an effect of gloom and impending disaster.
3. Make a list of these from the first paragraph.
4. Why are there so many references to the "tarn" in the first pages?
5. Find other such hints in the first part of the story.
6. What country is suggested? Is it important?
7. Note the details of the description of the room and of Usher. Do these fit in with what has already been told?
8. Might the feeling inspired have been due in part to the visitor's own temperament?
9. What do you think was the author's intention in this respect?
10. Note how the details of the unusual keep piling up, culminating momentarily in the appearance of the Lady Madeline.
11. As the character and accomplishments of Usher are developed, what is your feeling about him? Does he become more interesting? more likable? or not? Explain.
12. Why was the visitor never introduced to Madeline?
13. Does the appearance of the tomb recall a previous passage in the story? Be definite.

14. What bits of description of Madeline in the coffin are of special significance?
15. With "an observable change" in Usher the "terror" motive of the story speeds up. List details that are of importance later.
16. Is the "rising tempest" a fitting accompaniment for what follows?
17. Why does the visitor say, "You shall not behold this"?
18. The thrilling story of "Ethelred and the Dragon," as well as the name of the author, was invented by Poe to heighten the dramatic effect of this scene and to prepare for the startling climax.
19. Put into your own words a description of the climax.
20. Why does Usher repeat "I dared not speak"? What reasons can you give? Do you connect the doctor with this? Explain.
21. Does the story have a plot? If so, briefly state it.
22. Has the author succeeded in keeping his "atmosphere" throughout the story?

## SUBJECTS FOR COMPOSITION

1. Take an item of "horror" from a newspaper and try to turn it into an atmosphere story.
2. Write a story about a mysterious house on a cliff.
3. Sketch a character who is obsessed with some weird idea.

## OTHER STORIES BY EDGAR ALLAN POE

The Gold Bug
The Pit and the Pendulum
The Murders in the Rue Morgue
The Mystery of Marie Roget
The Purloined Letter

Masque of the Red Death
The Black Cat
The Cask of Amontillado
The Premature Burial
Descent into the Maelstrom

## ABOUT EDGAR ALLAN POE

*Life of Poe*, Richard Henry Stoddard
*Edgar Allan Poe*, G. E. Woodberry

# BRET HARTE
(1839–1902)

WHEN in 1868 Bret Harte became editor of the *Overland Monthly* of San Francisco he had already been writing fourteen years, and had achieved success without distinction, as such things went in the gold-crazed west. During those years he had made his living by working in the mining camps, by clerical positions, by teaching, and eventually as a typesetter in newspaper offices. From there he graduated into journalism proper, writing sketches and poems, and making many friends in Grub Street. When he was appointed secretary to the San Francisco mint, a job with good pay and little work, he definitely entered upon a literary career.

His early sketches were in the romantic manner of Irving, with a dash of Hawthorne, and his poems smacked loudly of Longfellow. This was to be expected of a young man born and bred in the East, for (Francis) Bret Harte was born in Albany, New York, in 1839. His father was a college professor, and the boy was to have had a regular college training, but frail health blocked that. His education was therefore obtained through an omnivorous devouring of books, his favorites being Irving and Dickens. Later he had an equal fondness for Spanish and French romances. In those days there were no " wild west " stories, a fact of some consequence.

After the death of his father he unwillingly accompanied his mother to California to join an older brother who had become infected with the gold fever. In 1853 the trip to California was still made by way of Panama, an adventure in itself. As editor of the *Overland Monthly* it was his pet ambition to make it the *Atlantic Monthly* of the west. The first number, in 1868, was wholly conventional, a real little sister to its near namesake in Boston. While Bret Harte had wanted just that, he nevertheless sensed that the thing was not quite right. Then he had the great idea, an idea destined quickly to lead him to the topmost pinnacle of contemporary fame. Not only that; it led to the most important element in the advance of the American short story since Irving and Poe.

Like all great ideas, that of Bret Harte was fundamentally simple; nothing other than to make his magazine a mirror of the stirring life and times immediately about him. In some of his earlier work there were hints of what might come, and other writers had unconsciously written in what was to be the new manner, notably Mark Twain, whose " Jumping Frog of Calaveras County " had appeared the year before. But Bret Harte now openly propagandized the idea, illustrating what he meant by his " Luck of Roaring Camp," " The Outcasts of Poker Flat," " Tennessee's Partner," and many others; also a poem in the same style, " Plain Language from Truthful James," better known as " The Heathen Chinee." Harte's triumph was complete, and he became the literary lion of two continents. And he thoroughly liked it. But Bret Harte was a child of the cultured East. Although he stayed in California seventeen years, he never became a full-blooded westerner. When in 1870 the *Atlantic Monthly* offered him $10,000 to come East and write for it a year he accepted and never went back.

When he returned east in 1870 he plunged gaily into the dress-suit life of the big cities. The large money returns from his writings were not large enough in the long run and he became hopelessly involved in debt. To get away from this embarrassment he accepted a position in the United States consular service, first in Germany and later in Glasgow. In the Scotch city it was said that you could always find Bret Harte anywhere except in his office. That tells its own story. When he was relieved of his duties, he went to England, where he died in 1902.

Bret Harte's special skill lay in making his background — " local color " — seem an inevitable part of the logic of the tale. The typical story smacks of the mining *camp,* not of the mines. His miner was a rough fellow, often a social outcast whose only law was lawlessness, who held life cheap, who wanted gold only for the immediate joy it would bring in saloon and gambling hall, and who was happiest in those instants when an issue was to be decided by the flash of a gun. These men Harte romanticized by seizing upon some moment when their innate better selves were brought into action, for he had an incorrigible belief that even the toughest tough had in him a streak of good.

Bret Harte's best and most characteristic work may be found in the volume entitled *The Luck of Roaring Camp and Other Stories,* published in 1870. Throughout the rest of his life he wrote many volumes of stories, poems, and novels, the best of which hark back to his California days, but never was he quite able to recapture the atmosphere and the flavor of the stories written on the spot. His final reputation will be determined by the stories in that first volume.

# THE POSTMISTRESS OF LAUREL RUN

THE mail stage had just passed Laurel Run — so rapidly that the whirling cloud of dust dragged with it down the steep grade from the summit hung over the level long after the stage had vanished, and then, drifting away, slowly sifted a red precipitate over the hot platform of the Laurel Run Post-Office.

Out of this cloud presently emerged the neat figure of the Postmistress with the mail bag which had been dexterously flung at her feet from the top of the passing vehicle. A dozen loungers eagerly stretched out their hands to assist her, but the warning, "It's agin the rules, boys, for any but her to touch it," from a bystander, and a coquettish shake of the head from the Postmistress herself — much more effective than any official interdict — withheld them. The bag was not heavy — Laurel Run was too recent a settlement to have attracted much correspondence — and the young woman, having pounced upon her prey with a certain feline instinct, dragged it, not without difficulty, behind the partitioned enclosure in the office, and locked the door. Her pretty face, momentarily visible through the window, was slightly flushed with the exertion, and the loose ends of her fair hair, wet with perspiration, curled themselves over her forehead into tantalizing little rings. But the window shutter was quickly closed, and this momentary but charming vision withdrawn from the waiting public.

"Gov'ment oughter have more sense than to make a woman pick mail bags outer the road," said Jo Simmons, sympathetically. "'Tain't in her day's work anyhow; Gov'ment oughter hand 'em over to her like a lady; it's rich enough and ugly enough."

"'Tain't Gov'ment; it's that Stage Company's airs and graces," interrupted a newcomer. "They think it mighty fine to go beltin' by, makin' everybody take their dust — just because stoppin' ain't in their contract. Why, if that expressman who chucked down the bag had any feelin's for a lady — " But he stopped here at the amused faces of his auditors.

"Guess you don't know much o' that expressman's feelin's, stranger," said Simmons grimly. "Why, you oughter see him just nussin' that bag like a baby as he comes tearin' down the grade, and then rise up and sorter heave it to Mrs. Baker ez if it was a five dollar bokay! His feelin's for her! Why, he's give himself so dead away to her that we're looking for him to forget what he's doin' next, and just come sailin' down hisself at her feet."

Meanwhile, on the other side of the partition, Mrs. Baker had brushed the red dust from the padlocked bag, and removed what seemed to be a supplementary package attached to it by a wire. Opening it she found a handsome scent-bottle, evidently a superadded gift from the devoted expressman. This she put aside with a slight smile and the murmured word, "Foolishness." But when she had unlocked the bag, even its sacred interior was also profaned by a covert parcel from the adjacent postmaster at Burnt Ridge, containing a gold "specimen" brooch and some circus tickets. It was laid aside with the other. This also was vanity and — presumably — vexation of spirit.

There were seventeen letters in all, of which five were for herself — and yet the proportion was small that morning. Two of them were marked "Official Business," and were promptly put by with feminine discernment; but in another compartment than that holding the presents. Then the shutter was opened, and the task of delivery commenced.

It was accompanied with a social peculiarity that had in time become a habit of Laurel Run. As the young woman delivered the letters, in turn, to the men who were patiently drawn up in Indian file, she made that simple act a medium of privileged but limited conversation on special or general topics — gay or serious as the case might be — or the temperament of the man suggested. That it was almost always of a complimentary character on their part may be readily imagined; but it was invariably characterized by an element of refined restraint, and — whether from some implied understanding or individual sense of honor — it never passed the bounds of conventionality or a certain delicacy of respect. The delivery was consequently more or less protracted, but when each man had exchanged his three or four minutes' conversation with the fair Postmistress — a conversation at times impeded by bashfulness or timidity, on his part solely, or restricted often to vague smiling — he resignedly made way for the next. It was a formal levee, mitigated by the informality of rustic tact, great good humor, and infinite patience, and would have been amusing, had it not always been terribly in earnest and at times touching. For it was peculiar to the place and the epoch, and indeed implied the whole history of Mrs. Baker.

She was the wife of John Baker, foreman of "The Last Chance," now for a year lying dead under half a mile of crushed and beaten in tunnel at Burnt Ridge. There had been a sudden outcry from the depths at high hot noontide one day, and John had rushed from his cabin — his young, foolish, flirting wife clinging to him — to answer that despairing cry of his imprisoned men. There was one exit that he alone knew which might be yet held open, among falling walls and tottering timbers, long enough to set them free. For one moment only the strong man hesitated between her entreating arms and his brothers' despairing cry. But she rose suddenly with a pale face, and said, " Go, John; I will wait for you here." He went, the men were freed — but she had waited for him ever since!

Yet in the shock of the calamity and in the after struggles of that poverty which had come to the ruined camp, she had scarcely changed. But the men had. Although she was to all appearances the same giddy, pretty Betsy Baker, who had been so disturbing to the younger members, they seemed to be no longer disturbed by her. A certain subdued awe and respect, as if the martyred spirit of John Baker still held his arm around her, appeared to have come upon them all. They held their breath as this pretty woman, whose brief mourning had not seemed to affect her cheerfulness or even playfulness of spirit, passed before them. But she stood by her cabin and the camp — the only woman in a settlement of forty men — during the darkest hours of their fortune. Helping them to wash and cook, and ministering to their domestic needs; the sanctity of her cabin was, however, always kept as inviolable as if it had been *his* tomb. No one exactly knew why, for it was only a tacit instinct; but even one or two who had not scrupled to pay court to Betsy Baker during John Baker's life shrank from even a suggestion of familiarity toward the woman who had said that she would " wait for him there."

When brighter days came and the settlement had increased by one or two families, and laggard capital had been hurried up to relieve the still beleaguered and locked-up wealth of Burnt Ridge, the needs of the community and the claims of the widow of John Baker were so well told in political quarters that the post-office of Laurel Run was created expressly for her. Every man participated in the building of the pretty yet substantial edifice — the only public building of Laurel Run — that stood in the dust of the great highway, half a mile from the settlement. There she was installed for certain hours of the day, for she could not be prevailed upon to abandon John's cabin, and here, with all the added respect due to a public functionary, she was secure in her privacy.

But the blind devotion of Laurel Run to John Baker's relict

## The Postmistress of Laurel Run 117

did not stop here. In its zeal to assure the Government authorities of the necessity for a post-office, and to secure a permanent competency to the postmistress, there was much embarrassing extravagance. During the first week the sale of stamps at Laurel Run Post-Office was unprecedented in the annals of the Department. Fancy prices were given for the first issue; then they were bought wildly, recklessly, unprofitably, and on all occasions. Complimentary congratulation at the little window invariably ended with "and a dollar's worth of stamps, Mrs. Baker." It was felt to be supremely delicate to buy only the highest priced stamps, without reference to their adequacy; then mere quantity was sought; then outgoing letters were all overpaid, and stamped in outrageous proportion to their weight and even size. The imbecility of this, and its probable effect on the reputation of Laurel Run at the General Post-Office, being pointed out by Mrs. Baker, stamps were adopted as local currency, and even for decorative purposes on mirrors and the walls of cabins. Everybody wrote letters, with the result, however, that those sent were ludicrously and suspiciously in excess of those received. To obviate this, select parties made forced journeys to Hickory Hill, the next post-office, with letters and circulars addressed to themselves at Laurel Run. How long the extravagance would have continued is not known, but it was not until it was rumored that, in consequence of this excessive flow of business, the Department had concluded that a post*master* would be better fitted for the place that it abated, and a compromise was effected with the General Office by a permanent salary to the Postmistress.

Such was the history of Mrs. Baker, who had just finished her afternoon levee, nodded a smiling "good-by" to her last customer, and closed her shutter again. Then she took up her own letters, but, before reading them, glanced, with a pretty impatience, at the two official envelopes addressed to herself, which she had shelved. They were generally a "lot of new rules," or notifications, or "absurd" questions which had nothing to do with Laurel Run, and only bothered her and "made her head ache," and she had usually referred them to her admiring neighbor at Hickory Hill for explanation, who had generally returned them to her with the brief endorsement, "Purp stuff, don't bother," or, "Hog wash, let it slide."

She remembered now that he had not returned the last two. With knitted brows and a slight pout she put aside her private correspondence and tore open the first one. It referred with official curtness to an unanswered communication of the previous week, and was "compelled to remind her of rule 47." Again those horrid rules! She opened the other; the frown deepened on her brow, and became fixed.

It was a summary of certain valuable money letters that had miscarried on the route, and of which they had given her previous information. For a moment her cheeks blazed. How dare they; what did they mean! Her way-bills and register were always right; she knew the names of every man, woman, and child in her district; no such names as those borne by the missing letters had ever existed at Laurel Run; no such addresses had ever been sent from Laurel Run Post-Office. It was a mean insinuation! She would send in her resignation at once! She would get "the boys" to write an insulting letter to Senator Slocumb — Mrs. Baker had the feminine idea of Government as a purely personal institution — and she would find out who it was that had put them up to this prying, crawling impudence! It was probably that wall-eyed old wife of the postmaster at Heavy Tree Crossing, who was jealous of her. "Remind her of their previous unanswered communication," indeed! Where was that communication, anyway? She remembered she had sent it to her admirer at Hickory Hill. Odd that he hadn't answered it. Of course, he knew all about this meanness — could he, too, have dared to suspect her! The thought turned her crimson again. He, Stanton Green, was an old "Laurel Runner," a friend of John's, a little "triflin'" and "presoomin'," but still an old loyal pioneer of the camp! "Why hadn't he spoke up?"

There was the soft muffled fall of a horse's hoof in the thick dust of the highway, the jingle of dismounting spurs, and a firm tread on the platform. No doubt, one of the boys returning for a few supplemental remarks under the feeble pretence of forgotten stamps. It had been done before, and she had resented it as "cayotin' round"; but now she was eager to pour out her wrongs to the first comer. She had her hand impulsively on the door of the partition, when she stopped with a new sense of her impaired dignity. Could she confess this to her worshipers? But here the door opened in her very face and a stranger entered.

He was a man of fifty, compactly and strongly built. A squarely cut goatee, slightly streaked with gray, fell straight from his thin-lipped but handsome mouth; his eyes were dark, humorous, yet searching. But the distinctive quality that struck Mrs. Baker was the blending of urban ease with frontier frankness. He was evidently a man who had seen cities and knew countries as well. And while he was dressed with the comfortable simplicity of a Californian mounted traveler, her inexperienced but feminine eye detected the keynote of his respectability in the carefully tied bow of his cravat. The Sierran throat was apt to be open, free, and unfettered.

"Good-morning, Mrs. Baker," he said, pleasantly, with his hat already in his hand. "I'm Harry Home, of San Francisco." As he spoke his eye swept approvingly over the neat enclosure, the primly tied papers, and well-kept pigeon-holes; the pot of flowers on her desk; her china silk mantle, and killing little chip hat and ribbons hanging against the wall; thence to her own pink flushed face, bright blue eyes, tendriled clinging hair, and then — fell upon the leathern mail bag still lying across the table. Here it became fixed on the unfortunate wire of the amorous expressman that yet remained hanging from the brass wards of the lock, and he reached his hand toward it.

But little Mrs. Baker was before him, and had seized it in her arms. She had been too preoccupied and bewildered to resent his first intrusion behind the partition, but this last familiarity with her sacred official property — albeit empty — capped the climax of her wrongs.

"How dare you touch it!" she said indignantly. "How dare you come in here! Who are you, anyway? Go outside at once!"

The stranger fell back with an amused, deprecatory gesture, and a long, silent laugh. "I'm afraid you don't know me, after all!" he said, pleasantly. "I'm Harry Home, the Department Agent from the San Francisco office. My note of advice, No. 201, with my name on the envelope, seems to have miscarried too."

Even in her fright and astonishment it flashed upon Mrs. Baker that she had sent that notice, too, to Hickory Hill.

But with it all the feminine secretive instinct within her was now thoroughly aroused, and she kept silent.

"I ought to have explained," he went on smilingly; "but you are quite right, Mrs. Baker," he added, nodding toward the bag. "As far as you knew, I had no business to go near it. Glad to see you know how to defend Uncle Sam's property so well. I was only a bit puzzled to know" (pointing to the wire) "if that thing was on the bag when it was delivered to you?"

Mrs. Baker saw no reason to conceal the truth. After all, this official was a man like the others, and it was just as well that he should understand her power. "It's only the expressman's foolishness," she said, with a slightly coquettish toss of her head. "He thinks it smart to tie some nonsense on that bag with the wire when he flings it down."

Mr. Home, with his eyes on her pretty face, seemed to think it a not inhuman or unpardonable folly. "As long as he doesn't meddle with the inside of the bag, I suppose you must put up with it," he said, laughingly. A dreadful recollection that the Hickory Hill postmaster had used the inside of the bag to convey *his* foolishness came across her. It would never do to confess it now. Her face must have shown some agitation, for the official resumed with a half-paternal, half-reassuring air: "But enough of this. Now, Mrs. Baker, to come to my business here! Briefly, then, it doesn't concern you in the least, except so far as it may relieve you and some others whom the Department knows equally well from a certain responsibility, and, perhaps, anxiety. We are pretty well posted down there in all that concerns Laurel Run, and I think" (with a slight bow), "we've known all about you and John Baker. My only business here is to take your place tonight in receiving the 'Omnibus Way Bag,' that you know arrives here at 9.30, doesn't it?"

"Yes, sir," said Mrs. Baker, hurriedly; "but it never has anything for us, except ——" (she caught herself up quickly, with a stammer, as she remembered the sighing Green's occasional offerings), "except a notification from Hickory Hill Post-Office. It leaves there," she went on with an affectation of precision, "at half-past eight exactly, and it's about an hour's run — seven miles by road."

"Exactly," said Mr. Home. "Well, I will receive the bag,

open it, and despatch it again. You can, if you choose, take a holiday."

"But," said Mrs. Baker, as she remembered that Laurel Run always made a point of attending her evening levee on account of the superior leisure it offered, "there are the people who come for letters, you know."

"I thought you said there were no letters at that time," said Mr. Home, quickly.

"No — but — but" (with a slight hysterical stammer) "the boys come all the same."

"Oh!" said Mr. Home, dryly.

"And — O Lord! ——" But here the spectacle of the possible discomfiture of Laurel Run at meeting the bearded face of Mr. Home, instead of her own smooth cheeks, at the window, combined with her nervous excitement, overcame her so that, throwing her little frilled apron over her head, she gave way to a paroxysm of hysterical laughter. Mr. Home waited with amused toleration for it to stop, and, when she had recovered, resumed: "Now, I should like to refer an instant to my first communication to you. Have you got it handy?"

Mrs. Baker's face fell. "No; I sent it over to Mr. Green, of Hickory Hill, for information."

"What!"

Terrified at the sudden seriousness of the man's voice, she managed to gasp out, however, that, after her usual habit, she had not opened the official letters, but had sent them to her more experienced colleague for advice and information; that she never could understand them herself — they made her head ache, and interfered with her other duties — but *he* understood them, and sent her word what to do. Remembering, also, his usual style of endorsement, she grew red again.

"And what did he say?"

"Nothing; he didn't return them."

"Naturally," said Mr. Home, with a peculiar expression. After a few moments' silent stroking of his beard, he suddenly faced the frightened woman.

"You oblige me, Mrs. Baker, to speak more frankly to you than I had intended. You have — unwittingly, I believe — given information to a man whom the Government suspects of peculation. You have, without knowing it, warned the Postmaster at Hickory Hill that he is suspected; and, as you might have frustrated our plans for tracing a series of embezzlements to their proper source, you will see that you might have also done great wrong to yourself as his only neighbor and the next responsible person. In plain words, we have traced the disappearance of money letters to a point when it lies between these two offices. Now, I have not the least hesitation in telling you that we do not suspect Laurel Run, and never have suspected it. Even the result of your thoughtless act, although it warned him, confirms our suspicion of his guilt. As to the warning, it has failed, or he has grown reckless, for another letter has been missed since. Tonight, however, will settle all doubt in the matter. When I open that bag in this office tonight, and do not find a certain decoy letter in it, which was last checked at Heavy Tree Crossing, I shall know that it remains in Green's possession at Hickory Hill."

She was sitting back in her chair, white and breathless. He glanced at her kindly, and then took up his hat. "Come, Mrs. Baker, don't let this worry you. As I told you at first, *you* have nothing to fear. Even your thoughtlessness and ignorance of rules has contributed to show your own innocence. Nobody will ever be the wiser for this; we do not advertise our affairs in the Department. Not a soul but yourself knows the real cause of my visit here. I will leave you here alone for a while, so as to divert any suspicion. You will come, as usual, this evening, and be seen by your friends; I will only be here when the bag arrives, to open it. Good-by, Mrs. Baker; it's a nasty bit of business, but it's all in the day's work. I've seen worse, and, thank God, you're out of it."

She heard his footsteps retreat into the outer office and die out on the platform; the jingle of his spurs, and the hollow beat of his horsehoofs that seemed to find a dull echo in her own heart, and she was alone.

The room was very hot and very quiet; she could hear the warping and creaking of the shingles under the relaxing of the nearly level sunbeams. The office clock struck seven. In the breathless silence that followed, a woodpecker took up his interrupted work on the roof, and seemed to beat out monotonously in her ear the last words of the stranger: Stanton Green — a thief! Stanton Green, one of the "boys"

John had helped out of the falling tunnel! Stanton Green, whose old mother in the States still wrote letters to him at Laurel Run, in a few hours to be a disgraced and ruined man forever! She remembered now, as a thoughtless woman remembers, tales of his extravagance and fast living, of which she had taken no heed, and, with a sense of shame, of presents sent her, that she now clearly saw must have been far beyond his means. What would the boys say? what would John have said? Ah! what would John have *done!*

She started suddenly to her feet, white and cold as on that day that she had parted from John Baker before the tunnel. She put on her hat and mantle, and going to that little iron safe that stood in the corner, unlocked it, and took out its entire contents of gold and silver. She had reached the door when another idea seized her, and opening her desk she collected her stamps to the last sheet, and hurriedly rolled them up under her cape. Then with a glance at the clock, and a rapid survey of the road from the platform, she slipped from it, and seemed to be swallowed up in the waiting woods beyond.

II

Once within the friendly shadows of the long belt of pines, Mrs. Baker kept them until she had left the limited settlement of Laurel Run far to the right, and came upon an open slope of Burnt Ridge, where she knew Jo Simmons's mustang, Blue Lightning, would be quietly feeding. She had often ridden him before, and when she had detached the fifty-foot riata from his headstall, he permitted her the further recognized familiarity of twining her fingers in his bluish mane and climbing on his back. The tool shed of Burnt Ridge Tunnel, where Jo's saddle and bridle always hung, was but a canter further on. She reached it unperceived, and — another trick of the old days — quickly extemporized a side saddle from Simmons's Mexican tree, with its high cantle and horn bow, and the aid of a blanket. Then leaping to her seat, she rapidly threw off her mantle, tied it by its sleeves around her waist, tucked it under one knee, and let it fall over her horse's flanks. By this time Blue Lightning was also struck with a flash of equine recollection, and pricked up his ears. Mrs. Baker uttered a little chirping cry which he remembered, and the next moment they were both careering over the Ridge.

The trail that she had taken, though precipitate, difficult, and dangerous in places, was a clear gain of two miles on the stage road. There was less chance of her being followed or meeting any one. The greater cañons were already in shadow; the pines on the further ridges were separating their masses, and showing individual silhouettes against the sky, but the air was still warm, and the cool breath of night, as she well knew it, had not yet begun to flow down the mountain. The lower range of Burnt Ridge was still uneclipsed by the creeping shadow of the mountain ahead of her. Without a watch, but with this familiar and slowly changing dial spread out before her, she knew the time to a minute. Heavy Tree Hill, a lesser height in the distance, was already wiped out by that shadowy index finger — half-past seven! The stage would be at Hickory Hill just before half-past eight; she ought to anticipate it, if possible — it would stay ten minutes to change horses — she *must* arrive before it left!

There was a good two-mile level before the rise of the next range. Now, Blue Lightning! all you know! And that was much — for with the little chip hat and fluttering ribbons well bent down over the bluish mane, and the streaming gauze of her mantle almost level with the horse's back, she swept down across the long table-land like a skimming blue jay. A few more bird-like dips up and down the undulations, and then came the long, cruel ascent of the Divide.

Acrid with perspiration, caking with dust, slithering in the slippery, impalpable powder of the road, groggily staggering in a red dusty dream, coughing, snorting, head-tossing; becoming suddenly dejected, with slouching haunch and limp legs on easy slopes, or wildly spasmodic and agile on sharp acclivities, Blue Lightning began to have ideas and recollections! Ah! she was a devil for a lark — this lightly-clinging, caressing, blarneying, cooing creature — up there! He remembered her now. Ha! very well then. Hoop la! And suddenly leaping out like a rabbit, bucking, trotting hard, ambling lightly, "loping" on three legs, and recreating himself — as only a Californian mustang could — the invincible Blue Lightning at last stood triumphantly upon the summit. The evening star had just pricked itself through the golden mist of the horizon line — eight o'clock! She could do it now! But here, suddenly, her first hesitation seized her. She knew her horse, she knew the trail, she knew herself — but did she know *the man* to whom she was riding? A cold chill crept over her, and then she shivered in a sudden blast; it was Night at last swooping down from the now invisible Sierras, and possessing all it touched. But it was only one long descent to Hickory Hill now, and she swept down securely on its wings. Half-past eight! The lights of the settlement were just ahead of her — but so, too, were the two lamps of the waiting stage before the post-office and hotel.

Happily the lounging crowd were gathered around the hotel, and she slipped into the post-office from the rear, unperceived. As she stepped behind the partition, its only occupant — a good-looking young fellow with a reddish mustache — turned toward her with a flush of delighted surprise. But it changed at the sight of the white, determined face and the brilliant eyes that had never looked once toward him, but were fixed upon a large bag, whose yawning mouth was still open and propped up beside his desk.

"Where is the through money letter that came in that bag?" she said, quickly.

"What — do — you — mean?" he stammered, with a face that had suddenly grown whiter than her own.

"I mean that it's a decoy, checked at Heavy Tree Crossing, and that Mr. Home, of San Francisco, is now waiting at my office to know if you have taken it!"

The laugh and lie that he had at first tried to summon to mouth and lips never reached them. For, under the spell of her rigid, truthful face, he turned almost mechanically to his desk, and took out a package.

"Good God! you've opened it already!" she cried, pointing to the broken seal.

The expression on her face, more than anything she had said, convinced him that she knew all. He stammered under the new alarm that her despairing tone suggested. "Yes! — I was owing some bills — the collector was waiting here for the money, and I took something from the packet. But I was going to make it up by next mail — I swear it."

"How much have you taken?"

"Only a trifle. I —— "

"How much?"

"A hundred dollars!"

She dragged the money she had brought from Laurel Run from her pocket, and, counting out the sum, replaced it in the open package. He ran quickly to get the sealing wax, but she motioned him away as she dropped the package back into the mail bag.

"No; as long as the money is found in the bag the package may have been broken *accidentally*. Now burst open one or two of those other packages a little — so"; she took out a packet of letters and bruised their official wrappings under her little foot until the tape fastening was loosened. "Now give me something heavy." She caught up a brass two-pound weight, and in the same feverish but collected haste wrapped it in paper, sealed it, stamped it, and, addressing it in a large printed hand to herself at Laurel Hill, dropped it in the bag. Then she closed it and locked it; he would have assisted her, but she again waved him away. "Send for the expressman, and keep yourself out of the way for a moment," she said curtly.

An attitude of weak admiration and foolish passion had taken the place of his former tremulous fear. He obeyed excitedly, but without a word. Mrs. Baker wiped her moist forehead and parched lips, and shook out her skirt. Well might the young expressman start at the unexpected revelation of those sparkling eyes and that demurely smiling mouth at the little window.

"Mrs. Baker!"

She put her finger quickly to her lips, and threw a world of unutterable and enigmatical meaning into her mischievous face.

"There's a big San Francisco swell takin' my place at Laurel tonight, Charley."

"Yes, ma'am."

"And it's a pity that the Omnibus Way Bag happened to get such a shaking up and banging round already, coming here."

"Eh?"

"I say," continued Mrs. Baker, with great gravity and dancing eyes, "that it would be just awful if that keerful city clerk found things kinder mixed up inside when he comes to open it. I wouldn't give him trouble for the world, Charley."

"No, ma'am, it ain't like you."

"So you'll be particularly careful on *my* account."

"Mrs. Baker," said Charley, with infinite gravity, "if that bag *should tumble off a dozen times* between this and Laurel Hill, I'll hop down and pick it up myself."

"Thank you! shake!"

They shook hands gravely across the window ledge.

"And you ain't goin' down with us, Mrs. Baker?"

"Of course not; it wouldn't do — for *I ain't here* — don't you see?"

"Of course!"

She handed him the bag through the door. He took it carefully, but in spite of his great precaution fell over it twice on his way to the road, where from certain exclamations and shouts it seemed that a like miserable mischance attended its elevation to the boot. Then Mrs. Baker came back into the office, and, as the wheels rolled away, threw herself into a chair, and inconsistently gave way for the first time to an outburst of tears. Then her hand was grasped suddenly, and she found Green on his knees before her. She started to her feet.

"Don't move," he said, with weak hysteric passion, "but listen to me, for God's sake! I am ruined, I know, even though you have just saved me from detection and disgrace. I have been mad! — a fool, to do what I have done, I know, but you do not know all — you do not know why I did it — you can not think of the temptation that has driven me to it. Listen, Mrs. Baker. I have been striving to get money, honestly, dishonestly — anyway, to look well in *your* eyes — to make myself worthy of you — to make myself rich, and to be able to offer you a home and take you away from Laurel Run. It was all for *you* — it was all for love of *you*, Betsy, my darling. Listen to me!"

In the fury, outraged sensibility, indignation, and infinite disgust that filled her little body at that moment, she should have been large, imperious, goddess-like, and commanding. But God is at times ironical with suffering womanhood. She could only writhe her hand from his grasp with childish contortions; she could only glare at him with eyes that were prettily and piquantly brilliant; she could only slap at his detaining hand with a plump and velvety palm, and when she found her voice it was high falsetto. And all she could say was: "Leave me be, loony, or I'll scream!"

He rose, with a weak, confused laugh, half of miserable affectation and half of real anger and shame.

"What did you come riding over here for, then? What did you take all this risk for? Why did you rush over here to share my disgrace — for *you* are as much mixed up with this now as *I* am — if you didn't calculate to share *everything else* with me? What did you come here for, then, if not for *me?*"

"What did *I* come here for?" said Mrs. Baker, with every drop of red blood gone from her cheek and trembling lip. "What — did — I — come here for? Well! — I came here for *John Baker's* sake! John Baker, who stood between you and death at Burnt Ridge, as I stand between you and damnation at Laurel Run, Mr. Green! Yes, John Baker, lying under half of Burnt Ridge, but more to me this day than any living man crawling over it — in — in " — oh, fatal climax! — "in a month o' Sundays! What did I come here for? I came here as John Baker's livin' wife to carry on dead John Baker's work. Yes, dirty work this time, maybe, Mr. Green! but his work, and for *him* only — precious! That's what I came here for; that's what I *live* for; that's what I'm waiting for — to be up to *him* and his work always! That's me — Betsy Baker!"

She walked up and down rapidly, tying her chip hat under her chin again. Then she stopped, and taking her chamois purse from her pocket, laid it sharply on the desk.

"Stanton Green, don't be a fool! Rise up out of this, and be a man again. Take enough out o' that bag to pay what you owe Gov'ment, send in your resignation, and keep the rest to start you in a honest life elsewhere. But light out o' Hickory Hill afore this time tomorrow."

She pulled her mantle from the wall and opened the door.

"You are going?" he said, bitterly.

"Yes." Either she could not hold seriousness long in her capricious little fancy, or, with feminine tact, she sought to make the parting less difficult for him, for she broke into a dazzling smile. "Yes, I'm goin' to run Blue Lightning agin Charley and that way-bag back to Laurel Run, and break the record."

It is said that she did! Perhaps owing to the fact that the grade of the return journey to Laurel Run was in her favor, and that she could avoid the long, circuitous ascent to the summit taken by the stage, or that, owing to the extraordinary difficulties in the carriage of the way-bag — which had to be twice rescued from under the wheels of the stage — she entered the Laurel Run Post-Office as the coach leaders came trotting up the hill. Mr. Home was already on the platform.

"You'll have to ballast your next way-bag, boss," said Charley, gravely, as it escaped his clutches once more in the dust of the road, "or you'll have to make a new contract with the company. We've lost ten minutes in five miles over that bucking thing."

Home did not reply, but quickly dragged his prize into the office, scarcely noticing Mrs. Baker, who stood beside him pale and breathless. As the bolt of the bag was drawn, revealing its chaotic interior, Mrs. Baker gave a little sigh. Home glanced quickly at her, emptied the bag upon the floor, and picked up the broken and half-filled money parcel. Then he collected the scattered coins and counted them. "It's all right, Mrs. Baker," he said gravely. "*He's* safe this time!"

"I'm so glad!" said little Mrs. Baker, with a hypocritical gasp.

"So am I," returned Home, with increasing gravity, as he took the coin, "for, from all I have gathered this afternoon, it seems he was an old prisoner of Laurel Run, a friend of your husband, and, I think, more fool than knave!" He was silent for a moment, clicking the coins against each other; then he said carelessly: "Did he get quite away, Mrs. Baker?"

"I'm sure I don't know what you're talking about," said Mrs. Baker, with a lofty air of dignity, but a somewhat debasing color. "I don't see why *I* should know anything about it, or why he should go away at all."

"Well," said Mr. Home, laying his hand gently on the widow's shoulder, "well, you see, it might have occurred to his friends that the *coins were marked!* That is, no doubt, the reason why he would take their good advice and go. But, as I said before, Mrs. Baker, *you're* all right, whatever happens — the Government stands by *you!*"

## QUESTIONS

1. What picture do you get from the opening paragraph?
2. What trait in the Postmistress is emphasized?
3. How do you account for the way the men treat her?
4. What type of men were these?
5. What expression gives the best clue to her character?
6. How had the men changed since the cave-in? Why?
7. Give two reasons why the men bought stamps so recklessly.
8. What was her attitude toward " official business " ?
9. How is this connected with the plot?
10. What hints at a complication?
11. With the appearance of the stranger were you prepared for a different complication?
12. Was the inspector a likable fellow? Give reasons.
13. Why was she " white and breathless " when she heard the facts about Stanton Green?
14. What was her motive in going to Hickory Hill?
15. How do you know?
16. Would " professional crooks " have used so primitive a method for covering up a theft?
17. Sketch the character of Stanton Green.
18. Was he entirely truthful in his explanations?
19. Did she at any time love him?
20. Why did she give a " hypocritical gasp " ?
21. Does the story end satisfactorily? Explain.
22. What might a modern " movie " do to this ending?

## SUBJECTS FOR COMPOSITION

1. Write an account of a cave-in.
2. The Inspector's Report.
3. Write a local color sketch of the street on which you live.
4. An episode of school life in the same manner.

## OTHER STORIES BY BRET HARTE

The Luck of Roaring Camp
The Outcasts of Poker Flat
Tennessee's Partner
The Idyl of Red Gulch

Miggles
M'liss
Left Out on Lone Star Mountain
A Protégé of Jack Hamlin's

## ABOUT BRET HARTE

*Bret Harte*, H. C. Merwin *Bret Harte*, H. W. Boynton

# NATHANIEL HAWTHORNE
## (1804-1864)

NATHANIEL HAWTHORNE was born on July 4, 1804, in Salem, Massachusetts. At the death of his father in 1808 his mother became a recluse, and the family lived a hermit-like existence in Salem. He was naturally shy and did not miss the companionship that most boys enjoy. There were hills and woods for tramping, streams in which to fish and swim, ice on which to skate, and the old harbor which still had enough shipping to stir the fanciful imagination of a romantic boy.

From 1821 to 1825 Hawthorne attended Bowdoin College, Maine, graduating in the same class with Longfellow. At college one of his best friends was Franklin Pierce. He returned to Salem and for twelve years remained in practical seclusion. In 1840 he wrote in his Note-Book: "Here I have written many tales — many that have been burned to ashes, many that doubtless deserved the same fate. . . . Here I have been glad and hopeful, and here I have been despondent. And here I sat a long, long time, waiting patiently for the world to know me, and sometimes wondering why it did not know me sooner, or whether it would ever know me at all. . . ."

In 1842 he married Miss Sophia Peabody, whom he had long known in Salem. He now wrote steadily but the money return was so small that he gladly accepted a position in the Salem Custom House. In 1853 his friend Pierce, now President, appointed him consul at Liverpool. He resigned after four years, but spent three more traveling in Europe before returning home in 1860. On account of failing health he wrote but little more. He died May 18, 1864.

In the history of the American short story Hawthorne followed Irving (1783-1859), and was almost the exact contemporary of Poe (1809-1849). Irving was content to present interestingly the ordinary details of life. To Hawthorne these outer details were important mainly as material for serious reflection on life and its problems. Most of his stories are full of moods, but he is never moody in the sense of being morbid. Hawthorne liked to adorn his tales with a moral. A favorite " mood " was his conviction that one's hopes and ambitions in life are seldom realized. The student will be interested to see how the author has worked out this idea in " The Ambitious Guest," as well as in some of the other stories listed below.

In many of the short stories, but more particularly in his novels, Hawthorne gave expression to his deep interest in the Puritan traditions of New England. In " The Gray Champion " he exults in the spirit of liberty. In *The Scarlet Letter* he points out how stern was the justice of his ancestors and how despicable the life of a moral coward. In *The House of the Seven Gables* he develops the idea that the sins of one generation must inevitably be paid for by another. These are strong themes, and often tragedy is involved, but Hawthorne never revels in the gruesome, as Poe often does. Whatever the outcome of a story, the reader is left satisfied that no other could have been possible.

Today, almost a hundred years since Hawthorne wrote his first stories, he is still ranked as one of the foremost of all writers of the short story, in English or any other language. It is one of the great glories of our literature that his only rival in this field is Edgar Allan Poe.

# THE AMBITIOUS GUEST

ONE September night a family had gathered round their hearth, and piled it high with the driftwood of mountain streams, the dry cones of the pine, and the splintered ruins of great trees that had come crashing down the precipice. Up the chimney roared the fire, and brightened the room with its broad blaze. The faces of the father and mother had a sober gladness; the children laughed; the eldest daughter was the image of Happiness at seventeen; and the aged grandmother, who sat knitting in the warmest place, was the image of Happiness grown old. They had found the "herb, heart's-ease," in the bleakest spot of all New England. This family was situated in the Notch of the White Hills, where the wind was sharp throughout the year, and pitilessly cold in the winter, — giving their cottage all its fresh inclemency before it descended on the valley of the Saco. They dwelt in a cold spot and a dangerous one; for a mountain towered above their heads, so steep that the stones would often rumble down its sides and startle them at midnight.

The daughter had just uttered some simple jest that filled them all with mirth, when the wind came through the Notch and seemed to pause before their cottage — rattling the door, with a sound of wailing and lamentation, before it passed into the valley. For a moment it saddened them, though there was nothing unusual in the tones. But the family were glad again when they perceived that the latch was lifted by some traveler, whose footsteps had been unheard amid the dreary blast which heralded his approach, and wailed as he was entering, and went moaning away from the door.

## The Ambitious Guest

Though they dwelt in such a solitude, these people held daily converse with the world. The romantic pass of the Notch is a great artery, through which the lifeblood of internal commerce is continually throbbing between Maine, on one side, and the Green Mountains and the shores of the St. Lawrence, on the other. The stagecoach always drew up before the door of the cottage. The wayfarer, with no companion but his staff, paused here to exchange a word, that the sense of loneliness might not utterly overcome him ere he could pass through the cleft of the mountain, or reach the first house in the valley. And here the teamster, on his way to Portland market, would put up for the night; and, if a bachelor, might sit an hour beyond the usual bedtime, and steal a kiss from the mountain maid at parting. It was one of those primitive taverns where the traveler pays only for food and lodging, but meets with a homely kindness beyond all price. When the footsteps were heard, therefore, between the outer door and the inner one, the whole family rose up, grandmother, children, and all, as if about to welcome some one who belonged to them, and whose fate was linked with theirs.

The door was opened by a young man. His face at first wore the melancholy expression, almost despondency, of one who travels a wild and bleak road, at nightfall and alone, but soon brightened up when he saw the kindly warmth of his reception. He felt his heart spring forward to meet them all, from the old woman, who wiped a chair with her apron, to the little child that held out its arms to him. One glance and smile placed the stranger on a footing of innocent familiarity with the eldest daughter.

"Ah, this fire is the right thing!" cried he; "especially when there is such a pleasant circle round it. I am quite benumbed; for the Notch is just like the pipe of a great pair of bellows; it has blown a terrible blast in my face all the way from Bartlett."

"Then you are going toward Vermont?" said the master of the house, as he helped to take a light knapsack off the young man's shoulders.

"Yes; to Burlington, and far enough beyond," replied he. "I meant to have been at Ethan Crawford's tonight; but a pedestrian lingers along such a road as this. It is no matter; for, when I saw this good fire, and all your cheerful faces, I felt as if you had kindled it on purpose for me, and were waiting my arrival. So I shall sit down among you, and make myself at home."

The frank-hearted stranger had just drawn his chair to the fire when something like a heavy footstep was heard without, rushing down the steep side of the mountain, as with long and rapid strides, and taking such a leap in passing the cottage as to strike the opposite precipice. The family held their breath, because they knew the sound, and their guest held his by instinct.

"The old mountain has thrown a stone at us, for fear we should forget him," said the landlord, recovering himself. "He sometimes nods his head and threatens to come down; but we are old neighbors, and agree together pretty well on the whole. Besides we have a sure place of refuge hard by if he should be coming in good earnest."

Let us now suppose the stranger to have finished his supper of bear's meat; and, by his natural felicity of manner, to have placed himself on a footing of kindness with the whole family, so that they talked as freely together as if he belonged to their mountain brood. He was of a proud, yet gentle spirit — haughty and reserved among the rich and great; but ever ready to stoop his head to the lowly cottage door, and be like a brother or a son at the poor man's fireside. In the household of the Notch he found warmth and simplicity of feeling, the pervading intelligence of New England, and a poetry of native growth, which they had gathered when they little thought of it from the mountain peaks and chasms, and at the very threshold of their romantic and dangerous abode. He had traveled far and alone; his whole life, indeed, had been a solitary path; for, with the lofty caution of his nature, he had kept himself apart from those who might otherwise have been his companions. The family, too, though so kind and hospitable, had that consciousness of unity among themselves, and separation from the world at large, which in every domestic circle, should still keep a holy place where no stranger may intrude. But this evening a prophetic sympathy impelled the refined and educated youth to pour out his heart before the simple mountaineers, and constrained them to answer him with the same free confidence. And thus it should have been. Is not the kindred of a common fate a closer tie than that of birth?

## The Ambitious Guest

The secret of the young man's character was a high and abstracted ambition. He could have borne to live an undistinguished life, but not to be forgotten in the grave. Yearning desire had been transformed to hope: and hope, long cherished, had become like certainty, that, obscurely as he journeyed now, a glory was to beam on all his pathway, — though not, perhaps, while he was treading it. But when posterity should gaze back into the gloom of what was now the present, they would trace the brightness of his footsteps, brightening as meaner glories faded, and confess that a gifted one had passed from his cradle to his tomb with none to recognize him.

"As yet," cried the stranger — his cheek glowing and his eye flashing with enthusiasm — " as yet, I have done nothing. Were I to vanish from the earth tomorrow, none would know so much of me as you; that a nameless youth came up at nightfall from the valley of Saco, and opened his heart to you in the evening, and passed through the Notch by sunrise, and was seen no more. Not a soul would ask, 'Who was he? Whither did the wanderer go?' But I cannot die till I have achieved my destiny. Then, let death come! I shall have built my monument!"

There was a continual flow of natural emotion, gushing forth amid abstracted reverie, which enabled the family to understand this young man's sentiments, though so foreign from their own. With quick sensibility of the ludicrous, he blushed at the ardor into which he had been betrayed.

"You laugh at me," said he, taking the eldest daughter's hand, and laughing himself. "You think my ambition as nonsensical as if I were to freeze myself to death on the top of Mount Washington, only that people might spy at me from the country round about. And, truly, that would be a noble pedestal for a man's statue!"

"It is better to sit here by this fire," answered the girl, blushing, "and be comfortable and contented, though nobody thinks about us."

"I suppose," said her father, after a fit of musing, "there is something natural in what the young man says; and if my mind had been turned that way, I might have felt just the same. It is strange, wife, how his talk has set my head running on things that are pretty certain never to come to pass."

"Perhaps they may," observed the wife. "Is the man thinking what he will do when he is a widower?"

"No, no!" cried he, repelling the idea with reproachful kindness. "When I think of your death, Esther, I think of mine, too. But I was wishing we had a good farm in Bartlett, or Bethlehem, or Littleton, or some other township round the White Mountains; but not where they could tumble on our heads. I should want to stand well with my neighbors and be called Squire, and sent to General Court for a term or two; for a plain, honest man may do as much good there as a lawyer. And when I should be grown quite an old man, and you an old woman, so as not to be long apart, I might die happy enough in my bed, and leave you all crying around me. A slate gravestone would suit me as well as a marble one — with just my name and age, and a verse of a hymn, and something to let people know that I lived an honest man and died a Christian."

"There now!" exclaimed the stranger; "it is our nature to desire a monument, be it slate or marble, or a pillar of granite, or a glorious memory in the universal heart of man."

"We're in a strange way, tonight," said the wife, with tears in her eyes. "They say it's a sign of something, when folks' minds go a-wandering so. Hark to the children!"

They listened accordingly. The younger children had been put to bed in another room, but with an open door between, so that they could be heard talking busily among themselves. One and all seemed to have caught the infection from the fireside circle, and were outvying each other in wild wishes, and childish projects of what they would do when they came to be men and women. At length a little boy, instead of addressing his brothers and sisters, called out to his mother.

"I'll tell you what I wish, mother," cried he. "I want you and father and grandma'm, and all of us, and the stranger too, to start right away, and go and take a drink out of the basin of the Flume!"

Nobody could help laughing at the child's notion of leaving a warm bed, and dragging them from a cheerful fire, to visit the basin of the Flume, — a brook which tumbles over the precipice, deep within the Notch. The boy had hardly spoken when a wagon rattled along the road, and stopped a moment before the door. It appeared to contain two or three men who were cheering their hearts with the rough chorus of a song, which resounded in broken notes between the cliffs, while the singers hesitated whether to continue their journey or put up here for the night.

"Father," said the girl, "they are calling you by name."

But the good man doubted whether they had really called him, and was unwilling to show himself too solicitous of gain by inviting people to patronize his house. He therefore did not hurry to the door; and the lash being soon applied, the travelers plunged into the Notch, still singing and laughing, though their music and mirth came back drearily from the heart of the mountain.

"There, mother!" cried the boy, again. "They'd have given us a ride to the Flume."

Again they laughed at the child's pertinacious fancy for a night ramble. But it happened that a light cloud passed over the daughter's spirit; she looked gravely into the fire, and drew a breath that was almost a sigh. It forced its way, in spite of a little struggle to repress it. Then starting and blushing, she looked quickly round the circle, as if they had caught a glimpse into her bosom. The stranger asked what she had been thinking of.

"Nothing," answered she, with a downcast smile. "Only I felt lonesome just then."

"Oh, I have always had a gift of feeling what is in other people's hearts," said he, half seriously. "Shall I tell the secrets of yours? For I know what to think when a young girl shivers by a warm hearth, and complains of lonesomeness at her mother's side. Shall I put these feelings into words?"

"They would not be a girl's feelings any longer if they could be put into words," replied the mountain nymph, laughing, but avoiding his eye.

All this was said apart. Perhaps a germ of love was springing in their hearts, so pure that it might blossom in Paradise, since it could not be matured on earth; for women worship such gentle dignity as his; and the proud, contemplative, yet kindly soul is oftenest captivated by simplicity like hers. But while they spoke softly, and he was watching the happy sadness, the lightsome shadows, the shy yearnings of a maiden's nature, the wind through the Notch took a deeper and drearier sound. It seemed, as the fanciful stranger said, like the choral strain of the spirits of the blast, who in old Indian times had their dwelling among these mountains, and made their heights and recesses a sacred region. There was a wail along the road, as if a funeral were passing. To chase away the gloom, the family threw pine branches on their fire, till the dry leaves crackled and the flame arose, discovering once again a scene of peace and humble happiness. The light hovered about them fondly, and caressed them all. There were the little faces of the children, peeping from their bed apart, and here the father's frame of strength, the mother's subdued and careful mien, the high-browed youth, the budding girl, and the good old grandma, still knitting in the warmest place. The aged woman looked up from her task, and, with fingers ever busy, was the next to speak.

"Old folks have their notions," said she, "as well as young ones. You've been wishing and planning, and letting your heads run on one thing and another, till you've set my mind a-wandering too. Now what should an old woman wish for, when she can go but a step or two before she comes to her grave? Children, it will haunt me night and day till I tell you."

"What is it, mother?" cried the husband and wife at once.

Then the old woman, with an air of mystery which drew the circle closer round the fire, informed them that she had provided her grave-clothes some years before — a nice linen shroud, a cap with a muslin ruff, and everything of a finer sort than she had worn since her wedding day. But this evening an old superstition had strangely recurred to her. It used to be said, in her younger days, that if anything were amiss with a corpse, if only the ruff were not smooth, or the cap did not set right, the corpse in the coffin and beneath the clods would strive to put up its cold hands and arrange it. The bare thought made her nervous.

"Don't talk so, grandmother!" said the girl, shuddering.

"Now," — continued the old woman, with singular earnestness, yet smiling strangely at her own folly, — "I want one of you, my children — when your mother is dressed and in the coffin — I want one of you to hold a looking-glass over my face. Who knows but I may take a glimpse at myself, and see whether all's right?"

"Old and young, we dream of graves and monuments,"

murmured the stranger youth. "I wonder how mariners feel when the ship is sinking, and they, unknown and undistinguished, are to be buried together in the ocean — that wide and nameless sepulcher?"

For a moment, the old woman's ghastly conception so engrossed the minds of her hearers that a sound abroad in the night, rising like the roar of a blast, had grown broad, deep, and terrible, before the fated group were conscious of it. The house and all within it trembled; the foundations of the earth seemed to be shaken, as if this awful sound were the peal of the last trump. Young and old exchanged one wild glance, and remained an instant, pale, affrighted, without utterance, or power to move. Then the same shriek burst simultaneously from all their lips.

"The slide! The slide!"

The simplest words must intimate, but not portray, the unutterable horror of the catastrophe. The victims rushed from their cottage, and sought refuge in what they deemed a safer spot — where, in contemplation of such an emergency, a sort of barrier had been reared. Alas! they had quitted their security, and fled right into the pathway of destruction. Down came the whole side of the mountain, in a cataract of ruin. Just before it reached the house, the stream broke into two branches — shivered not a window there, but overwhelmed the whole vicinity, blocked up the road, and annihilated everything in its dreadful course. Long ere the thunder of the great slide had ceased to roar among the mountains, the mortal agony had been endured, and the victims were at peace. Their bodies were never found.

The next morning, the light smoke was seen stealing from the cottage chimney up the mountain side. Within, the fire was yet smoldering on the hearth, and the chairs in a circle round it, as if the inhabitants had but gone forth to view the devastation of the slide, and would shortly return, to thank Heaven for their miraculous escape. All had left separate tokens, by which those who had known the family were made to shed a tear for each. Who has not heard their name? The story has been told far and wide, and will forever be a legend of these mountains. Poets have sung their fate.

There were circumstances which led some to suppose that a stranger had been received into the cottage on this awful night, and had shared the catastrophe of all its inmates. Others denied that there were sufficient grounds for such a conjecture. Woe for the high-souled youth, with his dream of earthly immortality! His name and person utterly unknown; his history, his way of life, his plans, a mystery never to be solved, his death and his existence equally a doubt! Whose was the agony of that death moment?

[This story is founded upon an actual occurrence as related in J. H. Spaulding's *Historical Relics of the White Mountains*. "Some time in June, before the great slide in August, 1826, there came a great storm, and the old veteran Abel Crawford, coming down the Notch, noticed the trees slipping down standing upright, and as he was passing Mr. Willey's he called and informed him of the wonderful fact. Immediately, in a less exposed place, Mr. Willey prepared a shelter to which to flee in case of immediate danger, and in the night of August 28 in that year he was, with his whole family, awakened by the thundering crash of the coming avalanche. Attempting to escape, that family, nine in number, rushed from the house and were overtaken and buried alive under a vast pile of rocks, earth, and water. By a remarkable coincidence the house remained uninjured, as the slide divided about four rods back of the house, against a high flat rock, and came down on either side with overwhelming power."]


## QUESTIONS

1. Is anything gained or lost by not naming the characters?
2. Why does the author begin his story with the fireside picture?
3. How is the cheerfulness of the inside emphasized?
4. Does the " situation " seem natural and real?
5. What does the author mean by saying that the family had found the " herb, heart's-ease " ?
6. Where are the White Hills?
7. What picture does the word " Notch " suggest?
8. Was the slope covered with trees?
9. What descriptive or other details justify the author in calling the " Notch " a " romantic pass " ?
10. Where does the story really begin?
11. What is the first hint that the young man's life may connect itself with that of the family?
12. Give a brief sketch of the young stranger.
13. What was his ambition?
14. How did the young man's enthusiasm affect: the father, the mother, the grandmother, the daughter, the children?
15. Under the circumstances, does all this seem natural and real?
16. How does the queer idea of the grandmother prepare the reader for what follows?

## The Ambitious Guest

17. What does it suggest to the young man?
18. What was the "unutterable horror" of the catastrophe?
19. What makes the "predominating incident" dramatic?
20. Are the last two paragraphs necessary for the story?
21. Do you agree with the ideas expressed in them?
22. Can you mention at least four places in the story where there is a hint of the end?
23. Is the somberness of the story anywhere relieved by a suggestion of humor?
24. Does the story show any of the characteristics of Hawthorne mentioned in the biographical sketch?
25. Ask yourself candidly whether or not you liked this story. Be prepared to give reasons.

### SUBJECTS FOR COMPOSITION

1. Give a brief summary of the story in your own words.
2. You, as a reporter for your local paper, arrive on the scene the morning after the tragedy. Prepare "copy," with headlines.
3. Write a biographical sketch of the young man, assuming that he lived.
4. Write a short story from the daughter's point of view, had the accident not occurred.
5. The newspapers contain many accounts of accidents. Select one that you think has story material. Then freely use your imagination and make up a story.

### OTHER STORIES BY NATHANIEL HAWTHORNE

The Gray Champion
The Minister's Black Veil
Mr. Higginbotham's Catastrophe
The Great Carbuncle
David Swan
Dr. Heidegger's Experiment

Rappaccini's Daughter
Peter Goldthwaite's Treasure
Drowne's Wooden Image
Roger Malvin's Burial
The Snow Image

### VOLUMES OF STORIES BY NATHANIEL HAWTHORNE

*Twice-Told Tales*
*Mosses from an Old Manse*
*Snow Image and Other Twice-Told Tales*

### ABOUT NATHANIEL HAWTHORNE AND NEW ENGLAND

*Hawthorne and His Wife,* Julian Hawthorne
*Hawthorne* (Great Writers Series), Moncure Conway
*Nathaniel Hawthorne* (American Men of Letters Series), G. E. Woodberry
*Customs and Fashions in Old New England,* Alice Morse Earle
*The Beginnings of New England,* John Fiske

# BOOTH TARKINGTON
(1869–    )

If Mr. Booth Tarkington's name did not appear with great frequency in magazines that feature the short story, it might easily be thought that he wrote long novels only. For some reason he, or perhaps his publishers, always arrange his short stories for book publication in such a way that their continuity gives the semblance of a novel. Today readers of the Penrod stories and *Seventeen* are forced to read them in book form, but it may be emphasized that originally the various chapters of these books appeared as separate stories. *In the Arena* (1905) is the only volume of his short stories that has not been rearranged for its book form, and it is the one least known to readers, although the reason lies in the nature of the stories and not in the lack of mechanical combination.

Among the major writers of modern America no writer has shown greater versatility, no one has enjoyed greater popularity, both personal and literary, no one has been more prolific than Booth Tarkington. It is therefore difficult to believe that there ever was a time when he could sell nothing, or that when he did finally begin to sell he earned only $22.50 in five years. When he graduated from Princeton in 1893 he returned to Indianapolis, the city in which he was born in 1869, and in which he still makes his home for part of each year. In college he was conspicuous for doing a great many things that did not pertain to class-room work, among them writing for the college papers. He thoroughly enjoyed his student life and no less the social life of his native town after he returned. Among his life-long friends was the poet James Whitcomb Riley.

But life was not all frivolity for him, in spite of the enviable social distinction that his family enjoyed in Indianapolis. Having determined to be a writer, he set about learning his trade very much as Stevenson did, by practice and imitation of successful authors. "We must learn by failure and by repeated effort how the thing should be done," he says. He wrote *Monsieur Beaucaire*, but it remained unsold until his first great success, *The Gentleman from Indiana* (1899). The novel *Cherry* also enjoyed seventeen rejections before it appeared in 1903, although in composition it was earlier than *The Gentleman from Indiana*. It is safe to say that Mr. Tarkington has "enjoyed" few rejections since that date.

His first short stories were those now contained in the volume *In the Arena*. They are political stories, based no doubt on his own career as a legislator, for he was a representative in the state legislature for one term. His chief activity seems to have been observation of how others did things, and from the stories those things were creditable neither to his colleagues nor to his state. His first real success in the short story dates from *Penrod,* published in book form in 1914, and *Penrod and Sam*, two years later. In these stories Mr. Tarkington accomplishes the difficult task of writing about boys of the age ten to twelve, their problems and ideals, without waxing sentimental. They present boy-life from the standpoint of the boy, intensely amusing to the older reader, but intensely serious to the boy himself. In *Seventeen* he depicts the life of an older boy with equal success. " Penrod's Busy Day," printed here, is an excellent example of Mr. Tarkington at his best in this type of story. Since 1916 he has written many similar stories involving both boys and girls, but they lack the vital qualities of the earlier ones. A volume of them appeared in 1923 entitled *The Fascinating Stranger and Other Stories*.

Mr. Tarkington spends a considerable part of each year in Kennebunkport, Maine. He writes with great regularity for six and eight hours a day, enjoys motoring and motor boating, goes to the movies and to football games once in a while, and stays away from New York as much as possible. His home in Kennebunkport is called The House That Penrod Built.

## PENROD'S BUSY DAY

ALTHOUGH the pressure had thus been relieved and Penrod found peace with himself, nevertheless there were times during the rest of that week when he felt a strong distaste for Margaret. His schoolmates frequently reminded him of such phrases in her letter as they seemed least able to forget, and for hours after each of these experiences he was unable to comport himself with human courtesy when constrained (as at dinner) to remain for any length of time in the same room with her. But by Sunday these moods had seemed to pass; he attended church in her close company, and had no thought of the troubles brought upon him by her correspondence with a person who throughout remained unknown to him.

Penrod slumped far down in the pew with his knees against the back of that in front, and he also languished to one side, so that the people sitting behind were afforded a view of him consisting of a little hair and one bored ear. The sermon — a noble one, searching and eloquent — was but a persistent sound in that ear, though, now and then, Penrod's attention would be caught by some detached portion of a sentence, when his mind would dwell dully upon the phrases for a little while — and lapse into a torpor. At intervals his mother, without turning her head, would whisper, " Sit up, Penrod," causing him to sigh profoundly and move his shoulders about an inch, this mere gesture of compliance exhausting all the energy that remained to him.

The black backs and gray heads of the elderly men in the congregation oppressed him; they gave him a lethargic and indefinite feeling that he was immersed among lives of repellent dullness. But he should have been grateful to the lady with the artificial cherries upon her hat. His gaze lingered there, wandered away, and hopelessly returned again and again, to be a little refreshed by the glossy scarlet of the cluster of tiny globes. He was not so fortunate as to be drowsy; that would have brought him some relief — and yet, after a while, his eyes became slightly glazed; he saw dimly, and what he saw was distorted.

The church had been built in the early 'Seventies, and it contained some naïve stained glass of that period. The arch at the top of a window facing Penrod was filled with a gigantic Eye. Of oyster-white and raw blues and reds, inflamed by the pouring sun, it had held an awful place in the infantile life of Penrod Schofield, for in his tenderer years he accepted it without question as the literal Eye of Deity. He had been informed that the church was the divine dwelling — and there was the Eye!

Nowadays, being no longer a little child, he had somehow come to know better without being told, and though the great flaming Eye was no longer the terrifying thing it had been to him during his childhood, it nevertheless retained something of its ominous character. It made him feel spied upon, and its awful glare still pursued him, sometimes, as he was falling asleep at night. When he faced the window his feeling was one of dull resentment.

His own glazed eyes, becoming slightly crossed with an *ennui* which was peculiarly intense this morning, rendered the Eye more monstrous than it was. It expanded to horrible size, growing mountainous; it turned into a volcano in the tropics, and yet it stared at him, indubitably an Eye implacably hostile to all rights of privacy forever. Penrod blinked and clinched his eyelids to be rid of this dual image, and he managed to shake off the volcano. Then, lowering the angle of his glance, he saw something most remarkable — and curiously out of place.

An inverted white soup-plate was lying miraculously balanced upon the back of a pew a little distance in front of him, and upon the upturned bottom of the soup plate was a brown coconut. Mildly surprised, Penrod yawned, and, in the effort to straighten his eyes, came to life temporarily. The coconut was revealed as Georgie Bassett's head, and the soup-plate as Georgie's white collar. Georgie was sitting up straight, as he always did in church, and Penrod found this vertical rectitude unpleasant. He knew that he had more to fear from the Eye than Georgie had, and he was under the impression (a correct one) that Georgie felt on intimate terms with it and was actually fond of it.

Penrod himself would have maintained that he was fond of it, if he had been asked. He would have said so because he feared to say otherwise; and the truth is that he never consciously looked at the Eye disrespectfully. He would have been alarmed if he thought the Eye had any way of finding out how he really felt about it. When not off his guard, he always looked at it placatively.

By and by, he sagged so far to the left that he had symptoms of a "stitch in the side," and, rousing himself, sat partially straight for several moments. Then he rubbed his shoulders slowly from side to side against the back of the seat, until his mother whispered, "Don't do that, Penrod."

Upon this, he allowed himself to slump inwardly till the curve in the back of his neck rested against the curved top of the back of the seat. It was a congenial fit, and Penrod again began to move slowly from side to side, finding the friction soothing. Even so slight a pleasure was denied him by a husky, "Stop that!" from his father.

Penrod sighed, and slid farther down. He scratched his head, his left knee, his right biceps, and his left ankle, after which he scratched his right knee, his right ankle, and his left biceps. Then he said, "Oh, hum!" unconsciously, but so loudly that there was a reproving stir in the neighborhood of the Schofield pew, and his father looked at him angrily.

Finally, his nose began to trouble him. It itched, and after scratching it, he rubbed it harshly. Another "Stop that!" from his father proved of no avail, being greeted by a desperate-sounding whisper, "I *got* to!"

And, continuing to rub his nose with his right hand, Penrod

began to search his pockets with his left. The quest proving fruitless, he rubbed his nose with his left hand and searched with his right. Then he abandoned his nose and searched feverishly with both hands, going through all of his pockets several times.

"What *do* you want?" whispered his mother.

But Margaret had divined his need, and she passed him her own handkerchief. This was both thoughtful and thoughtless — the latter because Margaret was in the habit of thinking that she became faint in crowds, especially at the theater or in church, and she had just soaked her handkerchief with spirits of ammonia from a small phial which she carried in her muff.

Penrod hastily applied the handkerchief to his nose and even more hastily exploded. He sneezed stupendously; he choked, sneezed again, wept, passed into a light convulsion of coughing and sneezing together — a mergence of sound which attracted much attention — and, after a few recurrent spasms, convalesced into a condition marked by silent tears and only sporadic instances of sneezing.

By this time his family were unanimously scarlet — his father and mother with mortification, and Margaret with the effort to control the almost irresistible mirth which the struggles and vociferations of Penrod had inspired within her. And yet her heart misgave her, for his bloodshot and tearful eyes were fixed upon her from the first and remained upon her, even when half-blinded with his agony; and their expression — as terrible as that of the windowed Eye confronting her — was not for an instant to be misunderstood. Absolutely, he considered that she had handed him the ammonia-soaked handkerchief deliberately and with malice, and well she knew that no power on earth could now or at any time henceforth persuade him otherwise.

"Of course I didn't mean it, Penrod," she said, at the first opportunity upon their homeward way. "I didn't notice — that is, I didn't think — " Unfortunately for the effect of sincerity which she hoped to produce, her voice became tremulous and her shoulders moved suspiciously.

"Just you wait! You'll see!" he prophesied, in a voice now choking, not with ammonia, but with emotion. "Poison a person, and then laugh in his face!"

## Penrod's Busy Day

He spake no more until they had reached their own house, though she made some further futile efforts at explanation and apology.

And after brooding abysmally throughout the meal that followed, he disappeared from the sight of his family, having answered with one frightful look his mother's timid suggestion that it was almost time for Sunday-school. He retired to his eyry — the sawdust box in the empty stable — and there gave rein to his embittered imaginings, incidentally forming many plans for Margaret.

Most of these were much too elaborate, but one was so alluring that he dwelt upon it, working out the details with gloomy pleasure, even after he had perceived its defects. It involved a considerable postponement — in fact, until Margaret should have become the mother of a boy about Penrod's present age. This boy would be precisely like Georgie Bassett — Penrod conceived that as inevitable — and, like Georgie, he would be his mother's idol. Penrod meant to take him to church and force him to blow his nose with an ammonia-soaked handkerchief in the presence of the Eye and all the congregation.

Then Penrod intended to say to this boy, after church, " Well, that's exac'ly what your mother did to me, and if you don't like it, you better look out! "

And the real Penrod in the sawdust-box clenched his fists. " Come ahead, then! " he muttered. " You talk too much! " Whereupon, the Penrod of his dream gave Margaret's puny son a contemptuous thrashing under the eyes of his mother, who besought in vain for mercy. This plan was finally dropped, not because of any lingering nepotism within Penrod, but because his injury called for action less belated.

One after another, he thought of impossible things; one after another, he thought of things merely inane and futile, for he was trying to do something beyond his power. Penrod was never brilliant, or even successful, save by inspiration.

At four o'clock he came into the house, still nebulous, and as he passed the open door of the library he heard a man's voice, not his father's.

" To me," said this voice, " the finest lines in all literature are those in Tennyson's ' Maud ' —

"'Had it lain for a century dead,
My dust would hear her and beat,
And blossom in purple and red,
There somewhere around near her feet.'

"I think I have quoted correctly," continued the voice nervously, "but, at any rate, what I wished to — ah — say was that I often think of those — ah — words; but I never think of them without thinking of — of — of *you*. I — ah ——"

The nervous voice paused, and Penrod took an oblique survey of the room, himself unobserved. Margaret was seated in an easy chair and her face was turned away from Penrod, so that her expression of the moment remained unknown to him. Facing her, and leaning toward her with perceptible emotion, was Mr. Claude Blakely — a young man with whom Penrod had no acquaintance, though he had seen him, was aware of his identity, and had heard speech between Mrs. Schofield and Margaret which indicated that Mr. Blakely had formed the habit of calling frequently at the house. This was a brilliantly handsome young man; indeed, his face was so beautiful that even Penrod was able to perceive something about it which might be explicably pleasing — at least to women. And Penrod remembered that, on the last evening before Mr. Robert Williams's departure for college, Margaret had been peevish because Penrod had genially spent the greater portion of the evening with Robert and herself upon the porch. Margaret made it clear, later, that she strongly preferred to conduct her conversations with friends unassisted — and as Penrod listened to the faltering words of Mr. Claude Blakely, he felt instinctively that, in a certain contingency, Margaret's indignation would be even more severe today than on the former occasion.

Mr. Blakely coughed faintly and was able to continue.

"I mean to say that when I say that what Tennyson says — ah — seems to — to apply to — to a feeling about you ——"

At this point, finding too little breath in himself to proceed, in spite of the fact that he had spoken in an almost inaudible tone, Mr. Blakely stopped again.

Something about this little scene was making a deep impression upon Penrod. What that impression was, he could not possibly have stated; but he had a sense of the imminence of a tender crisis, and he perceived that the piquancy of affairs in the library had reached a point which would brand an intentional interruption as the act of a cold-blooded ruffian. Suddenly it was as though a strong light shone upon him: he decided that it was Mr. Blakely who had told Margaret that her eyes were like blue stars in heaven — *this* was the person who had caused the hateful letter to be written! That decided Penrod; his inspiration, so long waited for, had come.

"I — I feel that perhaps I am not plain," said Mr. Blakely, and immediately became red, whereas he had been pale. He was at least modest enough about his looks to fear that Margaret might think he had referred to them. "I mean, not plain in another sense — that is, I mean not that *I* am not plain in saying what I mean to you — I mean, what you mean to *me!* I feel ——"

This was the moment selected by Penrod. He walked carelessly into the library, inquiring in a loud, bluff voice:

"Has anybody seen my dog around here anywheres?"

Mr. Blakely had inclined himself so far toward Margaret, and he was sitting so near the edge of the chair, that only a really wonderful bit of instinctive gymnastics landed him upon his feet instead of upon his back. As for Margaret, she said, "Good gracious!" and regarded Penrod blankly.

"Well," said Penrod breezily, "I guess it's no use lookin' for him — he isn't anywheres around. I guess I'll sit down." Herewith, he sank into an easy chair, and remarked, as in comfortable explanation, "I'm kind of tired standin' up, anyway."

Even in this crisis, Margaret was a credit to her mother's training.

"Penrod, have you met Mr. Blakely?"

"What?"

Margaret primly performed the rite.

"Mr. Blakely, this is my little brother Penrod."

Mr. Blakely was understood to murmur, "How d'ye do?"

"I'm well," said Penrod.

Margaret bent a perplexed gaze upon him, and he saw that she had not divined his intentions, though the expression of Mr. Blakely was already beginning to be a little compensation for the ammonia outrage. Then, as the protracted silence which followed the introduction began to be a severe strain upon all parties, Penrod felt called upon to relieve it.

"I didn't have anything much to do this afternoon, anyway," he said. And at that there leaped a spark in Margaret's eye; her expression became severe.

"You should have gone to Sunday-school," she told him crisply.

"Well, I didn't!" said Penrod, with a bitterness so significant of sufferings connected with religion, ammonia, and herself, that Margaret, after giving him a thoughtful look, concluded not to urge the point.

Mr. Blakely smiled pleasantly. "I was looking out of the window a minute ago," he said, "and I saw a dog run across the street and turn the corner."

"What kind of a lookin' dog was it?" Penrod inquired, with languor.

"Well," said Mr. Blakely, "it was a — it was a nice-looking dog."

"What color was he?"

"He was — ah — white. That is, I think ——"

"It wasn't Duke," said Penrod. "Duke's kind of brownish-gray-like."

Mr. Blakely brightened.

"Yes, that was it," he said. "This dog I saw first had another dog with him — a brownish-gray dog."

"Little or big?" Penrod asked, without interest.

"Why, Duke's a little dog!" Margaret intervened. "Of *course*, if it was little, it must have been Duke."

"It *was* little," said Mr. Blakely too enthusiastically. "It was a little bit of a dog. I noticed it because it was so little."

"Couldn't 'a' been Duke, then," said Penrod. "Duke's a kind of a middle-sized dog." He yawned, and added: "I don't want him now. I want to stay in the house this afternoon, anyway. And it's better for Duke to be out in the fresh air."

Mr. Blakely coughed again and sat down, finding little to say. It was evident, also, that Margaret shared his perplexity; and another silence became so embarrassing that Penrod broke it.

"I was out in the sawdust-box," he said, "but it got kind of chilly." Neither of his auditors felt called upon to offer any comment, and presently he added, "I thought I better come in here where it's warmer."

"It's too warm," said Margaret, at once. "Mr. Blakely, would you mind opening a window?"

"By all means!" the young man responded earnestly, as he rose. "Maybe I'd better open two?"

"Yes," said Margaret; "that would be much better."

But Penrod watched Mr. Blakely open two windows to their widest, and betrayed no anxiety. His remarks upon the relative temperatures of the sawdust-box and the library had been made merely for the sake of creating sound in a silent place. When the windows had been open for several minutes, Penrod's placidity, though gloomy, denoted anything but discomfort from the draft, which was powerful, the day being windy.

It was Mr. Blakely's turn to break a silence, and he did it so unexpectedly that Margaret started. He sneezed.

"Perhaps — " Margaret began, but paused apprehensively. "Perhaps-per-per — " Her apprehensions became more and more poignant; her eyes seemed fixed upon some incredible disaster; she appeared to inflate while the catastrophe she foresaw became more and more imminent. All at once she collapsed, but the power decorum had over her was attested by the mildness of her sneeze after so threatening a prelude.

"Perhaps I'd better put one of the windows down," Mr. Blakely suggested.

"Both, I believe," said Margaret. "The room has cooled off, now, I think."

Mr. Blakely closed the windows, and, returning to a chair near Margaret, did his share in the production of another long period of quiet. Penrod allowed this one to pass without any vocal disturbance on his part. It may be, however, that his gaze was disturbing to Mr. Blakely, upon whose person it was glassily fixed with a self-forgetfulness that was almost morbid.

"Didn't you enjoy the last meeting of the Cotillion Club?" Margaret said finally.

And upon Mr. Blakely's answer absently in the affirmative.

she suddenly began to be talkative. He seemed to catch a meaning in her fluency, and followed her lead, a conversation ensuing which at first had all the outward signs of eagerness. They talked with warm interest of people and events unknown to Penrod; they laughed enthusiastically about things beyond his ken; they appeared to have arranged a perfect way to enjoy themselves, no matter whether he was with them or elsewhere — but presently their briskness began to slacken; the appearance of interest became perfunctory. Within ten minutes the few last scattering semblances of gayety had passed, and they lapsed into the longest and most profound of all their silences indoors that day. Its effect upon Penrod was to make him yawn and settle himself in his chair.

Then Mr. Blakely, coming to the surface out of deep inward communings, snapped his finger against the palm of his hand impulsively.

"By George!" he exclaimed, under his breath.

"What is it?" Margaret asked. "Did you remember something?"

"No, it's nothing," he said. "Nothing at all. But, by the way, it seems a pity for you to be missing the fine weather. I wonder if I could persuade you to take a little walk?"

Margaret, somewhat to the surprise of both the gentlemen present, looked uncertain.

"I don't know ——" she said.

Mr. Blakely saw that she missed his point.

"One can talk better in the open, don't you think?" he urged, with a significant glance toward Penrod.

Margaret also glanced keenly at Penrod. "Well, perhaps." And then, "I'll get my hat," she said.

Penrod was on his feet before she left the room. He stretched himself.

"I'll get mine, too," he said.

But he carefully went to find it in a direction different from that taken by his sister, and he joined her and her escort not till they were at the front door, whither Mr. Blakely — with a last flickering of hope — had urged a flight in haste.

"I been thinkin' of takin' a walk, all afternoon," said Penrod pompously. "Don't matter to me which way we go."

The exquisite oval of Mr. Claude Blakely's face merged

into outlines more rugged than usual; the conformation of his jaw became perceptible, and it could be seen that he had conceived an idea which was crystallizing into a determination.

"I believe it happens that this is our first walk together," he said to Margaret, as they reached the pavement, "but, from the kind of tennis you play, I judge that you could go a pretty good gait. Do you like walking fast?"

She nodded. "For exercise."

"Shall we try it then?"

"You set the pace," said Margaret. "I think I can keep up."

He took her at her word, and the amazing briskness of their start seemed a little sinister to Penrod, though he was convinced that he could do anything that Margaret could do, and also that neither she nor her comely friend could sustain such a speed for long. On the contrary, they actually increased it with each fleeting block they covered.

"Here!" he panted, when they had thus put something more than a half-mile behind them. "There isn't anybody has to have a doctor, I guess! What's the use our walkin' so fast?"

In truth, Penrod was not walking, for his shorter legs permitted no actual walking at such a speed; his gait was a half-trot.

"Oh, *we're* out for a *walk!*" Mr. Blakely returned, a note of gayety beginning to sound in his voice. "Marg — ah — Miss Schofield, keep your head up and breathe through your nose. That's it! You'll find I was right in suggesting this. It's going to turn out gloriously! Now, let's make it a little faster."

Margaret murmured inarticulately, for she would not waste her breath in a more coherent reply. Her cheeks were flushed; her eyes were brimming with the wind, but when she looked at Penrod, they were brimming with something more. Gurgling sounds came from her.

Penrod's expression had become grim. He offered no second protest, mainly because he, likewise, would not waste his breath, and if he would, he could not. Of breath in the ordinary sense — breath, breathed automatically — he had none. He had only gasps to feed his straining lungs, and his half-trot, which had long since become a trot, was changed for a lope when Mr. Blakely reached his own best burst of speed.

And now people stared at the flying three. The gait of Margaret and Mr. Blakely could be called a walk only by courtesy, while Penrod's was becoming a kind of blind scamper. At times he zigzagged; other times, he fell behind, wabbling. Anon, with elbows flopping and his face sculptured like an antique mask, he would actually forge ahead, and then carom from one to the other of his companions as he fell back again.

Thus the trio sped through the coming of autumn dusk, outflying the fallen leaves that tumbled upon the wind. And still Penrod held to the task that he had set himself. The street lamps flickered into life, but on and on Claude Blakely led the lady, and on and on reeled the grim Penrod. Never once was he so far from them that they could have exchanged a word unchaperoned by his throbbing ear.

"*Oh!*" Margaret cried, and, halting suddenly, she draped herself about a lamp-post like a strip of bunting. "Guh-uh-guh-*goodness!*" she sobbed.

Penrod immediately drooped to the curb-stone, which he reached, by pure fortune, in a sitting position. Mr. Blakely leaned against a fence, and said nothing, though his breathing was eloquent. "We — we must go — go home," Margaret gasped. "We must, if — if we can drag ourselves!"

Then Penrod showed them what mettle they had tried to crack. A paroxysm of coughing shook him; he spoke through it sobbingly:

"'Drag!' 'S jus' lul-like a girl! Ha-why I walk — *oof!* — faster'n that every day — on my — way to school." He managed to subjugate a tendency to nausea. "What you — want to go — home for?" he said. "Le's go on!"

In the darkness Mr. Claude Blakely's expression could not be seen, nor was his voice heard. For these and other reasons, his opinions and sentiments may not be stated.

. . . Mrs. Schofield was looking rather anxiously forth from her front door when the two adult figures and the faithful smaller one came up the walk.

"I was getting uneasy," she said. "Papa and I came in and found the house empty. It's after seven. Oh, Mr. Blakely, is that you?"

"Good-evening," he said. "I fear I must be keeping an engagement. Good-night. Good-night, Miss Schofield."

"Good-night."

"Well, good-night," Penrod called, staring after him. But Mr. Blakely was already too far away to hear him, and a moment later Penrod followed his mother and sister into the house.

"I let Della go to church," Mrs. Schofield said to Margaret. "You and I might help Katie get supper."

"Not for a few minutes," Margaret returned gravely, looking at Penrod. "Come upstairs, mamma; I want to tell you something."

Penrod cackled hoarse triumph and defiance.

"Go on! Tell! What *I* care? You try to poison a person in church again, and then laugh in his face, you'll see what you get!"

But after his mother had retired with Margaret to the latter's room, he began to feel disturbed in spite of his firm belief that his cause was wholly that of justice victorious. Margaret had insidious ways of stating a case; and her point of view, no matter how absurd or unjust, was almost always adopted by Mr. and Mrs. Schofield in cases of controversy.

Penrod became uneasy. Perceiving himself to be in danger, he decided that certain measures were warranted. Unquestionably, it would be well to know beforehand in what terms Margaret would couch the charges which he supposed he must face in open court — that is to say, at the supper-table. He stole softly up the stairs, and, flattening himself against the wall, approached Margaret's door, which was about an inch ajar.

He heard his mother making sounds which appalled him — he took them for sobs. And then Margaret's voice rang out in a peal of insane laughter. Trembling, he crept nearer the door. Within the room Margaret was clinging to her mother, and both were trying to control their hilarity.

"He did it all to get even!" Margaret exclaimed, wiping her eyes. "He came in at just the right time. That *goose* was beginning to talk his silly, soft talk — the way he does with every girl in town — and he was almost proposing, and I didn't know how to stop him. And then Penrod came in and did it for me. I could have hugged Penrod, mamma, I actually could! And I saw he meant to stay to get even for that ammonia — and, oh, I worked so hard to make him think I wanted him to *go!* Mamma, mamma, if you could have *seen* that walk! That *goose* kept thinking he could wear Penrod out or drop him behind, but I knew he couldn't so long as Penrod believed he was worrying us and getting even. And that *goose* thought I *wanted* to get rid of Penrod, too; and the conceited thing said it would turn out 'gloriously,' meaning we'd be alone together pretty soon — I'd like to shake him! You see, I pretended so well, in order to make Penrod stick to us, that *goose* believed I meant it! And if he hadn't tried to walk Penrod off his legs, he wouldn't have wilted his own collar and worn himself out, and I think he'd have hung on until you'd have had to invite him to stay to supper, and he'd have stayed on all evening, and I wouldn't have had a chance to write to Robert Williams. Mamma, there have been lots of times when I haven't been thankful for Penrod, but today I could have got down on my knees to you and papa for giving me such a brother!"

In the darkness of the hall, as a small but crushed and broken form stole away from the crack in the door, a gigantic Eye seemed to form — seemed to glare down upon Penrod — warning him that the way of vengeance is the way of bafflement, and that genius may not prevail against the trickeries of women.

"This has been a *nice* day!" Penrod muttered hoarsely.

## QUESTIONS

1. Why was Georgie Bassett's "vertical rectitude" unpleasant to Penrod?
2. What impression do you get of Penrod from his thoughts in church?
3. Are these thoughts natural to a boy of Penrod's type?
4. What is the most amusing of Penrod's Sunday morning experiences?
5. Pick out the most amusing moments in the parlor scene.
6. Did Mr. Blakely have a sense of humor? Did Margaret?
7. Does Mr. Blakely make a dignified exit from the story?
8. Do you think he ever finished the interrupted speech to Margaret?
9. Why should Penrod have "cackled hoarse triumph"?
10. Why was his triumph short-lived?
11. What was his bitter disappointment?

# Penrod's Busy Day

12. Is there any plot?
13. Is Penrod's attitude toward an older sister true to life?
14. What kind of humor do you find, incident, situation, or what?
15. Do you like stories having children as characters?
16. Do you know any other child stories by modern writers?

## SUBJECTS FOR COMPOSITION

1. An embarrassing moment in your own life, funny to others.
2. Write this both from your point of view and from that of an observer.
3. A happening in school that was funny to you but awkward for the victim.

## OTHER STORIES BY BOOTH TARKINGTON

A Reward of Merit
Little Gentleman
Monsieur Beaucaire
Mrs. Protheroe

The Property-Man
Girl — Girl — Girl!
The Fascinating Stranger
The One Hundred Dollar Bill

## VOLUMES OF STORIES BY BOOTH TARKINGTON

*Penrod*
*Penrod and Sam*
*Seventeen*
*Penrod Jashber*

*In the Arena*
*Monsieur Beaucaire*
*The Fascinating Stranger*

## SINCLAIR LEWIS
## (1885–    )

LIKE Young Man Axelbrod, Mr. Sinclair Lewis comes from Minnesota, the northern tip of that section of our country vaguely called "The Middle West," a section that used to be famous only for its wheat and corn, but which today can boast of more prominent writers than all the other sections together. The career of Mr. Lewis is of the kind that we like to call typically American. Born of a Connecticut father and a Canadian mother, in 1885, he was raised in the prairie village of Sauk Center, Minnesota. After graduating from high school there he went to Yale. Unlike Axelbrod, he has not returned to live permanently in his home state.

To make a good American story better we should be able to record how young Lewis was captain of his high school football team, how he led his class at Yale in scholarship, and how, shortly after graduation, he startled the world by writing the great American novel. While the facts are different, they are none the less interesting. In high school his athletic career was limited to membership in a class relay team made up of four boys, the only boys in the class. He was undistinguished for scholarship both in high school and at Yale. At the end of three years he left college, but returned later for his degree.

During these formative years he read dime novels, poetry, and fiction; he studied Greek; and always he was interested in radical movements. At college he began to be seriously active in writing. He contributed to the college magazine and became one of its editors. At the end of his third year at college he joined a group of visionary radicals who were trying out a Utopian experiment in New Jersey. As in all similar attempts to make idealism practical, the basic idea was plain living and high thinking. To Lewis fell the job of janitor, and in his off moments from firing the furnace he wrote poetry. All this, however, together with further adventuring in different parts of the world, was only an interlude. His mind was set on writing fiction.

To prepare finally for what he had fully decided upon, he did all sorts of things except writing fiction. He did not yet feel ready for that. But there were poems, sketches, humorous bits, editorships of various kinds, and then, in 1914, his first novel, *Our Mr. Wrenn*. A year later his first short story was accepted by the *Saturday Evening Post*. Since then Mr. Lewis has devoted himself entirely to authorship.

Today Mr. Lewis is known as a winner of the Nobel Prize for Literature and the author of *Main Street* (1920), and other novels that have given him an enviable position among American writers. The so-called realism of Mr. Lewis is hard to define because of a definite romantic note underlying it, that of a vague but none the less decided longing for the beautiful in life, the sort of thing that would give happiness if we had it, the longing to get away from the sordidness and the humdrum of life as most of us know it.

*Main Street* is the story of a highly cultured woman placed in the drab village of Gopher Prairie, her futile attempts to raise it to a higher plane, her flight from it, and her return, with some sort of adjustment to it. *Babbitt* is the story of a middle-aged successful business man, who ought to be happy according to the standards of his class, but who becomes restless with the feeling that life is slipping away and he is not getting the " happiness " that should be his. He makes a few feeble efforts to obtain what he thinks he wants, only to find disappointment. He relapses into his ordinary routine.

After reading " Young Man Axelbrod " you will see how Mr. Lewis has used the same idea, with one very important variation. There is the same longing on the part of Axelbrod, more or less submerged by the grind of life on the farm, but emerging insistently when that grind is over. It is the feeling that somewhere somehow there must be something beautiful to relieve the drabness of life. He engages in what to others seems a silly proceeding, going to college at sixty-five.

If Mr. Lewis were writing that story today he might send Axelbrod back to his hill and his cat finally disillusioned. But here the variation comes in. Axelbrod has one night of riotous beauty with the young poet, one who also is following the gleam. He listens to the sympathetic reading of French poetry without understanding a word; he hears a world-famous violinist; the spark of eternal youth is fired by the romantic raptures of his young friend. He has found what he wanted, the glow of beauty, and wisely goes back home while the glow lasts to light his remaining years.

## YOUNG MAN AXELBROD

THE cottonwood is a tree of a slovenly and plebeian habit. Its woolly wisps turn gray the lawns and engender neighborhood hostilities about our town. Yet it is a mighty tree, a refuge and an inspiration; the sun flickers in its towering foliage, whence the tattoo of locusts enlivens our dusty summer afternoons. From the wheat-country out to the sagebrush plains between the buttes and the Yellowstone it is the cottonwood that keeps a little grateful shade for sweating homesteaders.

In Joralemon we called Knute Axelbrod " Old Cottonwood." As a matter of fact, the name was derived not so much from the quality of the man as from the wide grove about his gaunt, white house and red barn. He made a comely row of trees on each side of the country road, so that a humble, daily sort of man, driving beneath them in his lumber-wagon, might fancy himself lord of a private avenue. And at sixty-five Knute was like one of his own cottonwoods, his roots deep in the soil, his trunk weathered by rain and blizzard and baking August noons, his crown spread to the wide horizon of day and the enormous sky of a prairie night.

This immigrant was an American even in speech. Save for a weakness about his j's and w's, he spoke the twangy Yankee English of the land. He was the more American because in his native Scandinavia he had dreamed of America as a land of light. Always through disillusion and weariness he beheld America as the world's nursery for justice, for broad, fair towns, and eager talk; and always he kept a young soul that dared to desire beauty.

As a lad Knute Axelbrod had wished to be a famous scholar, to learn the ease of foreign tongues, the romance of history, to unfold in the graciousness of wise books. When he first came to America he worked in a sawmill all day and studied all evening. He mastered enough book-learning to teach district school for two terms; then, when he was only eighteen, a great-hearted pity for faded little Lena Wesselius moved him to marry her. Gay enough, doubtless, was their hike by prairie-schooner to new farm-lands, but Knute was promptly caught in a net of poverty and family. From eighteen to fifty-eight he was always snatching children away from death or the farm away from mortgages.

He had to be content — and generously content he was — with the second-hand glory of his children's success and, for himself, with pilfered hours of reading — that reading of big, thick, dismal volumes of history and economics which the lone, mature learner chooses. Without ever losing his desire for strange cities and the dignity of towers he stuck to his farm. He acquired a half-section, free from debt, fertile, well-stocked, adorned with a cement silo, a chicken-run, a new windmill. He became comfortable, secure, and then he was ready, it seemed, to die; for at sixty-three his work was done, and he was unneeded and alone.

His wife was dead. His sons had scattered afar, one a dentist in Fargo, another a farmer in the Golden Valley. He had turned over his farm to his daughter and son-in-law. They had begged him to live with them, but Knute refused.

"No," he said, " you must learn to stand on your own feet. I vill not give you the farm. You pay me four hundred dollars a year rent, and I live on that and vatch you from my hill."

On a rise beside the lone cottonwood which he loved best of all his trees Knute built a tar-paper shack, and here he " bached it "; cooked his meals, made his bed — sometimes, sat in the sun, read many books from the Joralemon library, and began to feel that he was free of the yoke of citizenship which he had borne all his life.

For hours at a time he sat on a backless kitchen-chair before the shack, a wide-shouldered man, white-bearded, motionless; a seer despite his grotesquely baggy trousers, his collarless shirt. He looked across the miles of stubble to the steeple of the Jack-rabbit Forks church and meditated upon the uses of life. At first he could not break the rigidity of habit. He rose at five, found work in cleaning his cabin and cultivating his garden, had dinner exactly at twelve, and went to bed by afterglow. But little by little he discovered that he could be irregular without being arrested. He stayed abed till seven or even eight. He got a large, deliberate, tortoise-shell cat, and played games with it; let it lap milk upon the table, called it the Princess, and confided to it that he had a " sneaking idee " that men were fools to work so hard. Around this coatless old man, his stained waistcoat flapping about a huge torso, in a shanty of rumpled bed and pine table covered with sheets of food-daubed newspaper, hovered all the passionate aspiration of youth and the dreams of ancient beauty.

He began to take long walks by night. In his necessitous life night had ever been a period of heavy slumber in close rooms. Now he discovered the mystery of the dark; saw the prairies wide-flung and misty beneath the moon, heard the voices of grass and cottonwoods and drowsy birds. He tramped for miles. His boots were dew-soaked, but he did not heed. He stopped upon hillocks, shyly threw wide his arms, and stood worshiping the naked, slumbering land.

These excursions he tried to keep secret, but they were bruited abroad. Neighbors, good, decent fellows with no nonsense about walking in the dew at night, when they were returning late from town, drunk, lashing their horses, and flinging whisky-bottles from their racing democrat wagons, saw him, and they spread the tidings that Old Cottonwood was "getting nutty since he give up his farm to that son-in-law of his and retired. Seen the old codger wandering around at midnight. Wish I had his chance to sleep. Wouldn't catch me out in the night air."

Any rural community from Todd Center to Seringapatam is resentful of any person who varies from its standard, and is morbidly fascinated by any hint of madness. The countryside began to spy on Knute Axelbrod, to ask him questions, and to stare from the road at his shack. He was sensitively aware of it, and inclined to be surly to inquisitive acquaintances. Doubtless that was the beginning of his great pilgrimage.

As a part of the general wild license of his new life, — really, he once roared at that startled cat, the Princess: "By gollies! I ain't going to brush my teeth tonight. All my life I've brushed 'em, and alvays wanted to skip a time vunce," — Knute took considerable pleasure in degenerating in his taste in scholarship. He wilfully declined to finish *The Conquest of Mexico,* and began to read light novels borrowed from the Joralemon library. So he rediscovered the lands of dancing and light wines, which all his life he had desired. Some economics and history he did read, but every evening he would stretch out in his buffalo-horn chair, his feet on the cot and the Princess in his lap, and invade Zenda or fall in love with Trilby.

Among the novels he chanced upon a highly optimistic story of Yale in which a worthy young man "earned his way through" college, stroked the crew, won Phi Beta Kappa, and had the most entertaining, yet moral, conversations on or adjacent to "the dear old fence."

As a result of this chronicle, at about three o'clock one morning when Knute Axelbrod was sixty-four years of age, he decided that he would go to college! All his life he had wanted to. Why not do it?

When he awoke in the morning he was not so sure about it as when he had gone to sleep. He saw himself as ridiculous, a ponderous, oldish man among clean-limbed youths, like a dusty cottonwood among silver birches. But for months he wrestled and played with that idea of a great pilgrimage to the Mount of Muses; for he really supposed college to be that sort of place. He believed that all college students, except for the wealthy idlers, burned to acquire learning. He pictured Harvard and Yale and Princeton as ancient groves set with marble temples, before which large groups of Grecian youths talked gently about astronomy and good government. In his picture they never cut classes or ate.

With a longing for music and books and graciousness such as the most ambitious boy could never comprehend, this thick-faced prairie farmer dedicated himself to beauty, and defied the unconquerable power of approaching old age. He sent for college catalogues and school-books, and diligently began to prepare himself for college.

He found Latin irregular verbs and the whimsicalities of algebra fiendish. They had nothing to do with actual life as he had lived it. But he mastered them; he studied twelve hours a day, as once he had plodded through eighteen hours a day in the hay-field. With history and English literature he had comparatively little trouble; already he knew much of them from his recreative reading. From German neighbors he had picked up enough Plattdeutsch to make German easy. The trick of study began to come back to him from his small school-teaching of forty-five years before. He began to believe that he could really put it through. He kept assuring himself that in college, with rare and sympathetic instructors to help him, there would not be this baffling search, this nervous strain.

But the unreality of the things he studied did disillusion him, and he tired of his new game. He kept it up chiefly because all his life he had kept up onerous labor without any taste for it. Toward the autumn of the second year of his eccentric life he no longer believed that he would ever go to college.

Then a busy little grocer stopped him on the street in Joralemon and quizzed him about his studies, to the delight of the informal club which always loafs at the corner of the hotel.

Knute was silent, but dangerously angry. He remembered just in time how he had once laid wrathful hands upon a hired man, and somehow the man's collarbone had been broken. He turned away and walked home, seven miles, still boiling. He picked up the Princess, and, with her mewing on his shoulder, tramped out again to enjoy the sunset.

He stopped at a reedy slough. He gazed at a hopping plover

without seeing it. He plucked at his beard. Suddenly he cried:

"I am going to college. It opens next veek. I t'ink that I can pass the examinations."

Two days later he had moved the Princess and his sticks of furniture to his son-in-law's house, had bought a new slouch hat, a celluloid collar, and a solemn suit of black, had wrestled with God in prayer through all of a star-clad night, and had taken the train for Minneapolis, on the way to New Haven.

While he stared out of the car-window Knute was warning himself that the millionaires' sons would make fun of him. Perhaps they would haze him. He bade himself avoid all these sons of Belial and cleave to his own people, those who "earned their way through."

At Chicago he was afraid with a great fear of the lightning flashes that the swift crowds made on his retina, the batteries of ranked motor-cars that charged at him. He prayed, and ran for his train to New York. He came at last to New Haven.

Not with gibing rudeness, but with politely quizzical eyebrows, Yale received him, led him through entrance examinations, which, after sweaty plowing with the pen, he barely passed, and found for him a room-mate. The room-mate was a large-browed, soft, white grub named Ray Gribble, who had been teaching school in New England, and seemed chiefly to desire college training so that he might make more money as a teacher. Ray Gribble was a hustler; he instantly got work tutoring the awkward son of a steel man, and for board he waited on table.

He was Knute's chief acquaintance. Knute tried to fool himself into thinking he liked the grub, but Ray couldn't keep his damp hands off the old man's soul. He had the skill of a professional exhorter of young men in finding out Knute's motives, and when he discovered that Knute had a hidden desire to dabble in gay, polite literature, Ray said in a shocked way:

"Strikes me a man like you, that's getting old, ought to be thinking more about saving your soul than about all these frills. You leave this poetry and stuff to these foreigners and artists, and you stick to Latin and math and the Bible. I tell you, I've taught school, and I've learned by experience."

With Ray Gribble, Knute lived grubbily, an existence of torn comforters and a smelly lamp, of lexicons and logarithm tables. No leisurely loafing by fireplaces was theirs. They roomed in West Divinity, where gather the theologues, the lesser sort of law students, a whimsical genius or two, and a horde of unplaced freshmen and " scrub seniors."

Knute was shockingly disappointed, but he stuck to his room because outside of it he was afraid. He was a grotesque figure, and he knew it, a white-polled giant squeezed into a small seat in a classroom, listening to instructors younger than his own sons. Once he tried to sit on the fence. No one but " ringers " sat on the fence any more, and at the sight of him trying to look athletic and young, two upper-class men snickered, and he sneaked away.

He came to hate Ray Gribble and his voluble companions of the submerged tenth of the class, the hewers of tutorial wood. It is doubtless safer to mock the flag than to question that best-established tradition of our democracy — that those who " earn their way through " college are necessarily stronger, braver, and more assured of success than the weaklings who talk by the fire. Every college story presents such a moral. But tremblingly the historian submits that Knute discovered that waiting on table did not make lads more heroic than did football or happy loafing. Fine fellows, cheerful and fearless, were many of the boys who " earned their way," and able to talk to richer classmates without fawning; but just as many of them assumed an abject respectability as the most convenient pose. They were pickers up of unconsidered trifles; they toadied to the classmates whom they tutored; they wriggled before the faculty committee on scholarships; they looked pious at Dwight Hall prayer-meetings to make an impression on the serious-minded; and they drank one glass of beer at Jake's to show the light-minded that they meant nothing offensive by their piety. In revenge for cringing to the insolent athletes whom they tutored, they would, when safe among their own kind, yammer about the " lack of democracy in colleges today." Not that they were so indiscreet as to do anything about it. They lacked the stuff of really rebellious souls. Knute listened to them and marveled. They sounded like young hired men talking behind his barn at harvest-time.

This submerged tenth hated the dilettantes of the class even more than they hated the bloods. Against one Gilbert Washburn, a rich esthete with more manner than any freshman ought to have, they raged righteously. They spoke of seriousness and industry till Knute, who might once have desired to know lads like Washburn, felt ashamed of himself as a wicked, wasteful old man.

With the friends of his room-mate began Knute's series of disillusions. Humbly though he sought, he found no inspiration and no comradeship. He was the freak of the class, and aside from the submerged tenth, his classmates were afraid of being "queered" by being seen with him.

As he was still powerful, one who could take up a barrel of pork on his knees, he tried to find friendship among the athletes. He sat at Yale Field, watching the football try-outs, and tried to get acquainted with the candidates. They stared at him and answered his questions grudgingly — beefy youths who in their simple-hearted way showed that they considered him plain crazy.

The place itself began to lose the haze of magic through which he had first seen it. Earth is earth, whether one sees it in Camelot or Joralemon or on the Yale campus — or possibly even in the Harvard yard! The buildings ceased to be temples to Knute; they became structures of brick or stone, filled with young men who lounged at windows and watched him amusedly as he tried to slip by.

The Gargantuan hall of Commons became a tri-daily horror because at the table where he dined were two youths who, having uncommonly penetrating minds, discerned that Knute had a beard, and courageously told the world about it. One of them, named Atchison, was a superior person, very industrious and scholarly, glib in mathematics and manners. He despised Knute's lack of definite purpose in coming to college. The other was a play-boy, a wit and a stealer of street-signs, who had a wonderful sense for a subtle jest; and his references to Knute's beard shook the table with jocund mirth three times a day. So these youths of gentle birth drove the shambling, wistful old man away from Commons, and thereafter he ate at the lunch-counter at the Black Cat.

Lacking the stimulus of friendship, it was the harder for Knute to keep up the strain of studying the long assignments.

What had been a week's pleasant reading in his shack was now thrown at him as a day's task. But he would not have minded the toil if he could have found one as young as himself. They were all so dreadfully old, the money-earners, the serious laborers at athletics, the instructors who worried over their life-work of putting marks in class-record books.

Then, on a sore, bruised day, Knute did meet one who was young.

Knute had heard that the professor who was the idol of the college had berated the too-earnest lads in his Browning class, and insisted that they read *Alice in Wonderland*. Knute floundered dustily about in a second-hand book-shop till he found an *Alice,* and he brought it home to read over his lunch of a hot-dog sandwich. Something in the grave absurdity of the book appealed to him, and he was chuckling over it when Ray Gribble came into the room and glanced at the reader.

"Huh!" said Mr. Gribble.

"That's a fine, funny book," said Knute.

"Huh! *Alice in Wonderland!* I've heard of it. Silly nonsense. Why don't you read something really fine, like Shakespeare or 'Paradise Lost'?"

"Vell —" said Knute, but that was all he could find to say.

With Ray Gribble's glassy eye on him, he could no longer roll and roar with the book. He wondered if indeed he ought not to be reading Milton's pompous anthropological misconceptions. He went unhappily out to an early history class, ably conducted by Blevins, Ph.D.

Knute admired Blevins, Ph.D. He was so tubbed and eye-glassed and terribly right. But most of Blevins's lambs did not like Blevins. They said he was a "crank." They read newspapers in his class and covertly kicked one another.

In the smug, plastered classroom, his arm leaning heavily on the broad tablet-arm of his chair, Knute tried not to miss one of Blevins's sardonic proofs that the correct date of the second marriage of Themistocles was two years and seven days later than the date assigned by that illiterate ass, Frutari of Padua. Knute admired young Blevins's performance, and he felt virtuous in application to these hard, unnonsensical facts.

He became aware that certain lewd fellows of the lesser sort were playing poker just behind him. His prairie-trained ear caught whispers of "Two to dole," and "Raise you two beans." Knute revolved, and frowned upon these mockers of sound learning. As he turned back he was aware that the offenders were chuckling, and continuing their game. He saw that Blevins, Ph.D., perceived that something was wrong; he frowned, but he said nothing. Knute sat in meditation. He saw Blevins as merely a boy. He was sorry for him. He would do the boy a good turn.

When class was over he hung about Blevins's desk till the other students had clattered out. He rumbled:

"Say, Professor, you're a fine fellow. I do something for you. If any of the boys make themselves a nuisance, you yust call on me, and I spank the son of a guns."

Blevins, Ph.D., spake in a manner of culture and nastiness:

"Thanks so much, Axelbrod, but I don't fancy that will ever be necessary. I am supposed to be a reasonably good disciplinarian. Good day. Oh, one moment. There's something I've been wishing to speak to you about. I do wish you wouldn't try quite so hard to show off whenever I call on you during quizzes. You answer at such needless length, and you smile as though there were something highly amusing about me. I'm quite willing to have you regard me as a humorous figure, privately, but there are certain classroom conventions, you know, certain little conventions."

"Why, Professor!" wailed Knute. "I never make fun of you! I didn't know I smile. If I do, I guess it's yust because I am so glad when my stupid old head gets the lesson good."

"Well, well, that's very gratifying, I'm sure. And if you will be a little more careful ——"

Blevins, Ph.D., smiled a toothy, frozen smile, and trotted off to the Graduates' Club, to be witty about old Knute and his way of saying "yust," while in the deserted classroom Knute sat chill, an old man and doomed. Through the windows came the light of Indian summer; clean, boyish cries rose from the campus. But the lover of autumn smoothed his baggy sleeve, stared at the blackboard, and there saw only the gray of October stubble about his distant shack. As he pictured the college watching him, secretly making fun of him and his smile, he was now faint and ashamed, now bull-angry. He was lonely for his cat, his fine chair of buffalo horns, the sunny doorstep of his shack, and the understanding land. He had been in college for about one month.

Before he left the classroom he stepped behind the instructor's desk and looked at an imaginary class.

"I might have stood there as a prof if I could have come earlier," he said softly to himself.

Calmed by the liquid autumn gold that flowed through the streets, he walked out Whitney Avenue toward the butte-like hill of East Rock. He observed the caress of the light upon the scarped rock, heard the delicate music of leaves, breathed in air pregnant with tales of old New England. He exulted:

"I could write poetry now if I yust — if I yust could write poetry!"

He climbed to the top of East Rock, whence he could see the Yale buildings like the towers of Oxford, Long Island Sound, and the white glare of Long Island itself beyond the water. He marveled that Knute Axelbrod of the cottonwood country was looking across an arm of the Atlantic to New York State.

He noticed a freshman on a bench at the edge of the rock, and he became irritated. The freshman was Gilbert Washburn, the snob, the dilettante, of whom Ray Gribble had once said: "That guy is the disgrace of the class. He doesn't go out for anything, high stand or Dwight Hall or anything else. Thinks he's so doggone much better than the rest of the fellows that he doesn't associate with anybody. Thinks he's literary, they say, and yet he doesn't even heel the 'Lit,' like the regular literary fellows! Got no time for a loafing, mooning snob like that."

As Knute stared at the unaware Gil, whose profile was fine in outline against the sky, he was terrifically public-spirited and disapproving and that sort of moral thing. Though Gil was much too well dressed, he seemed moodily discontented.

"What he needs is to vork in a thrashing-crew and sleep in the hay," grumbled Knute almost in the virtuous manner of Gribble. "Then he vould know when he vas vell off, and not look like he had the earache. Pff!"

Gil Washburn rose, trailed toward Knute, glanced at him, hesitated, sat down on Knute's bench.

"Great view!" he said. His smile was eager.

That smile symbolized to Knute all the art of life he had come to college to find. He tumbled out of his moral attitude with ludicrous haste, and every wrinkle of his weathered face creased deep as he answered:

"Yes; I t'ink the Acropolis must be like this here."

"Say, look here, Axelbrod; I've been thinking about you."

"Yas?"

"We ought to know each other. We two are the class scandal. We came here to dream, and these busy little goats like Atchison and Giblets, or whatever your room-mate's name is, think we're fools not to go out for marks. You may not agree with me, but I've decided that you and I are precisely alike."

"What makes you t'ink I come here to dream?" bristled Knute.

"Oh, I used to sit near you at Commons and hear you try to quell jolly old Atchison whenever he got busy discussing the reasons for coming to college. That old, moth-eaten topic! I wonder if Cain and Abel didn't discuss it at the Eden Agricultural College. You know, Abel the mark-grabber, very pious and high stand, and Cain wanting to read poetry."

"Yes," said Knute, "and I guess Prof Adam say, 'Cain, don't you read this poetry; it von't help you in algebry.'"

"Of course. Say, wonder if you'd like to look at this volume of Musset I was sentimental enough to lug up here today. Picked it up when I was abroad last year."

From his pocket Gil drew such a book as Knute had never seen before, a slender volume, in a strange language, bound in hand-tooled, crushed levant, an effeminate bibelot over which the prairie farmer gasped with luxurious pleasure. The book almost vanished in his big hands. With a timid forefinger he stroked the levant, ran through the leaves.

"I can't read it, but that's the kind of book I alvays t'ought there must be some like it," he sighed.

"Let me read you a little. It's French, poetry."

Gil read aloud. He made of the alien verses a music which satisfied Knute's sixty-five years of longing for he had never known what.

"That's — that's fine," he said.

"Listen!" cried Gil. "Ysaye is playing up at Hartford tonight. Let's go hear him. We'll trolley up, make it in plenty of time. Tried to get some of the fellows to come, but they thought I was a nut."

What an Ysaye was, Knute Axelbrod had no notion; but "Sure!" he boomed.

When they got to Hartford they found that between them they had just enough money to get dinner, hear Ysaye from gallery seats, and return only as far as Meriden.

At Meriden Gil suggested:

"Let's walk back to New Haven, then. Can you make it?"

Knute had no knowledge as to whether it was four miles or forty back to the campus, but "Sure!" he said. For the last few months he had been noticing that, despite his bulk, he had to be careful, but tonight he could have flown.

In the music of Ysaye, the first real musician he had ever heard, Knute had found all the incredible things of which he had slowly been reading in William Morris and "Idylls of the King." Tall knights he had beheld, and slim princesses in white samite, the misty gates of forlorn towns, and the glory of the chivalry that never was.

They did walk, roaring down the road beneath the October moon, stopping to steal apples and to exclaim over silvered hills, taking a puerile and very natural joy in chasing a profane dog. It was Gil who talked, and Knute who listened, for the most part; but Knute was lured into tales of the pioneer days, of blizzards, of harvesting, and of the first flame of the green wheat. Regarding the Atchisons and Gribbles of the class both of them were youthfully bitter and supercilious. But they were not bitter long, for they were atavisms tonight. They were wandering minstrels, Gilbert the troubadour with his man-at-arms.

They reached the campus at about five in the morning.

Fumbling for words that would express his feeling, Knute stammered:

"Vell, it vas fine. I go to bed now and I dream about ——"

"Bed? Rats! Never believe in winding up a party when it's going strong. Too few good parties. Besides, it's only the shank of the evening. Besides, we're hungry. Besides —

oh, besides! Wait here a second. I'm going up to my room to get some money, and we'll have some eats. Wait! Please do!"

Knute would have waited all night. He had lived sixty-five years and traveled fifteen hundred miles and endured Ray Gribble to find Gil Washburn.

Policemen wondered to see the celluloid-collared old man and the expensive-looking boy rolling arm in arm down Chapel Street in search of a restaurant suitable to poets. They were all closed.

"The Ghetto will be awake by now," said Gil. "We'll go buy some eats and take 'em up to my room. I've got some tea there."

Knute shouldered through dark streets beside him as naturally as though he had always been a night-hawk, with an aversion to anything as rustic as beds. Down on Oak Street, a place of low shops, smoky lights, and alley mouths, they found the slum already astir. Gil contrived to purchase boxed biscuits, cream-cheese, chicken-loaf, a bottle of cream. While Gil was chaffering, Knute stared out into the street milkily lighted by wavering gas and the first feebleness of coming day; he gazed upon Kosher signs and advertisements in Russian letters, shawled women and bearded rabbis; and as he looked he gathered contentment which he could never lose. He had traveled abroad tonight.

The room of Gil Washburn was all the useless, pleasant things Knute wanted it to be. There was more of Gil's Paris days in it than of his freshmanhood: cloisonné on the mantelpiece, Persian rugs, a silver tea-service, etchings, and books. Knute Axelbrod of the tar-paper shack and piggy farm-yards gazed in satisfaction. Vast-bearded, sunk in an easy-chair, he clucked amiably while Gil lighted a fire and spread a wicker table.

Over supper they spoke of great men and heroic ideals. It was good talk, and not unspiced with lively references to Gribble and Atchison and Blevins, all asleep now in their correct beds. Gil read snatches of Stevenson and Anatole France; then at last he read his own poetry.

It does not matter whether that poetry was good or bad. To Knute it was a miracle to find one who actually wrote it.

## Young Man Axelbrod      173

The talk grew slow, and they began to yawn. Knute was sensitive to the lowered key of their Indian-summer madness, and he hastily rose. As he said good-by he felt as though he had but to sleep a little while and return to this unending night of romance.

But he came out of the dormitory upon day. It was six-thirty of the morning, with a still, hard light upon red-brick walls.

"I can go to his room plenty times now; I find my friend," Knute said. He held tight the volume of Musset, which Gil had begged him to take.

As he started to walk the few steps to West Divinity Knute felt very tired. By daylight the adventure seemed more and more incredible.

As he entered the dormitory he sighed heavily:

"Age and youth, I guess they can't team together long." As he mounted the stairs he said: "If I saw the boy again, he vould get tired of me. I tell him all I got to say." And as he opened his door, he added: "This is what I come to college for — this one night; I live for it sixty-five years. I go avay before I spoil it."

He wrote a note to Gil, and began to pack his telescope. He did not even wake Ray Gribble, sonorously sleeping in the stale air.

At five that afternoon, on the day-coach of a westbound train, an old man sat smiling. A lasting content was in his eyes, and in his hands a small book in French, though the curious fact is that this man could not read French.

### QUESTIONS

1. From the first two paragraphs, what picture do you get of "Old Cottonwood"?
2. What note in Axelbrod's character is struck early in the story? Give a full statement in your own words.
3. Why should he wish to keep his "excursion" secret?
4. Were his struggles with Latin and algebra different from those of younger students?
5. Contrast his ideas of education with those of his room-mate.
6. What do you know about the "Yale fence"?
7. What is meant by the "submerged tenth" of a class?
8. Were Knute's early experiences and disillusionments common to many others, or due to his own peculiar position?

9. Note the types of students.  Are they common to schools?
10. What does Knute mean by " one as young as himself " ?
11. Does the reference to Cain and Abel fit in with what we are usually taught?
12. Is the reader prepared for Knute's appreciation of French poetry?
13. Try to catch this point, for it is the climax of the story.
14. Was Washburn's appreciation of Knute's spirit genuine?  Explain.
15. What is meant by " Indian-summer madness " ?
16. Is Knute's " morning after " feeling realistic?
17. What do you think of his " age and youth " philosophy?
18. Does the story end as you expected?
19. Throughout the rest of Knute's life, what symbolized his " success " at Yale?
20. Note how effectively the author uses contrasts in this story.  Select some of these.
21. Note also the use of concrete terms instead of vague generalities. How do these affect style?

## SUBJECTS FOR COMPOSITION

1. Write out in your own words the scene where Knute changes his ideas of Gil Washburn.
2. A picture of Knute in Washburn's room.
3. Write a possible different ending to the story.
4. Most schools have " freaks."  Write about one you know.

## OTHER STORIES BY SINCLAIR LEWIS

For the Zelda Bunch  
The Scarlet Sign  
Hobohemia  

Bronze Bars  
Willow Walk

## FANNIE HURST
(1889–    )

Miss Hurst has been called the literary descendant of O. Henry. Such a tag is often vicious because it is apt to be misunderstood. Miss Hurst is not an imitator of O. Henry except in one thing — she tries to write interesting stories interestingly, and imitation of that kind is a literary virtue. However, there are many similarities in the work of these two writers. Both write about New York. In some instances their subject matter is drawn from the same sources; boarding houses and apartment life, for instance. It happens that the stories here chosen to represent the work of O. Henry and Miss Hurst give the reader an opportunity for first-hand contrast.

Note how each writer opens his story. One flashes information of a boarding house, the other of a cheap but pretentious rooming apartment. Both depend much upon the manner of telling the story, but Miss Hurst's manner is not O. Henry's. While she has the same fondness for the trenchant word and the telling phrase, she subordinates these to the development of her theme and the working out of a plot, whereas O. Henry rarely bothers about a plot. His clever words and phrases are often mere interludes for the entertainment of his readers.

Miss Hurst writes about boarding houses from personal experience and direct observation, but fortunately it is not necessary to chronicle a harrowing tale of how she came to New York penniless, and how she had to wander around in search of a job, with all the accompanying horrors of a struggle to make ends meet while she pursued her ambitions to be a writer. Happily her advent was made with a pocketful of money and a trunk filled with unsold and unsellable manuscripts.

She came to New York from St. Louis, although she was born in Hamilton, Ohio, in 1889, in the home of her grandparents. Her family returned to St. Louis when, as Miss Hurst herself says, she was "still in the beety, underdone infantile stage," and where she "grew up a naughty, rather spoiled only child." She went through the public schools of St. Louis, and upon graduation from Central High School she entered Washington University in the same city, receiving her A.B. degree in 1909.

During these school years she wrote much but nobody knew anything about it. Hopefully she sent her "stuff" to editors who in those days had a heartless habit of immediately sending it back. In high school and college there were school papers, and in these some of her work appeared, especially when she herself became editor of the university magazine. But the old world wagged on in the same old way without being stirred. Miss Hurst was not dismayed. She was a girl full of energy and life, entering zestfully into whatever for the moment interested her.

After graduation from the university she came to New York, contrary to the wishes of her parents. At first she had a generous allowance and spent much of her time haunting editorial offices. Not succeeding in marketing any of her scripts, she took some graduate courses at Columbia University. Her father discontinued checks in the hope that she would return to St. Louis, but instead Miss Hurst secured a position as an actress at $20 a week. It was not a hard job, for she had to speak only twenty words, ten in the first act, and ten more in the fourth. During the wait she wrote "The Seventh Day," a story which she sold to *Smith's Magazine*.

Success was still "just around the corner," but she now characteristically began to lay up the material which was to become her medium. There were "weeks of rambling among the vivid poor of the vivid East Side," she says. And again: "I apprenticed myself as a salesgirl in New York's most gigantic cut-priced department store. Four and one-quarter yards of ribbon at seven and a half cents a yard proved my Waterloo there, and my resignation at the end of one week was not entirely voluntary."

Meanwhile she kept on writing, and with this enlarged background she began to write stories that sold, and handsomely. In a few years she was acclaimed America's greatest living writer of the short story. Since 1911 the story of her literary life has been one pæan of success. She has confined herself almost entirely to city types, the types she knows, from St. Louis and New York. Emphasis is upon character and plot, with an effective dash of emotion.

In 1914 she married Mr. Jacques Danielson, a pianist and composer, but the marriage was kept secret more than five years. Since 1911 she has written and published many stories, all of which are gradually finding their way into volumes. There have also been two novels and several plays, but Miss Hurst remains at her best in the short story.

## "ICE WATER, PL——!"

WHEN the two sides of every story are told Henry VIII may establish an alibi or two, Shylock and the public-school system meet over and melt that too, too solid pound of flesh, and Xantippe, herself the sturdier man than Socrates, give ready lie to what is called the shrew in her. Landladies, whole black bombazine generations of them — oh, so long unheard — may rise in one Indictment of the Boarder: the scarred bureau front and match-scratched wall paper; the empty trunk nailed to the floor in security for the unpaid bill; cigarette-burnt sheets and the terror of sudden fire; the silent newcomer in the third floor back hustled out one night in handcuffs; the day-long sobs of the blond girl so suddenly terrified of life-about-to-be and wringing her ringless hands in the fourth-floor hallroom; the smell of escaping gas and the tightly packed keyhole; the unsuspected flutes that lurk in boarders' trunks; towels, that querulous and endless pæan of the lodger; the high cost of liver and dried peaches, of canned corn and round steak!

Tired bombazine procession, wrapped in the greasy odors of years of carpet sweeping and emptying slops, airing the gassy slit of room after the coroner and padding from floor to floor on a mission of towels and towels and towels!

Sometimes climbing from floor to floor, a still warm supply of them looped over one arm, Mrs. Kaufman, who wore bombazine, but unspotted and with crisp net frills at the throat, and upon whose soft-looking face the years had written their chirography in invisible ink, would sit suddenly, there in the narrow gloom of her halls, head against the balustrade. Oftener than not the Katz boy from the third floor front would come lickety-clapping down the stairs and past her, jumping the last four steps of each flight.

" Irving, quit your noise in the hall."

" Aw! "

" Ain't you ashamed, a big boy like you, and Mrs. Suss with her neuralgia? "

" Aw! " — the slam of a door clipping off this insolence.

After a while she would resume her climb.

And yet in Mrs. Kaufman's private boarding house in West Eighty-ninth Street, one of a breastwork of brown-stone fronts, lined up stoop for stoop, story for story, and ash can for ash can, there were few enough greasy odors except upon the weekly occasion of Monday's boiled dinner; and, whatever the status of liver and dried peaches, canned corn and round steak, her menus remained static — so static that in the gas-lighted basement dining room and at a remote end of the long, well-surrounded table, Mrs. Katz, with her napkin tucked well under her third chin, turned *sotto* from the protruding husband at her right to her left neighbor, shielding her remark with her hand. " Am I right, Mrs. Finshriber? I just said to my husband in the five years we been here she should just give us once a change from Friday night lamb and noodles."

"Say, you should complain yet! With me it's six and a half years day after tomorrow, Easter Day, since I asked myself that question first."

"Even my Irving says to me tonight up in the room, jumping up and down on the hearth like he had four legs —— "

"I heard him, Mrs. Katz, on my ceiling like he had eight legs."

"'Mamma,' he says, 'guess why I feel like saying "Baa."'"

"Saying what?"

"Sheep talk, Mrs. Finshriber. B-a-a, like a sheep goes."

"Oh!"

"''Cause I got so many Friday nights' lamb in me, mamma,' he said. Quick like a flash that child is."

Mrs. Finshriber dipped her head and her glance, all her drooping features pulled even further down at their corners. "I ain't the one to complain, Mrs. Katz, and I always say when you come right down to it, maybe Mrs. Kaufman's house is as good as the next one, but —— "

"I wish, though, Mrs. Finshriber, you would hear what Mrs. Spritz says at her boarding house they get for breakfast: fried —— "

"You can imagine, Mrs. Katz, since my poor husband's death, how much appetite I got left; but I say, Mrs. Katz, just for the principle of the thing, it would not hurt once Mrs. Kaufman should give somebody else besides her own daughter and Vetsburg always the white meat from everything, ain't it?"

"It's a shame before the boarders! She knows, Mrs. Finshriber, how my husband likes breast from the chicken. You think once he gets it? No. I always tell him, not till chickens come double-breasted like overcoats can he get it in this house, with Vetsburg such a star boarder."

"Last night's chicken, let me tell you, I don't wish it to a dog! Such a piece of dark meat with gizzard I had to swallow."

Mrs. Katz adjusted with greater security the expanse of white napkin across her ample bosom. Gold rings and a quarter-inch marriage band flashed in and out among the litter of small tub-shaped dishes surrounding her, and a pouncing fork of a short, sure stab. "Right away my husband gets mad when I say the same thing. 'When we don't like it we should move,' he says."

"Like moving is so easy, if you got two chairs and a hair mattress to take with you. But I always say, Mrs. Katz, I don't blame Mrs. Kaufman herself for what goes on; there's *one* good woman if there ever was one!"

"They don't come no better or no better-looking, my husband always says. 'S-ay,' I tell him, 'she can stand her good looks.'"

"It's that big-ideaed daughter is more to blame. Did you see yet her new white spats tonight? Right away the minute they come out she has to have 'em. I'm only surprised she ain't got one of them red hats from Gimp's what is all the fad. *Oser,* if not such ideas, her mother could afford something better as succotash for us for supper."

"It's a shame, let me tell you, that a woman like Mrs. Kaufman can't see for herself such things. God forbid I should ever be so blind to my Irving. I tell you that Ruby has got it more like a queen than a boarding-house keeper's daughter. Spats, yet!"

"Rich girls could be glad to have it always so good."

"I don't say nothing how her mother treats Vetsburg, her oldest boarder, and for what he pays for that second floor front and no lunches she can afford to cater a little; but that such a girl shouldn't be made to take up a little stenography or help with the housework!"

"S-ay, when that girl even turns a hand, pale like a ghost her mother gets."

"How girls are raised nowadays, even the poor ones!"

"I ain't the one to complain, Mrs. Katz, but just look down there, that red stuff."

"Where?"

"Ain't it cranberry between Ruby and Vetsburg?"

"Yes, yes, and look such a dish of it!"

"Is it right extras should be allowed to be brought on a table like this where fourteen other boarders got to let their mouths water and look at it?"

"You think it don't hurt like a knife! For myself I don't mind, but my Irving! How that child loves 'em, and he should got to sit at the same table without cranberries."

From the head of the table the flashing implements of carving held in askance for stroke, her lips lifted to a smile and a simulation of interest for display of further carnivorous appetites, Mrs. Kaufman passed her nod from one to the other.

"Miss Arndt, little more? No? Mr. Krakower? Gravy? Mrs. Suss? Mr. Suss? So! Simon? Mr. Schloss? Miss Horowitz? Mr. Vetsburg, let me give you this little tender — No? Then, Ruby, here let mamma give you just a little more ——"

"No, no, mamma, please!" She caught at the hovering wrist to spare the descent of the knife.

By one of those rare atavisms by which a poet can be bred of a peasant or peasant be begot of poet, Miss Ruby Kaufman, who was born in Newark, posthumous, to a terrified little parent with a black ribbon at the throat of her gown, had brought with her from no telling where the sultry eyes and tropical-turned skin of spice-kissed winds. The corpuscles of a shah might have been running in the blood of her, yet Simon Kaufman and Simon Kaufman's father before him had sold wool remnants to cap factories on commission.

"Ruby, you don't eat enough to keep a bird alive. Ain't it a shame, Mr. Vetsburg, a girl should be so dainty?"

Mr. Meyer Vetsburg cast a beetling glance down upon Miss Kaufman, there so small beside him, and tinked peremptorily against her plate three times with his fork. "Eat, young lady, like your mamma wants you should, or, by golly, I'll string you up for my watch fob, not, Mrs. Kaufman?"

A smile lay under Mr. Vetsburg's gray-and-black mustache. Gray were his eyes too, and his suit, a comfortable baggy suit with the slouch of the wearer impressed into it, the coat hiking center back, the pocket flaps half in, half out, and the knees sagging out of press.

"That's right, Mr. Vetsburg, you should scold her when she don't eat."

Above the black bombazine basque, so pleasantly relieved at the throat by a V of fresh white net, a wave of color moved up Mrs. Kaufman's face into her architectural coiffure, the very black and very coarse skein of her hair wound into a large loose mound directly atop her head and pierced there with a ball-topped comb of another decade.

"I always say, Mr. Vetsburg, she minds you before she minds anybody else in the world."

"Ma," said Miss Kaufman, close upon that remark, "some succotash, please."

From her vantage down table, Mrs. Katz leaned a bit forward from the line.

"Look, Mrs. Finshriber, how for a woman her age she snaps her black eyes at him. It ain't hard to guess when a woman's got a marriageable daughter, not?"

"You can take it from me she'll get him for her Ruby yet! And take it from me, too, almost any girl I know, much less Ruby Kaufman, could do worse as get Meyer Vetsburg."

"S-say, I wish it to her to get him. For why once in a while shouldn't a poor girl get a rich man except in books and choruses?"

"Believe me, a girl like Ruby can manage what she wants. Take it from me, she's got it behind her ears."

"I should say so."

"*Oser* without it she could get in with such a crowd of rich girls like she does. I got it from Mrs. Abrams in the Arline Apartments how every week she plays five hundred with Nathan Shapiro's daughter."

"No! Shapiro and Stein?"

"And yesterday at matinée in she comes with a box of candy and laughing with that Rifkin girl! How she gets in with such swell girls, I don't know, but there ain't a nice Saturday afternoon I don't see that girl walking on Fifth Avenue with just such a crowd of fine-dressed girls, all with their noses powdered so white and their hats so little and stylish."

"I wouldn't be surprised if her mother don't send her down to Atlantic City over Easter again if Vetsburg goes. Every holiday she has to go lately like it was coming to her."

"Say, between you and me, I don't put it past her it's that Markovitch boy down there she's after. Ray Klein saw 'em on the Boardwalk once together, and she says it's a shame for the people how they sat so close in a rolling chair."

"I wouldn't be surprised she's fresh with the boys, but, believe me, if she gets the uncle she don't take the nephew!"

"Say, a clerk in his own father's hotel like the Markovitches got in Atlantic City ain't no crime."

"Her mother has got bigger thoughts for her than that. For why I guess she thinks her daughter should take the nephew when maybe she can get the uncle herself. Nowadays it ain't nothing no more that girls marry twice their own age."

"I always say I can tell when Leo Markovitch comes down by the way her mother's face gets long and the daughter's gets short."

"Can you blame her? Leo Markovitch, with all his monograms on his shirt sleeves and such black rims on his glasses, ain't the Rosenthal Vetsburg Hosiery Company, not by a long shot! There ain't a store in this town you ask for the No Hole guaranteed stocking, right away they don't show it to you. Just for fun always I ask."

"Cornstarch pudding! Irving, stop making that noise at Mrs. Kaufman! Little boys should be seen and not heard even at cornstarch pudding."

"Gott! Wouldn't you think, Mrs. Katz, how Mrs. Kaufman knows how I hate desserts that wobble, a little something extra she could give me?"

"*Oser* how she plays favorite, it's a shame. I wish you look, too, Mrs. Finshriber, how Flora Proskauer carries away from the table her glass milk with slice bread on top. I tell you it don't give tune to a house the boarders should carry away from the table like that. Irving, come and take with you that extra piece cake. Just so much board we pay as Flora Proskauer."

The line about the table broke suddenly, attended with a scraping of chairs and after-dinner chirrupings attended with toothpicks. A blowzy maid strained herself immediately across the strewn table and cloying lamb platter, and turned off two of the three gas jets.

In the yellow gloom, the odors of food permeating it, they filed out and up the dim-lit stairs into dim-lit halls, the line of conversation and short laughter drifting after.

A door slammed. Another. Irving Katz leaped from his third-floor threshold to the front hearth, quaking three layers of chandeliers. From Morris Krakower's fourth floor back the tune of a flute began to wind down the stairs. Out of her just-closed door, Mrs. Finshriber poked a frizzled gray head.

"Ice water, ple-ase, Mrs. Kauf-man."

At the door of the first floor back Mrs. Kaufman paused with her hand on the knob.

"Mamma, let me run and do it."

"Don't you move, Ruby. When Annie goes up to bed is time enough. Won't you come in for a while, Mr. Vetsburg?"

"Don't care if I do."

She opened the door, entering cautiously. "Let me light up, Mrs. Kaufman." He struck a phosphorescent line on the sole of his shoe, turning up three jets.

"You must excuse, Mr. Vetsburg, how this room looks; all day we been sewing for Ruby her new dress."

She caught up a litter of dainty pink frills in the making, clearing a chair for him.

"Sit down, Mr. Vetsburg."

They adjusted themselves around the shower of gaslight, Miss Kaufman fumbling in her flowered workbag, finally curling her foot up under her, her needle flashing and shirring through one of the pink flounces.

"Ruby, in such a light you shouldn't strain your eyes."

"All right, ma," stitching placidly on.

"What'll you give me, Ruby, if I tell you whose favorite color is pink?"

"Aw, Vetsy!" she cried, her face like a rose, "*your* color's pink!"

From the depths of an inverted sewing-machine top Mrs. Kaufman fished out another bit of the pink, ruffling it with deft needle.

The flute lifted its plaintive voice, feeling for high C.

Mr. Vetsburg lighted a loosely wrapped cigar and slumped in his chair.

"If anybody," he observed, "should ask right this minute where I'm at, tell 'em for me, Mrs. Kaufman, I'm in the most comfortable chair in the house."

"You should keep it, then, up in your room, Mr. Vetsburg, and not always bring it down again when I get Annie to carry it up to you."

"Say, I don't give up so easy my excuse for dropping in evenings."

"Honest, you — you two children, you ought to have a fence built around you the way you like always to be together."

He sat regarding her, puffing and chewing his live cigar. Suddenly he leaped forward, his hand closing rigidly over hers.

"Mrs. Kaufman!"

"What?"

"Quick, there's a hole in your chin."

"Gott, a — a — what?"

At that he relaxed at his own pleasantry, laughing and shrugging. With small white teeth Miss Kaufman bit off an end of thread.

"Don't let him tease you, ma; he's after your dimple again."

"*Ach, du* — tease, you! Shame! Hole in my chin he scares me with!"

She resumed her work with a smile and a twitching at her lips that she was unable to control. A warm flow of air came in, puffing the lace curtains. A faint odor of departed splendor lay in that room, its high calcimined ceiling with the floral rosette in the center, the tarnished pier glass tilted to reflect a great pair of walnut folding doors which cut off the room where once it had flowed on to join the great length of salon parlor. A folding bed with an inlay of mirror and a collapsible desk arrangement backed up against those folding doors. A divan with a winding back and sleek with horsehair was drawn across a corner, a marble-topped bureau alongside. A bronze clock ticked roundly from the mantel, balanced at either side by a pair of blue glass cornucopias with warts blown into them.

Mrs. Kaufman let her hands drop idly in her lap and her head fall back against the chair. In repose the lines of her mouth turned up, and her throat, where so often the years eat in first, was smooth and even slender above the rather round swell of bosom.

"Tired, mommy?"

"Always around Easter spring fever right away gets hold of me!"

Mr. Vetsburg bit his cigar, slumped deeper, and inserted a thumb in the arm of his waistcoat.

"Why, Mrs. Kaufman, don't you and Ruby come down by Atlantic City with me tomorrow over Easter? Huh? A few more or less don't make no difference to my sister the way they get ready for crowds."

Miss Kaufman shot forward, her face vivid.

"Oh, Vetsy," she cried, and a flush rushed up, completely dyeing her face. His face lit with hers, a sunburst of fine lines radiating from his eyes.

"Eh?"

"Why — why, we — we'd just love it, wouldn't we, ma? Atlantic City, Easter Day! Ma!"

Mrs. Kaufman sat upright with a whole procession of quick emotions flashing their expressions across her face. They ended in a smile that trembled as she sat regarding the two of them.

"I should say so, yes! I — you and Ruby go, Mr. Vetsburg. Atlantic City, Easter Day, I bet is worth the trip. I — you two go, I should say so, but you don't want an old woman to drag along with you."

"Ma! Just listen to her, Vetsy, ain't she — ain't she just the limit! Half the time when we go in stores together they take us for sisters, and then she — she begins to talk like that to get out of going!"

"Ruby don't understand; but it ain't right, Mr. Vetsburg, I should be away over Saturday and Sunday. On Easter always they expect a little extra, and with Annie's sore ankle, I — I ——"

"Oh, mommy, can't you leave this old shebang for only two days just for an Easter Sunday down at Atlantic, where — where everybody goes?"

"You know yourself, Ruby, how always on Annie's Sunday out ——"

"Well, what of it? It won't hurt all them old things upstairs that let you wait on them hand and foot all year to go without a few frills for their Easter dinner."

"Ruby!"

"I mean it. The old gossip pots! I just sat and looked at them there at supper just now, and I said to myself, I said, to think they drown kittens and let those poor lumps live!"

"Ruby, ain't you ashamed to talk like that?"

"Sat there and looked at poor old man Katz with his ear all ragged like it had been chewed off, and wondered why he didn't just go down to Brooklyn Bridge for a high jump."

"Ruby, I ——"

"If all those big, strapping women, Suss and Finshriber and

the whole gang of them, were anything but vegetables, they'd get out and hustle with keeping house, to work some of their flabbiness off and give us a chance to get somebody in besides a chocolate-eating, novel-reading crowd of useless women who think, mommy, you're a dumbwaiter, chambermaid, lady's maid, and French chef rolled in one! Honest, ma, if you carry that ice water up to Katz tonight on the sly, with that big son of hers to come down and get it, I — I'll go right up and tell her what I think of her if she leaves tomorrow."

"Mr. Vetsburg, you — you mustn't listen to her."

"Can't take a day off for a rest at Atlantic City because their old Easter dinner might go down the wrong side. Honest, mamma, to — to think how you're letting a crowd of old, flabby women that ain't fit even to wipe your shoes make a regular servant out of you! Mommy!"

There were tears in Miss Kaufman's voice and actual tears, big and bright, in her eyes, and two spots of color had popped out in her cheeks.

"Ruby, when — when a woman like me makes her living off her boarders, she can't afford to be so particular. You think it's a pleasure I can't slam the door right in Mrs. Katz's face when six times a day now she orders towels and ice water. You think it's a pleasure I got to take sass from such a bad boy like Irving. I tell you, Ruby, it's easy talk from a girl what don't understand. *Ach,* you — you make me ashamed before Mr. Vetsburg you should run down so the people we make our living off of."

Miss Kaufman flashed her vivid face toward Mr. Vetsburg, still low there in his chair. She was trembling. "Vetsy knows! He's the only one in this house does know! He ain't been here with us ten years, ever since we started in this big house, not — not to know he's the only one thinks you're here for anything except impudence and running stairs and standing sass from the bad boys of lazy mothers. You know, don't you, Vetsy?"

"Ruby! Mr. Vetsburg, you — you must excuse ——"

From the depths of his chair Mr. Vetsburg's voice came slow and carefully weighed. "My only complaint, Mrs. Kaufman, with what Ruby has got to say is it ain't strong enough. It maybe ain't none of my business, but always I have told you that for your own good you're too *gemütlich.* No wonder every boarder what you get stays year in and year out till even the biggest kickers pay more board sooner as go. In my business, Mrs. Kaufman, it's the same way right away if I get too easy with ——"

"But, Mr. Vetsburg, a poor woman can't afford to be so independent. I got big expenses and big rent; I got a daughter to raise ——"

"Mamma, haven't I begged you a hundred times to let me take up stenography and get out and hustle so you can take it easy, haven't I?"

A thick coating of tears sprang to Mrs. Kaufman's eyes and muddled the gaze she turned toward Mr. Vetsburg. "Is it natural, Mr. Vetsburg, a mother should want her only child should have always the best and do always the things she never herself could afford to do? All my life, Mr. Vetsburg. I had always to work. Even when I was five months married to a man what it looked like would some day do big things in the wool business, I was left all of a sudden with nothing but debts and my baby."

"But, mamma ——"

"Is it natural, Mr. Vetsburg, I should want to work off my hands my daughter should escape that? Nothing, Mr. Vetsburg, gives me so much pleasure she should go with all those rich girls who like her well enough poor to be friends with her. Always when you take her down to Atlantic City on holidays, where she can meet 'em, it — it ——"

"But, mommy, is it any fun for a girl to keep taking trips like that with — with her mother always at home like a servant? What do people think? Every holiday that Vetsy asks me, you — you back out. I — I won't go without you, mommy, and — and I *want* to go, ma, I — I *want* to!"

"My Easter dinner and ——"

"You, Mrs. Kaufman, with your Easter dinner! Ruby's right. When your mamma don't go this time, not one step we go by ourselves, ain't it?"

"Not a step."

"But ——"

"Tomorrow, Mrs. Kaufman, we catch that one-ten train. Twelve o'clock I call in for you. Put ginger in your mamma, Ruby, and we'll open her eyes on the Boardwalk, not?"

"Oh, Vetsy!"

He smiled regarding her.

Tears had fallen and dried on Mrs. Kaufman's cheeks; she wavered between a hysteria of tears and laughter.

" I — children — " She succumbed to tears, daubing her eyes shamefacedly.

He rose kindly. " Say, when such a little thing can upset her it's high time she took for herself a little rest. If she backs out, we string her up by the thumbs, not, Ruby? "

" We're going, ma. Going! You'll love the Markovitches' hotel, ma dearie, right near the Boardwalk, and the grandest glassed-in porch and — and chairs, and — and nooks and things. Ain't they, Vetsy? "

" Yes, you little Ruby, you," he said, regarding her with warm, insinuating eyes, even crinkling an eyelid in a wink.

She did not return the glance, but caught her cheeks in the vise of her hands as if to stem the too-quick flush. " Now you — you quit! " she cried, flashing her back upon him in quick pink confusion.

" She gets mad yet," he said, his shoulders rising and falling in silent laughter.

" Don't! "

" Well," he said, clicking the door softly after him, " good night and sleep tight."

" 'Night, Vetsy."

Upon the click of that door Mrs. Kaufman leaned softly forward in her chair, speaking through a scratch in her throat. " Ruby! "

With her flush still high, Miss Kaufman danced over toward her parent, then as suddenly ebbed in spirit, the color going. " Why, mommy, what — what you crying for, dearie? Why, there's nothing to cry for, dearie, that we're going off on a toot tomorrow. Honest, dearie, like Vetsy says, you're all nerves. I bet from the way Suss hollered at you today about her extra milk you're upset yet. Wouldn't I give her a piece of my mind, though! Here, move your chair, mommy, and let me pull down the bed."

" I — I'm all right, baby. Only I just tell you it's enough to make anybody cry we should have a friend like we got in Vetsburg. I — I tell you, baby, they just don't come no better than him. Not, baby? Don't be ashamed to say so to mamma."

"I ain't, mamma! And, honest, his — his whole family is just that way. Sweetlike and generous. Wait till you see the way his sister and brother-in-law will treat us at the hotel tomorrow. And — and Leo too."

"I always say the day what Meyer Vetsburg, when he was only a clerk in the firm, answered my furnished-room advertisement was the luckiest day in my life."

"You ought to heard, ma; I was teasing him the other day, telling him that he ought to live at the Savoy now that he's a two-thirds member of the firm."

"Ruby!"

"I was only teasing, ma. You just ought to seen his face. Any day he'd leave us!"

Mrs. Kaufman placed a warm, insinuating arm around her daughter's slim waist, drawing her around the chair side and to her. "There's only one way, baby, Meyer Vetsburg can ever leave me and make me happy when he leaves."

"Ma, what you mean?"

"You know, baby, without mamma coming right out in words."

"Ma, honest I don't. What?"

"You see it coming just like I do. Don't fool mamma, baby."

The slender lines of Miss Kaufman's waist stiffened, and she half slipped from the embrace.

"Now, now, baby, is it wrong a mother should talk to her own baby about what is closest in both their hearts?"

"I — I, mamma, I — I don't know!"

"How he's here in this room every night lately, Ruby, since you — you're a young lady. How right away he follows us upstairs. How lately he invited you every month down at Atlantic City. Baby, you ain't blind, are you?"

"Why, mamma — why, mamma, what is Meyer Vetsburg to — to me? Why, he — he's got gray hair, ma; he — he's getting bald. Why, he — he don't know I'm on earth. He — he's ——"

"You mean, baby, he don't know anybody else is on earth. What's, nowadays, baby, a man forty? Why — why, ain't mamma forty-one, baby, and didn't you just say yourself for sisters they take us?"

"I know, ma, but he — he —— Why, he's got an accent,

ma, just like old man Katz and — and all of 'em. He says 'too-sand' for thousand. He —— "

"Baby, ain't you ashamed like it makes any difference how a good man talks?" She reached out, drawing her daughter by the wrists down into her lap. "You're a bad little flirt, baby you, what pretends she don't know what a blind man can see."

Miss Kaufman's eyes widened, darkened, and she tugged for the freedom of her wrists. "Ma, quit scaring me!"

"Scaring you! That such a rising man like Vetsburg, with a business he worked himself into president from clerk looks every day more like he's falling in love with you, should scare you!"

"Ma, not — not him!"

In reply she fell to stroking the smooth black plaits wound coronet fashion about Miss Kaufman's small head. Large, hot tears sprang to her eyes. "Baby, when you talk like that it's you that scares mamma!"

"He — he —— "

"Why, you think, Ruby, I been making out of myself a servant like you call it all these years except for your future? For myself a smaller house without such a show and maybe five or six roomers without meals, you think ain't easier as this big barn? For what, baby, you think I always want you should have extravagances maybe I can't afford and should keep up with the fine girls what you meet down by Atlantic City if it ain't that a man like Meyer Vetsburg can be proud to choose you from the best?"

"Mamma, mamma!"

"Don't think, Ruby, when the day comes what I can give up this white-elephant house it won't be a happy one for me. Every night when I hear from upstairs how Mrs. Katz and all of them hollers down 'towels' and 'ice water' to me like I — I was their slave, you don't think, baby, I will be happiest woman in this world the day what I can slam the door, bang, right on the words."

"Mamma, mamma, and you pretending all these years you didn't mind!"

"I don't, baby. Not one minute while I got a future to look forward to with you. For myself, baby, you think I ask anything except my little girl's happiness? Anyways, when happiness come to you with a man like Meyer Vetsburg, don't — don't it come to me, too, baby?"

"Please, I —— "

"That's what my little girl can do for mamma, better as stenography. Set herself down well. That's why, since we got on the subject, baby, I — I hold off signing up the new lease with every day Shulif fussing so. Maybe, baby, I — well, just maybe, eh, baby?"

For answer a torrent of tears so sudden that they came in an avalanche burst from Miss Kaufman, and she crumpled forward face in hands and red rushing up the back of her neck and over her ears.

"Ruby!"

"No, no, ma! No, no!"

"Baby, the dream what I've dreamed five years for you!"

"No, no, no!"

She fell back regarding her.

"Why, Ruby. Why Ruby, girl!"

"It ain't fair. You mustn't!"

"Mustn't?"

"Mustn't! Mustn't!" Her voice had slipped up now and away from her.

"Why, baby, it's natural at first maybe a girl should be so scared. Maybe I shouldn't have talked so soon except how it's getting every day plainer, these trips to Atlantic City and —— "

"Mamma, mamma, you're killing me." She fell back against her parent's shoulder, her face frankly distorted.

A second, staring there into space, Mrs. Kaufman sat with her arm still entwining the slender but lax form. "Ruby, is — is it something you ain't telling mamma?"

"Oh, mommy, mommy!"

"Is there?"

"I — I don't know."

"Ruby, should you be afraid to talk to mamma, who don't want nothing but her child's happiness?"

"You know, mommy. You know!"

"Know what, baby?"

"I — er —— "

"Is there somebody else you got on your mind, baby?"

"You know, mommy."

"Tell mamma, baby. It ain't a — a crime if you got maybe somebody else on your mind."

"I can't say it, mommy. It — it wouldn't be — be nice."

"Nice?"

"He — he — We ain't even sure yet."

"He?"

"Not — yet."

"Who?"

"You know."

"So help me, I don't."

"Mommy, don't make me say it. Maybe if — when his uncle Meyer takes him in the business, we ——"

"Baby, not Leo?"

"Oh, mommy, mommy." And she buried her hot, revealing face into the fresh net V.

"Why — why, baby, a — a *boy* like that!"

"Twenty-three, mamma, ain't a boy!"

"But, Ruby, just a clerk in his father's hotel, and two older brothers already in it. A — a boy that ain't got a start yet."

"That's just it, ma. We — we're waiting! Waiting before we talk even — even much to each other yet. Maybe — maybe his uncle Meyer is going to take him in the business, but it ain't sure yet. We ——"

"A little yellow-haired boy like him that — that can't support you, baby, unless you live right there in his mother's and father's hotel away — away from me!"

"Ma!"

"Ruby, a smart girl like you. A little snip what don't make salt yet when you can have the uncle hisself!"

"I can't help it, ma! If — if — the first time Vetsy took me down to — to the shore, if — if Leo had been a king or a — or just what he is, it wouldn't make no difference. I — I can't help my — my feelings, ma. I can't!"

A large furrow formed between Mrs. Kaufman's eyes, darkening her brow.

"You wouldn't, Ruby," she said, clutching her.

"Oh, mommy, mommy, when a — a girl can't help a thing!"

"He ain't good enough for you, baby."

"He's ten times too good that — that's all you know about it. Mommy, please! I — I just can't help it, dearie. It's just like when I — I saw him a — a clock began to tick inside of me. I ——"

"Oh, my God," said Mrs. Kaufman, drawing her hand across her brow.

"His uncle Meyer, ma, 's been hinting all along he — he's going to give Leo his start and take him in the business. That's why we — we're waiting without saying much, till it looks more like — like we can all be together, ma."

"All my dreams! My dreams I could give up the house! My baby with a well-to-do husband maybe on Riverside Drive. A servant for herself, so I could pass maybe Mrs. Suss and Mrs. Katz by on the street. Ruby, you — you wouldn't, Ruby. After how I've built for you!"

"Oh, mamma, mamma, mamma!"

"If you ain't got ambitions for yourself, Ruby, think once of me and this long dream I been dreaming for — us."

"Yes, ma. Yes."

"Gott im Himmel, Ruby, I always thought, and how he must have thought it, too, when you was so glad for Atlantic City, it — it was for Vetsburg you liked his folks. How could I know it was ——"

"I never thought, mommy. Why — why Vetsy, he's just like a relation or something."

"I tell you, baby, it's just an idea you got in your head."

"No, no, mamma. No. No."

Suddenly Mrs. Kaufman threw up her hands, clasping them tight against her eyes, pressing them in frenzy. "Oh, my God," she cried, "all for nothing!" and fell to moaning through her laced fingers. "All for nothing! Years. Years. Years."

"Mommy, darling!"

"Oh — don't, don't! Just let me be. Let me be. Oh, my God! My God!"

"Mommy, please, mommy! I didn't mean it. I didn't mean it, mommy, darling."

"I can't go on all the years, Ruby. I'm tired. Tired, girl."

"Of course you can't, darling. We — I don't want you to. Shh-h-h!"

"It's only you and my hopes in you that kept me going all these years. The hope that with some day a good man to provide for you, I could find a rest maybe."

"Yes, yes."

"Every time what I think of that long envelope laying there on that desk with its lease waiting to be signed tomorrow, I — I could squeeze my eyes shut so tight, and wish I didn't never have to open them again on this — this house and this drudgery. If you marry wrong, baby, I'm caught. Caught in this house like a rat in a trap."

"No, no, mommy. Leo, he — his uncle ——"

"Don't make me sign that new lease, Ruby. Shulif hounds me every day now. Any day I expect he says is my last. Don't make me saddle another five years with the house. He's only a boy, baby, and years it will take, and — I'm tired, baby. Tired! Tired!" She lay back with her face suddenly held in rigid lines and her neck ribbed with cords.

At sight of her so prostrate there, Ruby Kaufman grasped the cold face in her ardent young hands, pressing her lips to the streaming eyes.

"Mommy, I didn't mean it. I didn't! I — we're just kids, flirting a little, Leo and me. I didn't mean it, mommy!"

"You didn't mean it, Ruby, did you? Tell mamma you didn't."

"I didn't, ma. Cross my heart. It's only I — I kinda had him in my head. That's all, dearie. That's all!"

"He can't provide, baby."

"Ehh-h-h, ma. Try to get calm, and maybe then — then things can come like you want 'em. Shh-h-h, dearie. I didn't mean it. Course Leo's only a kid. I — we — Mommy dear, don't. You're killing me. I didn't mean it. I didn't."

"Sure, baby! Sure?"

"Sure."

"Mamma's girl," sobbed Mrs. Kaufman, scooping the small form to her bosom and relaxing. "Mamma's own girl that minds."

They fell quiet, cheek to cheek, staring ahead into the gaslit quiet, the clock ticking into it.

The tears had dried on Mrs. Kaufman's cheeks, only her throat continuing to throb and her hand at regular intervals patting the young shoulder pressed to her. It was as if her heart lay suddenly very still in her breast.

"Mamma's own girl that minds."

"It — it's late, ma. Let me pull down the bed."

"You ain't mad at mamma, baby? It's for your own good

as much as mine. It is unnatural a mother should want to see her —— "

"No, no, mamma. Move, dearie; let me pull down the bed. There you are. Now! "

With a wrench Mrs. Kaufman threw off her recurring inclination to tears, moving casually through the processes of their retirement.

"Tomorrow, baby, I tighten the buttons on them new spats. How pretty they look."

"Yes, dearie."

"I told Mrs. Katz today right out her Irving can't bring any more his bicycle through my front hall. Wasn't I right? "

"Of course you were, ma."

"Miss Flora looked right nice in that pink waist tonight, not? Four-eighty-nine only, at Gimp's sale."

"She's too fat for pink."

"You get in bed first, baby, and let mamma turn out the lights."

"No, no, mamma; you."

In her white slip of a nightdress, her coronet braids unwound and falling down each shoulder, even her slightness had waned. She was like Juliet who at fourteen had eyes of maid and martyr.

They crept into bed, grateful for darkness.

The flute had died out, leaving a silence that was plaintive.

"You all right, baby? "

"Yes, ma." And she snuggled down into the curve of her mother's arm.

"Are you, mommy? "

"Yes, baby."

"Go to sleep then."

"Good night, baby."

"Good night, mommy."

Silence.

Lying there with her face upturned and her eyes closed, a stream of quiet tears found their way from under Miss Kaufman's closed lids, running down and toward her ears like spectacle frames.

An hour ticked past, and two damp pools had formed on her pillow.

"Asleep yet, baby? "

"Almost, ma."

"Are you all right?"

"Fine."

"You — you ain't mad at mamma?"

"Course not, dearie."

"I — thought it sounded like you was crying."

"Why, mommy, course not! Turn over now and go to sleep."

Another hour, and suddenly Mrs. Kaufman shot out her arm from the coverlet, jerking back the sheet and feeling for her daughter's dewy, upturned face where the tears were slashing down it.

"Baby!"

"Mommy, you — you mustn't!"

"Oh, my darling, like I didn't suspicion it!"

"It's only ——"

"You got, Ruby, the meanest mamma in the world. But you think, darling, I got one minute's happiness like this?"

"I'm all right, mommy, only ——"

"I been laying here half the night, Ruby, thinking how I'm a bad mother what thinks only of her own ——"

"No, no, mommy. Turn over and go to sl ——"

"My daughter falls in love with a fine, upright young man like Leo Markovitch, and I ain't satisfied yet! Suppose maybe for two or three years you ain't so much on your feet. Suppose even his uncle Meyer don't take him in. Don't any young man got to get his start slow?"

"Mommy!"

"Because I got for her my own ideas, my daughter shouldn't have in life the man she wants!"

"But, mommy, if ——"

"You think for one minute, Ruby, after all these years without this house on my hands and my boarders and their kicks, a woman like me would be satisfied! Why, the more, baby, I think of such a thing, the more I see it for myself. What you think, Ruby, I do all day without steps to run and my gedinks with housekeeping and marketing after eighteen years of it? At first, Ruby, ain't it natural it should come like a shock that you and that rascal Leo got all of a sudden so — so thick? I — it ain't no more, baby, I — I feel fine about it."

"Oh, mommy, if — if I thought you did!"

"I do. Why not? A fine young man what my girl is in love with. Every mother should have it so."

"Mommy, you mean it?"

"I tell you I feel fine. You don't need to feel bad or cry another minute. I can tell you I feel happy. Tomorrow at Atlantic City such a rascal don't tell me for himself. I — I ask him right out!"

"Ma."

"For why yet he should wait till he's got better prospects, so his mother-in-law can hang on? I guess not!"

"Mommy, darling. If you only truly feel like that about it. Why, you can keep putting off the lease, ma, if it's only for six months and then we — we'll all be to ——"

"Of course, baby. Mamma knows. Of course!"

"He — I just can't begin to tell you, ma, the kind of a fellow Leo is till you know him better, mommy dear."

"Always Vetsburg says he's a wide-awake one!"

"That's just what he is, ma. He's just a prince if — if there ever was one. One little prince of a fellow." She fell to crying softly, easy tears that flowed freely.

"I — I can tell you, baby, I'm happy as you."

"Mommy, dear, kiss me."

They talked, huddled arm in arm, until dawn flowed in at the window and dirty roofs began to show against a clean sky. Footsteps began to clatter through the asphalt court and there came the rattle of milk cans.

"I wonder if Annie left out the note for Mrs. Suss's extra milk!"

"Don't get up, dearie; it's only five."

"Right away, baby, with extra towels I must run up to Miss Flora's room. That six o'clock train for Trenton she gets."

"Ma, dear, let me go."

"Lay right where you are! I guess you want you should look all worn out when a young man what I know walks down to meet our train at Atlantic City this afternoon, eh?"

"Oh, mommy, mommy." And Ruby lay back against the luxury of pillows.

At eleven the morning rose to its climax — the butcher, the baker, and every sort of maker hustling in and out the basement way; the sweeping of upstairs halls; windows flung open and lace curtains looped high; the smell of spring pouring in even from asphalt; sounds of scrubbing from various stoops; shouts of drivers from a narrow street wedged with its Saturday morning blockade of delivery wagons, and a crosstown line of motor cars, tops back, and nosing for the speedway of upper Broadway. A homely bouquet of odors rose from the basement kitchen, drifting up through the halls, the smell of mutton bubbling as it stewed.

After a morning of upstairs and downstairs and in and out of chambers, Mrs. Kaufman, enveloped in a long-sleeved apron still angular with starch, hung up the telephone receiver in the hall just beneath the staircase and entered her bedroom, sitting down rather heavily beside the open shelf of her desk. A long envelope lay uppermost on that desk, and she took it up slowly, blinking her eyes shut and holding them squeezed tight as if she would press back a vision, even then a tear oozing through. She blinked it back, but her mouth was wry with the taste of tears.

A slatternly maid poked her head in through the open door.
" Mrs. Katz broke 'er mug! "
" Take the one off Mr. Krakow's washstand and give it to her, Tillie."

She was crying now frankly, and when the door swung closed, even though it swung back again on its insufficient hinge, she let her head fall forward into the pillow of her arms, the curve of her back rising and falling.

But after a while the greengrocer came on his monthly mission, in his white apron and shirt sleeves, and she compared stubs with him from a file on her desk and balanced her account with careful squinted glance and a keen eye for an overcharge on a cut of breakfast bacon.

On the very heels of him, so that they met and danced to pass one another in the doorway, Mr. Vetsburg entered with an overcoat flung across his right arm and his left sagging to a small black traveling bag.

" Well," he said, standing in the frame of the open door, his derby well back on his head and regarding her there beside the small desk, " is this what you call ready at twelve? "

She rose and moved forward in her crackly starched apron.
" I — please, Mr. Vetsburg, it ain't right I know —— "
" You don't mean you're not going! " he exclaimed, the lifted quality immediately dropping from his voice.

"You — you got to excuse me again, Mr. Vetsburg. It ain't no use I should try to get away on Saturdays, much less Easter Saturday."

"Well, of all things!"

"Right away the last minute, Mr. Vetsburg, right one things after another!"

He let his bag slip to the floor.

"Maybe, Mrs. Kaufman," he said, "it ain't none of my business, but ain't it a shame a good business woman like you should let herself always be tied down to such a house like she was married to it? Ain't it?"

"But ——"

"Can't get away on Saturdays, just like it ain't the same any other day in the week, I ask you! Saturday you blame it on yet!"

She lifted the apron from her hem, her voice hurrying. "You can see for yourself, Mr. Vetsburg, how in my brown silk all ready I was. Even — even Ruby don't know yet I don't go. Down by Gimp's I sent her she should buy herself one of them red straw hats is the fad with the girls now. She meets us down by the station."

"That's a fine come-off, ain't it, to disappoint ——"

"At the last minute, Mr. Vetsburg, how things can happen. Out of a clear sky Mrs. Finshriber has tomorrow for Easter dinner that skin doctor, Abrams, and his wife she's so particular about. And Annie with her sore ankle and ——"

"A little shyster doctor like Abrams with his advertisements all over the newspapers should sponge off you and your holiday. By golly, Mrs. Kaufman, just like Ruby says, how you let a whole household of old hens rule this roost it's a shame!"

"When you go down to the station, Mr. Vetsburg, so right away she ain't so disappointed I don't come, tell her maybe tomorrow I ——"

"I don't tell her nothing!" broke in Mr. Vetsburg and moved toward her with considerable strengthening of tone. "Mrs. Kaufman, I ask you, you think it right you should go back like this on Ruby and me, just when we want most you should ——"

At that she quickened and fluttered. "Ruby and you! Ach, it's a old saying, Mr. Vetsburg, like the twig is bent so the tree grows. That child won't be so surprised her mother changes her mind. Just so changeable as her mother, and more, is Ruby herself. With that girl, Mr. Vetsburg, it's — it's hard to know what she does one minute from the next. I always say no man — nobody can ever count on a little harum-scarum like — like she is."

He took up her hat, a small turban of breast feathers, laid out on the table beside him, and advanced with it clumsily enough. "Come," he said, "please now, Mrs. Kaufman. Please."

"I —— "

"I — I got plans made for us tomorrow down by the shore that's — that's just fine! Come now, Mrs. Kaufman."

"Please, Mr. Vetsburg, don't force. I — I can't! I always say nobody can count on such a little harum-scarum as —— "

"You mean to tell me, Mrs. Kaufman, that just because a little shyster doctor —— "

Her hand closed over the long envelope again, crunching it. "No, no, that — that ain't all, Mr. Vetsburg. Only I don't want you should tell Ruby, you promise me? How that child worries over little things. Shulif from the agency called up just now. He don't give me one more minute as two this afternoon I — I should sign. How I been putting them off so many weeks with this lease, it's a shame. Always you know how in the back of my head I've had it to take maybe a smaller place when this lease was done, but, like I say, talk is cheap and moving ain't so easy done, ain't it? If he puts in new plumbing in pantry and new hinges on the doors and papers my second floor and Mrs. Suss's alcove, like I said last night, after all I could do worse as stay here another five year, ain't it, Mr. Vetsburg?"

"I —— "

"A house what keeps filled so easy and such a location with the subway less as two blocks. I — So you see, Mr. Vetsburg, if I don't want I come back and find my house on the market, maybe rented over my head, I got to stay home for Shulif when he comes today."

A rush of dark blood had surged up into Mr. Vetsburg's face, and he twiddled his hat, his dry fingers moving around inside the brim.

"Mrs. Kaufman," he cried, "Mrs. Kaufman, sometimes when for years a man don't speak out his mind, sometimes he busts all of a sudden right out. I — oh — e-e-e!" And, immediately and thickly inarticulate, he made a tremendous feint at clearing his throat, tossed up his hat and caught it, and rolled his eyes.

"Mr. Vetsburg?"

"A man, Mrs. Kaufman, can bust!"

"Bust?"

He was still violently dark but swallowing with less labor. "Yes, from holding in. Mrs. Kaufman, should a woman like you — the finest woman in the world, and I can prove it — a woman, Mrs. Kaufman, who in her heart and my heart and — Should such a woman not come to Atlantic City when I got everything fixed like a stage set!"

She threw out an arm that was visibly trembling. "Mr. Vetsburg, for God's sake, ain't I just told you how that she — harum-scarum — she ——"

"Will you, Mrs. Kaufman, come or won't you? Will you, I ask you, or won't you?" He threw a gesture now with mastery, one arm before and one behind.

"I — I can't, Mr. ——"

"All right, then, I — I bust out now. Today can be as good as tomorrow! Not with my say in a t'ousand years, Mrs. Kaufman, you sign that lease! I ain't a young man any more with fine speeches, Mrs. Kaufman, but not in a t'ousand years you sign that lease."

"Mr. Vetsburg, Ruby, I ——"

"If anybody's got a lease on you, Mrs. Kaufman, I — I want it! I want it! That's the kind of a lease would suit me. To be leased to you for always, the rest of your life!"

She could not follow him down the vista of fancy, but stood interrogating him with her heartbeats at her throat. "Mr. Vetsburg, if he puts on the doors and hinges and new plumbing in ——"

"I'm a plain man, Mrs. Kaufman, without much to offer a woman what can give out her heart's blood like it was so much water. But all these years I been waiting, Mrs. Kaufman, to bust out, until — till things got riper. I know with a woman like you, whose own happiness always is last, that first your girl must be fixed ——"

"She's a young girl, Mr. Vetsburg, you — you mustn't depend —— If I had my say ——"

"He's a fine fellow, Mrs. Kaufman. With his uncle to help 'em, they got, let me tell you, a better start as most young ones!"

She rose, holding on to the desk.

"I — I ——" she said. "What?"

"Lena," he uttered very softly.

"Lena, Mr. Vetsburg?"

"It ain't been easy, Lenie, these years while she was only growing up, to keep off my lips that name. A name just like a leaf off a rose. Lena!" he reiterated, and advanced.

Comprehension came quietly and dawning like a morning.

"I — I — Mr. Vetsburg, you must excuse me," she said and sat down suddenly.

He crossed to the little desk and bent low over the back of her chair with his hand, not on her shoulder, but at the knob of her chair. His voice had a swift rehearsed quality.

"Maybe tomorrow, if you didn't back out, it would sound finer by the ocean, Lenie, but it don't need the ocean a man should tell a woman when she's the first and the finest woman in the world. Does it, Lenie?"

"I — I thought Ruby. She ——"

"He's a good boy, Leo is, Lenie. A good boy what can be good to a woman like his father before him. Good enough even for a fine girl like our Ruby, Lenie — *our* Ruby!"

"*Gott im Himmel*, then you ——"

"Wide-awake, too. With a start like I can give him in my business, you ain't got to worry Ruby ain't fixed herself with the man what she chooses. Tomorrow at Atlantic City all fixed I had it I should tell ——"

"You!" she said, turning around in her chair to face him, "you — all along you been fixing ——"

He turned sheepish. "Ain't it fair, Lenie, in love and war and business a man has got to scheme for what he wants out of life? Long enough it took she should grow up. I knew all along once those two, each so full of life and gedinks, got together it was natural what should happen. Mrs. Kaufman! Lenie! Lenie!"

From two flights up, in through the open door and well above the harsh sound of scrubbing, a voice curled down through the hallways and in. "Mrs. Kaufman, ice water — ple-ase!"

"Lenie," he said, his singing, tingling fingers closing over her wrist.

"Mrs. Kauf-man, ice water, pl —— ! "

With her free arm she reached and slammed the door, let her cheek lie to the back of his hand, and closed her eyes.

## QUESTIONS

1. How is boarding-house life described?
2. Would you call the author's style vague or direct? Illustrate.
3. How does the author impart a dash of humor?
4. What are the first hints of a possible plot? Be definite.
5. Was it a poor boarding house, really? Give reasons.
6. What are your first impressions of Vetsburg?
7. Where is the first hint of a complication in the plot?
8. Does the after-dinner scene in the sitting room prepare for what is coming later? Explain.
9. What does Ruby's outburst indicate about her character?
10. Under the conditions of the story, is the relation between mother and daughter natural?
11. In the situation, which shows up the better? Give reasons.
12. Had Ruby really been ignorant of her mother's rather transparent scheme? Explain.
13. Were Ruby's objections to Vetsburg natural? Explain.
14. After the girl reveals her real love, is the pathos in the mother's outburst genuine? Explain.
15. What does the "long envelope" symbolize to Mrs. Kaufman?
16. Explain the sudden change in the mother's attitude?
17. How is the tension of the night scene relieved in the morning?
18. Why had Vetsburg not "busted out" before?
19. Had he suspected Mrs. Kaufman's scheme?
20. Is there an early hint that Vetsburg knew about Ruby and Leo?
21. Did the "surprise" ending surprise you?
22. This story is told almost entirely by conversation. Do you like that method?

## SUBJECTS FOR COMPOSITION

1. Ruby and Leo at the seashore.
2. A friend tells you about an experience in his boarding house.
3. Write a short love story, being careful to avoid the sentimental.

## OTHER STORIES BY FANNIE HURST

Humoresque
Get Ready the Wreaths
T — B
The Solitary Reaper

The Sob Sister
Forty-Five
7 Candles

## VOLUMES OF STORIES BY FANNIE HURST

Just Around the Corner
Every Soul Hath Its Song
Gaslight Sonatas
Humoresque

The Vertical City
Song of Life
Procession

## DOROTHY CANFIELD
(1879-    )

PERHAPS nowhere but in America could a woman born in the last quarter of the 19th century have piled up so much of real achievement as that of Mrs. Dorothy Canfield Fisher. A partial explanation may be found in "The Heyday of the Blood." " Live while you live," she makes old Gran'ther say, and to her, as to him, life means doing something interesting. Linguist, scholar, novelist, short story writer, translator; traveler, war worker, wife, mother — that is a condensed summary of her varied lines of interest.

Her father was president of the University of Kansas, at Lawrence, where she was born in 1879. When she had finished high school her father accepted the presidency of Ohio State University, and there Miss Canfield took her A. B. degree. Still later Dr. Canfield became Librarian at Columbia University; there Miss Canfield received the degree of Doctor of Philosophy in 1904. She specialized in Romance languages, but her first published work was a textbook on rhetoric, written in collaboration with Professor Carpenter of Columbia in 1906. About the same time she began to write short stories for the magazines. In 1907 she married Mr. John R. Fisher, a former Columbia football captain.

How many young women, brought up in a college atmosphere culminating in the city of New York, would deliberately choose to live in a small country community? Mrs. Fisher says, " City dwellers make money, make reputations (good and bad), make museums and subways, make charitable institutions, make with a hysteric rapidity, like excited spiders, more and yet more complications in the mazy labyrinths of their lives, but they never make each other's acquaintance . . . and that is all that is worth doing in the world. . . ."

To live and work according to their ideals Mr. and Mrs. Fisher chose Arlington, Vermont, as their home. When they desire a change from village life they take a trip to the city, or to Europe, staying as long as they please; but they always return to their home among the Green Mountains. From Mrs. Fisher's first collection of short stories, *Hillsboro People*, from which our story is taken, the reader might easily think that she was New England born and bred, so sympathetically does she portray the life and people of her adopted state. All the stories in *Hillsboro People* are laid in Vermont, but she has also written about the Middle West, about New York, and about Europe. She is best known as a novelist, but her fame in this particular field grew through the volumes of short stories which came from her experiences in France during the war. These were *Home Fires in France* and *The Day of Glory*. Today she is one of our most popular writers of fiction, both novel and short story.

In 1923 Mrs. Fisher published a translation of Papini's *Life of Christ*, a book that at once achieved a place among important books of the day. More recent works are *Raw Material*, a series of sketches in the manner of the short story, and *The Home Maker*, a novel.

"The Heyday of the Blood," as already indicated, is typical of her style and method in the short story, and more especially, of the wholesome spirit which is never absent from her work. The story is first of all a character sketch, hardly more than an anecdote, but she has cleverly contrived to clothe this bit with her philosophy of life.

# THE HEYDAY OF THE BLOOD

THE older professor looked up at the assistant, fumbling fretfully with a pile of papers. "Farrar, what's the *matter* with you lately?" he said sharply.

The younger man started, "Why . . . why . . ." The brusqueness of the other's manner shocked him suddenly into confession. "I've lost my nerve, Professor Mallory, that's what's the matter with me. I'm frightened to death," he said melodramatically.

"What *of?*" asked Mallory, with a little challenge in his tone.

The flood-gates were open. The younger man burst out in exclamations, waving his thin, nervous, knotted fingers, his face twitching as he spoke. "Of myself . . . no, not myself, but my body! I'm not well . . . I'm getting worse all the time. The doctors don't make out what is the matter . . . I don't sleep . . . I worry . . . I forget things, I take no interest in life . . . the doctors intimate a nervous breakdown ahead of me . . . and yet I rest . . . I rest . . . more than I can afford to! I never go out. Every evening I'm in bed by nine o'clock. I take no part in college life beyond my work, for fear of the nervous strain. I've refused to take charge of that summer-school in New York, you know, that would be such an opportunity for me . . . if I could only sleep! But though I never do anything exciting in the evening . . . heavens! what nights I have. Black hours of seeing myself in a sanitarium, dependent on my brother! I never . . . why, I'm in hell . . . that's what's the matter with me, a perfect hell of ignoble terror!"

# The Heyday of the Blood

He sat silent, his drawn face turned to the window. The older man looked at him speculatively. When he spoke it was with a cheerful, casual quality in his voice which made the other look up at him surprised.

"You don't suppose those great friends of yours, the nerve specialists, would object to my telling you a story, do you? It's very quiet and unexciting. You're not too busy?"

"Busy! I've forgotten the meaning of the word! I don't dare to be!"

"Very well, then; I mean to carry you back to the stony little farm in the Green Mountains, where I had the extreme good luck to be born and raised. You've heard me speak of Hillsboro; and the story is all about my great-grandfather, who came to live with us when I was a little boy."

"Your great-grandfather?" said the other incredulously. "People don't remember their great-grandfathers!"

"Oh, yes, they do, in Vermont. There was my father on one farm, and my grandfather on another, without a thought that he was no longer young, and there was 'gran'ther' as we called him, eighty-eight years old and just persuaded to settle back, let his descendants take care of him, and consent to be an old man. He had been in the War of 1812 — think of that, you mushroom! — and had lost an arm and a good deal of his health there. He had lately begun to get a pension of twelve dollars a month, so that for an old man he was quite independent financially, as poor Vermont farmers look at things; and he was a most extraordinary character, so that his arrival in our family was quite an event.

"He took precedence at once of the oldest man in the township, who was only eighty-four and not very bright. I can remember bragging at school about Gran'ther Pendleton, who'd be eighty-nine come next Woodchuck day, and could see to read without glasses. He had been ailing all his life, ever since the fever he took in the war. He used to remark triumphantly that he had now outlived six doctors who had each given him but a year to live; 'and the seventh is going downhill fast, so I hear!' This last was his never-failing answer to the attempts of my conscientious mother and anxious, dutiful father to check the old man's reckless indifference to any of the rules of hygiene.

"They were good disciplinarians with their children, and

this naughty old man, who would give his weak stomach frightful attacks of indigestion by stealing out to the pantry and devouring a whole mince pie because he had been refused two pieces at the table — this rebellious, unreasonable, whimsical old madcap was an electric element in our quiet, orderly life. He insisted on going to every picnic and church sociable, where he ate recklessly of all the indigestible dainties he could lay his hands on, stood in drafts, tired himself to the verge of fainting away by playing games with the children, and returned home, exhausted, animated, and quite ready to pay the price of a day in bed, groaning and screaming out with pain as heartily and unaffectedly as he had laughed with the pretty girls the evening before.

"The climax came, however, in the middle of August, when he announced his desire to go to the county fair, held some fourteen miles down the valley from our farm. Father never dared let gran'ther go anywhere without himself accompanying the old man, but he was perfectly sincere in saying that it was not because he could not spare a day from the haying that he refused pointblank to consider it. The doctor who had been taking care of gran'ther since he came to live with us said that it would be crazy to think of such a thing. He added that the wonder was that gran'ther lived at all, for his heart was all wrong, his asthma was enough to kill a young man, and he had no digestion; in short, if father wished to kill his old grandfather, there was no surer way than to drive fourteen miles in the heat of August to the noisy excitement of a county fair.

"So father for once said 'No,' in the tone that we children had come to recognize as final. Gran'ther grimly tied a knot in his empty sleeve — a curious, enigmatic mode of his to express strong emotion — put his one hand on his cane, and his chin on his hand, and withdrew himself into that incalculable distance from the life about him where very old people spend so many hours.

"He did not emerge from this until one morning toward the middle of fair-week, when all the rest of the family were away — father and the bigger boys on the far-off upland meadows haying, and mother and the girls off blackberrying. I was too little to be of any help, so I had been left to wait on gran'ther, and to set out our lunch of bread and milk and huckleberries. We had not been alone half an hour when gran'ther sent me to extract, from under the mattress of his bed, the wallet in which he kept his pension money. There was six dollars and forty-three cents — he counted it over carefully, sticking out his tongue like a schoolboy doing a sum, and when he had finished he began to laugh and snap his fingers and sing out in his high, cracked old voice:

"'We're goin' to go a skylarkin'! Little Jo Mallory is going to the county fair with his Gran'ther Pendleton, an' he's goin' to have more fun than ever was in the world, and he ——'

"'But, gran'ther, father said we mustn't!' I protested, horrified.

"'But I say we *shall!* I was your gre't-gran'father long before he was your feyther, and anyway I'm here and he's not — so, *march!* Out to the barn!'

"He took me by the collar and, executing a shuffling fandango of triumph, he pushed me ahead of him to the stable, where old white Peggy, the only horse left at home, looked at us amazed.

"'But it'll be twenty-eight miles, and Peg's never driven over eight!' I cried, my old-established world of rules and orders reeling before my eyes.

"'Eight — and — twenty-eight!
But I — am — *eighty*-eight!'

"Gran'ther improvised a sort of whooping chant of scorn as he pulled the harness from the peg. 'It'll do her good to drink some pink lemonade — old Peggy! An' if she gits tired comin' home, I'll git out and carry her part way myself!'

"His adventurous spirit was irresistible. I made no further objection, and we hitched up together, I standing on a chair to fix the check-rein, and gran'ther doing wonders with his one hand. Then, just as we were — gran'ther in a hickory shirt, and with an old hat flapping over his wizened face, I bare-legged, in ragged old clothes — so we drove out of the grassy yard, down the steep, stony hill that led to the main valley road, and along the hot, white turnpike, deep with the dust which had been stirred up by the teams on their way to the fair. Gran'ther sniffed the air jubilantly, and exchanged hilarious greetings with the people who constantly overtook old Peg's jogging trot. Between times he regaled me with spicy stories of the hundreds of thousands — they seemed no less numerous to me then — of county fairs he had attended in his youth. He was horrified to find that I had never been even to one.

"'Why, Joey, how old be ye? 'Most eight, ain't it? When I was your age I had run away and been to two fairs an' a hangin'.'

"'But didn't they lick you when you got home?' I asked shudderingly.

"'You *bet* they did!' cried gran'ther with gusto.

"I felt the world changing into an infinitely larger place with every word he said.

"'Now, this is somethin' *like!*' he exclaimed, as we drew near to Granville and fell into a procession of wagons all filled with country people in their best clothes, who looked with friendly curiosity at the little, shriveled cripple, his face shining with perspiring animation, and at the little boy beside him, his bare feet dangling high above the floor of the battered buckboard, overcome with the responsibility of driving a horse for the first time in his life, and filled with such a flood of new emotions and ideas that he must have been quite pale."

Professor Mallory leaned back and laughed aloud at the vision he had been evoking — laughed with so joyous a relish in his reminiscences that the drawn, impatient face of his listener relaxed a little. He drew a long breath, he even smiled a little absently.

"Oh, that was a day!" went on the professor, still laughing and wiping his eyes. "Never will I have such another! At the entrance to the grounds gran'ther stopped me while he solemnly untied the knot in his empty sleeve. I don't know what kind of hairbrained vow he had tied up in it, but with the little ceremony disappeared every trace of restraint, and we plunged head over ears into the saturnalia of delights that was an old-time county fair.

"People had little cash in those days, and gran'ther's six dollars and forty-three cents lasted like the widow's cruse of oil. We went to see the fat lady, who, if she was really as big as she looked to me then, must have weighed at least a ton. My admiration for gran'ther's daredevil qualities rose to infinity when he entered into free-and-easy talk with her, about how much she ate, and could she raise her arms enough to do up her own hair, and how many yards of velvet it took to make her gorgeous, gold-trimmed robe. She laughed a great deal at us, but she was evidently touched by his human interest, for she confided to him that it was not velvet at all, but furniture covering; and when we went away she pressed on us a bag of peanuts. She said she had more peanuts than she could eat — a state of unbridled opulence which fitted in for me with all the other superlatives of that day.

"We saw the dog-faced boy, whom we did not like at all; gran'ther expressing, with a candidly outspoken cynicism, his belief that 'them whiskers was glued to him.' We wandered about the stock exhibit, gazing at the monstrous oxen, and hanging over the railings where the prize pigs lived to scratch their backs. In order to miss nothing, we even conscientiously passed through the Woman's Building, where we were very much bored by the serried ranks of preserve jars.

"'Sufferin' Hezekiah!' cried gran'ther irritably. 'Who cares how gooseberry jell *looks?* If they'd give a felly a taste, now ——'

"This reminded him that we were hungry, and we went to a restaurant under a tent, where, after taking stock of the wealth that yet remained of gran'ther's hoard, he ordered the most expensive things on the bill of fare."

Professor Mallory suddenly laughed out again. "Perhaps in heaven, but certainly not until then, shall I ever taste anything so ambrosial as that fried chicken and coffee ice-cream! I have not lived in vain that I have such a memory back of me!"

This time the younger man laughed with the narrator, settling back in his chair as the professor went on:

"After lunch we rode on the merry-go-round, both of us, gran'ther clinging desperately with his one hand to his red camel's wooden hump, and crying out shrilly to me to be sure and not lose his cane. The merry-go-round had just come in at that time, and gran'ther had never experienced it before. After the first giddy flight we retired to a lemonade-stand to exchange impressions, and finding that we both alike had fallen completely under the spell of the new sensation, gran'ther said that we 'sh'd keep on a-ridin' till we'd had enough! King Solomon couldn't tell when we'd ever git a chance again!' So we returned to the charge, and rode and rode and rode, through blinding clouds of happy excitement, so it seems to me now, such as I was never to know again. The sweat was pouring off from us, and we had tried all the different animals on the machine before we could tear ourselves away to follow the crowd to the race-track.

"We took reserved seats, which cost a quarter apiece, instead of the unshaded ten-cent benches, and gran'ther began at once to pour out to me a flood of horse-talk and knowing race-track aphorisms, which finally made a young fellow sitting next to us laugh superciliously. Gran'ther turned on him heatedly.

"'I bet-che fifty cents I pick the winner in the next race!' he said sportily.

"'Done!' said the other, still laughing.

"Gran'ther picked a big black mare, who came in almost last, but he did not flinch. As he paid over the half-dollar he said: 'Everybody's likely to make mistakes about *some* things; King Solomon was a fool in the head about womenfolks! I bet-che a dollar I pick the winner in *this* race!' and 'Done!' said the disagreeable young man, still laughing. I gasped, for I knew we had only eighty-seven cents left, but gran'ther shot me a command to silence out of the corner of his eyes, and announced that he bet on the sorrel gelding.

"If I live to be a hundred and break the bank at Monte Carlo three times a week," said Mallory, shaking his head reminiscently, "I could not know a tenth part of the frantic excitement of that race or of the mad triumph when our horse won. Gran'ther cast his hat upon the ground, screaming like a steam-calliope with exultation as the sorrel swept past the judges' stand ahead of all the others, and I jumped up and down in an agony of delight which was almost more than my little body could hold.

"After that we went away, feeling that the world could hold nothing more glorious. It was five o'clock, and we decided to start back. We paid for Peggy's dinner out of the dollar we had won on the race — I say 'we,' for by that time we were welded into one organism — and we still had a dollar and a quarter left. 'While ye're about it, always go the whole hog!' said gran'ther, and we spent twenty minutes in laying out that money in trinkets for all the folks at home. Then, dusty, penniless, laden with bundles, we bestowed our exhausted bodies and our uplifted hearts in the old buckboard, and turned Peg's head toward the mountains. We did not talk much during that drive, and though I thought at the time only of the carnival of joy we had left, I can now recall every detail of the trip — how the sun sank behind Indian Mountain, a peak I had known before only through distant views; then, as we journeyed on, how the stars came out above Hemlock Mountain — our own home mountain behind our house, and later, how the fireflies filled the darkening meadows along the river below us, so that we seemed to be floating between the steady stars of heaven and their dancing, twinkling reflection in the valley.

"Gran'ther's dauntless spirit still surrounded me. I put out of mind doubts of our reception at home, and lost myself in delightful ruminatings on the splendors of the day. At first, every once in a while, gran'ther made a brief remark, such as, ' 'Twas the hind-quarters of the sorrel I bet on. He was the only one in the hull kit and bilin' of 'em that his quarters didn't fall away'; or, 'You needn't tell *me* that them Siamese twins ain't unpinned every night as separate as you and me!' But later on, as the damp evening air began to bring on his asthma, he subsided into silence, only broken by great gasping coughs.

"These were heard by the anxious, heart-sick watchers at home, and, as old Peg stumbled wearily up the hill, father came running down to meet us. 'Where you be'n?' he demanded, his face pale and stern in the light of his lantern. 'We be'n to the county fair!' croaked gran'ther with a last flare of triumph, and fell over sideways against me. Old Peg stopped short, hanging her head as if she, too, were at the limit of her strength. I was frightfully tired myself, and frozen with terror of what father would say. Gran'ther's collapse was the last straw. I began to cry loudly, but father ignored my distress with an indifference which cut me to the heart. He lifted gran'ther out of the buckboard, carrying the unconscious little old body into the house without a glance backward at me. But when I crawled down to the ground, sobbing and digging my fists into my eyes, I felt mother's arms close around me.

"'Oh, poor, naughty little Joey!' she said. 'Mother's bad, dear little boy!'"

Professor Mallory stopped short.

"Perhaps that's something else I'll know again in heaven," he said soberly, and waited a moment before he went on: "Well, that was the end of our day. I was so worn out that I fell asleep over my supper, in spite of the excitement in the house about sending for a doctor for gran'ther, who was, so one of my awe-struck sisters told me, having some kind of 'fits.' Mother must have put me to bed, for the next thing I remember, she was shaking me by the shoulder and saying, 'Wake up, Joey. Your great-grandfather wants to speak to you. He's been suffering terribly all night, and the doctor think's he's dying.'

"I followed her into gran'ther's room, where the family was assembled about the bed. Gran'ther lay drawn up in a ball, groaning so dreadfully that I felt a chill like cold water at the roots of my hair; but a moment or two after I came in, all at once he gave a great sigh and relaxed, stretching out his legs and laying his arms down on the coverlid. He looked at me and attempted a smile.

"'Well, it was wuth it, warn't it, Joey?' he said gallantly, and closed his eyes peacefully to sleep."

"Did he die?" asked the younger professor, leaning forward eagerly.

"Die? Gran'ther Pendleton? Not much! He came tottering down to breakfast the next morning, as white as an old ghost, with no voice left, his legs trembling under him, but he kept the whole family an hour and a half at the table, telling them in a loud whisper all about the fair, until father said really he would have to take us to the one next year. Afterward he sat out on the porch watching old Peg graze around the yard. I thought he was in one of his absent-minded fits, but when I came out, he called me to him, and, setting his lips to my ear, he whispered:

"'An' the seventh is a-goin' down-hill fast, so I hear!' He chuckled to himself over this for some time, wagging his head feebly, and then he said: 'I tell ye, Joey, I've lived a long time, and I've larned a lot about the way folks is made.

## The Heyday of the Blood

The trouble with most of 'em is, they're 'fraid-cats! As Jeroboam Warner used to say — he was in the same rigiment with me in 1812 — the only way to manage this business of livin' is to give a whoop and let her rip! If ye just about half-live, ye just the same as half-die; and if ye spend yer time half-dyin', some day ye turn in and die all over, without rightly meanin' to at all — just a kind o' bad habit ye've got yerself inter.' Gran'ther fell into a meditative silence for a moment. 'Jeroboam, he said that the evenin' before the battle of Lundy's Lane, and he got killed the next day. Some live, and some die; but folks that live all over die happy, anyhow! Now I tell you what's my motto, an' what I've lived to be eighty-eight on —— "

Professor Mallory stood up and, towering over the younger man, struck one hand into the other as he cried: " This was the motto he told me: 'Live while you live, and then die and be done with it!'"

### QUESTIONS

1. What do you think of the way the story opens?
2. How does the older man catch the interest of the younger?
3. What is meant by " Woodchuck day " ?
4. How is the reader at once interested in gran'ther? in Joey?
5. Is Joey a " natural " boy? Explain.
6. Do you detect any plot? Explain.
7. Is the emphasis on local color or character? Explain.
8. Did you expect gran'ther to die?
9. If he had, would there have been any point to the story?
10. What is the point, finally, of this story?
11. What do you think of it, in a general way?
12. Did the younger professor profit by hearing it, do you think? Explain.

### SUBJECTS FOR COMPOSITION

1. Describe gran'ther and Joey driving to the fair.
2. My Grandfather's Favorite Story.
3. Adventures at the County Fair.
4. Joey at the fair twenty years later.

### VOLUMES OF STORIES BY DOROTHY CANFIELD

*Hillsboro People*
*The Real Motive*
*Home Fires in France*

*The Day of Glory*
*Raw Material*
*Basque People*

## ANZIA YEZIERSKA
### (1885–    )

THE story "Hunger," reprinted from *Hungry Hearts,* is one of a number of stories based upon direct observation or personal experience of the author. There have been other writers who drew their material from immigrants, but when Miss Yezierska's stories first began to appear in the magazines in 1918 it was evident that the subject had not been exhausted. Poverty and wretchedness in the ghetto and other immigrant sections were familiar themes to readers, and these are not absent from Miss Yezierska's stories. But she showed a new aspect of this old subject by frank personality in voicing her own ambitions and ideals in the process of being Americanized. With the utmost persistency and sincerity, she has continued her drive on what she feels to be the only solution for the immigrant problem, that of providing the means by which the newcomers will be able to realize their dreams of America as the Promised Land.

That sounds simple enough. But the facts are far otherwise, as Miss Yezierska knows, for she was born in Russia in 1885, and came to America with her immigrant parents in 1901. When she was compelled to strike out for herself she had little knowledge of English, and experienced all the hardships that fall to the lot of the friendless foreigner. She did housework in an Americanized Russian family, but one month was all she could stand. She left, not because of the work but because of the snobbishness of the newly-rich foreigner. Her next job was sewing on buttons in a basement "kept by an old wrinkled woman who looked like a witch." From there she graduated into what she calls "a regular factory job," of the kind described in "Hunger." In the meanwhile she studied the English language and read much, constantly feeling that she had within herself something crying for expression, something that the American reader ought to know, something that would be appreciated if only she could put it into the proper form.

In 1918 she began to write her stories of life in the East Side of New York. The following year she had the satisfaction of having "The Fat of the Land," declared the best short story for 1919 in Mr. Edward J. O'Brien's annual collection. Since then she has written many stories and two novels, all dealing with the life that she knows best.

Miss Yezierska's stories invite comparison with those of Miss Fannie Hurst, yet no two writers could be more different, as the reader of this volume will know. Miss Hurst usually writes of the immigrant and his problems after he has become Americanized, when his problems have become as American as those of Americans themselves. Her style is much more sophisticated, there is more of a conscious effort to write according to the established short story modes. Miss Yezierska, on the other hand, writes with a spontaneous naturalness that makes no effort to conceal primitive emotions. Miss Hurst adds touches of humor, while Miss Yezierska does so rarely, and never purposely. The sincerity in Miss Yezierska's work is an expression of her own personality, for she is a serious woman, and works conscientiously to create the effect of reality that she wants to convey to her readers.

## HUNGER

SHENAH PESSAH paused in the midst of scrubbing the stairs of the tenement. "Ach!" she sighed. "How can his face still burn so in me when he is so long gone? How the deadness in me flames up with life at the thought of him!"

The dark hallway seemed flooded with white radiance. She closed her eyes that she might see more vividly the beloved features. The glowing smile that healed all ills of life and changed her from the weary drudge into the vibrant creature of joy.

It was all a miracle — his coming, this young professor from one of the big colleges. He had rented a room in the very house where she was janitress so as to be near the people he was writing about. But more wonderful than all was the way he stopped to talk to her, to question her about herself as though she were his equal. What warm friendliness had prompted him to take her out of her dark basement to the library where there were books to read!

And then — that unforgettable night on the way home, when the air was poignant with spring! Only a moment — a kiss — a pressure of hands! And the world shone with light — the empty, unlived years filled with love!

She was lost in dreams of her one hour of romance when a woman elbowed her way through the dim passage, leaving behind her the smell of herring and onions.

Shenah Pessah gripped the scrubbing-brush with suppressed fury. "Meshugeneh! Did you not swear to yourself that you would tear his memory out from your heart? If he would have been only a man I could have forgotten him. But he was not a man! He was God Himself! On whatever I look shines his face!"

The white radiance again suffused her. The brush dropped from her hand. "He — he is the beating in my heart! He is the life in me — the hope in me — the breath of prayer in me! If not for him in me, then what am I? Deadness — emptiness — nothingness! You are going out of your head. You are living only on rainbows. He is no more real —

"What is real? These rags I wear? This pail? This black hole? Or him and the dreams of him?" She flung her challenge to the murky darkness.

"Shenah Pessah! A black year on you!" came the answer from the cellar below. It was the voice of her uncle, Moisheh Rifkin.

"Oi weh!" she shrugged young shoulders, wearied by joyless toil. "He's beginning with his hollering already." And she hurried down.

"You piece of earth! Worms should eat you! How long does it take you to wash up the stairs?" he stormed. "Yesterday, the eating was burned to coal; and today you forget the salt."

"What a fuss over a little less salt!"

"In the Talmud it stands a man has a right to divorce his wife for only forgetting him the salt in his soup."

"Maybe that's why Aunt Gittel went to the grave before her time — worrying how to please your taste in the mouth."

The old man's yellow, shriveled face stared up at her out of the gloom. "What has he from life? Only his pleasure in eating and going to the synagogue. How long will he live yet?" And moved by a surge of pity, "Why can't I be a little kind to him?"

"Did you chop me some herring and onions?" he interrupted harshly.

She flushed with conscious guilt. Again she wondered why ugly things and ugly smells so sickened her.

"What don't you forget?" His voice hammered upon her ears. "No care lays in your head. You're only dreaming in the air."

Her compassion was swept away in a wave of revolt that left her trembling. "I can't no more stand it from you! Get yourself somebody else!" She was surprised at her sudden spirit.

"You big mouth, you! That's your thanks for saving you from hunger."

"Two years already I'm working the nails off my fingers and you didn't give me a cent."

"Beggerin! Money yet, you want? The minute you get enough to eat you turn up your head with freshness. Are you used to anything from home? What were you out there in Savel? The dirt under people's feet. You're already forgetting how you came off from the ship — a bundle of rags full of holes. If you lived in Russia a hundred years would you have lived to wear a pair of new shoes on your feet?"

"Other girls come naked and with nothing to America and they work themselves up. Everybody gets wages in America ——"

"Americanerin! Didn't I spend out enough money on your ship-ticket to have a little use from you? A thunder should strike you!"

Shenah Pessah's eyes flamed. Her broken finger-nails pierced the callous flesh of her hands. So this was the end — the awakening of her dreams of America! Her memory went back to the time her ship-ticket came. In her simple faith she had really believed that they wanted her — her father's brother and his wife who had come to the new world before ever she was born. She thought they wanted to give her a chance for happiness, for life and love. And then she came — to find the paralytic aunt — housework — janitor's drudgery. Even after her aunt's death, she had gone on uncomplainingly, till her uncle's nagging had worn down her last shred of self-control.

"It's the last time you'll holler on me!" she cried. "You'll never see my face again if I got to go begging in the street." Seizing her shawl, she rushed out. "Woe is me! Bitter is me! For what is my life? Why didn't the ship go under and drown me before I came to America?"

Through the streets, like a maddened thing, she raced, not knowing where she was going, not caring. "For what should I keep on suffering? Who needs me? Who wants me? I got nobody — nobody!"

And then the vision of the face she worshiped flashed before her. His beautiful kindness that had once warmed her into new life breathed over her again. "Why did he ever come but to lift me out of my darkness into his light?"

Instinctively her eyes sought the rift of blue above the tenement roofs and were caught by a boldly printed placard: " HANDS WANTED." It was as though the sign swung open on its hinges like a door and arms stretched out inviting her to enter. From the sign she looked to her own hands — vigorous, young hands — made strong through toil.

Hope leaped within her. " Maybe I got yet luck to have it good in this world. Ach! God from the sky! I'm so burning to live — to work myself up for a somebody! And why not? " With clenched fist she smote her bosom. " Ain't everything possible in the new world? Why is America but to give me the chance to lift up my head with everybody alike? "

Her feet scarcely touched the steps as she ran up. But when she reached the huge, iron door of Cohen Brothers, a terror seized her. " Oi weh! They'll give a look on my greenhorn rags, and down I go —— For what are you afraid, you fool? " she commanded herself. " You come not to beg. They need hands. Don't the sign say so? And you got good, strong hands that can turn over the earth with their strength. America is before you. You'll begin to earn money. You'll dress yourself up like a person and men will fall on their knees to make love to you — even him — himself! "

All fear had left her. She flung open the door and beheld the wonder of a factory — people — people — seas of bent heads and busy hands of people — the whir of machinery — flying belts — the clicking clatter of whirling wheels — all seemed to blend and fuse into one surging song of hope — of new life — a new world — America!

A man, his arms heaped with a bundle of shirts, paused at sight of the radiant face. Her ruddy cheeks, the film of innocence shining out of eyes that knew no guile, carried him back to the green fields and open plains of his native Russia.

" Her mother's milk is still fresh on her lips," he murmured, as his gaze enveloped her.

The bundle slipped and fell to her feet. Their eyes met in spontaneous recognition of common race. With an embarrassed laugh they stooped to gather up the shirts.

" I seen downstairs hands wanted," came in a faltering voice.

" Then you're looking for work? " he questioned with keen

interest. She was so different from the others he had known in his five years in this country. He was seized with curiosity to know more.

"You ain't been long in America?" His tone was an unconscious caress.

"Two years already," she confessed. "But I ain't so green like I look," she added quickly, overcome by the old anxiety.

"Trust yourself on me," Sam Arkin assured her. "I'm a feller that knows himself on a person first off. I'll take you to the office myself. Wait only till I put away these things."

Grinning with eagerness, he returned and together they sought the foreman.

"Good luck to you! I hope you'll be pushed up soon to my floor," Sam Arkin encouraged, as he hurried back to his machine.

Because of the rush of work and the scarcity of help, Shenah Pessah was hired without delay. Atremble with excitement, she tiptoed after the foreman as he led the way into the workroom.

"Here, Sadie Kranz, is another learner for you." He addressed a big-bosomed girl, the most skillful worker in the place.

"Another greenhorn with a wooden head!" she whispered to her neighbor as Shenah Pessah removed her shawl. "Gevalt! All these greenhorn hands tear the bread from our mouths by begging to work so cheap."

But the dumb appeal of the immigrant stirred vague memories in Sadie Kranz. As she watched her run her first seam, she marveled at her speed. "I got to give it to you, you have a quick head." There was conscious condescension in her praise.

Shenah Pessah lifted a beaming face. "How kind it was from you to learn me! You good heart!"

No one had ever before called Sadie Kranz "good heart." The words lingered pleasantly.

"Ut! I like to help anybody, so long it don't cost me nothing. I get paid by the week anyhow," she half apologized.

Shenah Pessah was so thrilled with the novelty of the work, the excitement of mastering the intricacies of her machine, that she did not realize that the day was passed until the bell rang, the machines came to a halt, and the "hands" made a wild rush for the cloak-room.

"Oi weh! Is it a fire?" Shenah Pessah blanched with dread.

Loud laughter quelled her fears. "Greenie! It's six o'clock. Time to go home," chorused the voices.

"Home?" The cry broke from her. "Where will I go? I got no home." She stood bewildered, in the fast-dwindling crowd of workers. Each jostling by her had a place to go. Of them all, she alone was friendless, shelterless!

"Help me find a place to sleep!" she implored, seizing Sadie Kranz by the sleeve of her velvet coat. "I got no people, I ran away."

Sadie Kranz narrowed her eyes at the girl. A feeling of pity crept over her at sight of the outstretched, hungry hands.

"I'll fix you by me for the while." And taking the shawl off the shelf, she tossed it to the forlorn bundle of rags. "Come along. You must be starved for some eating."

As Shenah Pessah entered the dingy hall-room which Sadie Kranz called home, its chill and squalor carried her back to the janitor's basement she had left that morning. In silence she watched her companion prepare the hot dogs and potatoes on the oil-stove atop the trunk. Such pressing sadness weighed upon her that she turned from even the smell of food.

"My heart pulls me so to go back to my uncle." She swallowed hard her crust of black bread. "He's so used to have me help him. What'll he do — alone?"

"You got to look out for yourself in this world." Sadie Kranz gesticulated with a hot potato. "With your quickness, you got a chance to make money and buy clothes. You can go to shows — dances. And who knows — maybe meet a man to get married."

"Married? You know how it burns in every girl to get herself married — that's how it burns in me to work myself up for a person."

"Ut! For what need you to work yourself up. Better marry yourself up to a rich feller and you're fixed for life."

"But him I want — he ain't just a man. He is ——" She

paused seeking for words and a mist of longing softened the heavy peasant features. "He is the golden hills on the sky. I'm as far from him as the earth is from the stars."

"Yok! Why wills itself in you the stars?" her companion ridiculed between swallows.

Shenah Pessah flung out her hands with Jewish fervor. "Can I help it what's in my heart? It always longs in me for the higher. Maybe he has long ago forgotten me, but only one hope drives in me like madness — to make myself alike to him."

"I'll tell you the truth," laughed Sadie Kranz, fishing in the pot for the last frankfurter. "You are a little out of your head — plain mehsugeh."

"Mehsugeh?" Shenah Pessah rose to her feet vibrant with new resolve. "Mehsugeh?" she challenged, her peasant youth afire with ambition. "I'll yet show the world what's in me. I'll not go back to my uncle — till it rings with my name in America."

She entered the factory, the next day, with a light in her face, a sureness in her step that made all pause in wonder. "Look only! How high she holds herself her head! Has the matchmaker promised her a man?"

Then came her first real triumph. Shenah Pessah was raised above old hands who had been in the shop for years and made assistant to Sam Arkin, the man who had welcomed her that first day in the factory. As she was shown to the bench beside him, she waited expectantly for a word of welcome. None came. Instead, he bent the closer to his machine and the hand that held the shirt trembled as though he were cold, though the hot color flooded his face.

Resolutely, she turned to her work. She would show him how skillful she had become in those few weeks. The seams sped under her lightning touch when a sudden clatter startled her. She jumped up terror-stricken.

"The belt! The belt slipped! But it's nothing, little bird," Sam Arkin hastened to assure her. "I'll fix it." And then the quick warning, "Sh-h! The foreman is coming!"

Accustomed to her uncle's harsh bickering, this man's gentleness overwhelmed her. There was something she longed to say that trembled on her lips, but her voice refused to come.

Sam Arkin, too, was inarticulate. He felt he must talk to her, must know more of her. Timidly he touched her sleeve. "Lunch-time — here — wait for me," he whispered, as the foreman approached.

A shrill whistle — the switch thrown — the slowing-down of the machines, then the deafening hush proclaiming noon. Followed the scraping of chairs, raucous voices, laughter, and the rush on the line to reach the steaming cauldron. One by one, as their cups of tea were filled, the hungry workers dispersed into groups. Seated on window-sills, table-tops, machines, and bales of shirts, they munched black bread and herring and sipped tea from saucers. And over all rioted the acrid odor of garlic and onions.

Rebecca Feist, the belle of the shop, pulled up the sleeve of her georgette waist and glanced down at her fifty-nine-cent silk stocking. "A lot it pays for a girl to kill herself to dress stylish. Give only a look on Sam Arkin, how stuck he is on that new hand."

There followed a chorus of voices. "Such freshness! We been in the shop so long and she just gives a come-in and grabs the cream as if it's coming to her."

"It's her innocent-looking baby eyes that fools him in ——"

"Innocent! Pfui! These make-believe innocent girls! Leave it to them! They know how to shine themselves up to a feller!"

Bleemah Levine, a stoop-shouldered, old hand, grown gray with the grayness of unrelieved drudgery, cast a furtive look in the direction of the couple. "Ach! The little bit of luck! Not looks, not smartness, but only luck, and the world falls to your feet." Her lips tightened with envy. "It's her greenhorn, red cheeks ——"

Rebecca Feist glanced at herself in the mirror of her vanity bag. It was a pretty, young face, but pale and thin from undernourishment. Adroitly applying a lip-stick, she cried indignantly: "I wish I could be such a false thing like her. But only, I'm too natural — the hypocrite!"

Sadie Kranz rose to her friend's defense. "What are you falling on her like a pack of wild dogs, just because Sam Arkin gives a smile on her? He ain't marrying her yet, is he?"

"We don't say nothing against her," retorted Rebecca Feist, tapping her diamond-buckled foot, "only, she pushes herself too much. Give her a finger and she'll grab your whole hand. Is there a limit to the pushings of such a green animal? Only a while ago, she was a learner, a nobody, and soon she'll jump over all our heads and make herself for a forelady."

Sam Arkin, seated beside Shenah Pessah on the window-sill, had forgotten that it was lunch-hour and that he was savagely hungry. "It shines so from your eyes," he beamed. "What happy thoughts lay in your head?"

"Ach! When I give myself a look around on all the people laughing and talking, it makes me so happy I'm one of them."

"Ut! These Americanerins! Their heads is only on ice-cream soda and style."

"But it makes me feel so grand to be with all these hands alike. It's as if I just got out from the choking prison into the open air of my own people."

She paused for breath — a host of memories overpowering her. "I can't give it out in words," she went on. "But just as there ain't no bottom to being poor, there ain't no bottom to being lonely. Before, everything I done was alone, by myself. My heart hurt so with hunger for people. But here, in the factory, I feel I'm with everybody together. Just the sight of people lifts me on wings in the air."

Opening her bag of lunch which had lain unheeded in her lap, she turned to him with a queer, little laugh, "I don't know why I'm so talking myself out to you ——"

"Only talk more. I want to know everything about yourself." An aching tenderness rushed out of his heart to her, and in his grave simplicity he told her how he had overheard one of the girls say that she, Shenah Pessah, looked like a "greeneh yenteh," just landed from the ship, so that he cried out, "Gottuniu! If only the doves from the sky were as beautiful!"

They looked at each other solemnly — the girl's lips parted, her eyes wide and serious.

"That first day I came to the shop, the minute I gave a look on you, I felt right away, here's somebody from home. I used to tremble so to talk to a man, but you — you — I could talk myself out to you like thinking in myself."

"You're all soft silk and fine velvet," he breathed reverently. "In this hard world, how could such fineness be?"

An embarrassed silence fell between them as she knotted and knotted her colored kerchief.

"I'll take you home? Yes?" he found voice at last.

Under lowered lashes she smiled her consent.

"I'll wait for you downstairs, closing time." And he was gone.

The noon hour was not yet over, but Shenah Pessah returned to her machine. "Shall I tell him?" she mused. "Sam Arkin understands so much, shall I tell him of this man that burns in me? If I could only give out to some one about him in my heart — it would make me a little clear in the head." She glanced at Sam Arkin furtively. "He's kind, but could he understand? I only made a fool from myself trying to tell Sadie Kranz." All at once she began to sob without reason. She ran to the cloak-room and hid from prying eyes, behind the shawls and wraps. The emptiness of all for which she struggled pressed upon her like a dead weight, dragging her down, down — the reaction of her ecstasy.

As the gong sounded, she made a desperate effort to pull herself together and returned to her work.

The six o'clock whistles still reverberated when Sam Arkin hurried down the factory stairs and out to the corner where he was to meet Shenah Pessah. He cleared his throat to greet her as she came, but all he managed was a bashful grin. She was so near, so real, and he had so much to say — if he only knew how to begin.

He cracked his knuckles and bit his fingertips, but no words came. "Ach! You yok! Why ain't you saying something?" He wrestled with his shyness in vain. The tense silence remained unbroken till they reached her house.

"I'm sorry" — Shenah Pessah colored apologetically — "but I got no place to invite you. My room is hardly big enough for a push-in of one person."

"What say you to a bite of eating with me?" he blurted.

She thought of her scant supper upstairs and would have responded eagerly, but glancing down at her clothes, she hesitated. "Could I go dressed like this in a restaurant?"

"You look grander plain, like you are, than those twisted up with style. I'll take you to the swellest restaurant on Grand Street and be proud with you!"

She flushed with pleasure. "Nu, come on, then. It's good to have a friend that knows himself on what's in you and not what's on you, but still, when I go to a place, I like to be dressed like a person so I can feel like a person."

"You'll yet live to wear diamonds that will shine up the street when you pass!" he cried.

Through streets growing black with swarming crowds of toil-released workers they made their way. Sam Arkin's thick hand rested with a lightness new to him upon the little arm tucked under his. The haggling pushcart peddlers, the newsboys screaming, "*Tageblatt, Abendblatt, Herold,*" the roaring noises of the elevated trains resounded the pæan of joy swelling his heart.

"America was good to me, but I never guessed how good till now." The words were out before he knew it. "Tell me only, what pulled you to this country?"

"What pulls anybody here? The hope for the better. People who got it good in the old world don't hunger for the new."

A mist filled her eyes at memory of her native village. "How I suffered in Savel! I never had enough to eat. I never had shoes on my feet. I had to go barefoot even in the freezing winter. But still I love it. I was born there. I love the houses and the straw roofs, the mud streets, the cows, the chickens and the goats. My heart always hurts me for what is no more."

The brilliant lights of Levy's Café brought her back to Grand Street.

"Here it is." He led her in and over to a corner table. "Chopped herring and onions for two," he ordered with a flourish.

"Ain't there some American eating on the card?" interposed Shenah Pessah.

He laughed indulgently. "If I lived in America for a hundred years I couldn't get used to the American eating. What can make the mouth so water like the taste and the smell from herring and onions?"

"There's something in me — I can't help — that so quickly takes on to the American taste. It's as if my outside skin only was Russian; the heart in me is for everything of the new world — even the eating."

"Nu, I got nothing to complain against America. I don't like the American eating, but I like the American dollar. Look only on me!" He expanded his chest. "I came to America a ragged nothing — and — see —" He exhibited a bank-book in four figures, gesticulating grandly, "And I learned in America how to sign my name!"

"Did it come hard to learn?" she asked under her breath.

"Hard?" His face purpled with excitement. "It would be easier for me to lift up this whole house on my shoulders than to make one little dot of a letter. When I took my pencil — Oi weh! The sweat would break out on my face! 'I can't, I can't!' I cried, but something in me jumped up. 'You can — you yok — you must!' — Six months, night after night, I stuck to it — and I learned to twist around the little black hooks till it means — me — Sam Arkin."

He had the rough-hewn features of the common people, but he lifted his head with the pride of a king. "Since I can write out my name, I feel I can do anything. I can sign checks, put money in the bank, or take it out without nobody to help me."

As Shenah Pessah listened, unconsciously she compared Sam Arkin, glowing with the frank conceit of the self-made man, his neglected teeth, thick, red lips, with that of the Other One — made ever more beautiful with longings and dreams.

"But in all these black years, I was always hoping to get to the golden country," Sam Arkin's voice went on, but she heard it as from afar. "Before my eyes was always the shine of the high wages and the easy money and I kept pushing myself from one city to another, and saving and saving till I saved up enough for my ship-ticket to the new world. And then when I landed here, I fell into the hands of a cockroach boss."

"A cockroach boss?" she questioned absently and reproached herself for her inattention.

"A black year on him! He was a landsman, that's how he fooled me in. He used to come to the ship with a smiling face of welcome to all the greenhorns what had nobody to go to. And then he'd put them to work in his sweatshop and sweat them into their grave."

"Don't I know it?" she cried with quickened understanding. "Just like my uncle, Moisheh Rifkin."

# Hunger

"The bloodsucker!" he gasped. "When I think how I slaved for him sixteen hours a day — for what? Nothing!"

She gently stroked his hand as one might a child in pain. He looked up and smiled gratefully.

"I want to forget what's already over. I got enough money now to start for myself — maybe a tailor-shop — and soon — I — I want to marry myself — but none of those crazy chickens for me." And he seemed to draw her unto himself by the intensity of his gaze.

Growing bolder, he exclaimed: "I got a grand idea. It's Monday and the bank is open yet till nine o'clock. I'll write over my bank-book on your name? Yes?"

"My name?" She fell back, dumbstruck.

"Yes — you — everything I only got — you — " he mumbled. "I'll give you dove's milk to drink — silks and diamonds to wear — you'll hold all my money."

She was shaken by this supreme proof of his devotion.

"But I — I can't — I got to work myself up for a person. I got a head. I got ideas. I can catch on to the Americans quicker'n lightning."

"My money can buy you everything. I'll buy you teachers. I'll buy you a piano. I'll make you for a lady. Right away you can stop from work." He leaned toward her, his eyes welling with tears of earnestness.

"Take your hard-earned money? Could I be such a beggerin?"

"God from the world! You are dearer to me than the eyes from my head! I'd give the blood from under my nails for you! I want only to work for you — to live for you — to die for you — " He was spent with the surge of his emotion.

Ach! To be loved as Sam Arkin loved! She covered her eyes, but it only pressed upon her the more. Home, husband, babies, a bread-giver for life!

And the Other — a dream — a madness that burns you up alive. "You might as well want to marry yourself to the President of America as to want him. But I can't help it. *Him and him only* I want."

She looked up again. "No — no!" she cried, cruel in the self-absorption of youth and ambition. "You can't make me for a person. It's not only that I got to go up higher, but I got to push myself up by myself, by my own strength ——"

"Nu, nu," he sobbed. "I'll not bother you with me — only give you my everything. My bank-book is more than my flesh and blood — only take it, to do what you want with it."

Her eyes deepened with humility. "I know your goodness — but there's something like a wall around me — him in my heart."

"Him?" The word hurled itself at him like a bomb-shell. He went white with pain. And even she, immersed in her own thoughts, lowered her head before the dumb suffering on his face. She felt she owed it to him to tell him.

"I wanted to talk myself out to you about him yet before. — He ain't just a man. He is all that I want to be and am not yet. He is the hunger of me for the life that ain't just eating and sleeping and slaving for bread."

She pushed back her chair and rose abruptly. "I can't be inside walls when I talk of him. I need the earth, the whole free sky to breathe when I think of him. Come out in the air."

They walked for a time before either spoke. Sam Arkin followed where she led through the crooked labyrinth of streets. The sight of the young mothers with their nursing infants pressed to their bared bosoms stabbed anew his hurt.

Shenah Pessah, blind to all but the vision that obsessed her, talked on. "All that my mother and father and my mother's mother and father ever wanted to be is in him. This fire in me, it's not just the hunger of a woman for a man — it's the hunger of all my people back of me, from all ages, for light, for the life higher!"

A veil of silence fell between them. She felt almost as if it were a sacrilege to have spoken of that which was so deeply centered within her.

Sam Arkin's face became lifeless as clay. Bowed like an old man, he dragged his leaden feet after him. The world was dead — cold — meaningless. Bank-book, money — of what use were they now? All his years of saving couldn't win her. He was suffocated in emptiness.

On they walked till they reached a deserted spot in the park. So spent was he by his sorrow that he lost the sense of time or place or that she was near.

Leaning against a tree, he stood, dumb, motionless, unutterable bewilderment in his sunken eyes.

"I lived over the hunger for bread — but this — " He clutched at his aching bosom. "Highest One, help me!" With his face to the ground he sank, prostrate.

"Sam Arkin!" She bent over him tenderly. "I feel the emptiness of words — but I got to get it out. All that you suffer I have suffered, and must yet go on suffering. I see no end. But only — there is a something — a hope — a help out — it lifts me on top of my hungry body — the hunger to make from myself a person that can't be crushed by nothing nor nobody — the life higher!"

Slowly, he rose to his feet, drawn from his weakness by the spell of her. "With one hand you throw me down and with the other you lift me up to life again. Say to me only again, your words," he pleaded, helplessly.

"Sam Arkin! Give yourself your own strength!" She shook him roughly. "I got no pity on you, no more than I got pity on me."

He saw her eyes fill with light as though she were seeing something far beyond them both. "This," she breathed, "is only the beginning of the hunger that will make from you a person who'll yet ring in America."

### QUESTIONS

1. How does the first paragraph at once suggest the atmosphere?
2. How is contrast used to intensify this atmosphere?
3. What is the real theme of this story?
4. Where does it first show?
5. What was Shenah's ambition?
6. How does it help the complication?
7. How is possible sentimentalism avoided?
8. Was Sam justified in his characterization of "Americanerins"?
9. Was his proposal in line with his character? Explain.
10. Would Rebecca Feist have accepted him on the spot? Explain.
11. Was Shenah disgusted with Sam's offer? Explain.
12. How is the theme of the story bound up in "him"?
13. Does Sam at last understand?
14. Find examples of the author's emotionalisms in style.
15. Is the atmosphere of the story depressing? Explain.

## SUBJECTS FOR COMPOSITION

1. Write a short story involving Americanization.
2. Write a sequel to the story of Shenah and Sam.
3. Tell orally something that you know about sweat shops.

## VOLUMES OF STORIES BY ANZIA YEZIERSKA

*Hungry Hearts*                      *Children of Loneliness*

# FRANK R. STOCKTON
## (1834–1902)

IN THE literary career of Frank R. Stockton there are many things that remind us of Bret Harte. Both were dissatisfied with their first name; one dropped it entirely, the other changed it from "Francis" to "Frank." They were almost exact contemporaries; both worked at other things before turning to writing; both began to write as newspaper men before achieving magazine editorships; the work of both has a distinct touch of humor; and both popularized a new variety of the short story, Harte that of local color, and Stockton that of the "trick" story. The analogy might be continued by saying that both wrote too much and that both are today almost entirely neglected with the exception of a few of their earlier stories.

About Stockton we may at once say that his chief note is humor, secured by a "trick" which keeps the reader guessing. He takes an utterly impossible situation in all seriousness and treats it as a commonplace. The charm of his stories lies in the manner of telling and the surprise at the end, almost invariably the opposite of what the reader suspects. Often he is as whimsical in his conceptions as the author of *Alice in Wonderland*. He had a romantic imagination tinged with the fantastic, always working to play some delightful joke on the reader.

Stockton was born in Philadelphia in 1834. His first literary work consisted of "wonder" stories for children, done before he had definitely decided to make writing a profession. At first he wanted to be a doctor, but he gave that up in favor of wood engraving. After some success in the juvenile magazines he accepted a newspaper position in Philadelphia. Shortly after beginning his work on the paper he had his first story accepted by a "grown-up" magazine in New York, *Scribner's*, and in that same year, 1872, he moved to New York. In that city he held various editorial positions. It was only after ten years that he felt able to depend entirely upon writing as a career.

Like Bret Harte, he enjoyed the social life of the big cities and his prestige as a popular author. Although Stockton acquired several farms, and lived on one in New Jersey, he spent part of each year, usually the winter months, in New York City. He continued to write novels and short stories in great numbers, the kind which he could do best, the kind for which he had an insatiable public. But the humorous story only too often is of an ephemeral interest, and Stockton has shared the fate of most humorists, that of being remembered for a few stories.

Of these few he is best known today for "The Lady or the Tiger?" first published in 1882. That story in its day created a sensation almost as big as that of Bret Harte's "Luck of Roaring Camp."

It is in the manner of a practical joke, except that the point is left in suspension. Its power lies in the straightforward manner of presenting an impossible situation, with all the details in mechanical perfection, but instead of the expected surprise there is the surprise of its not being " sprung " at all. It is perhaps the cleverest " trick " story in the English language.

" The Remarkable Wreck of the *Thomas Hyke*," printed here, has all the characteristic earmarks of Stockton.

# THE REMARKABLE WRECK OF THE *THOMAS HYKE*[1]

IT WAS half-past one by the clock in the office of the Registrar of Woes. The room was empty, for it was Wednesday, and the Registrar always went home early on Wednesday afternoons. He had made that arrangement when he accepted the office. He was willing to serve his fellow-citizens in any suitable position to which he might be called, but he had private interests which could not be neglected. He belonged to his country, but there was a house in the country which belonged to him; and there were a great many things appertaining to that house which needed attention, especially in pleasant summer weather. It is true he was often absent on afternoons which did not fall on the Wednesday, but the fact of his having appointed a particular time for the furtherance of his outside interests so emphasized their importance that his associates in the office had no difficulty in understanding that affairs of such moment could not always be attended to in a single afternoon of the week.

But although the large room devoted to the especial use of the Registrar was unoccupied, there were other rooms connected with it which were not in that condition. With the suite of offices to the left we have nothing to do, but will confine our attention to a moderate-sized room to the right of the Registrar's office, and connected by a door, now closed, with that large and handsomely furnished chamber. This was the office of the Clerk of Shipwrecks, and it was at present occupied by five persons. One of these was the clerk himself,

[1] From *The Christmas Wreck and Other Stories*. Copyright, 1886, 1914, by Charles Scribner's Sons. By permission of the publishers.

a man of goodly appearance, somewhere between twenty-five and forty-five years of age, and of a demeanor such as might be supposed to belong to one who had occupied a high position in state affairs, but who, by the cabals of his enemies, had been forced to resign the great operations of statesmanship which he had been directing, and who now stood, with a quite resigned air, pointing out to the populace the futile and disastrous efforts of the incompetent one who was endeavoring to fill his place. The Clerk of Shipwrecks had never fallen from such a position, having never occupied one, but he had acquired the demeanor referred to without going through the preliminary exercises.

Another occupant was a very young man, the personal clerk of the Registrar of Woes, who always closed all the doors of the office of that functionary on Wednesday afternoons, and at other times when outside interests demanded his principal's absence, after which he betook himself to the room of his friend the Shipwreck Clerk.

Then there was a middle-aged man named Mathers, also a friend of the clerk, and who was one of the eight who had made application for a sub-position in this department, which was now filled by a man who was expected to resign when a friend of his, a gentleman of influence in an interior county, should succeed in procuring the nomination as congressional representative of his district of an influential politician, whose election was considered assured in case certain expected action on the part of the administration should bring his party into power. The person now occupying the sub-position hoped then to get something better, and Mathers, consequently, was very willing, while waiting for the place, to visit the offices of the department and acquaint himself with its duties.

A fourth person was J. George Watts, a juryman by profession, who had brought with him his brother-in-law, a stranger in the city.

The Shipwreck Clerk had taken off his good coat, which he had worn to luncheon, and had replaced it by a lighter garment of linen, much bespattered with ink; and he now produced a cigar-box, containing six cigars.

"Gents," said he, "here is the fag end of a box of cigars. It's not like having the pick of the box, but they are all I have left."

Mr. Mathers, J. George Watts, and the brother-in-law each took a cigar with that careless yet deferential manner which always distinguishes the treatee from the treator; and then the box was protruded in an offhand way toward Harry Covare, the personal clerk of the Registrar; but this young man declined, saying that he preferred cigarettes, a package of which he drew from his pocket. He had very often seen that cigar-box with a Havana brand, which he himself had brought from the other room after the Registrar had emptied it, passed around with six cigars, no more nor less, and he was wise enough to know that the Shipwreck Clerk did not expect to supply him with smoking material. If that gentleman had offered to the friends who generally dropped in on him on Wednesday afternoon the paper bag of cigars sold at five cents each when bought singly, but half a dozen for a quarter of a dollar, they would have been quite as thankfully received; but it better pleased his deprecative soul to put them in an empty cigar-box, and thus throw around them the halo of the presumption that ninety-four of their imported companions had been smoked.

The Shipwreck Clerk, having lighted a cigar for himself, sat down in his revolving chair, turned his back to his desk, and threw himself into an easy cross-legged attitude, which showed that he was perfectly at home in that office. Harry Covare mounted a high stool, while the visitors seated themselves in three wooden arm-chairs. But few words had been said, and each man had scarcely tossed his first tobacco ashes on the floor when some one wearing heavy boots was heard opening an outside door and entering the Registrar's room. Harry Covare jumped down from his stool, laid his half-smoked cigarette thereon, and bounced into the next room, closing the door after him. In about a minute he returned, and the Shipwreck Clerk looked at him inquiringly.

"An old cock in a pea-jacket," said Mr. Covare, taking up his cigarette, and mounting his stool. "I told him the Registrar would be here in the morning. He said he had something to report about a shipwreck; and I told him the Registrar would be here in the morning. Had to tell him that three times, and then he went."

"School don't keep Wednesday afternoons," said Mr. J. George Watts, with a knowing smile.

"No, sir," said the Shipwreck Clerk, emphatically, changing the crossing of his legs. "A man can't keep grinding on day in and day out without breaking down. Outsiders may say what they please about it, but it can't be done. We've got to let up sometimes. People who do the work need the rest just as much as those who do the looking on."

"And more too, I should say," observed Mr. Mathers.

"Our little let-up Wednesday afternoons," modestly observed Harry Covare, "is like death; it is sure to come, while the let-ups we get other days are more like the diseases which prevail in certain areas; you can't be sure whether you're going to get them or not."

The Shipwreck Clerk smiled benignantly at this remark, and the rest laughed. Mr. Mathers had heard it before, but he would not impair the pleasantness of his relations with a future colleague by hinting that he remembered it.

"He gets such ideas from his beastly statistics," said the Shipwreck Clerk.

"Which come pretty heavy on him sometimes, I expect," observed Mr. Mathers.

"They needn't," said the Shipwreck Clerk, "if things were managed here as they ought to be. If John J. Laylor," meaning thereby the Registrar, "was the right kind of a man, you'd see things very different here from what they are now. There'd be a larger force."

"That's so," said Mr. Mathers.

"And not only that, but there'd be better buildings, and more accommodations. Were any of you ever up to Anster? Well, take a run up there some day, and see what sort of buildings the department has there. William Q. Green is a very different man from John J. Laylor. You don't see him sitting in his chair and picking his teeth the whole winter, while the representative from his district never says a word about his department from one end of a session of Congress to the other. Now if I had charge of things here, I'd make such changes that you wouldn't know the place. I'd throw two rooms off here, and a corridor and entrance door at that end of the building. I'd close up this door," pointing toward the Registrar's room, "and if John J. Laylor wanted to come in here he might go round to the end door like other people."

The thought struck Harry Covare that in that case there would be no John J. Laylor, but he would not interrupt.

"And what is more," continued the Shipwreck Clerk, "I'd

close up this whole department at twelve o'clock on Saturdays. The way things are managed now, a man has no time to attend to his own private business. Suppose I think of buying a piece of land, and want to go out and look at it, or suppose any one of you gentlemen were here and thought of buying a piece of land and wanted to go out and look at it, what are you going to do about it? You don't want to go on Sunday, and when are you going to go?"

Not one of the other gentlemen had ever thought of buying a piece of land, nor had they any reason to suppose that they ever would purchase an inch of soil unless they bought it in a flower-pot; but they all agreed that the way things were managed now there was no time for a man to attend to his own business.

"But you can't expect John J. Laylor to do anything," said the Shipwreck Clerk.

However, there was one thing which that gentleman always expected John J. Laylor to do. When the clerk was surrounded by a number of persons in hours of business, and when he had succeeded in impressing them with the importance of his functions, and the necessity of paying deferential attention to himself if they wished their business attended to, John J. Laylor would be sure to walk into the office and address the Shipwreck Clerk in such a manner as to let the people present know that he was a clerk and nothing else, and that he, the Registrar, was the head of that department. These humiliations the Shipwreck Clerk never forgot.

There was a little pause here, and then Mr. Mathers remarked:

"I should think you'd be awfully bored with the long stories of shipwrecks that the people come and tell you."

He hoped to change the conversation, because, although he wished to remain on good terms with the subordinate officers, it was not desirable that he be led to say much against John J. Laylor.

"No, sir," said the Shipwreck Clerk, "I am not bored. I did not come here to be bored, and as long as I have charge of this office I don't intend to be. The long-winded old salts who come here to report their wrecks never spin out their prosy yarns to me. The first thing I do is to let them know just what I want of them; and not an inch beyond that does a man of them go, at least while I am managing the business. There are times when John J. Laylor comes in, and puts in his oar, and wants to hear the whole story, which is pure stuff and nonsense, for John J. Laylor doesn't know anything more about a shipwreck than he does about ———"

"The endemies in the Lake George area," suggested Harry Covare.

"Yes; or any other part of his business," said the Shipwreck Clerk; "and when he takes it into his head to interfere, all business stops till some second mate of a coal-schooner has told his whole story, from his sighting land on the morning of one day to his getting ashore on it on the afternoon of the next. — Now I don't put up with any such nonsense. There's no man living that can tell me anything about shipwrecks. I've never been to sea myself, but that's not necessary; and if I had gone, it's not likely I'd been wrecked. But I've read about every kind of shipwreck that ever happened. When I first came here I took care to post myself upon these matters, because I knew it would save trouble. I have read *Robinson Crusoe*, *The Wreck of the Grosvenor*, *The Sinking of the Royal George*, and wrecks by waterspouts, tidal waves, and every other thing which would knock a ship into a cocked hat, and I've classified every sort of wreck under its proper head; and when I've found out to what class a wreck belongs, I know all about it. Now, when a man comes here to report a wreck, the first thing he has to do is just to shut down on his story, and to stand up square and answer a few questions that I put to him. In two minutes I know just what kind of shipwreck he's had; and then, when he gives me the name of his vessel, and one or two other points, he may go. I know all about that wreck, and I make a much better report of the business than he could have done if he'd stood here talking three days and three nights. The amount of money that's been saved to our tax-payers by the way I've systematized the business of this office is not to be calculated in figures."

The brother-in-law of J. George Watts knocked the ashes from the remnant of his cigar, looked contemplatively at the coal for a moment, and then remarked:

"I think you said there's no kind of shipwreck you don't know about?"

"That's what I said," replied the Shipwreck Clerk.

"I think," said the other, "I could tell you of a shipwreck, in which I was concerned, that wouldn't go into any of your classes."

The Shipwreck Clerk threw away the end of his cigar, put both his hands into his trousers pockets, stretched out his legs, and looked steadfastly at the man who had made this unwarrantable remark. Then a pitying smile stole over his countenance, and he said: "Well, sir, I'd like to hear your account of it; and before you get a quarter through I can stop you just where you are, and go ahead and tell the rest of the story myself."

"That's so," said Harry Covare. "You'll see him do it just as sure pop as a spread rail bounces the engine."

"Well, then," said the brother-in-law of J. George Watts, "I'll tell it." And he began:

"It was just two years ago, the first of this month, that I sailed for South America in the *Thomas Hyke*."

At this point the Shipwreck Clerk turned and opened a large book at the letter T.

"That wreck wasn't reported here," said the other, "and you won't find it in your book."

"At Anster, perhaps?" said the Shipwreck Clerk, closing the volume, and turning round again.

"Can't say about that," replied the other. "I've never been to Anster, and haven't looked over their books."

"Well, you needn't want to," said the clerk. "They've got good accommodations at Anster, and the Registrar has some ideas of the duties of his post, but they have no such system of wreck reports as we have here."

"Very like," said the brother-in-law. And he went on with his story. "The *Thomas Hyke* was a small iron steamer of six hundred tons, and she sailed from Ulford for Valparaiso with a cargo principally of pig iron."

"Pig iron for Valparaiso?" remarked the Shipwreck Clerk. And then he knitted his brows thoughtfully, and said, "Go on."

"She was a new vessel," continued the narrator, "and built with water-tight compartments; rather uncommon for a vessel of her class, but so she was. I am not a sailor, and don't know anything about ships. I went as passenger, and there was another one named William Anderson, and his son

Sam, a boy about fifteen years old. We were all going to Valparaiso on business. I don't remember just how many days we were out, nor do I know just where we were, but it was somewhere off the coast of South America, when, one dark night, with a fog besides, for aught I know, for I was asleep, we ran into a steamer coming north. How we managed to do this, with room enough on both sides for all the ships in the world to pass, I don't know; but so it was. When I got on deck the other vessel had gone on, and we never saw anything more of her. Whether she sunk or got home is something I can't tell. But we pretty soon found that the *Thomas Hyke* had some of the plates in her bow badly smashed, and she took in water like a thirsty dog. The captain had the forward water-tight bulkhead shut tight, and the pumps set to work, but it was no use. That forward compartment just filled up with water, and the *Thomas Hyke* settled down with her bow clean under. Her deck was slanting forward like the side of a hill, and the propeller was lifted up so that it wouldn't have worked even if the engine had been kept going. The captain had the masts cut away, thinking this might bring her up some, but it didn't help much. There was a pretty heavy sea on, and the waves came rolling up the slant of the deck like the surf on the seashore. The captain gave orders to have all the hatches battened down so that water couldn't get in, and the only way by which anybody could go below was by the cabin door, which was far aft. This work of stopping up all openings in the deck was a dangerous business, for the decks sloped right down into the water, and if anybody had slipped, away he'd have gone into the ocean, with nothing to stop him; but the men made a line fast to themselves, and worked away with a good will, and soon got the deck and the house over the engine as tight as a bottle. The smoke-stack, which was well forward, had been broken down by a spar when the masts had been cut, and as the waves washed into the hole that it left, the captain had this plugged up with old sails, well fastened down. It was a dreadful thing to see the ship a-lying with her bows clean under water, and her stern sticking up. If it hadn't been for her water-tight compartments that were uninjured, she would have gone down to the bottom as slick as a whistle. On the afternoon of the day after the collision the wind fell,

and the sea soon became pretty smooth. The captain was
quite sure that there would be no trouble about keeping us
afloat until some ship came along and took us off. Our flag
was flying, upside down, from a pole in the stern; and if
anybody saw a ship making such a guy of herself as the
*Thomas Hyke* was then doing, they'd be sure to come to see
what was the matter with her, even if she had no flag of distress flying. We tried to make ourselves as comfortable as we
could, but this wasn't easy with everything on such a dreadful
slant. But that night we heard a rumbling and grinding
noise down in the hold, and the slant seemed to get worse.
Pretty soon the captain roused all hands, and told us that
the cargo of pig iron was shifting and sliding down to the
bow, and that it wouldn't be long before it would break
through all the bulkheads, and then we'd fill and go to the
bottom like a shot. He said we must all take to the boats,
and get away as quick as we could. It was an easy matter
launching the boats. They didn't lower them outside from
the davits, but they just let 'em down on deck and slid 'em
along forward into the water, and then held 'em there with
a rope until everything was ready to start. They launched
three boats, put plenty of provisions and water in 'em, and
then everybody began to get aboard. But William Anderson,
and me, and his son Sam, couldn't make up our minds to get
into those boats and row out on the dark, wide ocean. They
were the biggest boats we had, but still they were little things
enough. The ship seemed to us to be a good deal safer, and
more likely to be seen when day broke, than those three
boats, which might be blown off if the wind rose, nobody
knew where. It seemed to us that the cargo had done all
the shifting it intended to, for the noise below had stopped;
and, altogether, we agreed that we'd rather stick to the ship
than go off in those boats. The captain, he tried to make us
go, but we wouldn't do it; and he told us if we chose to stay
behind and be drowned it was our affair, and he couldn't
help it; and then he said there was a small boat aft, and we'd
better launch her, and have her ready in case things should
get worse, and we should make up our minds to leave the
vessel. He and the rest then rowed off so as not to be caught
in the vortex if the steamer went down, and we three stayed
aboard. We launched the small boat in the way we'd seen

the others launched, being careful to have ropes tied to us while we were doing it; and we put things aboard that we thought we should want. Then we went into the cabin and waited for morning. It was a queer kind of a cabin, with a floor inclined like the roof of a house, but we sat down in the corners, and were glad to be there. The swinging lamp was burning, and it was a good deal more cheerful in there than it was outside. But, about daybreak, the grinding and rumbling down below began again, and the bow of the *Thomas Hyke* kept going down more and more; and it wasn't long before the forward bulkhead of the cabin, which was what you might call its front wall when everything was all right, was under our feet, as level as a floor, and the lamp was lying close against the ceiling that it was hanging from. You may be sure that we thought it was time to get out of that. There were benches with arms to them fastened to the floor, and by these we climbed up to the foot of the cabin stairs, which, being turned bottom upward, we went down in order to get out. When we reached the cabin door we saw part of the deck below us, standing up like the side of a house that is built in the water, as they say the houses in Venice are. We had made our boat fast to the cabin door by a long line, and now we saw her floating quietly on the water, which was very smooth, and about twenty feet below us. We drew her up as close under us as we could, and then we let the boy Sam down by a rope, and after some kicking and swinging he got into her; and then he took the oars, and kept her right under us while we scrambled down by the ropes which we had used in getting her ready. As soon as we were in the boat we cut her rope and pulled away as hard as we could; and when we got to what we thought was a safe distance we stopped to look at the *Thomas Hyke*. You never saw such a ship in all your born days. Two-thirds of the hull was sunk in the water, and she was standing straight up and down with the stern in the air, her rudder up as high as the topsail ought to be, and the screw propeller looking like the wheel on the top of one of these windmills that they have in the country for pumping up water. Her cargo had shifted so far forward that it had turned her right up on end, but she couldn't sink, owing to the air in the compartments that the water hadn't gotten into; and on the top of the whole thing was the distress flag flying from the pole which stuck out over the stern. It was broad daylight, but not a thing did we see of the other boats. We'd supposed that they wouldn't row very far, but would lay off at a safe distance until daylight; but they must have been scared and rowed farther than they intended. Well, sir, we stayed in that boat all day, and watched the *Thomas Hyke;* but she just kept as she was, and didn't seem to sink an inch. There was no use of rowing away, for we had no place to row to; and besides, we thought that passing ships would be much more likely to see that stern sticking high in the air than our little boat. We had enough to eat, and at night two of us slept while the other watched, dividing off the time, and taking turns to this. In the morning there was the *Thomas Hyke* standing stern up just as before. There was a long swell on the ocean now, and she'd rise and lean over a little on each wave, but she'd come up again just as straight as before. That night passed as the last one had, and in the morning we found we'd drifted a good deal farther from the *Thomas Hyke,* but she was floating just as she had been, like a big buoy that's moored over a sand-bar. We couldn't see a sign of the boats, and we about gave them up. We had our breakfast, which was a pretty poor meal, being nothing but hard-tack and what was left of a piece of boiled beef. After we'd sat for a while doing nothing, but feeling mighty uncomfortable, William Anderson said: 'Look here, do you know that I think we would be three fools to keep on shivering all night and living on hard-tack in the day-time, when there's plenty on that vessel for us to eat, and to keep us warm. If she's floated that way for two days and two nights, there's no knowing how much longer she'll float, and we might as well go on board and get the things we want as not.' 'All right,' said I, for I was tired of doing nothing, and Sam was as willing as anybody. So we rowed up to the steamer, and stopped close to the deck, which, as I said before, was standing straight up out of the water like the wall of a house. The cabin door, which was the only opening into her, was about twenty feet above us, and the ropes which we had tied to the rails of the stairs inside were still hanging down. Sam was an active youngster, and he managed to climb up one of these ropes; but when he got to the door he drew it up and tied knots in it about a foot apart, and then he let it down to us, for neither William Anderson nor me could go up a rope hand over hand without knots or something to hold on to. As it was, we had a lot of bother getting up, but we did it at last, and then we walked up the stairs, treading on the front part of each step instead of the top of it, as we would have done if the stairs had been in their proper position. When we got to the floor of the cabin, which was now perpendicular like a wall, we had to clamber down by means of the furniture, which was screwed fast, until we reached the bulkhead, which was now the floor of the cabin. Close to this bulkhead was a small room which was the steward's pantry, and here we found lots of things to eat, but all jumbled up in a way that made us laugh. The boxes of biscuits and the tin cans, and a lot of bottles in wicker covers, were piled up on one end of the room, and everything in the lockers and drawers was jumbled together. William Anderson and me set to work to get out what we thought we'd want, and we told Sam to climb up into some of the state-rooms, of which there were four on each side of the cabin, and get some blankets to keep us warm, as well as a few sheets, which we thought we could rig up for an awning to the boat; for the days were just as hot as the nights were cold. When we'd collected what we wanted, William Anderson and me climbed into our own rooms, thinking we'd each pack a valise with what we most wanted to save of our clothes and things; and while we were doing this, Sam called out to us that it was raining. He was sitting at the cabin door looking out. I first thought to tell him to shut the door so's to keep the rain from coming in; but when I thought how things really were, I laughed at the idea. There was a sort of little house built over the entrance to the cabin, and in one end of it was the door; and in the way the ship now was the open doorway was underneath the little house, and of course no rain could come in. Pretty soon we heard the rain pouring down, beating on the stern of the vessel like hail. We got to the stairs and looked out. The rain was falling in perfect sheets, in a way you never see except round about the tropics. 'It's a good thing we're inside,' said William Anderson, ' for if we'd been out in this rain we'd been drowned in the boat.' I agreed with him, and we made up our minds to stay where we were until the rain was over.

Well, it rained about four hours; and when it stopped, and we looked out, we saw our little boat nearly full of water, and sunk so deep that if one of us had stepped on her she'd have gone down, sure. 'Here's a pretty kittle of fish,' said William Anderson; 'there's nothing for us to do now but to stay where we are.' I believe in his heart he was glad of that, for if ever a man was tired of a little boat, William Anderson was tired of that one we'd been in for two days and two nights. At any rate there was no use talking about it, and we set to work to make ourselves comfortable. We got some mattresses and pillows out of the state-rooms, and when it began to get dark we lighted the lamp, which we had filled with sweet-oil from a flask in the pantry, not finding any other kind, and we hung it from the railing of the stairs. We had a good night's rest, and the only thing that disturbed me was William Anderson lifting up his head every time he turned over, and saying how much better this was than that blasted little boat. The next morning we had a good breakfast, even making some tea with a spirit lamp we found, using brandy instead of alcohol. William Anderson and I wanted to get into the captain's room, which was near the stern, and pretty high up, so as to see if there was anything there that we ought to get ready to save when a vessel should come along and pick us up; but we were not good at climbing, like Sam, and we didn't see how we could get up there. Sam said he was sure he had once seen a ladder in the compartment just forward of the bulkhead, and as William was very anxious to get up to the captain's room, we let the boy go and look for it. There was a sliding door in the bulkhead under our feet, and we opened this far enough to let Sam get through; and he scrambled down like a monkey into the next compartment, which was light enough, although the lower half of it, which was next to the engine-room, was under the water-line. Sam actually found a ladder with hooks at one end of it, and while he was handing it up to us, which was very hard to do, for he had to climb up on all sorts of things, he let it topple over, and the end with the iron hooks fell against the round glass of one of the port-holes. The glass was very thick and strong, but the ladder came down very heavy and shivered it. As bad luck would have it, this window was below the water-line, and the water came rushing in, in a big spout. We chucked blankets down to Sam for him to stop up the hole, but 'twas of no use; for it was hard for him to get at the window, and when he did the water came in with such force that he couldn't get a blanket into the hole. We were afraid he'd be drowned down there, and told him to come out as quick as he could. He put up the ladder again, and hooked it on to the door in the bulkhead, and we held it while he climbed up. Looking down through the doorway, we saw, by the way the water was pouring in at the opening, that it wouldn't be long before that compartment was filled up; so we shoved the door to and made it all tight, and then said William Anderson: 'The ship'll sink deeper and deeper as that fills up, and the water may get up to the cabin door, and we must go and make that as tight as we can.' Sam had pulled the ladder up after him, and this we found of great use in getting to the foot of the cabin stairs. We shut the cabin door, and locked and bolted it; and as it fitted pretty tight, we didn't think it would let in much water if the ship sunk that far. But over the top of the cabin stairs were a couple of folding doors, which shut down horizontally when the ship was in its proper position, and which were only used in very bad, cold weather. These we pulled to and fastened tight, thus having a double protection against the water. Well, we didn't get this done any too soon, for the water did come up to the cabin door, and a little trickled in from the outside door, and through the cracks in the inner one. But we went to work and stopped these up with strips from the sheets, which we crammed well in with our pocket knives. Then we sat down on the steps, and waited to see what would happen next. The doors of all the state-rooms were open, and we could see through the thick plate-glass windows in them, which were all shut tight, that the ship was sinking more and more as the water came in. Sam climbed up into one of the after state-rooms, and said the outside water was nearly up to the stern; and pretty soon we looked up to the two port-holes in the stern, and saw that they were covered with water; and as more and more water could be seen there, and as the light came through less easily, we knew that we were sinking under the surface of the ocean. 'It's a mighty good thing,' said William Anderson, 'that no water can get in here.' William had a hopeful kind of mind, and always looked on the bright side of things; but I must say that I was dreadfully scared when I looked through those stern windows and saw water instead of sky. It began to get duskier and duskier as we sank lower and lower, but still we could see pretty well, for it's astonishing how much light comes down through the water. After a little while we noticed that the light remained about the same; and then William Anderson, he sings out: 'Hooray, we've stopped sinking!' 'What difference does that make?' says I. 'We must be thirty or forty feet under water, and more yet for aught I know.' 'Yes, that may be,' said he; 'but it is clear that all the water has got into that compartment that can get in, and we have sunk just as far down as we are going.' 'But that don't help matters,' said I; 'thirty or forty feet under water is just as bad as a thousand to a drowning man.' 'Drowning!' said William; 'how are you going to be drowned? No water can get in here.' 'Nor no air, either,' said I; 'and people are drowned for want of air, as I take it.' 'It would be a queer sort of thing,' said William, 'to be drowned in the ocean and yet stay as dry as a chip. But it's no use being worried about air. We've got air enough here to last us for ever so long. This stern compartment is the biggest in the ship, and it's got lots of air in it. Just think of that hold! It must be nearly full of air. The stern compartment of the hold has nothing in it but sewing-machines. I saw 'em loading her. The pig-iron was mostly amidships, or at least forward of this compartment. Now, there's no kind of a cargo that'll accommodate as much air as sewing-machines. They're packed in wooden frames, not boxes, and don't fill up half the room they take. There's air all through and around 'em. It's a very comforting thing to think that the hold isn't filled up solid with bales of cotton or wheat in bulk.' It might be comforting, but I couldn't get much good out of it. And now Sam, who'd been scrambling all over the cabin to see how things were going on, sung out that the water was leaking in a little again at the cabin door, and around some of the iron frames of the windows. 'It's a lucky thing,' said William Anderson, 'that we didn't sink any deeper, or the pressure of the water would have burst in those heavy glasses. And what we've got to do now is to stop up all the cracks. The more we work, the livelier we'll feel.' We tore off more strips of sheets and went all round, stopping up cracks wherever we found them. 'It's fortunate,' said William Anderson, 'that Sam found that ladder, for we would have had hard work getting to the windows of the stern state-rooms without it; but by resting it on the bottom step of the stairs, which now happens to be the top one, we can get to any part of the cabin.' I couldn't help thinking that if Sam hadn't found the ladder it would have been a good deal better for us; but I didn't want to damp William's spirits, and I said nothing.

"And now I beg your pardon, sir," said the narrator, addressing the Shipwreck Clerk, "but I forgot that you said you'd finish this story yourself. Perhaps you'd like to take it up just here?"

The Shipwreck Clerk seemed surprised, and had, apparently, forgotten his previous offer. "Oh, no," he said, "tell your own story. This is not a matter of business."

"Very well, then," said the brother-in-law of J. George Watts, "I'll go on. We made everything as tight as we could, and then we got our supper, having forgotten all about dinner, and being very hungry. We didn't make any tea, and we didn't light the lamp, for we knew that would use up air; but we made a better meal than three people sunk out of sight in the ocean had a right to expect. 'What troubles me most,' said William Anderson, as he turned in, 'is the fact that if we are forty feet under water, our flag-pole must be covered up. Now, if the flag was sticking out, upside down, a ship sailing by would see it and would know there was something wrong.' 'If that's all that troubles you,' said I, 'I guess you'll sleep easy. And if a ship was to see the flag, I wonder how they'd know we were down here, and how they'd get us out if they did!' 'Oh, they'd manage it,' said William Anderson; 'trust those sea-captains for that.' And then he went to sleep. The next morning the air began to get mighty disagreeable in the part of the cabin where we were, and then William Anderson he says: 'What we've got to do is to climb up into the stern state-rooms, where the air is purer. We can come down here to get our meals, and then go up again to breathe comfortable.' 'And what are we going to do when the air up there gets foul?' says I to William, who seemed to be making arrangements for spending the summer in our present quarters. 'Oh, that'll be all right,' said he. 'It don't do to be extravagant with air any more than with anything else. When we've used up all there is in this cabin, we can bore holes through the floor into the hold and let in air from there. If we're economical, there'll be enough to last for dear knows how long.' We passed the night each in a state-room, sleeping on the end wall instead of the berth, and it wasn't till the afternoon of the next day that the air of the cabin got so bad we thought we'd have some fresh; so we went down on the bulkhead, and with an auger that we found in the pantry, we bored three holes, about a yard apart in the cabin floor, which was now one of the walls of the room, just as the bulkhead was the floor, and the stern end, where the two round windows were, was the ceiling or roof. We each took a hole, and I tell you it was pleasant to breathe the air which came in from the hold. 'Isn't this jolly?' said William Anderson. 'And we ought to be mighty glad that hold wasn't loaded with codfish or soap. But there's nothing that smells better than new sewing-machines that haven't ever been used, and this air is pleasant enough for anybody.' By William's advice we made three plugs, by which we stopped up the holes when we thought we'd had air enough for the present. 'And now,' says he, 'we needn't climb up into those awkward state-rooms any more. We can just stay down here and be comfortable, and let in air when we want it.' 'And how long do you suppose that air in the hold is going to last?' said I. 'Oh, ever so long,' said he, 'using it so economically as we do; and when it stops coming out lively through these little holes, as I suppose it will after a while, we can saw a big hole in this flooring and go into the hold, and do our breathing, if we want to.' That evening we did saw a hole about a foot square, so as to have plenty of air while we were asleep, but we didn't go into the hold, it being pretty well filled up with machines; though the next day Sam and I sometimes stuck our heads in for a good sniff of air, though William Anderson was opposed to this, being of the opinion that we ought to put ourselves on short rations of breathing so as to make the supply of air hold out as long as possible. 'But what's the good,' said I to William, 'of trying to make the air hold out if we've got to be suffocated in this place after all?' 'What's the good?' says he. 'Haven't you enough biscuits, and canned meats, and plenty of other things to eat, and a barrel of water in that room opposite the pantry, not to speak of wine and brandy if you want to cheer yourself up a bit, and haven't we good mattresses to sleep on, and why shouldn't we try to live and be comfortable as long as we can?' 'What I want,' said I, 'is to get out of this box. The idea of being shut up in here down under the water is more than I can stand. I'd rather take my chances going up to the surface and swimming about till I found a piece of the wreck, or something to float on.' 'You needn't think anything of that sort,' said William, 'for if we were to open a door or a window to get out, the water'd rush in and drive us back and fill up this place in no time; and then the whole concern would go to the bottom. And what would you do if you did get to the top of the water? It's not likely you'd find anything there to get on, and if you did you wouldn't live very long floating about with nothing to eat. No, sir,' says he, 'what we've got to do is to be content with the comforts we've got around us, and something will turn up to get us out of this; you see if it don't.' There was no use talking against William Anderson, and I didn't say anything more about getting out. As for Sam, he spent his time at the windows of the state-rooms a-looking out. We could see a good way into the water, further than you would think, and we sometimes saw fishes, especially porpoises, swimming about, most likely trying to find out what a ship was doing hanging bows down under the water. What troubled Sam was that a sword-fish might come along and jab his sword through one of the windows. In that case it would be all up, or rather down, with us. Every now and then he'd sing out, 'Here comes one!' And then, just as I'd give a jump, he'd say, 'No, it isn't; it's a porpoise.' I thought from the first, and I think now, that it would have been a great deal better for us if that boy hadn't been along. That night there was a good deal of motion to the ship, and she swung about and rose up and down more than she had done since we'd been left in her. 'There must be a big sea running on top,' said William Anderson, 'and if we were up there we'd be tossed about dreadful. Now the motion down here is just as easy as a cradle, and, what's more, we can't be sunk very deep; for if we were there wouldn't be any motion at all.' About noon next day we felt a sudden tremble and shake run through the whole ship, and far down under us we heard a rumbling and grinding that nearly scared me out of my wits. I first thought we'd struck bottom, but William said that couldn't be, for it was just as light in the cabin as it had been, and if we'd gone down it would have grown much darker, of course. The rumbling stopped after a little while, and then it seemed to grow lighter instead of darker; and Sam, who was looking up at the stern windows over our heads, he sung out, 'Sky!' And, sure enough, we could see the blue sky, as clear as daylight, through those windows! And then the ship, she turned herself on the slant, pretty much as she had been when her forward compartment first took in water, and we found ourselves standing on the cabin floor instead of the bulkhead. I was near one of the open state-rooms, and as I looked in there was the sunlight coming through the wet glass in the window, and more cheerful than anything I ever saw before in this world. William Anderson, he just made one jump, and, unscrewing one of the state-room windows, he jerked it open. We had thought the air inside was good enough to last some time longer; but when that window was open and the fresh air came rushing in, it was a different sort of thing, I can tell you. William put his head out and looked up and down and all around. 'She's nearly all out of water!' he shouted, 'and we can open the cabin door.' Then we all three rushed at those stairs, which were nearly right side up now, and we had the cabin doors open in no time. When we looked out we saw that the ship was truly floating pretty much as she had been when the captain and crew left her, though we all agreed that her deck didn't slant as much forward as it did then. 'Do you know what's happened?' sung out William Anderson, after he'd stood still for a minute to look around and think. 'That bobbing up and down that the vessel got last night shook up and settled down the pig iron inside of her, and the iron plates in the bow, that were smashed and loosened by the collision, have given way under the weight, and the whole cargo of pig iron has burst through and gone to the bottom. Then, of course, up we came. Didn't I tell you something would happen to make us all right?'

"Well, I won't make this story any longer than I can help. The next day after that we were taken off by a sugar-ship bound north, and we were carried safe back to Ulford, where we found our captain and the crew, who had been picked up by a ship after they'd been three or four days in their boats. This ship had sailed our way to find us, which, of course, she couldn't do, as at that time we were under water and out of sight.

"And now, sir," said the brother-in-law of J. George Watts to the Shipwreck Clerk, "to which of your classes does this wreck of mine belong?"

"Gents," said the Shipwreck Clerk, rising from his seat, "it's four o'clock, and at that hour this office closes."

## QUESTIONS

1. What do you think of the elaborate introduction?
2. Is it necessary for the effect desired by the author?
3. Do you know other authors who use a similar method?
4. Is the Shipwreck Clerk typical of certain minor officials?
5. How is he used to prepare the way for the story?
6. Is the explanation for the peculiar wreck satisfying to the reader?
7. What was their signal of distress?
8. Is it still in use? Explain.
9. What reasons did the three give for staying with the ship?
10. Is the group more interesting because one of the three was a boy?
11. Note the small details used by the author to make the situation seem more real.
12. Just exactly what is the situation when the narrator is willing to turn the story over to the Shipwreck Clerk?
13. What do you think of Anderson's explanation?
14. Do you find any element of suspense? of surprise?
15. Is the story made more plausible by being told in the first person?
16. What other type of story succeeds best told in that way?
17. Is this a story of plot, character, or setting? Explain.
18. What elements of humor do you find?
19. Is the ending too abrupt?
20. Does the title fit the story? Explain.

## SUBJECTS FOR COMPOSITION

1. Write a character sketch of the Shipwreck Clerk.
2. Describe some freak happening, imitating Stockton's use of minute detail.
3. Tell orally some strange occurrence of which you have heard or read.

## OTHER STORIES BY FRANK R. STOCKTON

The Lady or the Tiger?  A Tale of Negative Gravity
The Christmas Wreck  The Transferred Ghost
The Casting Away of Mrs. Lecks and Mrs. Aleshine

## ABOUT FRANK R. STOCKTON

*Famous Authors,* E. F. Harkness
*Frank R. Stockton,* A. T. Quiller-Couch

## HENRY CUYLER BUNNER
(1855–1896)

ALTHOUGH born in Oswego, N. Y., in 1855, Bunner belongs to New York City, where he was reared and educated. After a short fling in business he turned to newspaper work. When, in 1877 a German-American humorous weekly called *Puck* decided to print an English edition, Bunner was chosen its editor. It is the business of a humorous paper to be funny, and to that end Bunner devoted himself both as editor and as a writer of verse and stories. Before long *Puck* was the foremost humorous weekly in this country. Like O. Henry, Bunner was a delightful personality, but less seclusive. He was a great reader, and shared with the later writer a fondness for New York and its countless oddities — queer restaurants, foreign quarters, and the types of characters that haunted both.

Bunner frequently used in his stories the "surprise" ending to gain his purpose. This now common device was tried upon the reading public in 1873 in a story by Thomas Bailey Aldrich called "Marjorie Daw," and at once became a popular fad.

After his marriage Bunner moved to a New Jersey suburb. Many of his later stories have a country atmosphere, true of "Zenobia's Infidelity," printed here. Bunner made no secret of his adoration for Maupassant. He even went so far as to paraphrase a number of his stories, giving them an American setting and casting them in a lighter vein. Concise crisp narrative was what he admired in the Frenchman, and this he hoped to attain by these paraphrases. Bunner and O. Henry conclusively prove by their work that a terse vigorous style can be as effective for humor as for the somber aims of Maupassant. While "Zenobia's Infidelity" does not have a surprise ending, it nevertheless falls within the "surprise" category because of its central situation. What could be more surprising than the elephantine courtship of the grateful Zenobia and its ignoble finish in the gutter? Bunner was exceedingly apt in devising a humorous situation, and in developing it most entertainingly. He rarely bothers with a moral or a theme. And for sheer entertainment the best of Bunner's stories have rarely been excelled.

# ZENOBIA'S INFIDELITY [1]

DR. TIBBITT stood on the porch of Mrs. Pennypepper's boarding house, and looked up and down the deserted Main Street of Sagawaug with a contented smile, the while he

[1] From *The Stories of H. C. Bunner*, copyright, 1890, 1896, by Alice Larned Bunner; published by Charles Scribner's Sons. By permission of the publishers.

buttoned his driving gloves. The little doctor had good cause to be content with himself and with everything else — with his growing practice, with his comfortable boarding house, with his own good looks, with his neat attire, and with the world in general. He could not but be content with Sagawaug, for there never was a prettier country town. The doctor looked across the street and picked out the very house that he proposed to buy when the one remaining desire of his soul was gratified. It was a house with a hip roof and with a long garden running down to the river.

There was no one in the house today, but there was no one in any of the houses. Not even a pair of round bare arms were visible among the clothes that waved in the August breeze in every backyard. It was circus day in Sagawaug.

The doctor was climbing into his gig when a yell startled him. A freckled boy with saucer eyes dashed around the corner.

"Doctor!" he gasped, "come quick! The circus got afire an' the trick elephant's most roasted!"

"Don't be silly, Johnny," said the doctor, reprovingly.

"Hope to die — honest Injun — cross my breast!" said the boy. The doctor knew the sacredness of this juvenile oath.

"Get in here with me," he said, "and if I find you're trying to be funny, I'll drop you in the river."

As they drove toward the outskirts of the town, Johnny told his tale.

"Now," he began, "the folks was all out of the tent after the show was over, and one of the circus men, he went to the oil barrel in the green wagon with Dan'l in the Lion's Den onto the outside of it, an' he took in a candle an' left it there, and fust thing the barrel busted, an' he wasn't hurted a bit, but the trick elephant she was burned awful, an' the ringtailed baboon, he was so scared he had a fit. Say, did you know baboons had fits?"

When they reached the circus grounds, they found a crowd around a small side-show tent. A strong odor of burnt leather confirmed Johnny's story. Dr. Tibbitt pushed his way through the throng, and gazed upon the huge beast, lying on her side on the grass, her broad shoulder charred and quivering. Her bulk expanded and contracted with spasms of agony, and from time to time she uttered a moaning sound. On her head was a structure of red cloth, about the size of a bushel basket, apparently intended to look like a British soldier's forage cap. This was secured by a strap that went under her chin — if an elephant has a chin. This scarlet cheese box every now and then slipped down over her eye, and the faithful animal patiently, in all her anguish, adjusted it with her prehensile trunk.

By her side stood her keeper and the proprietor of the show, a large man with a dyed mustache, a wrinkled face, and hair oiled and frizzed. These two bewailed their loss alternately.

"The boss elephant in the business!" cried the showman. "Barnum never had no trick elephant like Zenobia. And them lynes and Dan'l was painted in new before I took the road this season. Oh, there's been a hoodoo on me since I showed ag'inst the Sunday-school picnic!"

"That there elephant's been like my own child," groaned the keeper, "or my own wife, I may say."

The doctor had been carefully examining his patient.

"If there is any analogy —" he began.

"Neuralogy!" snorted the indignant showman; "'tain't neuralogy, you jay pill box, she's *cooked!*"

"If there is any analogy," repeated Dr. Tibbitt, flushing a little, "between her case and that of a human being, I think I can save your elephant. Get me a barrel of linseed oil, and drive these people away."

The doctor's orders were obeyed with eager submission. He took off his coat and went to work. He had never doctored an elephant, and the job interested him. At the end of an hour, Zenobia's sufferings were somewhat alleviated. She lay on her side, chained tightly to the ground, and swaddled in bandages. Her groans had ceased.

"I'll call tomorrow at noon," said the doctor — "good gracious, what's that?" Zenobia's trunk was playing around his waistband.

"She wants to shake hands with you," her keeper explained "She's a lady, she is, and she knows you done her good."

"I'd rather not have anything of the sort," said the doctor decisively.

When Dr. Tibbitt called at twelve on the morrow, he found Zenobia's tent nearly roped in. an amphitheater of circus

## Zenobia's Infidelity

benches constructed around her, and this amphitheater packed with people.

"Got a quarter apiece from them jays," whispered the showman, "jest to see you dress them wownds." Subsequently the showman relieved his mind to a casual acquaintance. "He's got a heart like a gunflint, that doctor," he said, "made me turn out every one of them jays and give 'em their money back before he'd lay a hand on Zenobia."

But if the doctor suppressed the clinic, neither he nor the showman suffered. From dawn till dusk people came from miles around to stare a quarter's worth at the burnt elephant. Once in a while, as a rare treat, the keeper lifted a corner of her bandages, and revealed the seared flesh. The show went off in a day or two, leaving Zenobia to recover at leisure; and as it wandered westward, it did an increased business simply because it had had a burnt trick elephant. Such, dear friends, is the human mind.

The doctor fared even better. The fame of his new case spread far and wide. People seemed to think that if he could cure an elephant he could cure anything. He was called into consultation in neighboring towns. Women in robust health imagined ailments, so as to send for him and ask him shuddering questions about "that *wretched* animal." The trustees of the orphan asylum made him staff physician — in this case the doctor thought he could trace a connection of ideas, in which children and a circus were naturally associated. And the local newspaper called him a *savant*.

He called every day upon Zenobia, who greeted him with trumpetings of joyful welcome. She also desired to shake hands with him, and her keeper had to sit on her head and hold her trunk to repress the familiarity. In two weeks she was cured, except for extensive and permanent scars, and she waited only for a favorable opportunity to rejoin the circus.

The doctor had got his fee in advance.

Upon a sunny afternoon in the last of August, Dr. Tibbitt jogged slowly toward Sagawaug in his neat little gig. He had been to Pelion, the next town, to call upon Miss Minetta Bunker, the young lady whom he desired to install in the house with the garden running down to the river. He had found her starting out for a drive in Tom Matson's dogcart.

Now, the doctor feared no foe, in medicine or in love; but when a young woman is inscrutable as to the state of her affections, when the richest young man in the county is devoting himself to her, and when the young lady's mother is backing the rich man, a young country doctor may well feel perplexed and anxious over his chance of the prize.

The doctor was so troubled, indeed, that he paid no heed to a heavy, repeated thud behind him, on the macadamized road. His gentle little mare heard it, though, and began to curvet and prance. The doctor was pulling her in, and calming her with a " soo — soo — down, girl, down! " when he interrupted himself to shout,

" Great Cæsar! get off me! "

Something like a yard of rubber hose had come in through the side of the buggy, and was rubbing itself against his face. He looked around, and the cold sweat stood out on him as he saw Zenobia, her chain dragging from her hind foot, her red cap a-cock on her head, trotting along by the side of his vehicle, snorting with joy, and evidently bent on lavishing her pliant, serpentine, but leathery caresses upon his person.

His fear vanished in a moment. The animal's intentions were certainly pacific, to put it mildly. He reflected that if he could keep his horse ahead of her, he could toll her around the block and back toward her tent. He had hardly guessed, as yet, the depth of the impression which he had made upon Zenobia's heart, which must have been a large organ, if the size of her ears was any indication — according to the popular theory.

The doctor tolled his elephant around the block without further misadventure, and they started up the road toward Zenobia's tent, Zenobia caressing her benefactor while shudders of antipathy ran over his frame. In a few minutes the keeper hove in sight. Zenobia saw him first, blew a shrill blast on her trumpet, close to the doctor's ear, bolted through a snake fence, lumbered across a turnip field, and disappeared in a patch of woods, leaving the doctor to quiet his excited horse and to face the keeper, who advanced with rage in his eye.

"What do you mean, you cuss," he began, "weaning a man's elephant's affections away from him? You ain't got no more morals than a Turk, you ain't. That elephant an' me has been side-partners for fourteen years, an' here you come between us."

"I don't want your confounded elephant," roared the doctor. "Why don't you keep it chained up?"

"She busted her chain to git after you," replied the keeper. "Oh, I seen you two lally-gaggin' all along the road. I knowed you wa'n't no good the first time I set eyes on yer, a-sayin' hoodoo words over the poor dumb beast."

The doctor resolved to banish "analogy" from his vocabulary.

The next morning, about four o'clock, Dr. Tibbitt awoke with a troubled mind. He had driven home after midnight from a late call, and he had had an uneasy fancy that he saw a great shadowy bulk ambling along in the mist-hid fields by the roadside. He jumped out of bed and went to the window. Below him, completely covering Mrs. Pennypepper's nasturtium bed, her prehensile trunk ravaging the early chrysanthemums, stood Zenobia, swaying to and fro, the dew glistening on her seamed sides beneath the early morning sunlight. The doctor hastily dressed himself and slipped downstairs and out, to meet this Frankenstein's-monster of affection.

There was but one thing to do. Zenobia would follow him wherever he went — she rushed madly through Mrs. Pennypepper's roses to greet him — and his only course was to lead her out of the town before people began to get up, and to detain her in some remote meadow until he could get her keeper to come for her and secure her by force or stratagem. He set off by the least frequented streets, and he experienced a pang of horror as he remembered that his way led him past the house of his one professional rival in Sagawaug. Suppose Dr. Pettengill should be coming home or going out as he passed!

The doctor found a secluded pasture, near the woods that encircled the town, and there he sat him down, in the corner of a snake fence, to wait until some farmer or market gardener should pass by, to carry his message to the keeper. He had another message to send, too. He had several cases that must be attended to at once. Unless he could get away from his pachydermatous familiar, Dr. Pettengill must care for his cases that morning. It was hard — but what was he to do?

Zenobia stood by his side, dividing her attention between the caresses she bestowed on him and the care she was obliged to take of her red cap, which was not tightly strapped on, and slipped in various directions at every movement of her gigantic head. She was unmistakably happy. From time to time she trumpeted cheerily. She plucked up tufts of grass, and offered them to the doctor. He refused them, and she ate them herself. Once he took a daisy from her, absent-mindedly, and she was so greatly pleased that she smashed his hat in her endeavors to pet him. The doctor was a kind-hearted man. He had to admit that Zenobia meant well. He patted her trunk, and made matters worse. Her elephantine ecstasy came near being the death of him.

Still the farmer came not, nor the market gardener. Dr. Tibbitt began to believe that he had chosen a meadow that was *too* secluded. At last two boys appeared. After they had stared at him and at Zenobia for half an hour, one of them agreed to produce Dr. Pettengill and Zenobia's keeper for fifty cents. Dr. Pettengill was the first to arrive. He refused to come nearer than the farthest limit of the pasture.

"Hello, doctor," he called out, "hear you've been seeing elephants. Want me to take your cases? Guess I can. Got a half hour free. Brought some bromide down for you, if you'd like to try it."

To judge from his face, Zenobia was invisible. But his presence alarmed that sensitive animal. She crowded up close to the fence, and every time she flicked her skin to shake off the flies she endangered the equilibrium of the doctor, who was sitting on the top rail, for dignity's sake. He shouted his directions to his colleague, who shouted back professional criticisms.

"Salicylate of soda for that old woman? What's the matter with salicylate of cinchonidia? Don't want to kill her before you get out of this swamp, do you?"

Dr. Tibbitt was not a profane man, but at this moment he could not restrain himself.

"D—— *you!*" he said, with such vigor that the elephant gave a convulsive start. The doctor felt his seat depart from under him — he was going — going into space for a brief moment, and then he scrambled up out of the soft mud of the cow-wallow back of the fence on which he had been sitting. Zenobia had backed against the fence.

The keeper arrived soon after. He had only reached the meadow when Zenobia lifted her trunk in the air, emitted a mirthful toot, and struck out for the woods with the picturesque and cumbersome gallop of a mastodon pup.

"Dern *you*," said the keeper to Dr. Tibbitt, who was trying to fasten his collar, which had broken loose in his fall; "if the boys was here, and I hollered 'Hey, Rube!'—there wouldn't be enough left of yer to spread a plaster fer a baby's bile!"

The doctor made himself look as decent as the situation allowed, and then he marched toward the town with the light of a firm resolve illuminating his face. The literature of his childhood had come to his aid. He remembered the unkind tailor who pricked the elephant's trunk. It seemed to him that the tailor was a rather good fellow.

"If that elephant's disease is gratitude," thought the doctor, "I'll give her an antidote."

He went to the drug store, and, as he went, he pulled out a blank pad and wrote down a prescription, from mere force of habit. It read thus:

**PESSELS & MORTON,**
DRUGGISTS,
*Commercial Block, Main Street, Sagawaug.*

PRESCRIPTIONS CAREFULLY COMPOUNDED.

When the druggist looked at it, he was taken short of breath.
"What's this?" he asked — "a bombshell?"

"Put it up," said the doctor, "and don't talk so much." He lingered nervously on the druggist's steps, looking up and down the street. He had sent a boy to order the stableman to harness his gig. By and by, the druggist put his head out of the door.

"I've got some asafetida pills," he said, "that are kind o' tired, and half a pound of whale-oil soap that's higher 'n Haman ——"

"Put 'em in!" said the doctor, grimly, as he saw Zenobia coming in sight far down the street.

She came up while the doctor was waiting for the bolus. Twenty-three boys were watching them, although it was only seven o'clock in the morning.

"Down, Zenobia!" said the doctor, thoughtlessly, as he might have addressed a dog. He was talking with the druggist, and Zenobia was patting his ear with her trunk. Zenobia sank to her knees. The doctor did not notice her. She folded her trunk about him, lifted him to her back, rose with a heave and a sway to her feet, and started up the road. The boys cheered. The doctor got off on the end of an elm-branch. His descent was watched from nineteen second-story windows.

His gig came to meet him at last, and he entered it and drove rapidly out of town, with Zenobia trotting contentedly behind him. As soon as he had passed Deacon Burgee's house, he drew rein, and Zenobia approached, while his perspiring mare stood on her hind legs.

"Zenobia — pill!" said the doctor.

As she had often done in her late illness, Zenobia opened her mouth at the word of command, and swallowed the infernal bolus. Then they started up again, and the doctor headed for Zenobia's tent.

But Zenobia's pace was sluggish. She had been dodging about the woods for two nights, and she was tired. When the doctor whipped up, she seized the buggy by any convenient projection, and held it back. This damaged the buggy and frightened the horse; but it accomplished Zenobia's end. It was eleven o'clock before Jake Bumgardner's "Half-Way-House" loomed up white, afar down the dusty road, and the doctor knew that his roundabout way had at length brought him near to the field where the circus tent had been pitched. He drove on with a lighter heart in his bosom. He had not heard Zenobia behind him for some time. He did not know what had become of her, or what she was doing, but he learned later.

The doctor had compounded a pill well calculated to upset Zenobia's stomach. That it would likewise give her a consuming thirst he had not considered. But chemistry was doing its duty without regard to him. A thirst like a furnace burned within Zenobia. Capsicum and chloride of lime were doing their work. She gasped and groaned. She searched for water. She filled her trunk at a wayside trough and poured the contents into her mouth. Then she sucked up a puddle or two. Then she came to Bumgardner's, where a dozen kegs of lager beer and a keg of what passed at Bumgardner's for gin stood on the sidewalk. Zenobia's circus experience had taught her what a water barrel meant. She applied her knowledge. With her forefoot she deftly staved in the head of one keg after another, and with her trunk she drew up the beer and the gin, and delivered them to her stomach. If you think her taste at fault, remember the bolus.

Bumgardner rushed out and assailed her with a bung-starter. She turned upon him and squirted lager beer over him until he was covered with an iridescent lather of foam from head to foot. Then she finished the kegs and went on her way to overtake the doctor.

The doctor was speeding his mare merrily along, grateful for even a momentary relief from Zenobia's attentions, when, at one and the same time, he heard a heavy, uncertain thumping on the road behind him, and the quick patter of a trotter's hoofs on the road ahead of him. He glanced behind him first, and saw Zenobia. She swayed from side to side, more than was her wont. Her red cap was far down over her left eye. Her aspect was rakish, and her gait was unsteady. The doctor did not know it, but Zenobia was drunk.

Zenobia was sick, but intoxication dominated her sickness. Even sulphide of calcium withdrew courteously before the might of beer and gin. Rocking from side to side, reeling across the road and back, trumpeting in imbecile inexpressive tones, Zenobia advanced.

The doctor looked forward. Tom Matson sat in his dogcart, with Miss Bunker by his side. His horse had caught sight of Zenobia, and he was rearing high in air, and whinnying in terror. Before Tom could pull him down, he made a sudden break, overturned the dogcart, and flung Tom and Miss Minetta Bunker on a bank by the side of the road. It was a soft bank, well-grown with mint and stinging nettles, just above a creek. Tom had scarce landed before he was up and off, running hard across the fields.

Miss Minetta rose and looked at him with fire in her eyes.

"Well!" she said aloud, "I'd like mother to see you *now!*"

The doctor had jumped out of his gig and let his little mare go galloping up the road. He had his arm about Miss Minetta's waist when he turned to face his familiar demon — which may have accounted for the pluck in his face.

But Zenobia was a hundred yards down the road, and she was utterly incapable of getting any farther. She trumpeted once or twice, then she wavered like a reed in the wind; her legs weakened under her, and she sank on her side. Her red cap had slipped down, and she picked it up with her trunk, broke its band in a reckless swing that resembled the wave of jovial farewell, gave one titanic hiccup, and fell asleep by the roadside.

An hour later, Dr. Tibbitt was driving toward Pelion, with Miss Bunker by his side. His horse had been stopped at the tollgate. He was driving with one hand. Perhaps he needed the other to show how they could have a summer-house in the garden that ran down to the river.

But it was evening when Zenobia awoke to find her keeper sitting on her head. He jabbed a cotton hook firmly and decisively into her ear, and led her homeward down the road lit by the golden sunset. That was the end of Zenobia's infidelity.

### QUESTIONS

1. From the title of the story and its opening paragraphs, what type of story did you think it was? Explain.
2. Where does the story really begin?
3. How does the author obtain humorous effects?
4. Compare his manner with that of O. Henry

5. What was the story of the tailor and the elephant's trunk?
6. What elements of plot do you find?
7. Are they interesting?
8. Show how Zenobia is after all connected with the plot.
9. Whose story is this, Zenobia's or the doctor's?
10. Contrast it with "The Elephant Remembers," elsewhere in this book.
11. Don't fail to read Kipling's "Moti Guj — Mutineer," and then compare it with the other two.
12. Would this story have been equally funny if the animal had been a dog or a horse? Explain.
13. Does the story end satisfactorily? Explain.
14. Might it have ended sooner without being spoiled?
15. Would the story have gained by more episodes?
16. In modern magazines, what animals are used in stories?
17. Do you like animal stories? What is your favorite animal in stories?
18. Compare Bunner with Irving, Poe, and Maupassant.

## SUBJECTS FOR COMPOSITION

1. The Circus Arrives
2. My First Circus
3. Make up a story of a horse or a dog in an amusing situation.
4. Tell orally an episode illustrating so-called "animal intelligence."

## VOLUMES OF STORIES BY H. C. BUNNER

*Short Sixes*  *More Short Sixes*

## OTHER STORIES BY H. C. BUNNER

The Tenor
The Love-letters of Smith
The Nice People

Hector
A Sisterly Scheme

## WASHINGTON IRVING
## (1783-1859)

THE city of New York was still in the hands of the British when Washington Irving was born, April 3, 1783. That his English-born parents were good American patriots may be inferred by the name they gave to their eleventh child. Because of frail health, and because he was the youngest child, Irving was the pet of the family. His schooling was more or less erratic, and stopped at the age of sixteen, for he refused to go to college.

The family wanted him to become a lawyer; hence he was articled to a practicing attorney. While fond of reading, he was not a bookworm, and the ponderous law books interested him not at all. Much more inviting to young Irving were the docks and the queer nooks of New York, many still distinctively Dutch at that time. With an eye for the quaint and the picturesque, he perhaps did actually draw Diedrich Knickerbocker from some type casually encountered on one of his rambles. Everywhere he gathered stories and legends of the old Dutch days and the later life of the colonists. Where legends were lacking his ready imagination fabricated them. A long journey up the Hudson brought to Irving the inspiration which gave the United States its first short story in " Rip Van Winkle " (1819), and another equally good in " The Legend of Sleepy Hollow " (1820).

But Irving's literary career had begun earlier, in 1809, with *A History of New York by Diedrich Knickerbocker,* a satirically humorous work purporting to be a history of New York under the Dutch. The device of the discovery of the manuscript is borrowed from the eighteenth century English writers, especially Defoe, except that Irving elaborated the idea by previously advertising in the papers the strange disappearance of Diedrich Knickerbocker, " a small, elderly gentleman, dressed in a black coat and a cocked hat." Unless he showed up or was found, his belongings were to be sold to pay his board bill. He had left a curious manuscript, and this, Irving stated, included the history of New York. The idea worked so well that he found it agreeable to attribute the stories of Rip Van Winkle and Ichabod Crane to the same mythical source, although they were written ten years later when the author was in England, whither his roving propensities had taken him in 1815.

Irving disliked regular work of all kinds, including writing, and so far in his life he had been indulged by his family. In 1818 his brothers' business failed, and Irving, suddenly left without funds, for the first time turned seriously to writing. A series of short pieces published serially in this country under the title " The Sketch Book of Geoffrey Crayon, Gent." came out as a book both here and in England and became tremendously popular. In England it was the first American book that received recognition as literature.

Irving had now found his profession. After his first great success with the *Sketch Book* he visited France and Germany, and then settled down to a longer stay in Spain. The stories of the *Alhambra* he sketched while actually living in the old Moorish palace in Granada, the government having given him special permission to do so. To this day Irving's room is shown to visitors.

In 1829 Irving unwillingly accepted the position of Secretary of the Legation in London, but he was now full of literary plans and returned to America in 1832, after an absence of seventeen years. He was received almost as a conquering hero by his admirers, with banquets and receptions. Then followed a prolonged tour of the South and West, which gave him material for books written after he had settled down at Tarrytown, a small town on the Hudson. He fixed for himself a comfortable bachelor home, with the cheerful name of "Sunnyside," where he expected to live out his days undisturbed.

But Irving, by virtue of his personality, his literary accomplishments, his long experience abroad, his knowledge of European countries and their languages, had made himself an international figure. It was therefore most creditable of President Tyler to appoint him Minister to Spain in 1842. After four years he returned finally to Sunnyside, where he lived happily the remainder of his life, surrounded by friends and relatives. He died Nov. 28, 1859.

For all practical purposes it may be said that Irving was the pioneer writer of the short story in English, and certainly of America. Bearing in mind our definition of the short story, we at once notice outstanding differences between the practice of modern writers and Irving. He concerned himself little with plot. In "The Legend of Sleepy Hollow" there is something approaching a plot in the wooing of the two rivals, but even here the interest really lies in the character of the rustic pedagogue. And here, as in "Rip Van Winkle," much of the charm arises from the author's rambling on about everything that interested him — bits of description, hints at local folklore, miscellaneous observations.

Above all, Irving is America's first humorist. He was not obsessed with the somber moral conscience of the New England writers, as exemplified in the stories of Hawthorne, nor did life present to him the pictures of horror that are found in Poe. To Irving life was something to be enjoyed, and literature something to bring pleasure to the reader. His hope, he said, was to be able to "rub out one wrinkle from the brow of care, or beguile the heavy heart of one moment's sadness." Who can read his two great stories and deny that he succeeded?

# THE LEGEND OF SLEEPY HOLLOW

## FOUND AMONG THE PAPERS OF THE LATE DIEDRICH KNICKERBOCKER

> A pleasing land of drowsy-head it was,
>   Of dreams that wave before the half-shut eye
> And of gay castles in the clouds that pass,
>   For ever flushing round a summer sky.
>                           CASTLE OF INDOLENCE.

IN THE bosom of one of those spacious coves which indent the eastern shore of the Hudson, at that broad expansion of the river denominated by the ancient Dutch navigators the Tappan Zee, and where they always prudently shortened sail and implored the protection of St. Nicholas when they crossed, there lies a small market-town or rural port which by some is called Greensburg, but which is more generally and properly known by the name of Tarry Town. This name was given, we are told, in former days by the good housewives of the adjacent country from the inveterate propensity of their husbands to linger about the village tavern on market days. Be that as it may, I do not vouch for the fact, but merely advert to it for the sake of being precise and authentic. Not far from this village, perhaps about two miles, there is a little valley, or rather lap of land, among high hills, which is one of the quietest places in the whole world. A small brook glides through it, with just murmur enough to lull one to repose, and the occasional whistle of a quail or tapping of a woodpecker is almost the only sound that ever breaks in upon the uniform tranquillity.

I recollect that when a stripling my first exploit in squirrel-shooting was in a grove of tall walnut trees that shades one side of the valley. I had wandered into it at noontime, when all Nature is peculiarly quiet, and was startled by the roar of my own gun as it broke the Sabbath stillness around and was prolonged and reverberated by the angry echoes. If ever I should wish for a retreat whither I might steal from the world and its distractions and dream quietly away the remnant of a troubled life, I know of none more promising than this little valley.

From the listless repose of the place and the peculiar character of its inhabitants, who are descendants from the original Dutch settlers, this sequestered glen has long been known by the name of SLEEPY HOLLOW, and its rustic lads are called the Sleepy Hollow Boys throughout all the neighboring country. A drowsy, dreamy influence seems to hang over the land and to pervade the very atmosphere. Some say that the place was bewitched by a High German doctor during the early days of the settlement; others, that an old Indian chief, the prophet or wizard of his tribe, held his powwows there before the country was discovered by Master Hendrick Hudson. Certain it is, the place still continues under the sway of some witching power that holds a spell over the minds of the good people, causing them to walk in a continual reverie. They are given to all kinds of marvelous beliefs, are subject to trances and visions, and frequently see strange sights and hear music and voices in the air. The whole neighborhood abounds with local tales, haunted spots, and twilight superstitions; stars shoot and meteors glare oftener across the valley than in any other part of the country, and the nightmare, with her whole ninefold, seems to make it the favorite scene of her gambols.

The dominant spirit, however, that haunts this enchanted region, and seems to be commander-in-chief of all the powers of the air, is the apparition of a figure on horseback without a head. It is said by some to be the ghost of a Hessian trooper whose head had been carried away by a cannon-ball in some nameless battle during the Revolutionary War, and who is ever and anon seen by the country-folk hurrying along in the gloom of night as if on the wings of the wind. His haunts are not confined to the valley, but extend at times to the adjacent roads, and especially to the vicinity of a church at no great distance. Indeed, certain of the most authentic historians of those parts, who have been careful in collecting and collating the floating facts concerning this specter, allege that, the body of the trooper having been buried in the churchyard, the ghost rides forth to the scene of battle in nightly quest of his head, and that the rushing speed with which he sometimes passes along the Hollow, like a midnight blast, is owing to his being belated and in a hurry to get back to the churchyard before daybreak.

Such is the general purport of this legendary superstition, which has furnished materials for many a wild story in that region of shadows; and the specter is known at all the country firesides by the name of the Headless Horseman of Sleepy Hollow.

It is remarkable that the visionary propensity I have mentioned is not confined to the native inhabitants of the valley, but is unconsciously imbibed by every one who resides there for a time. However wide awake they may have been before they entered that sleepy region, they are sure in a little time to inhale the witching influence of the air and begin to grow imaginative — to dream dreams and see apparitions.

I mention this peaceful spot with all possible laud, for it is in such little retired Dutch valleys, found here and there embosomed in the great State of New York, that population, manners, and customs remain fixed, while the great torrent of migration and improvement, which is making such incessant changes in other parts of this restless country, sweeps by them unobserved. They are like those little nooks of still water which border a rapid stream where we may see the straw and bubble riding quietly at anchor or slowly revolving in their mimic harbor, undisturbed by the rush of the passing current. Though many years have elapsed since I trod the drowsy shades of Sleepy Hollow, yet I question whether I should not still find the same trees and the same families vegetating in its sheltered bosom.

In this by-place of Nature there abode, in a remote period of American history — that is to say, some thirty years since — a worthy wight of the name of Ichabod Crane, who sojourned, or, as he expressed it, "tarried," in Sleepy Hollow for the purpose of instructing the children of the vicinity. He was a native of Connecticut, a State which supplies the Union with pioneers for the mind as well as for the forest, and sends forth yearly its legions of frontier woodmen and country schoolmasters. The cognomen of Crane was not inapplicable to his person. He was tall, but exceedingly lank, with narrow shoulders, long arms and legs, hands that dangled a mile out of his sleeves, feet that might have served for shovels, and his whole frame most loosely hung together. His head was small, and flat at top, with huge ears, large green glassy eyes, and a long snip nose, so that it looked like a weathercock perched upon his spindle neck to tell which way the wind blew. To see him striding along the profile of a hill on a windy day, with his clothes bagging and fluttering about him, one might have mistaken him for the genius of Famine descending upon the earth or some scarecrow eloped from a cornfield.

His school-house was a low building of one large room, rudely constructed of logs, the windows partly glazed and partly patched with leaves of old copy-books. It was most ingeniously secured at vacant hours by a withe twisted in the handle of the door and stakes set against the window-shutters, so that, though a thief might get in with perfect ease, he would find some embarrassment in getting out — an idea most probably borrowed by the architect, Yost Van Houten, from the mystery of an eelpot. The school-house stood in a rather lonely but pleasant situation, just at the foot of a woody hill, with a brook running close by and a formidable birch tree growing at one end of it. From hence the low murmur of his pupils' voices, conning over their lessons, might be heard in a drowsy summer's day like the hum of a bee-hive, interrupted now and then by the authoritative voice of the master in the tone of menace or command, or, peradventure, by the appalling sound of the birch as he urged some tardy loiterer along the flowery path of knowledge. Truth to say, he was a conscientious man, and ever bore in mind the golden maxim, " Spare the rod and spoil the child." Ichabod Crane's scholars certainly were not spoiled.

I would not have it imagined, however, that he was one of those cruel potentates of the school who joy in the smart of their subjects; on the contrary, he administered justice with discrimination rather than severity, taking the burden off the backs of the weak and laying it on those of the strong. Your mere puny stripling, that winced at the least flourish of the rod, was passed by with indulgence; but the claims of justice were satisfied by inflicting a double portion on some little tough, wrong-headed, broad-skirted Dutch urchin, who sulked and swelled and grew dogged and sullen beneath the birch. All this he called " doing his duty by their parents "; and he never inflicted a chastisement without following it by the assurance, so consolatory to the smarting urchin, that "he would remember it and thank him for it the longest day he had to live."

When school-hours were over he was even the companion and playmate of the larger boys, and on holiday afternoons would convoy some of the smaller ones home who happened to have pretty sisters or good housewives for mothers noted for the comforts of the cupboard. Indeed it behooved him to keep on good terms with his pupils. The revenue arising from his school was small, and would have been scarcely sufficient to furnish him with daily bread, for he was a huge feeder, and, though lank, had the dilating powers of an anaconda; but to help out his maintenance he was, according to country custom in those parts, boarded and lodged at the houses of the farmers whose children he instructed. With these he lived successively a week at a time, thus going the rounds of the neighborhood with all his worldly effects tied up in a cotton handkerchief.

That all this might not be too onerous on the purses of his rustic patrons, who are apt to consider the costs of schooling a grievous burden and schoolmasters as mere drones, he had various ways of rendering himself both useful and agreeable. He assisted the farmers occasionally in the lighter labors of their farms, helped to make hay, mended the fences, took the horses to water, drove the cows from pasture, and cut wood for the winter fire. He laid aside, too, all the dominant dignity and absolute sway with which he lorded it in his little empire, the school, and became wonderfully gentle and ingratiating. He found favor in the eyes of the mothers by petting the children, particularly the youngest; and like the lion bold, which whilom so magnanimously the lamb did hold, he would sit with a child on one knee and rock a cradle with his foot for whole hours together.

In addition to his other vocations, he was the singing-master of the neighborhood and picked up many bright shillings by instructing the young folks in psalmody. It was a matter of no little vanity to him on Sundays to take his station in front of the church-gallery with a band of chosen singers, where, in his own mind, he completely carried away the palm from the parson. Certain it is, his voice resounded far above all the rest of the congregation, and there are peculiar quavers still to be heard in that church, and which may even be heard half a mile off, quite to the opposite side of the mill-pond on a still Sunday morning, which are said to be legitimately descended from the nose of Ichabod Crane. Thus, by divers little makeshifts in that ingenious way which is commonly denominated "by hook and by crook," the worthy pedagogue got on tolerably enough, and was thought, by all who understood nothing of the labor of headwork, to have a wonderfully easy life of it.

The schoolmaster is generally a man of some importance in the female circle of a rural neighborhood, being considered a kind of idle, gentleman-like personage of vastly superior taste and accomplishments to the rough country swains, and, indeed, inferior in learning only to the parson. His appearance, therefore, is apt to occasion some little stir at the tea-table of a farmhouse and the addition of a supernumerary dish of cakes or sweetmeats, or, peradventure, the parade of a silver tea-pot. Our man of letters, therefore, was peculiarly happy in the smiles of all the country damsels. How he would figure among them in the churchyard between services on Sundays, gathering grapes for them from the wild vines that overrun the surrounding trees; reciting for their amusement all the epitaphs on the tombstones; or sauntering, with a whole bevy of them, along the banks of the adjacent mill-pond, while the more bashful country bumpkins hung sheepishly back, envying his superior elegance and address.

From his half-itinerant life, also, he was a kind of traveling gazette, carrying the whole budget of local gossip from house to house, so that his appearance was always greeted with satisfaction. He was, moreover, esteemed by the women as a man of great erudition, for he had read several books quite through, and was a perfect master of Cotton Mather's *History of New England Witchcraft,* in which, by the way, he most firmly and potently believed.

He was, in fact, an odd mixture of small shrewdness and simple credulity. His appetite for the marvelous and his powers of digesting it were equally extraordinary, and both had been increased by his residence in this spellbound region. No tale was too gross or monstrous for his capacious swallow. It was often his delight, after his school was dismissed in the afternoon, to stretch himself on the rich bed of clover bordering the little brook that whimpered by his school-house, and there con over old Mather's direful tales until the gathering dusk of the evening made the printed page a mere mist before his eyes. Then, as he wended his way by swamp and stream and awful woodland to the farmhouse where he happened to be quartered, every sound of Nature at that witching hour fluttered his excited imagination — the moan of the whippoorwill from the hillside; the boding cry of the tree-toad, that harbinger of storm; the dreary hooting of the screech-owl, or the sudden rustling in the thicket of birds frightened from their roost. The fire-flies, too, which sparkled most vividly in the darkest places, now and then startled him as one of uncommon brightness would stream across his path; and if, by chance, a huge blockhead of a beetle came winging his blundering flight against him, the poor varlet was ready to give up the ghost, with the idea that he was struck with a witch's token. His only resource on such occasions, either to drown thought or drive away evil spirits, was to sing psalm tunes; and the good people of Sleepy Hollow, as they sat by their doors of an evening, were often filled with awe at hearing his nasal melody, " in linked sweetness long drawn out," floating from the distant hill or along the dusky road.

Another of his sources of fearful pleasure was to pass long winter evenings with the old Dutch wives as they sat spinning by the fire, with a row of apples roasting and spluttering along the hearth, and listen to their marvelous tales of ghosts and goblins, and haunted fields, and haunted brooks, and haunted bridges, and haunted houses, and particularly of the headless horseman, or Galloping Hessian of the Hollow, as they sometimes called him. He would delight them equally by his anecdotes of witchcraft and of the direful omens and portentous sights and sounds in the air which prevailed in the earlier times of Connecticut, and would frighten them woefully with speculations upon comets and shooting stars, and with the alarming fact that the world did absolutely turn round and that they were half the time topsy-turvy.

But if there was a pleasure in all this while snugly cuddling in the chimney-corner of a chamber that was all of a ruddy glow from the crackling wood-fire, and where, of course, no specter dared to show its face, it was dearly purchased by the terrors of his subsequent walk homewards. What fearful shapes and shadows beset his path amidst the dim and ghastly glare of a snowy night! With what wistful look did he eye every trembling ray of light streaming across the waste fields from some distant window! How often was he appalled by some shrub covered with snow, which, like a sheeted specter, beset his very path! How often did he shrink with curdling awe at the sound of his own steps on the frosty crust beneath his feet, and dread to look over his shoulder, lest he should behold some uncouth being tramping close behind him! And how often was he thrown into complete dismay by some rushing blast howling among the trees, in the idea that it was the Galloping Hessian on one of his nightly scourings!

All these, however, were mere terrors of the night, phantoms of the mind that walk in darkness; and though he had seen many specters in his time, and been more than once beset by Satan in divers shapes in his lonely perambulations, yet daylight put an end to all these evils; and he would have passed a pleasant life of it, in spite of the devil and all his works, if his path had not been crossed by a being that causes more perplexity to mortal man than ghosts, goblins, and the whole race of witches put together, and that was — a woman.

Among the musical disciples who assembled one evening in each week to receive his instructions in psalmody was Katrina Van Tassel, the daughter and only child of a substantial Dutch farmer. She was a blooming lass of fresh eighteen, plump as a partridge, ripe and melting and rosy-cheeked as one of her father's peaches, and universally famed, not merely for her beauty, but her vast expectations. She was withal a little of a coquette, as might be perceived even in her dress, which was a mixture of ancient and modern fashions, as most suited to set off her charms. She wore the ornaments of pure yellow gold which her great-great-grandmother had brought over from Saardam, the tempting stomacher of the olden time, and withal a provokingly short petticoat to display the prettiest foot and ankle in the country round.

Ichabod Crane had a soft and foolish heart towards the sex, and it is not to be wondered at that so tempting a morsel soon found favor in his eyes, more especially after he had visited her in her paternal mansion. Old Baltus Van Tassel was a perfect picture of a thriving, contented, liberal-hearted farmer. He seldom, it is true, sent either his eyes or his thoughts beyond the boundaries of his own farm, but within those everything was snug, happy, and well-conditioned. He was satisfied with his wealth, but not proud of it, and piqued himself upon the hearty abundance, rather than the style, in which he lived. His stronghold was situated on the banks of the Hudson, in one of those green, sheltered, fertile nooks in which the Dutch farmers are so fond of nestling. A great elm tree spread its broad branches over it, at the foot of which bubbled up a spring of the softest and sweetest water in a little well formed of a barrel, and then stole sparkling away through the grass to a neighboring brook that bubbled along among alders and dwarf willows. Hard by the farmhouse was a vast barn, that might have served for a church, every window and crevice of which seemed bursting forth with the treasures of the farm; the flail was busily resounding within it from morning to night; swallows and martins skimmed twittering about the eaves; and rows of pigeons, some with one eye turned up, as if watching the weather, some with their heads under their wings or buried in their bosoms, and others, swelling, and cooing, and bowing about their dames, were enjoying the sunshine on the roof. Sleek, unwieldy porkers were grunting in the repose and abundance of their pens, whence sallied forth, now and then, troops of sucking pigs as if to snuff the air. A stately squadron of snowy geese were riding in an adjoining pond, convoying whole fleets of ducks; regiments of turkeys were gobbling through the farmyard, and guinea-fowls fretting about it, like ill-tempered housewives, with their peevish, discontented cry. Before the barn-door strutted the gallant cock, that pattern of a husband, a warrior, and a fine gentleman, clapping his burnished wings and crowing in the pride and gladness of his heart — sometimes tearing up the earth with his feet, and then generously calling his ever-hungry family of wives and children to enjoy the rich morsel which he had discovered.

The pedagogue's mouth watered as he looked upon his sumptuous promise of luxurious winter fare. In his devouring mind's eye he pictured to himself every roasting-pig running about with a pudding in his belly and an apple in his mouth; the pigeons were snugly put to bed in a comfortable pie and tucked in with a coverlet of crust; the geese were swimming in their own gravy; and the ducks pairing cozily in dishes, like snug married couples, with a decent competency of onion sauce. In the porkers he saw carved out the future sleek side of bacon and juicy relishing ham; not a turkey but he beheld daintily trussed up, with its gizzard under its wing, and, peradventure, a necklace of savory sausages; and even bright Chanticleer himself lay sprawling on his back in a side-dish, with uplifted claws, as if craving that quarter which his chivalrous spirit disdained to ask while living.

As the enraptured Ichabod fancied all this, and as he rolled his great green eyes over the fat meadow-lands, the rich fields of wheat, of rye, of buckwheat, and Indian corn, and the orchards burdened with ruddy fruit, which surrounded the warm tenement of Van Tassel, his heart yearned after the damsel who was to inherit these domains, and his imagination expanded with the idea how they might be readily turned into cash and the money invested in immense tracts of wild land and shingle palaces in the wilderness. Nay, his busy fancy already realized his hopes, and presented to him the blooming Katrina, with a whole family of children, mounted on the top of a wagon loaded with household trumpery, with pots and kettles dangling beneath, and he beheld himself bestriding a pacing mare, with a colt at her heels, setting out for Kentucky, Tennessee, or the Lord knows where.

When he entered the house the conquest of his heart was complete. It was one of those spacious farmhouses with high-ridged but lowly-sloping roofs, built in the style handed down from the first Dutch settlers, the low projecting eaves forming a piazza along the front capable of being closed up in bad weather. Under this were hung flails, harness, various utensils of husbandry, and nets for fishing in the neighboring river. Benches were built along the sides for summer use, and a great spinning-wheel at one end and a churn at the other showed the various uses to which this important porch might be devoted. From this piazza the wondering Ichabod entered the hall, which formed the center of the mansion and the place of usual residence. Here rows of resplendent pewter, ranged on a long dresser, dazzled his eyes. In one corner stood a huge bag of wool ready to be spun; in another a quantity of linsey-woolsey just from the loom; ears of Indian corn and strings of dried apples and peaches hung in gay festoons along the walls, mingled with the gaud of red peppers; and a door left ajar gave him a peep into the best parlor, where the claw-footed chairs and dark mahogany tables shown like mirrors; andirons, with their accompanying shovel and tongs, glistened from their covert of asparagus tops; mock-oranges and conch-shells decorated the mantelpiece; strings of various-colored birds' eggs were suspended above it; a great ostrich egg was hung from the center of the room, and a corner cupboard, knowingly left open, displayed immense treasures of old silver and well-mended china.

From the moment Ichabod laid his eyes upon these regions of delight the peace of his mind was at an end, and his only study was how to gain the affections of the peerless daughter of Van Tassel. In this enterprise, however, he had more real difficulties than generally fell to the lot of a knight-errant of yore, who seldom had anything but giants, enchanters, fiery dragons, and such-like easily conquered adversaries to contend with, and had to make his way merely through gates of iron and brass and walls of adamant to the castle keep, where the lady of his heart was confined; all which he achieved as easily as a man would carve his way to the center of a Christmas pie, and then the lady gave him her hand as a matter of course. Ichabod, on the contrary, had to win his way to the heart of a country coquette beset with a labyrinth of whims and caprices, which were forever presenting new difficulties and impediments, and he had to encounter a host of fearful adversaries of real flesh and blood, the numerous rustic admirers who beset every portal to her heart, keeping a watchful and angry eye upon each other, but ready to fly out in the common cause against any new competitor.

Among these the most formidable was a burly, roaring, roistering blade of the name of Abraham — or, according to the Dutch abbreviation, Brom — Van Brunt, the hero of the country round, which rang with his feats of strength and hardihood. He was broad-shouldered and double-jointed, with short curly black hair and a bluff but not unpleasant countenance, having a mingled air of fun and arrogance. From his Herculean frame and great powers of limb, he had received the nickname of BROM BONES, by which he was universally known. He was famed for great knowledge and skill in horsemanship, being as dextrous on horseback as a Tartar. He was foremost at all races and cock-fights, and, with the ascendency which bodily strength acquires in rustic life, was the umpire in all disputes, setting his hat on one side and giving his decisions with an air and tone admitting of no gainsay or appeal. He was always ready for either a fight or a frolic, but had more mischief than ill-will in his composition; and with all his overbearing roughness there was a strong dash of waggish good-humor at bottom. He had three or four boon companions who regarded him as their model, and at the head of whom he scoured the country, attending every scene of feud or merriment for miles around. In cold weather he was distinguished by a fur cap surmounted with a flaunting fox's tail; and when the folks at a country gathering descried this well-known crest at a distance, whisking about among a squad of hard riders, they always stood by for a squall. Sometimes his crew would be heard dashing along past the farmhouses at midnight with whoop and halloo, like a troop of Don Cossacks, and the old dames, startled out of their sleep, would listen for a moment till the hurry-scurry had clattered by, and then exclaim, "Ay, there goes Brom Bones and his gang!" The neighbors looked upon him with a mixture of awe, admiration, and good-will, and when any madcap prank of rustic brawl occurred in the vicinity always shook their heads and warranted Brom Bones was at the bottom of it.

This rantipole hero had for some time singled out the blooming Katrina for the object of his uncouth gallantries, and, though his amorous toyings were something like the gentle caresses and endearments of a bear, yet it was whispered that she did not altogether discourage his hopes. Certain it is, his advances were signals for rival candidates to retire who felt no inclination to cross a line in his amours; insomuch that, when his horse was seen tied to Van Tassel's paling on a Sunday night, a sure sign that his master was courting — or, as it is termed, "sparking" — within, all other suitors passed by in despair and carried the war into other quarters.

Such was the formidable rival with whom Ichabod Crane had to contend, and, considering all things, a stouter man than he would have shrunk from the competition and a wiser man would have despaired. He had, however, a happy mixture of pliability and perseverance in his nature; he was in form and spirit like a supple jack — yielding, but tough; though he bent, he never broke; and though he bowed beneath the slightest pressure, yet the moment it was away, jerk! he was as erect and carried his head as high as ever.

To have taken the field openly against his rival would have been madness; for he was not a man to be thwarted in his amours any more than that stormy lover, Achilles. Ichabod, therefore, made his advances in a quiet and gently-insinuating manner. Under cover of his character of singing-master he made frequent visits at the farmhouse; not that he had anything to apprehend from the meddlesome interference of parents, which is so often a stumbling-block in the path of lovers. Balt Van Tassel was an easy, indulgent soul; he loved his daughter better even than his pipe, and, like a reasonable man and an excellent father, let her have her way in everything. His notable little wife, too, had enough to do to attend to her housekeeping and manage her poultry; for, as she sagely observed, ducks and geese are foolish things and must be looked after, but girls can take care of themselves. Thus while the busy dame bustled about the house or plied her spinning-wheel at one end of the piazza, honest Balt would sit smoking his evening pipe at the other, watching the achievements of a little wooden warrior who, armed with a sword in each hand, was most valiantly fighting the wind on the pinnacle of the barn. In the meantime, Ichabod would carry on his suit with the daughter by the side of the spring under the great elm or sauntering along in the twilight, that hour so favorable to the lover's eloquence. I profess not to know how women's hearts are wooed and won. To me they have always been matters of riddle and admiration. Some seem to have but one vulnerable point or door of access, while others have a thousand avenues and may be captured in a thousand different ways. It is a great triumph of skill to gain the former, but a still greater proof of generalship to maintain possession of the latter, for a man must battle for his fortress at every door and window. He who wins a thousand common hearts is therefore entitled to some renown, but he who keeps undisputed sway over the heart of a coquette is indeed a hero. Certain it is, this was not the case with the redoubtable Brom Bones; and from the moment Ichabod Crane made his advances the interests of the former evidently declined; his horse was no longer seen tied at the palings on Sunday nights, and a deadly feud gradually arose between him and the preceptor of Sleepy Hollow.

Brom, who had a degree of rough chivalry in his nature, would fain have carried matters to open warfare, and have settled their pretensions to the lady according to the mode of those most concise and simple reasoners, the knights-errant of yore — by single combat; but Ichabod was too conscious of the superior might of his adversary to enter the lists against him; he had overheard a boast of Bones, that he would " double the schoolmaster up and lay him on a shelf of his own school-house; " and he was too wary to give him an opportunity. There was something extremely provoking in this obstinately pacific system; it left Brom no alternative but to draw upon the funds of rustic waggery in his disposition and to play off boorish practical jokes upon his rival. Ichabod became the object of whimsical persecution to Bones and his gang of rough riders. They harried his hitherto peaceful domains; smoked out his singing school by stopping up the chimney; broke into the school-house at night, in spite of its formidable fastenings of withe and window stakes, and turned everything topsy-turvy; so that the poor schoolmaster began to think all the witches in the country held their meetings there. But, what was still more annoying, Brom took all opportunities of turning him into ridicule in presence of his mistress, and had a scoundrel dog whom he taught to whine in the most ludicrous manner, and introduced as a rival of Ichabod's to instruct her in psalmody.

In this way matters went on for some time without producing any material effect on the relative situation of the contending powers. On a fine autumnal afternoon Ichabod in pensive mood sat enthroned on the lofty stool whence he usually watched all the concerns of his little literary realm. In his hand he swayed a ferule, that scepter of despotic power; the birch of justice reposed on three nails behind the throne, a constant terror to evildoers; while on the desk before him might be seen sundry contraband articles and prohibited weapons detected upon the persons of idle urchins, such as half-munched apples, popguns, whirligigs, fly-cages, and whole legions of rampant little paper game-cocks. Apparently there had been some appalling act of justice recently inflicted, for his scholars were all busily intent upon their books or slyly whispering behind them with one eye kept upon the master, and a kind of buzzing stillness reigned throughout the school-room. It was suddenly interrupted by the appearance of a negro in tow-cloth jacket and trowsers, a round-crowned fragment of a hat like the cap of Mercury, and mounted on the back of a ragged, wild, half-broken colt, which he managed with a rope by way of halter. He came clattering up to the school door with an invitation to Ichabod to attend a merrymaking or " quilting frolic " to be held that evening at Mynheer Van Tassel's; and, having delivered his message with that air of importance and effort at fine language which a negro is apt to display on petty embassies of the kind, he dashed over the brook, and was seen scampering away up the hollow, full of the importance and hurry of his mission.

All was now bustle and hubbub in the late quiet schoolroom. The scholars were hurried through their lessons without stopping at trifles; those who were nimble skipped over half with impunity, and those who were tardy had a smart application now and then in the rear to quicken their speed or help them over a tall word. Books were flung aside without being put away on the shelves, inkstands were overturned, benches thrown down, and the whole school was turned loose an hour before the usual time, bursting forth like a legion of young imps, yelping and racketing about the green in joy at their early emancipation.

The gallant Ichabod now spent at least an extra half hour at his toilet, brushing and furbishing up his best, and indeed only, suit of rusty black and arranging his locks by a bit of broken looking-glass that hung up in the school-house. That he might make his appearance before his mistress in the true style of a cavalier, he borrowed a horse from the farmer with whom he was domiciliated, a choleric old Dutchman of the name of Hans Van Ripper, and, thus gallantly mounted, issued forth like a knight-errant in quest of adventures. But it is meet I should, in the true spirit of romantic story, give some account of the looks and equipments of my hero and his steed. The animal he bestrode was a broken-down plow-horse that had outlived almost everything but his viciousness. He was gaunt and shagged, with a ewe neck and a head like a hammer; his rusty mane and tail were tangled and knotted with burrs; one eye had lost its pupil and was glaring and spectral, but the other had the gleam of a genuine devil in it. Still, he must have had fire and mettle in his day, if we may judge from the name he bore of Gunpowder. He had, in fact, been a favorite steed of his master's, the choleric Van Ripper, who was a furious rider, and had infused, very probably, some of his own spirit into the animal; for, old and broken down as he looked, there was more of the lurking devil in him than in any young filly in the country.

Ichabod was a suitable figure for such a steed. He rode with short stirrups, which brought his knees nearly up to the pommel of the saddle; his sharp elbows stuck out like grasshoppers'; he carried his whip perpendicularly in his hand like a scepter; and as his horse jogged on the motion of his arms was not unlike the flapping of a pair of wings. A small wool hat rested on the top of his nose, for so his scanty strip of forehead might be called, and the skirts of his black coat fluttered out almost to his horse's tail. Such was the appearance of Ichabod and his steed as they shambled out of the gate of Hans Van Ripper, and it was altogether such an apparition as is seldom to be met with in broad daylight.

It was, as I have said, a fine autumnal day, the sky was clear and serene, and Nature wore that rich and golden livery which we always associate with the idea of abundance. The forests had put on their sober brown and yellow, while some trees of the tender kind had been nipped by the frosts into brilliant dyes of orange, purple, and scarlet. Streaming files of wild ducks began to make their appearance high in the air; the bark of the squirrel might be heard from the groves of beech and hickory nuts, and the pensive whistle of the quail at intervals from the neighboring stubble-field.

The small birds were taking their farewell banquets. In the fulness of their revelry they fluttered, chirping and frolicking, from bush to bush and tree to tree, capricious from the very profusion and variety around them. There was the honest cock robin, the favorite game of stripling sportsmen, with its loud querulous note; and the twittering blackbirds, flying in sable clouds; and the golden-winged woodpecker, with his crimson crest, his broad black gorget, and splendid plumages, and the cedar-bird, with its red-tipt wings and yellow-tipt tail and its little monteiro cap of feathers; and the blue jay, that noisy coxcomb, in his gay light-blue coat and white underclothes, screaming and chattering, bobbing and nodding and bowing, and pretending to be on good terms with every songster of the grove.

As Ichabod jogged slowly on his way his eye, ever open to every symptom of culinary abundance, ranged with delight over the treasures of jolly Autumn. On all sides he beheld vast store of apples — some hanging in oppressive opulence on the trees, some gathered into baskets and barrels for the market, others heaped up in rich piles for the cider-press. Farther on he beheld great fields of Indian corn, with its golden ears peeping from their leafy coverts and holding out the promise of cakes and hasty pudding; and the yellow pumpkins lying beneath them, turning up their fair round bellies to the sun, and giving ample prospects of the most luxurious of pies; and anon he passed the fragrant buckwheat-fields, breathing the odor of the bee-hive, and as he beheld them soft anticipations stole over his mind of dainty slapjacks, well buttered and garnished with honey or treacle by the delicate little dimpled hand of Katrina Van Tassel.

Thus feeding his mind with many sweet thoughts and "sugared suppositions," he journeyed along the sides of a range of hills which look out upon some of the goodliest scenes of the mighty Hudson. The sun gradually wheeled his broad disk down into the west. The wide bosom of the Tappan Zee lay motionless and glassy, excepting that here and there a gentle undulation waved and prolonged the blue shadow of the distant mountain. A few amber clouds floated in the sky, without a breath of air to move them. The horizon was of a fine golden tint, changing gradually into a pure apple green, and from that into the deep blue of the mid-heaven. A slanting ray lingered on the woody crests of the precipices that overhung some parts of the river, giving greater depth to the darkgray and purple of their rocky sides. A sloop was loitering in the distance, dropping slowly down with the tide, her sail hanging uselessly against the mast, and as the reflection of the sky gleamed along the still water it seemed as if the vessel was suspended in the air.

It was toward evening that Ichabod arrived at the castle of the Heer Van Tassel, which he found thronged with the pride and flower of the adjacent country — old farmers, a spare, leathern-faced race, in homespun coats and breeches, blue stockings, huge shoes, and magnificent pewter buckles; their brisk withered little dames, in close crimped caps, long-waisted gowns, homespun petticoats, with scissors and pincushions and gay calico pockets hanging on the outside; buxom lasses, almost as antiquated as their mothers, excepting where a straw hat, a fine ribbon, or perhaps a white frock, gave symptoms of city innovation; the sons, in short square-skirted coats with rows of stupendous brass buttons, and their hair generally queued in the fashion of the times, especially if they could procure an eel-skin for the purpose, it being esteemed throughout the country as a potent nourisher and strengthener of the hair.

Brom Bones, however, was the hero of the scene, having come to the gathering on his favorite steed Daredevil — a creature, like himself full of metal and mischief, and which no one but himself could manage. He was, in fact, noted for preferring vicious animals, given to all kinds of tricks, which kept the rider in constant risk of his neck, for he held a tractable, well-broken horse as unworthy of a lad of spirit.

Fain would I pause to dwell upon the world of charms that burst upon the enraptured gaze of my hero as he entered the state parlor of Van Tassel's mansion. Not those of the bevy of buxom lasses with their luxurious display of red and white, but the ample charms of a genuine Dutch country tea-table in the sumptuous time of autumn. Such heaped-up platters of cakes of various and almost indescribable kinds, known only to experienced Dutch housewives! There was the doughty doughnut, the tenderer oily koek, and the crisp and crumbling cruller; sweet cakes and short cakes, ginger cakes and honey cakes, and the whole family of cakes. And then there were apple pies and peach pies and pumpkin pies; besides slices of ham and smoked beef; and moreover delectable dishes of preserved plums and peaches and pears and quinces; not to mention broiled shad and roasted chickens; together with bowls of milk and cream, — all mingled higgledy-piggledy, pretty much as I have enumerated them, with the motherly tea-pot sending up its clouds of vapor from the midst. Heaven bless the mark! I want breath and time to discuss this banquet as it deserves, and am too eager to get on with my story. Happily, Ichabod Crane was not in so great a hurry as his historian, but did ample justice to every dainty.

He was a kind and thankful creature, whose heart dilated in proportion as his skin was filled with good cheer, and whose spirits rose with eating as some men's do with drink. He could not help, too, rolling his large eyes round him as he ate, and chuckling with the possibility that he might one day be lord of all this scene of almost unimaginable luxury and splendor. Then, he thought, how soon he'd turn his back upon the old school-house, snap his fingers in the face of Hans Van Ripper and every other niggardly patron, and kick any itinerant pedagogue out of doors that should dare to call him comrade!

Old Baltus Van Tassel moved about among his guests with a face dilated with content and good-humor, round and jolly as the harvest moon. His hospitable attentions were brief, but expressive, being confined to a shake of the hand, a slap on the shoulder, a loud laugh, and a pressing invitation to " fall to and help themselves."

And now the sound of the music from the common room, or hall, summoned to the dance. The musician was an old gray-headed negro who had been the itinerant orchestra of the neighborhood for more than half a century. His instrument was as old and battered as himself. The greater part of the time he scraped on two or three strings, accompanying every movement of the bow with a motion of the head, bowing almost to the ground and stamping with his foot whenever a fresh couple were to start.

Ichabod prided himself upon his dancing as much as upon his vocal powers. Not a limb, not a fiber about him was idle; and to have seen his loosely hung frame in full motion and clattering about the room you would have thought Saint Vitus himself, that blessed patron of the dance, was figuring before you in person. He was the admiration of all the negroes, who, having gathered, of all ages and sizes, from the farm and the neighborhood, stood forming a pyramid of shining black faces at every door and window, gazing with delight at the scene, rolling their white eyeballs, and showing grinning rows of ivory from ear to ear. How could the flogger of urchins be otherwise than animated and joyous? The lady of his heart was his partner in the dance, and smiling graciously in reply to all his amorous oglings, while Brom Bones, sorely smitten with love and jealousy, sat brooding by himself in one corner.

When the dance was at an end Ichabod was attracted to a knot of the sager folks, who, with old Van Tassel, sat smoking at one end of the piazza gossiping over former times and drawing out long stories about the war.

This neighborhood, at the time of which I am speaking, was one of those highly favored places which abound with chronicle and great men. The British and American line had run near it during the war; it had therefore been the scene of marauding and infested with refugees, cow-boys, and all kinds of border chivalry. Just sufficient time had elapsed to enable each story-teller to dress up his tale with a little becoming fiction, and in the indistinctness of his recollection to make himself the hero of every exploit.

There was the story of Doffue Martling, a large blue-bearded Dutchman, who had nearly taken a British frigate with an old iron nine-pounder from a mud breastwork, only that his gun burst at the sixth discharge. And there was an old gentleman who shall be nameless, being too rich a mynheer to be lightly mentioned, who, in the battle of Whiteplains, being an excellent master of defence, parried a musket-ball with a small sword, insomuch that he absolutely felt it whiz round the blade and glance off at the hilt: in proof of which he was ready at any time to show the sword, with the hilt a little bent. There were several more that had been equally great in the field, not one of whom but was persuaded that he had a considerable hand in bringing the war to a happy termination.

But all these were nothing to the tales of ghosts and apparitions that succeeded. The neighborhood is rich in legendary treasures of the kind. Local tales and superstitions thrive best in these sheltered, long-settled retreats, but are trampled under foot by the shifting throng that forms the population of most of our country places. Besides, there is no encouragement for ghosts in most of our villages, for they have scarcely had time to finish their first nap and turn themselves in their graves before their surviving friends have traveled away from the neighborhood; so that when they turn out at night to walk their rounds they have no acquaintance left to call upon. This is perhaps the reason why we so seldom hear of ghosts except in our long-established Dutch communities.

The immediate cause, however, of the prevalence of supernatural stories in these parts was doubtless owing to the vicinity of Sleepy Hollow. There was a contagion in the very air that blew from that haunted region; it breathed forth an atmosphere of dreams and fancies infecting all the land. Several of the Sleepy Hollow people were present at Van

Tassel's, and, as usual, were doling out their wild and wonderful legends. Many dismal tales were told about funeral trains and mourning cries and wailings heard and seen about the great tree where the unfortunate Major André was taken, and which stood in the neighborhood. Some mention was made also of the woman in white that haunted the dark glen at Raven Rock, and was often heard to shriek on winter nights before a storm, having perished there in the snow. The chief part of the stories, however, turned upon the favorite specter of Sleepy Hollow, the headless horseman, who had been heard several times of late patrolling the country, and, it was said, tethered his horse nightly among the graves in the churchyard.

The sequestered situation of this church seems always to have made it a favorite haunt of troubled spirits. It stands on a knoll surrounded by locust trees and lofty elms, from among which its decent whitewashed walls shine modestly forth, like Christian purity beaming through the shades of retirement. A gentle slope descends from it to a silver sheet of water bordered by high trees, between which peeps may be caught at the blue hills of the Hudson. To look upon its grass-grown yard, where the sunbeams seem to sleep so quietly, one would think that there at least the dead might rest in peace. On one side of the church extends a wide woody dell, along which raves a large brook among broken rocks and trunks of fallen trees. Over a deep black part of the stream, not far from the church, was formerly thrown a wooden bridge; the road that led to it and the bridge itself were thickly shaded by overhanging trees, which cast a gloom about it even in the daytime, but occasioned a fearful darkness at night. Such was one of the favorite haunts of the headless horseman, and the place where he was most frequently encountered. The tale was told of old Brouwer, a most heretical disbeliever in ghosts, how he met the horseman returning from his foray into Sleepy Hollow, and was obliged to get up behind him; how they galloped over bush and brake, over hill and swamp, until they reached the bridge, when the horseman suddenly turned into a skeleton, threw old Brouwer into the brook, and sprang away over the tree-tops with a clap of thunder.

This story was immediately matched by a thrice-marvelous adventure of Brom Bones, who made light of the galloping Hessian as an arrant jockey. He affirmed that on returning one night from the neighboring village of Sing-Sing he had been overtaken by this midnight trooper; that he had offered to race with him for a bowl of punch, and should have won it too, for Daredevil beat the goblin horse all hollow, but just as they came to the church bridge the Hessian bolted and vanished in a flash of fire.

All these tales, told in that drowsy undertone with which men talk in the dark, the countenances of the listeners only now and then receiving a casual gleam from the glare of a pipe, sank deep in the mind of Ichabod. He repaid them in kind with large extracts from his invaluable author, Cotton Mather, and added many marvelous events that had taken place in his native state of Connecticut and fearful sights which he had seen in his nightly walks about Sleepy Hollow.

The revel now gradually broke up. The old farmers gathered together their families in their wagons, and were heard for some time rattling along the hollow roads and over the distant hills. Some of the damsels mounted on pillions behind their favorite swains, and their light-hearted laughter, mingling with the clatter of hoofs, echoed along the silent woodlands, sounding fainter and fainter until they gradually died away, and the late scene of noise and frolic was all silent and deserted. Ichabod only lingered behind, according to the custom of country lovers, to have a tête-à-tête with the heiress, fully convinced that he was now on the high road to success. What passed at this interview I will not pretend to say, for in fact I do not know. Something, however, I fear me, must have gone wrong, for he certainly sallied forth, after no very great interval, with an air quite desolate and chop-fallen. Oh these women! these women! Could that girl have been playing off any of her coquettish tricks? Was her encouragement of the poor pedagogue all a mere sham to secure her conquest of his rival? Heaven only knows, not I! Let it suffice to say, Ichabod stole forth with the air of one who has been sacking a hen-roost, rather than a fair lady's heart. Without looking to the right or left to notice the scene of rural wealth on which he had so often gloated, he went straight to the stable, and with several hearty cuffs and kicks roused his steed most uncourteously from the comfortable quarters in which he was soundly sleeping, dreaming of mountains of corn and oats and whole valleys of timothy and clover.

It was the very witching time of night that Ichabod, heavyhearted and crestfallen, pursued his travel homewards along the sides of the lofty hills which rise above Tarry Town, and which he had traversed so cheerily in the afternoon. The hour was as dismal as himself. Far below him the Tappan Zee spread its dusky and indistinct waste of waters, with here and there the tall mast of a sloop riding quietly at anchor under the land. In the dead hush of midnight he could even hear the barking of the watch-dog from the opposite shore of the Hudson; but it was so vague and faint as only to give an idea of his distance from this faithful companion of man. Now and then, too, the long-drawn crowing of a cock, accidentally awakened, would sound far, far off, from some farmhouse away among the hills; but it was like a dreaming sound in his ear. No signs of life occurred near him, but occasionally the melancholy chirp of a cricket, or perhaps the guttural twang of a bullfrog from a neighboring marsh, as if sleeping uncomfortably and turning suddenly in his bed.

All the stories of ghosts and goblins that he had heard in the afternoon now came crowding upon his recollection. The night grew darker and darker; the stars seemed to sink deeper in the sky, and driving clouds occasionally hid them from his sight. He had never felt so lonely and dismal. He was, moreover, approaching the very place where many of the scenes of the ghost stories had been laid. In the center of the road stood an enormous tulip tree which towered like a giant above all the other trees of the neighborhood and formed a kind of landmark. Its limbs were gnarled and fantastic, large enough to form trunks for ordinary trees, twisting down almost to the earth and rising again into the air. It was connected with the tragical story of the unfortunate André, who had been taken prisoner hard by, and was universally known by the name of Major André's tree. The common people regarded it with a mixture of respect and superstition, partly out of sympathy for the fate of its ill-starred namesake, and partly from the tales of strange sights and doleful lamentations told concerning it.

As Ichabod approached this fearful tree he began to whistle: he thought his whistle was answered; it was but a blast sweeping sharply through the dry branches. As he approached a little nearer he thought he saw something white hanging in the midst of the tree: he paused and ceased whistling, but on looking more narrowly perceived that it was a place where the tree had been scathed by lightning and the white wood laid bare. Suddenly he heard a groan: his teeth chattered and his knees smote against the saddle; it was but the rubbing of one huge bough upon another as they were swayed about by the breeze. He passed the tree in safety, but new perils lay before him.

About two hundred yards from the tree a small brook crossed the road and ran into a marshy and thickly-wooded glen known by the name of Wiley's Swamp. A few rough logs, laid side by side, served for a bridge over the stream. On that side of the road where the brook entered the wood a group of oaks and chestnuts, matted thick with wild grapevines, threw a cavernous gloom over it. To pass this bridge was the severest trial. It was at this identical spot that the unfortunate André was captured, and under the covert of those chestnuts and vines were the sturdy yeomen concealed who surprised him. This has ever since been considered a haunted stream, and fearful are the feelings of the schoolboy who has to pass it alone after dark.

As he approached the stream his heart began to thump; he summoned up, however, all his resolution, gave his horse half a score of kicks in the ribs, and attempted to dash briskly across the bridge; but instead of starting forward, the perverse old animal made a lateral movement and ran broadside against the fence. Ichabod, whose fears increased with the delay, jerked the reins on the other side and kicked lustily with the contrary foot: it was all in vain; his steed started, it is true, but it was only to plunge to the opposite side of the road into a thicket of brambles and alder-bushes. The schoolmaster now bestowed both whip and heel upon the starveling ribs of old Gunpowder, who dashed forward, snuffling and snorting, but came to a stand just by the bridge with a suddenness that had nearly sent his rider sprawling over his head. Just at this moment a plashy tramp by the side of the bridge caught the sensitive ear of Ichabod. In the dark shadow of the grove on the margin of the brook he beheld something huge, misshapen, black, and towering. It stirred not, but seemed gathered up in the gloom, like some gigantic monster ready to spring upon the traveler.

The hair of the affrighted pedagogue rose upon his head with terror. What was to be done? To turn and fly was now too late; and besides, what chance was there of escaping ghost or goblin, if such it was, which could ride upon the wings of the wind? Summoning up, therefore, a show of courage, he demanded in stammering accents, "Who are you?" He received no reply. He repeated his demand in a still more agitated voice. Still there was no answer. Once more he cudgeled the sides of the inflexible Gunpowder, and, shutting his eyes, broke forth with involuntary fervor into a psalm tune. Just then the shadowy object of alarm put itself in motion, and with a scramble and a bound stood at once in the middle of the road. Though the night was dark and dismal, yet the form of the unknown might now in some degree be ascertained. He appeared to be a horseman of large dimensions and mounted on a black horse of powerful frame. He made no offer of molestation or sociability, but kept aloof on one side of the road, jogging along on the blind side of old Gunpowder, who had now got over his fright and waywardness.

Ichabod, who had no relish for this strange midnight companion, and bethought himself of the adventure of Brom Bones with the Galloping Hessian, now quickened his steed in hopes of leaving him behind. The stranger, however, quickened his horse to an equal pace. Ichabod pulled up, and fell into a walk, thinking to lag behind; the other did the same. His heart began to sink within him; he endeavored to resume his psalm tune, but his parched tongue clove to the roof of his mouth and he could not utter a stave. There was something in the moody and dogged silence of this pertinacious companion that was mysterious and appalling. It was soon fearfully accounted for. On mounting a rising ground, which brought the figure of his fellow-traveler in relief against the sky, gigantic in height and muffled in a cloak, Ichabod was horror-struck on perceiving that he was headless; but his horror was still more increased on observing that the head, which should have rested on his shoulders, was carried before him on the pommel of the saddle. His terror rose to desperation, he rained a shower of kicks and blows upon Gunpowder, hoping by a sudden movement to give his companion the slip; but the specter started full jump with him. Away, then, they dashed through thick and thin, stones flying and sparks flashing at every bound. Ichabod's flimsy garments fluttered in the air as he stretched his long lank body away over his horse's head in the eagerness of his flight.

They had now reached the road which turns off to Sleepy Hollow; but Gunpowder, who seemed possessed with a demon, instead of keeping up it, made an opposite turn and plunged headlong downhill to the left. This road leads through a sandy hollow shaded by trees for about a quarter of a mile, where it crosses the bridge famous in goblin story, and just beyond swells the green knoll on which stands the whitewashed church.

As yet the panic of the steed had given his unskilful rider an apparent advantage in the chase; but just as he had got halfway through the hollow the girths of the saddle gave way and he felt it slipping from under him. He seized it by the pommel and endeavored to hold it firm, but in vain, and had just time to save himself by clasping old Gunpowder round the neck, when the saddle fell to the earth, and he heard it trampled under foot by his pursuer. For a moment the terror of Hans Van Ripper's wrath passed across his mind, for it was his Sunday saddle; but this was no time for petty fears; the goblin was hard on his haunches, and (unskilled rider that he was) he had much ado to maintain his seat, sometimes slipping on one side, sometimes on another, and sometimes jolted on the high ridge of his horse's backbone with a violence that he verily feared would cleave him asunder.

An opening in the trees now cheered him with the hopes that the church bridge was at hand. The wavering reflection of a silver star in the bosom of the brook told him that he was not mistaken. He saw the walls of the church dimly glaring under the trees beyond. He recollected the place where Brom Bones' ghostly competitor had disappeared. "If I can but reach that bridge," thought Ichabod, "I am safe." Just then he heard the black steed panting and blowing close behind him; he even fancied that he felt his hot breath. Another convulsive kick in the ribs, and old Gunpowder sprang upon the bridge; he thundered over the resounding planks; he gained the opposite side; and now Ichabod cast a look behind to see if his pursuer should vanish, according to rule, in a flash of fire and brimstone. Just then he saw the goblin rising in his stirrups, and in the very act of hurling his head at him. Ichabod endeavored to dodge the missile, but too late. It encountered his cranium with a tremendous crash; he was tumbled headlong into the dust, and Gunpowder, the black steed, and the goblin rider passed by like a whirlwind.

The next morning the old horse was found, without his saddle and with the bridle under his feet, soberly cropping the grass at his master's gate. Ichabod did not make his appearance at breakfast; dinner-hour came, but no Ichabod. The boys assembled at the school-house and strolled idly about the banks of the brook; but no schoolmaster. Hans Van Ripper now began to feel some uneasiness about the fate of poor Ichabod and his saddle. An inquiry was set on foot, and after diligent investigation they came upon his traces. In one part of the road leading to the church was found the saddle trampled in the dirt; the tracks of horses' hoofs, deeply dented in the road and evidently at furious speed, were traced to the bridge, beyond which, on the bank of a broad part of the brook, where the water ran deep and black, was found the hat of the unfortunate Ichabod, and close beside it a shattered pumpkin.

The brook was searched, but the body of the schoolmaster was not to be discovered. Hans Van Ripper, as executor of his estate, examined the bundle which contained all his worldly effects. They consisted of two shirts and a half, two stocks for the neck, a pair or two of worsted stockings, an old pair of corduroy small-clothes, a rusty razor, a book of psalm tunes full of dog's ears, and a broken pitch-pipe. As to the books and furniture of the school-house, they belonged to the community, excepting Cotton Mather's *History of Witchcraft,* a *New England Almanac,* and a book of dreams and fortune-telling; in which last was a sheet of foolscap much scribbled and blotted in several fruitless attempts to make a copy of verses in honor of the heiress of Van Tassel. These magic books and the poetic scrawl were forthwith consigned to the flames by Hans Van Ripper, who from that time forward determined to send his children no more to school, observing that he never knew any good come of this same reading and writing. Whatever money the schoolmaster possessed — and he had received his quarter's pay but a day or two before — he must have had about his person at the time of his disappearance.

The mysterious event caused much speculation at the church on the following Sunday. Knots of gazers and gossips were collected in the churchyard, at the bridge, and at the spot where the hat and pumpkin had been found. The stories of Brouwer, of Bones, and a whole budget of others were called to mind, and when they had diligently considered them all, and compared them with the symptoms of the present case, they shook their heads and came to the conclusion that Ichabod had been carried off by the Galloping Hessian. As he was a bachelor and in nobody's debt, nobody troubled his head any more about him, the school was removed to a different quarter of the hollow and another pedagogue reigned in his stead.

It is true an old farmer, who had been down to New York on a visit several years after, and from whom this account of the ghostly adventure was received, brought home the intelligence that Ichabod Crane was still alive; that he had left the neighborhood, partly through fear of the goblin and Hans Van Ripper, and partly in mortification at having been suddenly dismissed by the heiress; that he had changed his quarters to a distant part of the country; had kept school and studied law at the same time, had been admitted to the bar, turned politician, electioneered, written for the newspapers, and finally had been made a justice of the Ten Pound Court. Brom Bones too, who shortly after his rival's disappearance conducted the blooming Katrina in triumph to the altar, was observed to look exceedingly knowing whenever the story of Ichabod was related, and always burst into a hearty laugh at the mention of the pumpkin; which led some to suspect that he knew more about the matter than he chose to tell.

The old country wives, however, who are the best judges of these matters, maintain to this day that Ichabod was spirited away by supernatural means; and it is a favorite story often told about the neighborhood round the winter evening fire. The bridge became more than ever an object of superstitious awe, and that may be the reason why the road has been altered of late years, so as to approach the church by the border of the mill-pond. The school-house, being deserted, soon fell to decay, and was reported to be haunted by the ghost of the unfortunate pedagogue; and the plow-boy, loitering homeward of a still summer evening, has often fancied his voice at a distance chanting a melancholy psalm tune among the tranquil solitudes of Sleepy Hollow.

## POSTSCRIPT,

#### FOUND IN THE HANDWRITING OF MR. KNICKERBOCKER

THE preceding tale is given almost in the precise words in which I heard it related at a Corporation meeting of the ancient city of Manhattoes, at which were present many of its sagest and most illustrious burghers. The narrator was a pleasant, shabby, gentlemanly old fellow in pepper-and-salt clothes, with a sadly humorous face, and one whom I strongly suspected of being poor, he made such efforts to be entertaining. When his story was concluded there was much laughter and approbation, particularly from two or three deputy aldermen who had been asleep the greater part of the time. There was, however, one tall, dry-looking old gentleman, with beetling eyebrows, who maintained a grave and rather severe face throughout, now and then folding his arms, inclining his head, and looking down upon the floor, as if turning a doubt over in his mind. He was one of your wary men, who never laugh but upon good grounds — when they have reason and the law on their side. When the mirth of the rest of the company had subsided and silence was restored, he leaned one arm on the elbow of his chair, and sticking the other akimbo, demanded, with a slight but exceedingly sage motion of the head and contraction of the brow, what was the moral of the story and what it went to prove.

The story-teller, who was just putting a glass of wine to his lips as a refreshment after his toils, paused for a moment, looked at his inquirer with an air of infinite deference, and, lowering the glass slowly to the table, observed that the story was intended most logically to prove —

"That there is no situation in life but has its advantages and pleasures — provided we will but take a joke as we find it;

"That, therefore, he that runs races with goblin troopers is likely to have rough riding of it.

"Ergo, for a country schoolmaster to be refused the hand of a Dutch heiress is a certain step to high preferment in the state."

## The Legend of Sleepy Hollow

The cautious old gentleman knit his brows tenfold closer after this explanation, being sorely puzzled by the ratiocination of the syllogism, while methought the one in pepper-and-salt eyed him with something of a triumphant leer. At length he observed that all this was very well, but still he thought the story a little on the extravagant — there were one or two points on which he had his doubts.

"Faith, sir," replied the story-teller, "as to that matter I don't believe one-half of it myself." D. K.

### QUESTIONS

1. In the first few pages of the story find evidence of what is said in the final paragraphs of the sketch.
2. Find expressions that tend to show that Irving made up some of the legends.
3. Who was Master Hendrick Hudson?
4. What early paragraphs give "atmosphere"? Explain.
5. Would "The Headless Horseman of Sleepy Hollow" have been a better title? Explain.
6. Where is the real beginning of the story? Contrast this with "Rip Van Winkle."
7. From memory, describe Ichabod.
8. Where are the first hints of the plot?
9. What was a "traveling gazette"?
10. What side of Ichabod's character prepares the reader for the climax?
11. Characterize Katrina. What traits are vital for the conclusion?
12. Name ten material things that helped to disturb Ichabod's "peace of mind."
13. Why was his task more difficult than "the lot of a knight-errant of yore"?
14. Describe and characterize the villain.
15. How did girls wear their hair in those days?
16. How would you spell the word "metal" as used in the text?
17. What feature of the party once more suggests the atmosphere of the climax?
18. What had gone wrong in Ichabod's tête-à-tête with Katrina?
19. Is the author's explanation correct?
20. Contrast Ichabod's ride home with the ride earlier in the evening. Give definite details.
21. From memory, describe the scene where Ichabod meets the "Headless Horseman." Does it fit in with your idea of a ghost story?
22. Exactly where is the climax?
23. In spite of the "old wives' tales," is the reader in any doubt as to Ichabod's fate?
24. Do you know a poem by Robert Burns that tells a similar tale?

25. Does the frequent use of terms of chivalry suggest that Irving was fond of Scott?
26. What do you make of the " tall, dry-looking old gentleman " of the " Postscript " ?

## FOR COMPOSITION

1. Tell orally the story of Major André.
2. Katrina Prepares for the Party.
3. Brom Bones Prepares for the Party.
4. A Morning in Ichabod's School.

## OTHER STORIES BY WASHINGTON IRVING

Rip Van Winkle
The Spectre Bridegroom
Legend of the Moor's Legacy (*Alhambra*)
Legend of the Three Beautiful Princesses (*Alhambra*)
Legend of the Arabian Astrologer (*Alhambra*)
The Student of Salamanca (*Bracebridge Hall*)
Tales of a Traveler (a collection)

## ABOUT WASHINGTON IRVING

*Washington Irving*, Charles Dudley Warner
*Washington Irving*, H. W. Boynton

## EDNA FERBER
## (1887-    )

BORN in Kalamazoo, Michigan, August 15, 1887, Edna Ferber moved at an early age to Appleton, Wisconsin, where she attended grade and high school. When only seventeen she became a reporter on *The Daily Crescent* of Appleton. While she admits that it was a harrowing job, she got her first sharp insight into humanity. Her knowledge of people was increased by her early habit of observing her fellow creatures as they went their daily way. Later, she was correspondent for two Milwaukee papers, and later still, for the *Chicago Tribune*. When she was twenty-four she had completed her first novel, *Dawn O'Hara*. This was so successful that she had no difficulty in disposing of her short stories to which she then turned her attention. The earlier ones were based upon the background of her life in Appleton. Most of these are to be found in the volume, *Buttered Side Down*.

After Appleton came Beloit and Slatersville, then Chicago, and finally New York, where she continues to live. However, she has always found time for travels in far countries, but always and everywhere her interest is in human beings.

In her early stories she writes about men and women going about their daily business, such as clerks, traveling salesmen, and stenographers. Her most interesting character creation, Emma McChesney, is a traveling saleswoman, first introduced in the volume, *Roast Beef Medium*, and appearing in several later volumes. But Miss Ferber also likes to write about cooks and women who allow themselves to become household drudges.

With her abiding interest in character study, it is easy to understand why Miss Ferber's short stories are usually weak in plot. While this has often been pointed out as a fault by her critics, she nevertheless continues to write according to her own ideas. She once replied to a critic: "People's insides are so much more interesting than their outsides." It is interesting to note that in many of her stories there is a particular emphasis on food, as suggested by the title of her first book of short stories. Watch for this element in the following story. Her lack of interest in plot is compensated for by her careful attention to details and the description of character. These characteristics are almost all well exemplified in "Meadow Lark," which is taken from Miss Ferber's latest collection (1933), *They Brought Their Women*.

The meadow lark is a fairly common bird in most sections of our country. One of its most noteworthy characteristics is its graceful flight as it rises slowly from the ground and spirals upward. Hence, it is natural enough that the author should see it as a suitable title for a story about an airplane. But, true to her usual interest in the ordinary man, Miss Ferber does not write about one of the epoch-making flights that have become so well known since Lindbergh's great flight to Paris some years ago, but rather about the ambition of an ordinary farm boy to sit in a cockpit and handle the controls of one of these marvelous machines — the ambition of almost every normal modern boy. However, amongst the parents of today, there are still oldtimers like Pa Trost who see in new things only the ridiculous and curse them because they are so different from what they have been accustomed to. Such attitudes inevitably lead to a lack of understanding between the older and the newer generations. In this story there is this element. For young Theodore, the planes which he constantly sees and hears flying over the farm are the very essence of Romance, as well as the symbols of freedom from the hard, narrow life of his home which he looked upon as a monotonous physical grind leading nowhere. While for Pa Trost, those same airplanes were symbols of evil and destruction that threatened the productiveness of the farm which was the concrete evidence of his thrift and conformance to the standards of success held by his generation — a precious possession to a man like Pa Trost.

The determination of Theodore to escape despite the opposition of his father, and the maneuvers of his mother to get him safely married to a girl of her own type so that he will settle down on a farm and carry on in the family tradition form what plot there is of the story. But, as one would expect of a story by Miss Ferber, the plot of " Meadow Lark " is less important than the characterization, for the author shows vividly and interestingly how and why each character is what he is; and, being what they are, the result of the situation in the story is inevitable.

By watching for all these points you will find a thoroughly satisfying story in " Meadow Lark " and you will also be able to see why Miss Ferber ranks in the very forefront of modern American short story writers.

## MEADOW LARK

WHEN first the winged things had come zooming out of the sky above the Kansas prairie land old man Trost used to stand there in the middle of the field he was plowing — or even when the threshing crew was there — and shake his great brown fist at them. A stout and ridiculous Ajax,[1] yet not quite ridiculous, either, in his impotent wrath, he would turn his face toward the heavens and utter imprecations in his native tongue.

" *Gott verdammt noch e' mal!* " he would roar. " *Die Dinger da — die verfluchten Dinger!* "[2] But presently they became so numerous that the fist-shaking had to be abandoned. It would have taken too much of his time, for the government established an airport not four miles distant from the Trost farm, and glass-roofed airplane factories glittered like bubbles all over the prairies skirting the city of Wichita.

Wichita boasted of this, trumpeting: More Airplanes Made in Wichita Than in Any Other City. But the Kansas farmers were furious. None so furious, though, as old man Trost. He threatened to sue the government on the grounds that his farm was being ruined.

The night planes, roaring overhead, disturbed the chickens in their roosts, so that they refused to lay; the stock grew thin with nervousness; the milk dried up in the cows' udders; the mares, maddened by the strange roar always overhead, ramped across the pastures, manes tossing, wild eyes rolling, their hoofs beating a smart tattoo of panic on the fence posts.

Some of that same madness seemed to take hold of old man Trost as the things multiplied — those things swooping and roaring and taunting him from the skies. Here he was, tied to the earth. There they soared, free.

As time went on, the neighboring farmers accepted the new order of things, but Trost never. One of the more daring souls said, " Why don't you take a ride in one? Try it once. Say, you take a look at that farm of yours from five thousand feet up and you'll get a different idea how big it is. It's like you was God and nothing down here is anything. Whole Wichita looks like a toy set for kids."

Trost's face would go mahogany with choler. " If I would get hold once of one of those *verfluchten Dinger* [3] I would show you how it would go up." His brown hands would curve into claws as though he were tearing the soaring thing wing from wing.

Old man Trost was not really old at all; forty-eight at most. But he had married at eighteen, and his was the settled aspect of one long used to the marital yoke. A powerful man, and dark with a strange darkness belying his Saxon ancestry. A firm barrel of a body, a neck like an ox, short strong legs. A solid-looking man, pot-bellied, burned by the Kansas sun and wind; brusque of speech.

Except for his swarthy coloring he was unromantic of mien; commonplace, almost. A prosperous Midwest farmer, German born, conforming on the surface at least to all the conventional rules for husband, father, citizen. No one knew, no one suspected, that in this unremarkable body rushed the hot blood of the adventurer. Inside, old man Trost was a figure of romance.

Perhaps sometimes Ma Trost wondered about him; but his occasional vagaries she put down to temper or to indigestion. Certainly his temper was something to be reckoned with in that household; a smoldering thing that blazed high and hot into sudden unreasonable rages.

At such times the Trost children, when young, had feared him. When he made for them, arm raised, the scarlet flood of temper turning his brown face to purple, they had scurried for the shelter of their mother's broad haunches and had hidden in the folds of her ample skirts, peering fearfully from this shelter to watch her quelling the storm they had raised.

"Now, Trost, now! Some day by mistake you will hit me, and then you will see. I start for you with the rolling pin like in the movies. Here — get away, all of you — out of my kitchen. *Tapfer, tapfer!*"[4]

His anger would go as quickly as it had come. The brooding darkness, that sat so oddly on this stout farmer, would settle down on him again. Perhaps far, far back in his line there was a seafaring Spaniard; or an Italian from the north of Italy; or, even more remotely still, a plundering Gaul.

He had come to America a boy of twelve. The sea had stayed ever in his mind, though he never looked upon it again. The Kansas prairie on which he settled and thrived knew no water except the rain, and even that sometimes withheld itself grudgingly when it was most needed. No one knew that as he plowed the Midwest fields, row on row, the furrows that turned so voluptuously under the plow were waves before the prow of a ship that cut through the green-black waters.

Often enough, in those days of his early youth, one heard of this or that inland farm boy who had run away to sea. He, perhaps, might have been one of them, but the lively girl who now was Ma Trost had caught him and held him fast; and there followed the children, four girls and, last, the boy Theodore; and the Kansas fields to be plowed and planted and added to, acre on acre. They had him now, safe enough from the sea. The neighboring farmers put him down as odd, this portly man with the big paunch and the bright dark eyes. He grew on his farm things that they never thought of, and would not have attempted if they had.

Strange fowl pecked in his barnyard — birds with odd colorings and haughty struttings. Hens snow-white; roosters like a sunset; speckled things with markings foreign to the common coop. Then he actually attempted to grow peanuts and did, burying them in mounds in a patch of sandy soil and tending them slavishly. They proved little shriveled things at first, but he persisted, and they grew in firmness and plumpness until they were a marvel in this temperate climate.

He planted a vineyard for love of the exotic. With infinite pains and many difficulties he succeeded in perfecting rare varieties — small, sweet, pale green Lady Washingtons; Spanish grapes, purple-black ovals with a down on their dusky cheeks. These he tended in the evening when the others of the family had rattled off to town in the car, to see Laura Lovely in *Passion's Playground*.[5]

He walked alone, softly, in his felt slippers, this burgher, smoking his seasoned pipe; weeding here, spading there, spending in dalliance with his loves the hours that in his thrifty daytime he begrudged them. His hand, with its thick brown fingers, passed tenderly, lingeringly, over the clustered grapes, like a lover's hand.

Not one of the children would have dared to eat those grapes unbidden. They sometimes longed to pluck surreptitiously a sweet juicy glove from the under side of a cluster nestling almost hidden in its dark leaves. But they never did. Sometimes — rarely — Ma Trost would cut a whole bunch in a fit of frisky defiance and pass it round as though the green things were emeralds and the blue, sapphires.

Certainly Ma Trost was not the drab farm drudge of fiction. A vast and sprightly woman in a bungalow apron and boudoir cap, with a kind of rich gayety for her husband's dourness. It was she who planted and tended the bright patch of flower garden with its hardy staring blossoms — zinnias, verbenas, asters, blue flag, broad-faced sunflowers.

Even in the winter there stood in the kitchen window a wooden rack holding pots and slips, tier on tier; fuchsias bloomed; there were bleeding heart, geraniums scarlet and pink, bits of cactus. She filled the room with green and growing things and with a kind of hearty abundance; she gave to the house a friendly aspect that offset her husband's dark sullenness; a woman with floury arms, an ample aproned front, little merry eyes that disappeared in wrinkles of laughter.

The four girls had given them a fright, coming like that — one, two, three, four — one after the other. But then, when they were almost despairing, the boy Theodore had come, and everything was all right. In good time the four girls had married readily enough, being healthy, bouncing, red-cheeked creatures with their mother's hearty laugh and her knack with the baking board and kettle. They had gone off with their strapping husbands to near-by farms or to Wichita to live.

Ma Trost saw them often enough, welcomed their growing brood, fed the whole tribe from time to time as they drove up to the Trost farm on Sundays and spilled out of their chunky automobiles. But whether the girls and their families came or went, she had Theodore.

She had Theodore in the house, and she had Theodore there in the near-by fields, but she no more knew Theodore than she knew this dark husband of hers. For while the four girls were fair, the boy was dark like his father, and the two men worked the fields and tended the stock, and both looked up at the darting, droning, winged things high in the sky or swooping impudently close to the Trost housetop and patch of woods.

Try to catch me, you worms down there — you grubs burrowing in the earth. And the dour man of forty-eight looked up and was choked with baffled rage and futility; but the dark boy of nineteen looked up and his eyes had the glow, the hope, the resolve of a man who, gazing at his love as she coquets with him, teases him, devils him, is serene in the knowledge that this wild free thing will one day be his, tamed, submissive under his hand.

To Theo there was nothing new or strange about these flying things as there was to an older generation. He had seen them and heard them since early childhood. They were an accepted fact — as much a part of the order of things as the automobile, the telephone, the phonograph. He loved all things motor-driven, but this thing he worshipped. It not only moved; it flew, spurning the ground. It was more than a motor, more than a ship. An air ship.

"Stop reading them magazines once and go like the other boys," Ma Trost was forever saying. Or, "You ain't going to work again in that shed, tinkering all hours of the night! Why'n't you take Bertha to the movie in town? How she sits there in the evening with her pa, that poor girl, with her education and all, so smart, and pretty, too, Bertha Muller is. H'm? Why don't you, once, Theo?"

He would glance absently up at her from the magazine he was reading or the bench at which he was working.

The magazines were always the same — *Mechanical Age; Air; Motor; The Pilot; Aviation.* Their ads said: Are You Hungry for Popularity, Adventure, Big Pay? Then Choose Aviation.

Are You a Red-Blooded, Daring He-Man?

A picture accompanying this of a helmeted Lindberghian youth.

He had made for himself a workshop in an old shed that had been an abandoned henroost. Little by little, painfully, with the dimes, quarters, and half-dollars that came his way in that thrifty German farm household — the small change that other lads of his age spent for movies, soft drinks, girls, fancy shirts — he had acquired tools, a motor, all the necessities of a workshop.

Before he was sixteen he had practically built for himself an automobile out of such odds and ends as only a born mechanic could assemble and invest magically with the power of locomotion. Shivering, snarling, rattling in every bolt and screw, it still could miraculously outdistance the plump middle-class family car.

Ma Trost would trot out to the shed after their early supper and stand in the doorway, surveying her last-born with a mingled pride and impatience. "Such a grand girl, poor Bertha, and there she sits on a lovely evening like this with her sick pa."

At her importuning he glanced up abstractedly. He had the clear childlike eyes, the wise guileless face of the natural mechanic — of one to whom a motor is a more living thing than a human being. Sweetness was there, and strength and utter detachment.

"Leave her sit."

It was not that he disliked the Muller girl. He liked her

well enough. He did not love her. Perhaps he realized, vaguely, that the Muller girl and Ma Trost were conspiring to take from him his real love — his real love with whom he spent every evening far into the night, and who was in his thoughts all through the long bright day.

The thought of her was all that sustained him during the day as he plowed and sowed and garnered under the Kansas sun. An exquisite thing, his love, frail, yet strong; slim, vibrant, infinitely exciting; all steel and light, light spruce wood, and cotton. Sometimes, when he thought of her, the blood ebbed from his heart and rushed into his head, almost blinding him, suffocating him, then surged back again to his heart so that he thought it would burst.

The Bertha Muller girl indeed!

Sometimes he saw her and even took her to the pictures or to a picnic. He liked being with her, in a vague, remote sort of way. She let him kiss her once or twice, primly, and he had rather enjoyed that. She was a good girl, the Muller girl, and smart. Ma Trost kept dinning that into his ears. Not like those other girls, running around Wichita all the time, in silk stockings and skirts to their knees and high heels, and no more know how to cook or keep house than *Gott weiss was*.[6]

She had gone to the normal school at Emporia, and after that had taught for a whole year at good pay. Then, in one year, her mother had died, her father had suffered a stroke, and there was the rich Muller farm to be worked by strangers, with Bertha called home to act as housekeeper and nurse.

Old Muller could whirl himself about in a wheel chair now, and the Wichita doctor promised that in another year perhaps he could walk. But the Muller farm, with its bountiful acres, needed a guiding hand. Bertha's husband was the man for the place. But Bertha had no husband, though a few came wooing.

It was surprising that more did not come, for she was comely enough, strong, capable. They seemed to prefer the new order of farm girl — the flutter-budget of whom Ma Trost spoke with such contempt. Bertha Muller frightened them with her serious face, her determined mien, her bossy ways, her manner of coming down hard on her heels, as though to crush something underfoot. They were troubled to explain it, these inarticulate Kansas farm swains.

"It's like she was teacher all the time, and you was pupil and she caught you throwing spitballs."

Still, she could have married one of them, and would have; but the Muller girl, so strong, so independent, was in love with Trosts' Theodore, who looked at her with the eyes of one who sees through her and beyond her, to something far distant and dear.

Airplanes. Airplanes. Always reading and studying about those crazy airplanes. She and Ma Trost put their heads together. Theirs was a silent understanding. They would tame this meadow lark, and cage him.

They did not say to each other: We will tame him. We will sprinkle crumbs on the doorsill and he will be afraid at first, but he will hop nearer and nearer, though at the slightest sound he will fly away. But pretty soon he will not be afraid, and he will come every day to eat, and then one day we will reach down softly, softly — and have him, and hold him.

"Bertha invited us to dinner Sunday, Pa and me and you. It will be nice I don't have to cook a big dinner once on Sunday."

"I don't want to go."

"Theo, what is got into you? That poor Bertha, she fixes all week we should come to dinner on Sunday and cheer her pa up a little. I guess you can do that much for somebody that has got trouble and not always have to sit in that shed with your face full of grease from a engine, and your clothes. It's bad enough to wash farm clothes clean without your dirty engine clothes that the grease won't come out at all."

He went sulkily. The Muller girl received them, and it was as though she were panting with a breathless energy. She went back and forth between stove and table, though they had a hired girl.

Bertha's cheeks were pink with the heat and excitement. There were tiny beads of moisture on her upper lip and her temples and in the cleft of her firm round chin. She had the short sturdy fibula of the energetic woman and seemed to take more steps and to come down harder than was absolutely necessary.

"My, this is good!" chanted Ma Trost, over and over. "My, Bertha, did you cook this all yourself?"

"Every bite." Her firm cheeks flushed pinker. She glanced at Theo. His eyes were on his plate.

"Well, I thought I was a cook, but I guess you make me take a back seat, all right. Dumplings I can never get light like this. Some man is going to be lucky some day."

"Oh, now, Mrs. Trost!"

"Pa Trost will be complaining about how I fix his eating after this, with mayonnaise and whipped cream and puff paste and such little finger rolls and what."

"You cook good enough for me," Pa Trost muttered, somberly. Both he and Theo had pushed the golden crown of mayonnaise off their unaccustomed salad with an investigating fork, had looked down at the mixed fruit mass beneath and had sat back with the mien of the male who disdains feminized food.

The paralytic, silent through most of the meal, at this unfortunate moment piped up in his reedy voice.

"Now'days boys don't marry girls because they can cook, like when I was young. They would sooner eat out of a tin can and a paper bag from the delicatessen in Wichita if she is got a cute shape and can switch her hips around when she walks."

Pink deepened to red in the Muller girl's cheeks.

Mrs. Trost bridled. "I'm surprised, Mr. Muller, how you can talk like that in front of Bertha here and Theo."

The boy, hearing his name, looked up, "What?"

"Mr. Muller, talking like that."

"I didn't hear him," said Theo.

What could you do with a boy like that?

Bertha tried the wiles of those other girls — the new farm girls of the district with their bobbed hair and small close hats and silk stockings and silk dresses bought out of the window of the department store in Wichita. She knew. Those other boys who had come courting Bertha had pressed against her meaningly with a knee, a thigh, a hard-muscled arm or shoulder. So now, on those rare occasions when she rode with him and sat with him a moment in his work shed as she visited the Trost farm on some flimsy neighborly pretext, she experimented, using age-old instinct as her guide.

Goaded, doubtless, by Ma Trost, Theo had driven Bertha into town one evening in late May. They had seen a picture. They had had an ice-cream soda at the drugstore counter. Now they were driving back to the farm in Theo's homemade and feverish car. Its whole frame was shaken as by a palsy when you started its engine, but it leaped like the mad thing it was, once set going.

The Kansas sky hung low. From the east a crouching storm, about to spring, showed its fangs from time to time, and growled in warning. As they rattled along the road they passed the signal lights that marked the aviator's course toward the landing field. It was well past eleven o'clock.

"Let's us go out to the field and see the mail plane come in, huh?"

"Oo, it's going to storm. Look. And anyway, it's late."

"That's anyway a half an hour off, that storm. I can tell. Come on. Let's."

"Well — all right, Theo."

As the generations before them, craving adventure even at second hand, had lounged down to the railway depot to watch Number Nine or Number Twelve rush, panting, into the town and out again, coming from strange lands east and bound for unseen plains west, so now these of the newest adult generation achieved a vicarious thrill from the arrival and departure of that traveler of the air — the midnight mail plane.

Bertha Muller inched her way cautiously toward him as he sat so quiet, so quiet and remote, at the wheel of his crazy car. She had known the warm prickling thrill that had come when those others had met her in momentary contact — those other boys of her experience; hearty fellows, strong, with the good hard flesh on them from manual labor and the plain plentiful food of the region — bread, pies, pork, mashed potatoes, beans, gravy. So she pressed against him a little as they sat there side by side — not boldly, but hopefully, askingly — a warm touch of the knee, the soft hip, the shoulder. But when she pressed against him like that it was like pressing against steel, so hard he was, so unyielding, so unresponsive.

She, too, fell silent a moment. Nothing. Well, she would try another tack.

"I always think," she began, in her prim normal-school accents, "how wonderful it is that we should be driving along like this, farmer folks that we are. Here we have been into town and seen a movie, and are coming back and going to see the night plane come in, and all. Electricity on the farms, and all kinds of modern inventions.

" We don't have to work like your ma and pa did, and mine. That's all past, that kind of slaving on a farm. When I think of my folks. My mother never had any fun in her life — anyway, not after she married. But now'days farming is fun, really.

" I would be perfectly happy on the farm, really. I used to miss my teaching, and the — uh — mental contacts I had. If I only had somebody to help me, and advise, and look to. Papa won't live long. I might as well face that, because it's coming, and you have to face the facts of life. And then I will be left all alone, with that big valuable farm on my hands — a woman, alone."

" Yeh," said Theo. " That's tough."

She gave an impatient movement, then controlled herself, relaxed again, patient, patient. " I suppose I could get married to one of the boys that's always hanging around. But I'm not the kind of a girl that would marry just to have a man on my farm. My, no! "

" Good a reason as any," said Theo, and stepped on the gas. They shot into the parking space behind the low shed that marked the landing field.

There was always a gathering of people on the field on warm summer nights, to watch the midnight mail plane come in. Something of mystery still was in it, and romance, and daring, even to this community accustomed to the wheeling, whirring, swooping things in the sky above their farms and houses. People drove out from Wichita itself.

The shed was warmly lighted, and stifling. Outside stood little scattered groups. The landing-field light went off, and on, and off, and on, a Cyclops eye turned toward the sky. But the gravel-covered landing field itself was flooded with a strong white light, made more unreal and blinding because of the brooding darkness just beyond.

The sky now was low and black and ominous. The jagged thrusts were more venomous, more frequent, and the growl more urgent.

" He better step on it if he's going to make it," the onlookers said, peering into the blackness. Women's figures in light summer dresses. Men smoking and looking up at the sky. Their faces were strangely pure, raised like that to the heavens, with something of wonder in them, and expectation.

A tiny light, closer and closer, out of the east. "Here she comes."

A man ran out of the shed, shooing the crowd back to safety. Keep away, folks. Keep clear. Don't want to get hurt. Get back, now.

Nearer, nearer. A movement of panic; a darting back to safety. The incredible thing swooped down out of the air, came scuttling along the field scattering dust and gravel in a cloud as it came to a stop.

A lean young figure in corduroy and leather slung a lank leg over the cockpit. He unstrapped from about his waist a clumsy-looking contraption that the wise knew to be his parachute. His shoulders, in the limp blue shirt, slumped. He walked stiffly toward the shed.

"Hello, Fred."

"'Lo, Otto."

"How's she blowing?"

"Pretty good. Guess I can make Denver before she hits me. Got to step on it, though."

The crowd closed about the birdlike thing curiously, as though they were seeing its like for the first time. Inside the shed the boy in the blue shirt made his report, deposited his sack, gathered up the west-bound mail. He emerged again, quickly, with a final bite of ham sandwich bulging his cheek.

He wiped his mouth with the back of his hard palm, climbed into the cockpit, was off, with another scattering of gravel and dust, another backward surge from the crowd. Off. Up, up. Higher. The growling, flashing animal was close behind him now, leaping just behind him from the east, showing its fangs like a ravenous thing. The tail light suddenly turned. He was coming back.

He encircled the field once, in farewell. Showing off. The crowd, sensing this, laughed with a kind of excited admiration, such as they would give a lion tamer who plays with the ferocious animal in its cage at the circus. The tail light grew smaller, dimmer, winked once, vanished into the high blackness.

The crowd gave a sigh, deep, as though awakened from a

dream. They stumbled a little as they walked toward their waiting cars.

Theo and Bertha climbed into their little car, were off with a shiver and a leap. A tight cold band of steel was tightening around the girl's heart. She laughed in mirthless pretense of laughter.

"Well, I'd rather it would be him than me," she quavered, forgetting her normal-school training. "I'll take my farm and my nice safe bed, thank you."

The boy said nothing. Absolutely nothing. If he had protested; if only he had sneered at her fear, or laughed at her, or defended this lean sky god in the soiled blue shirt. But he said nothing, sitting there, tight-lipped, at the wheel.

But he was, after all, human and male. And here was a woman — admiring, wondering — in whom to confide the secret of his strength. So, a scant quarter of a mile before they reached her farmyard, this young Samson confided in his Delilah.[7]

"I'll be up in a day or two."

"Up?"

"Don't you let on to my folks. Pa and Ma, they don't understand. I been making a plane. I been a year at it. That's why I come out tonight. I wanted to get away from her for one evening, to get fresh, so I could look her over tomorrow with new eyes. She's in the lean-to, behind my work shed. Nobody knows but you. I kept that door locked. Day after tomorrow I knock out the whole side of the lean-to, and trundle her out, and up in her at sunset, after supper."

"But Theo, how do you know — maybe it isn't right or something — what if you fall? Oh, Theo, your ma — you ought to tell your ma, anyway."

"That's right. Go on and blab."

"I won't. I won't."

But he left her angrily at the gate, not troubling to get out of the car to help her. He was off, the thing snarling and chattering down the road in a fury of anger against her, against all womankind. She stood there, in the farm gateway. The rain came; great pelting drops, heavy, like warm lead.

He seemed to sense that in her love for him he could not trust her. She cared more for his bones than her honor.

Next evening, after supper, she left the sick man and was down the road in her own car toward the Trost farm. She drove swiftly and well, her strong brown hands capable at the wheel.

Ma Trost was watering her flowers. Pa Trost, in his slippers and shirt sleeves, was smoking an after-supper pipe in the cool of the kitchen doorway.

"Hello," called Bertha, very casual. "Hello. Where's Theo?"

"Hello, Bertha. How's your Pa?"

"All right. He's all right. Where's Theo?"

Ma Trost laughed her hearty laugh that shook her vast bosom. "In that shed of his, tinkering. Go back, once, and talk to him. My, you look cute in that pink dress. Don't she, Pa? Like a rose."

From the shed came the sound of hammering, loud on the still evening air. Hammering, and boards being rent from their nailings. A sudden premonition seized Bertha Muller. Her whole body stiffened as she stood there. The hammering ceased. A whirring sound then, loud, loud, louder. Her pink cheeks went putty-colored.

"Come!" she screamed suddenly, like a madwoman. "Come Quick. It's Theo. He's going up."

She began to run. The man and the woman stared at her a moment. Then they, too, began to run toward the roaring, whirring sound, clumsily, heavily. They looked ridiculous, running like that, the fat woman in her apron, the paunchy man with his pipe.

The thing, awkward yet fleet and somehow graceful in its awkwardness, careened across the open field as they reached the ruined lean-to. A tiny winged thing, almost moth-like against the green of the field.

Across the field it went, into the meadow beyond, wheeled, turned, came toward them, so that they ran back fearfully; turned again, made off at higher speed, wheeled, turned, again and again and again and again, so that the three standing there in an agony of fear and suspense finally realized that this winged thing was tied to the earth — that its wings were powerless to lift it. Again it came toward them, turned, made off, turned, raced back. Stopped.

Theo stepped out of the tiny cockpit. His face was set and

terrible. He looked at the man and the woman and the girl. He seemed not to see them.

"She won't lift," he said simply. Then, suddenly, in a louder voice, "She won't lift." His set expression broke, then, in a grimace of sickening disappointment and impotent rage, so that the three involuntarily turned their eyes away, ashamed to look upon his agony.

Ma Trost went toward him then. "Oh, Theo, what do you — how you can scare me like that?"

"Leave me alone. Leave me alone. She won't lift. She's no good. God damn it! She's no good." He began to cry — the horrible crying of a man betrayed by the thing he loves.

Here was a situation for Pa Trost's handling. He advanced on the boy, his face darker than was its wont. His great hands were clenched into fists. "You try to go up in one of them things again I break every bone in your body. You hear me! I smash it into a thousand pieces, that *Gott verdammte Ding!*"

Theodore picked up a hammer from the ground near the work shed. He raised it high, threateningly. "You touch it and I'll break your head. Yes, you!"

Then, as his father stood, open-mouthed, purple with rage and astonishment, the boy swung the hammer back and brought it down on the wings of the frail light craft — down, and up, and down and up and down and up, until the white cotton stuff, so strong, so flimsy, fluttered in ribbons.

"Oh, Theo!" whimpered Bertha Muller; and covered her face with her hands.

The boy threw the hammer far away into the field. He faced them then, set and stern. His hysteria was past. "Look," he said. "I'm going to the factory. I'm through."

"Through!" echoed Ma Trost feebly. "What — through?"

"I'm through farming, see? I'm going to get a job in the factory and learn to make planes right, not like that piece of junk. And fly. I'm going to fly a mail plane yet. You'll see."

Pa Trost again. "You crazy, you! You crazy! You stay here on the farm and work, you fool, you. I've got enough now of this airplanes. You with your airplane, it won't even go one inch off the muck in the field. A fine airplane flyer you are. You go in the house now, and first you take that junk and kindling and old rags off my good field. I show you who is a flyer in this house. I make you fly, all right, with my foot behind you."

" Good-bye," said the boy. He walked past them.

" Theo, where are you going? "

" You come back here, *du Narr du! Du — du Verrückter!* [8] You stay here or I make you."

" Yeh? How you going to make me stay? Put me in jail! "

The Eagle Aircraft Company's plant had, curiously, the brilliant airy look of a huge playroom. It was all windows, or almost all, so that the golden Kansas sun shone on steel and wire and on pieces of wood that were broad and thick, and yet light as a feather when you lifted them. Spruce, or balsam from South America, weighing no more than paper.

You saw other boys there, like Theo, with the look of the farm still on them; corn-colored hair, cornflower-blue eyes, working patiently at this or that menial task, the brimless crown of an old straw hat atop their heads as they worked. They dreamed of the clouds as they worked, but they worked carefully, none the less. Large printed signs were tacked up here, there, everywhere.

REPORT ALL MISTAKES IMMEDIATELY.
FAILURE TO DO SO MAY MEAN THE
DEATH OF A BRAVE MAN

They set him to mopping floors, this farm boy who had been the pet of the woman-ridden household, the apple of his mother's eyes. And he scrubbed them. He was farther from flying than he ever had been in his work-shed days on the farm. They wouldn't let him go near a plane, or scarcely.

Theo come home your pa will forgive you you are breaking my hart your ma.

Bertha wrote, too, in her firm round hand:

Dear Theodore, I am writing to you, though you haven't written a word to poor me, because I think somebody ought to tell you how your mother is grieving, and your father too, though he doesn't let on. I think you ought to remember that they are old people now, and that we young people ought to make life happier and easier for them . . .

He answered his mother briefly; Bertha, too.

When you see me flying over the farm you'll know I am willing to come home. But not to stay home. I will let you know.

They paid him an infinitesimal wage, and he pulled in his belt and lived on it. Sometimes, at night — and in the daytime, too — he dreamed of the bountiful steaming noon-board that Ma Trost had always spread.

He was a natural mechanic and a natural flyer. Born in the age of flying, in the region where flying was thickest, it was as inevitable that he should one day learn to fly, and fly always thereafter, as that another should learn to walk.

He picked up the trade slang and work phases readily enough. He learned to call the cockpit the " office." Aileron. Dural. Dope. The three types of plane that stood all about the huge bright room in every stage, from the metal skeleton to the completed ship, had, for him, the definite personalities of so many human beings.

The mail plane, big, substantial, businesslike, dependable, a thing built to stand the daily grind, summer and winter, in all kinds of weather. The sport plane, like a pretty, frivolous girl, made for pleasure — a butterfly thing, white and scarlet and gay. The army plane, gray, grim, sinister.

One day they let him hand things to a friendly pilot. Weeks passed. One day they let him clean a spark plug. Weeks passed. He got a ride now and again, and was silent. He had a feel for the air as a born automobile racer has a feel for the road.

One day a silent, good-natured pilot took him up and in a burst of generosity let him have the controls for one moment, when they were high enough to be safe. Theo took them, his young face stern. The pilot watched him narrowly, though he appeared casual enough. Once he had been up with a kid who froze to the sticks, and he had barely had time to hammer and wrench the kid's fingers loose and grab the controls himself, and right her.

Six months. Ten. A year. Ma Trost had driven out to see him, of course, many times, and brought him baskets, napkin-covered. Bertha Muller, too. But always his face had set in those lines of resolve. Pa Trost never came.

The Trost telephone rang at half-past five on a June night,

as Ma Trost was getting the supper. Her hearty chuckling laugh was heard less often these days.

A mysterious voice over the telephone. A voice strange to her. " Tonight at half-past six over the farm three times."

" What? " shrieked Ma Trost, who always talked too loudly on the telephone. " What you say? "

" Tonight at half-past six over the farm three times. Watch the sky."

" What? "

But the voice had gone.

She knew. She telephoned Bertha then. She tried to get Theodore at the airplane factory, but there was no answer; at his boarding house. He was not there.

Bertha arrived, white and shaking. " Did you tell Pa Trost? "

" No. I don't know should I."

" I wouldn't. Call him out. No — you'd better tell him first."

She told him. Half-past six, over the farm. Three times. He said nothing.

Pa Trost ate his supper as usual; silent, somber. Ma Trost ate nothing. Bertha explained that she had had her supper early. The two women listened. The man pretended not to.

The two women went to the back porch and stood there, in the June evening light. The man stayed within. The smell of his pipe drifted out to them.

They heard the humming, the buzzing, the roaring before they saw it.

Their sharp eyes, accustomed to distances, saw him then, a speck, a tiny winged thing like a meadow lark high up in the evening sky. Then it came lower, lower, still.

" That's him," said Bertha simply. " Here. Do you want the glasses? " She had brought the binoculars with her.

" I don't need no glasses . . . Pa! Pa, come out. It's Theo. Up there."

They stood, their faces raised to the sky. It circled the farm once. It circled the farm twice. Old man Trost drew a deep breath, like a sob, and his face went the color of dark red wine. He shook his fist in the air, a gesture of futility and bafflement. Then he turned, walking heavily in his soft felt slippers, and went into the house and shut the door with a violence that caused the two women watchers to start and cry out.

Three times. And now the graceful, whirring, wheeling thing dipped, swooped, banked, spiraled. Ma Trost covered her face with her shaking hand. Then, fascinated, she must look up again. Her left hand, with the broad gold band deeply embedded in the flesh of the fourth finger, pleated and unpleated her kitchen apron in an agony of terror.

"I'm afraid for him. Look how he makes! [9] I'm afraid he is killed. I'm afraid he drops down in the field, and is killed."

The winged thing, its third circle completed, darted off now toward the west.

Bertha Muller lowered her binoculars slowly. She looked, suddenly, old. Her voice, when she spoke, was hard and without life.

"Don't you worry. He won't come down. He won't — ever come down."

## NOTES FOR *MEADOW LARK*

1. Ajax, a character in Homer who defied the lightning.
2. German cursing expressions.
3. Cursed things.
4. *Tapfer,* brave, but here used in the sense of hurry up.
5. A reference to a common type of movie.
6. God knows what.
7. A reference to a famous story in the Bible.
8. You fool, you crazy one.
9. A German idiom meaning does or acts.

## QUESTIONS

1. Why is old man Trost's action called ridiculous?
2. Why did he stop shaking his fists at the planes?
3. Tell what his objections to the planes were and whether or not they were justified?
4. What in Pa Trost's ancestry tended to make him different in temperament from Ma Trost. By what physical details is this heritage indicated?
5. Show how this description of Trost is vital to the story.
6. Is there any evidence that Pa Trost had ever had a romantic yearning similar to Theodore's? What was it?
7. How did he eventually satisfy this yearning?
8. Show why the word "burgher" adequately describes Pa Trost at this particular hour of the day. Could this term be used to describe him at other hours of the day equally well? Why not?
9. How does the expression "frisky defiance" strike a humorous note with reference to Ma Trost?

# Meadow Lark

10. Would you say that the kinds of things Ma Trost grew indicated a different type of personality from that of her husband? How?
11. In what way is the fact that Theodore is like his father and not like his mother or sisters significant for the story?
12. Tell how Theodore's view of airplanes differed from that of his father.
13. Why was Theodore " serene " when he looked at the planes? How does this prepare the reader for what is to follow in the story?
14. Is such a preparation on the part of an author a desirable bit of technique in story writing? Why?
15. How did Theodore spend his spare time?
16. In what way did Theodore's lack of interest in Bertha differ from the lack also shown by other boys in her?
17. Does this in any way make Theodore's character more vivid to the reader? Explain.
18. Miss Ferber is the author of several Broadway stage successes. Find two scenes in this story which show a dramatic touch.
19. Why did Theodore take Bertha to town?
20. What was Bertha attempting to do by her description of modern farm life? Was she successful? How do you know?
21. Explain " Cyclops eye."
22. In what way does the description of the arrival and departure of the mail plane tend to make the unfolding of the story smoother and more natural?
23. What important fact does Bertha learn about Theodore? Were you prepared for it? Why?
24. Why did his first attempt at a flight fail?
25. Why did the attempted flight affect Pa Trost as it did?
26. Why did the Aircraft Company set the men to doing such menial tasks at first? What would you say about the characters of the men who were willing to do these things?
27. List the number of times food is mentioned in this story.
28. Why do you think that a reconciliation between Theodore and his father is impossible? Would the youthful yearnings of old Trost help to explain his final attitude toward his son? Explain.
29. What is meant by the last paragraph in the story?
30. With whom are your sympathies at the end of the story. Why?

## SUBJECTS FOR COMPOSITION

1. Pretend that Pa Trost does take a trip in an airplane and describe his reactions to his farm when he comes down.
2. Suppose that Theodore later achieves distinction either in an endurance test or a long distance flight and then returns home to see his parents.

## VOLUMES OF STORIES BY EDNA FERBER

*Buttered Side Down*
*Roast Beef Medium*
*Personality Plus*
*Cheerful by Request*

*Emma McChesney and Company*
*Half Portions*
*They Brought Their Women*

# PEARL S. BUCK
## (1892–    )

PEARL S. BUCK was born in Hillsboro, West Virginia in 1892. Her parents were missionaries in China. After a long period of hardship in the interior of China they spent the year of 1892 in England and America. At the age of four months she was taken to China, where, as she has said, " I grew up much alone. My parents lived in many places, but when I was a child moved to a city on the Yangste River called Chinkiang." There she spent her childhood very quietly in a small bungalow picturesquely situated on the top of a hill overlooking the great river. She learned to speak Chinese before English, but when it came time to read she studied English because of the difficulty of the Chinese language.

Mrs. Buck's first literary influence came from her Chinese nurse who told her many tales of magic which she had heard from the Buddhist and Taoist priests. From her father and mother she learned the stories of the pioneers in America. She went to a Chinese school to learn to read the native language. Her mother thought it wise that her daughter should learn to work and assigned her certain daily tasks such as sweeping and straightening up her own room, but her nurse thought this undesirable and did the work for her, mumbling, " Why should the child work since she is to be as learned as a boy? "

Mrs. Buck's father made frequent journeys to remote parts of China and always brought back stories of startling adventures. The mother frequently told the daughter about her own childhood in West Virginia. It was from her also that Pearl Buck learned about art, beauty, and music, especially about the beauty that lies in words. Mrs. Buck says, " From my earliest childhood she helped me to see beauty everywhere and taught me to write down what I saw and felt, and not a week passed without my giving her something to read that I had written and she was fearless though kind in her criticism." Some of these little pieces were sent to the *Shanghai Mercury,* an English language newspaper which had a weekly edition for children. For a period of several years many of these were printed over the signature " Novice." The paper paid her in cash for them and she came to think of these little articles as a regular source of spending money.

When Pearl Buck was fifteen she went to a boarding school in Shanghai for her first formal schooling, and at seventeen she came to America to enter Randolph-Macon College. She did not enjoy college life very much because it was too confining as compared with her free life in China. Nevertheless, she became a leader and president of her class. She wrote for the college paper and in her senior year won two literary prizes, one of which was for a short story.

After graduation Pearl Buck returned to China which she regarded as home. For two years she took care of her mother, who was ill. Then she married a young American and went with him to a town in the north of China where his work was. They lived there for five years. She says that these years were the richest as well as the hardest of their lives. They were the only white people in that town and countryside. She went about among the people and came into a close and intimate knowledge of the lives of the Chinese. During this period the young couple experienced a time of famine and battles between bandits who attacked the city.

Then her husband took charge of the department of rural economics in the University of Nanking. There for ten years they watched the nation in revolution. Mrs. Buck knew all the time that she wanted to write, but for some years she was kept busy with the care of her home, her children and her parents. She also took a strong interest in her husband's researches in Chinese farming. Besides, as a part of her job as a Presbyterian missionary she taught English literature in the University of Nanking and later in Chung Yung University.

Although there was no time to write her mind was constantly framing stories. Reading some articles in the *Atlantic Monthly* about the younger generation, Mrs. Buck was inspired to write an article on the subject. This was sent to the *Atlantic,* promptly accepted, and printed in January, 1923. The editor of the *Forum* asked for an article and she sent him one and this appeared in March, 1924.

In 1925 Mr. and Mrs. Buck, on furlough, came to America. She went to study at Cornell for her Masters degree. Although her studies were conducted in the English department, she won the Laura Messenger Prize in history. On the voyage to America she had begun to write a story. At the urgent request of a friend, she sent the manuscript to the magazine, *Asia,* which promptly accepted it.

When Mrs. Buck returned to China in 1926 she began to write regularly and took up, as a major project, a history of the Chinese novel. She also started a novel but this was interrupted in March, 1927 by the uprising of the Communist soldiers who looted the city and killed foreigners. Mr. and Mrs. Buck barely escaped being killed. The next day all the white members of the colony were taken away by an American destroyer. She spent a year in Japan and Shanghai and then returned to Nanking.

After her return to China in 1926 a publisher wrote her that with some changes to make a full length novel, he would be glad to publish, as a novel, the story she had sent to *Asia.* She felt that she could not do this without spoiling the story but offered to let them publish it together with a sequel that she had written in the meantime. They refused her offer. Eventually, however, she sent the manuscript and its sequel to a literary agency in New York which found a great prejudice among publishers against anything Chinese. But at last it was taken. This was in 1929 and in that same year the Bucks made a hurried business trip to America. When Mrs. Buck visited the office of her publishers she found that they did not like her title so she and the publisher compromised on " East Wind: West Wind " instead of " Winds of Heaven." The book appeared in 1930. Mrs. Buck says that the best thing about all this was that it gave her confidence to go on writing about the things she knew best.

Her second novel, *The Good Earth,* was finished in 1930 and published in March of 1931. This book was at once hailed by all critics and for nearly two years it headed the list of best sellers. It was also awarded the Pulitzer Prize for the best novel of the year. The sequel, *Sons,* came out in 1932. Meanwhile, Mrs. Buck has contributed numerous articles to American journals about herself and her work in China.

In the summer of 1932 Mrs. Buck returned to America once more and in November she addressed a large body of Presbyterian women in New York City on the subject of foreign missions. This led to an attack on Mrs. Buck's doctrinal beliefs, whereupon she resigned as a missionary. She now gives her whole time to research and writing. She has completed a fourth novel, *Mother,* and has published, under the title of *All Men Are Brothers,* one of China's most famous novels.

All of Mrs. Buck's novels, short stories and articles have to do with China both before and since the revolution. "The Frill" printed in this volume was selected as one of the O. Henry Memorial Award prize stories for 1933.

# THE FRILL

"MY DEAR, the only way to manage these native tailors is to be firm!"

Mrs. Lowe, the postmaster's wife, settled herself with some difficulty into the wicker rocking-chair upon the wide veranda of her house. She was a large woman, red-faced from more food than necessary and little exercise over the ten-odd years she had spent in a port town on the China coast. Now as she looked at her caller and thus spoke, her square hard-fleshed face grew a little redder. Beside her stood a Chinese manservant who had just announced in a mild voice:

"Tailor have come, missy."

Little Mrs. Newman looked at her hostess with vague admiration.

"I'm sure I wish I had your way with them, Adeline," she murmured, fanning herself slowly with a palm-leaf fan. She went on in a plaintive complaining way: "Sometimes I think it is scarcely worth while to bother with new clothes, although they are so cheap here, especially if you buy the native silks. But it is so much trouble to have them made, and these tailors say — my dear, my tailor promises me faithfully he will make a dress in three days and then he doesn't come for a week or two!" Her weak voice dwindled and ended in a sigh and she fanned herself a trifle more quickly.

# The Frill

"Watch me, now," said Mrs. Lowe commandingly. She had a deep firm voice and round hard gray eyes set a little near together beneath closely waved dead brown hair. She turned these eyes upon the Chinese manservant as he stood looking decorously down to the floor, his head drooping slightly, and said, "Boy, talkee tailor come this side!"

"Yes, missy," murmured the servant and disappeared.

Almost instantly there was the sound of soft steady footsteps through the open doors, and from the back of the house through the hall following the manservant there came the tailor. He was a tall man, taller than the servant, middle-aged, his face quiet with a sort of closed tranquillity. He wore a long robe of faded blue grasscloth, patched neatly at the elbows and very clean. Under his arm he carried a bundle wrapped in a white cloth. He bowed to the two white women and then squatting down put this bundle upon the floor of the veranda and untied its knots. Inside was a worn and frayed fashion book from some American company and a half-finished dress of a spotted blue and white silk. This dress he shook out carefully and held up for Mrs. Lowe to see. From its generous proportions it could be seen that it was made for her. She surveyed it coldly and with hostility, searching its details.

Suddenly she spoke in a loud voice: "No wantchee that collar, tailor! I have talkee you wantchee frill — see, so fashion!" She turned the pages of the book rapidly to a section devoted to garments for ample women. "See, all same fashion this lady. What for you makee flat collar? No wantchee — no wantchee — take it away!"

Upon the tailor's calm patient face a perspiration broke forth. "Yes, missy," he said faintly. And then he pressed his lips together slightly and took a breath and began: "Missy, you first talkee frill, then you say no frill. Other day you say wantchee flat collar, frill too fat."

He looked imploringly at the white woman. But Mrs. Lowe waved him away with a fat ringed hand.

"No, you talkee lie, tailor," she cried sternly. "I know how I talkee. I never say I wantchee flat collar — never! No lady have flat collar now. What for you talkee so fashion?"

"Yes, missy," said the tailor. Then brightening somewhat he suggested. "Have more cloth, missy. Suppose I makee frill, never mind."

But Mrs. Lowe was not to be thus easily appeased. "Yes, never mind you, but you have spoil so much my cloth. What you think, I buy this cloth no money? Plenty money you make me lose." She turned to her guest. "I have been counting on that dress, Minnie, and now look at it! I wanted to wear it to the garden party at the consulate day after tomorrow. I told him a frill — just look at that silly collar!"

"Yes, I know. It's just what I was saying," said Mrs. Newman in her tired peevish voice. "What I want to know is how will you manage it?"

"Oh, I'll manage it," replied Mrs. Lowe grimly.

She ignored the tailor for a while and stared out over her trim garden. In the hot sunshine a blue-coated coolie squatted over a border of zinnias, glittering in the September noon. A narrow sanded path ran about a square of green lawn. She said nothing, and the tailor stood acutely uncomfortable, the dress still held delicately by the shoulders. A small trickle of perspiration ran down each side of his face. He wet his lips and began in a trembling voice:

"Missy wantchee try?"

"No, I do not," snapped Mrs. Lowe. "What for wantchee try? All wrong — collar all wrong — what for try?" She continued to stare out into the shining garden.

"Can makee all same frill," said the tailor eagerly, persuasively. "Yes, yes, missy, I makee all same you say. What time you want?"

"I want it tomorrow," replied the white woman. "You bring tomorrow twelve o'clock. Suppose you no bring, then I no pay — savee? All time you talkee what time you bring and you never bring."

"Can do, missy," said the tailor quietly. He squatted gracefully, folded the dress into the cloth again and tied it tenderly, careful to crush nothing. Then he rose and stood waiting, upon his face some agony of supplication. His whole soul rose in this silent supplication, so that it was written upon his quiet high-cheeked face, upon his close-set lips. Sweat broke out upon him afresh. Even Mrs. Lowe could feel dimly that imploring soul. She paused in her rocking, and looked up.

"What is it?" she asked sharply. "What more thing?"

The tailor wet his lips again and spoke in a faint voice. "Missy, can you give me litty money — one dollar, two dollar ———" Before her outraged look his voice dropped yet lower. "My brother's son he die today, I think — he have three piecee baby, one woman — no money buy coffin — no nothing — he very ill today ———"

Mrs. Lowe looked at her caller. "Well, of all the nerve!" she breathed, genuinely aghast. Mrs. Newman answered her look.

"It's just what I said," she replied. "They are more trouble than they are worth — and the way they *cut* — and then they think about nothing but money!"

Mrs. Lowe turned her rolling gray eyes upon the tailor. He did not look up, but he wiped his lip furtively with his sleeve. She stared at him an instant and then her voice came forth filled with righteous anger.

"No," she said. "No. You finish dress all proper with frill, I pay you. No finish dress, no pay. Never. You savee, tailor?"

"Yes, missy," sighed the tailor. All vestige of hope had now disappeared from his face. The atmosphere of supplication died away. A look of cold despair came over his face like a curtain. "I finish tomorrow twelve o'clock, missy," he said and turned away.

"See that you do," shouted Mrs. Lowe triumphantly after him and she watched his figure with contempt as it disappeared into the hall. Then she turned to her caller. "If I say tomorrow," she explained, "perhaps it will be ready by the day after." She thought of something and reaching forward in her chair pressed a bell firmly. The servant appeared.

"Boy," she said, "look see tailor — see he no takee something."

Her loud voice penetrated into the house, and the tailor's body, still visible at the end of the hall, straightened itself somewhat and then passed out of sight.

"You never can tell," said Mrs. Lowe. "You can't tell whether they are making up these stories or not. If they need money — but they always do need money. I never saw such people. They must make a lot, though, sewing for all these foreigners here in the port. But this tailor is worse than most. He is forever wanting money before his work is done. Three separate times he has come and said a child was dying or something. I don't believe a word of it. Probably smokes opium or gambles. They all gamble — you can't believe a word they say!"

"Oh, I know ——" sighed Mrs. Newman rising to depart. Mrs. Lowe rose also.

"After all, one simply has to be firm," she said again.

Outside the big white foreign house the tailor went silently and swiftly through the hot street. Well, he had asked her, and she would not give him anything. After all his dread and fear of her refusal, all his summoning of courage, she would not give him anything. The dress was more than half done, except for the frill, too. She had given him the silk two days ago, and he had been glad because it would bring him in a few dollars for this nephew of his who was like his own son now that the gods had taken away his own little children, three of them.

He had therefore clung the more to this only son of his dead younger brother, a young man apprenticed to an ironsmith, and he had three little children now too. Such a strong young man — who could have thought he would have been seized for death like this? Two months ago it was that the long piece of red-hot iron he was beating into the shape of a plowshare had slipped somehow from his pincers and had fallen upon his leg and foot and seared the flesh away almost to the bone. It had fallen on his naked flesh, for it was summer and the little shop was hot and he had only his thin cotton trousers on rolled to his thighs.

Well, and they had tried every sort of ointment, but what ointment will grow sound flesh again, and what balm is there for such a wound? The whole leg had swollen and now on this hot day in the ninth moon the young man lay dying. There were black plasters on his leg from hip to foot, but they were of no avail.

Yes, the tailor had seen that for himself this morning when he went to see his nephew — he had seen death there plainly. The young wife sat weeping in the doorway of the one room that was their home and the two elder children stared at her gravely, too stricken for play. The third was but a babe she held in her bosom.

# The Frill

The tailor turned down an alleyway and into a door in a wall. He passed through a court filled with naked children screaming and quarreling and shouting at play.

Above his head were stretched bamboo poles upon which were hung ragged garments washed in too scanty water and without any soap. Here about these courts a family lived in every room and poured its waste into the court so that even though it was a dry day — and the days had been dry for a moon or more — yet the court was slimy and running with waste water.

But he did not notice this. He passed through three more courts like the first and turned to an open door at the right and went into the dark windowless room. There was a different odor here. It was the odor of dying rotten flesh. The sound of a woman's wailing rose from beside the curtained bed and thither the tailor went, his face not changed from the look it had borne away from the white woman's house. The young wife did not look up at his coming. She sat crouched on the ground beside the bed and her face was wet with tears. Her long black hair had come uncoiled and stretched over her shoulder and hung to the earth. Over and over she moaned: "Oh, my husband — oh, my man — I am left alone — oh, my husband ——"

The babe lay on the ground beside her crying feebly now and again. The two elder children sat close to their mother, each of them holding fast to a corner of her coat. They had been weeping too but now they were silent, their streaked faces upturned to look at their uncle.

But the tailor paid no heed to them now. He looked into the hempen curtains of the bed and said gently:

"Are you still living, my son?"

The dying man turned his eyes with difficulty. He was horribly swollen, his hands, his naked upper body, his neck, his face. But these were nothing to the immense log-like swelling of his burned leg. It lay there so huge it seemed he was attached to it, rather than it to him. His glazed eyes fixed themselves upon his uncle. He opened his puffed lips and after a long time and a mighty effort of concentration his voice came forth in a hoarse whisper:

"These children ——"

The tailor's face was suddenly convulsed with suffering.

He sat down upon the edge of the bed and began to speak earnestly:

"You need not grieve for your children, my son. Die peacefully. Your wife and your children shall come to my house. They shall take the place of my own three. Your wife shall be daughter to me and to my wife, and your children shall be our grandchildren. Are you not my own brother's son? And he dead too, and only I left now."

He began to weep quietly, and it could be seen that the lines upon his face were set there by other hours of this repressed silent weeping, for as he wept his face hardly changed at all, only the tears rolled down his cheeks.

After a long time the dying man's voice came again with the same rending effort, as though he tore himself out of some heavy stupor to say what must be said:

"You — are poor — too ——"

But the uncle answered quickly, bending toward the dying man, for the swollen eyes were now closed and he could not be sure he was heard: "You're not to worry. Rest your heart. I have work — these white women are always wanting new dresses. I have a silk dress now nearly finished for the postmaster's wife — nearly done, except for a frill, and then she will give me money for it and perhaps more sewing. We shall do very well ——"

But the young man made no further reply. He had gone into that stupor forever and he could rouse himself no more.

Nevertheless, he still breathed slightly throughout that long hot day. The tailor rose once to place his bundle in a corner and to remove his robe, and then he took his place again beside the dying man and remained immovable through the hours. The woman wailed on and on, but at last she was exhausted and sat leaning against the end of the bed, her eyes closed, sobbing now and again softly. But the children grew used to it. They grew used even to their father's dying, and they ran out into the court to play. Once or twice a kindly neighbor woman came and put her head into the door and the last time she picked up the babe and carried him away, holding him to her own full breast to comfort him. Outside her voice could be heard shouting in cheerful pity:

"Well, his hour is come, and he is foul already as though he had been dead a month!"

So the hot day drew on at last to its end and when twilight came the young man ceased breathing and was dead.

Only then did the tailor rise. He rose and put on his gown and took his bundle and he said to the crouching woman, " He is dead. Have you any money at all? "

Then the young woman rose also and looked at him anxiously, smoothing the hair back from her face. It could now be seen that she was still very young — not more than twenty years of age — a young common creature such as may be seen anywhere on any street in any day, neither pretty nor ugly, slight, and somewhat slovenly even on ordinary occasions, and now unwashed for many days. Her grimy face was round, the mouth full and projecting, the eyes a little stupid. It was clear that she had lived from day to day, never foreseeing the catastrophe that had now befallen her. She looked at the tailor humbly and anxiously.

" We have nothing left," she said. " I pawned his clothes and my winter clothes and the table and stools and we have only that bed on which he lies."

The look of despair deepened on the man's face. " Is there anyone of whom you might borrow? " he asked.

She shook her head. " I do not know anyone except these people in the court. And what have they? " Then as the full terror of her position came upon her she cried out shrilly, " Uncle, we have no one but you in the world! "

" I know," he said simply. He looked once more at the bed. " Cover him," he said in a low voice. " Cover him against the flies."

He passed through the courts quickly then and the neighbor woman, who was still holding the babe, bawled at him as he went, " Is he dead yet? "

" He is dead," said the tailor and went through the gate into the street and turned to the west where his own home was.

It seemed to him that this was the most hot day of that whole summer. So is the ninth moon hot sometimes, and so does summer often pass burning fiercely into autumn. The evening had brought no coolness and thunderous clouds towered over the city. The streets were filled with half-naked men and with women in thinnest garb, sitting upon little low bamboo couches they had moved out of their houses. Some lay flat upon the street on mats of reed or strips of woven matting. Children wailed everywhere and mothers fanned their babes wearily, dreading the night.

Through this crowd the tailor passed swiftly, his head bent down. He was now very weary but still not hungry although he had fasted the whole day. He could not eat — no, not even when he reached the one room in a court which was his home, and he could not eat even when his poor stupid old wife, who could not keep her babies alive, came shuffling and panting out of the street and placed a bowl of cold rice gruel on the table for him to eat. There was that smell about his clothes — it filled his nostrils still. He thought suddenly of the silk dress. Suppose the white woman noticed the odor there! He rose suddenly and opened the bundle and shook out the dress, and turning it carefully inside out he hung it to air upon a decrepit dressmaker's form that stood by the bed.

But it could not hang there long. He must finish it and have the money. He took off his robe and his undershirt and his shoes and stockings and sat in his trousers. He must be careful in this heat that his sweat did not stain the dress. He found a gray towel and wrapped it about his head to catch the drops of sweat and put a rag upon the table on which to wipe his hands from time to time.

While he sewed swiftly, not daring to hasten beyond what he was able to do well lest she be not pleased, he pondered on what he could do. He had had one apprentice last year, but the times were so evil he had had to let the lad go, and so had now but his own ten fingers to use. But that was not altogether ill because the lad had made so many mistakes and the white woman said insistently, "You must makee yourself, tailor — no give small boy makee spoil." Yes, but with just these ten fingers of his could he hope to make another dress in three days — suppose she had another silk dress — that would be ten dollars for the two. He could buy a coffin for ten dollars down and the promise of more later.

But supposing she had no more work to give him now — then what could he do? What indeed, but go to a usurer? And yet that he did not dare to do. A man was lost if he went to a usurer for the interest ran faster than a tiger upon him — in a few months double and triple what he had borrowed. Then when the coffin was buried he must bring the young wife and the three babies here. There was only this one room for them all, too. His heart warmed somewhat at the thought of the babies and then stopped in terror at the thought that he must feed them.

Midnight drew on and he was not finished. There was the worst of all yet to be made — the frill. He fetched his fashion book and pored over it beneath the flickering light of the small tin kerosene lamp. So the frill went, here it turned, a long wide frill, closely pleated. He folded the small pleats, his hands trembling with fatigue. His wife lay snoring in the bed now. Nothing would wake her, not even the rackety noisy sewing machine with which he set fast the carefully basted frill. At dawn there remained but the edge to whip by hand and the irons to heat on the charcoal brazier. Well, he would sleep a little and rest his aching eyes and then get up to finish it. He hung the dress upon the form, and then he lay down beside his wife and fell instantly into deep sleep.

But not for long could he sleep. At seven he rose and went to his work again and worked until nearly noon, stopping only for a mouthful of the food he could not eat the night before. Then he was finished. It had taken him longer than he hoped it would. He squinted up at the sun. Yes, he could just get to the house by noon. He must hasten. He must not make her angry so that she would perhaps refuse him the other dress. No, somehow he must have the other dress. Then if he sewed this afternoon and tonight he could finish it in another day. He smelled the finished dress anxiously. A little odor, perhaps — would she notice it?

But fortunately she did not notice it. She was sitting in that strange moving chair she had on the veranda, and she looked at the dress critically.

" All finish? " she asked in her loud sudden way.

" Yes, missy," he answered humbly.

" All right, I go try."

She had gone into her room, then and he held his breath, waiting. Perhaps there was some odor to it yet? But she came back wearing the dress, a satisfied look upon her face; but not too satisfied.

" How much? " she said abruptly.

He hesitated. " Five dollar, missy, please." Then seeing

her angry eyes he added hastily. " Silk dress, five dollar, please, missy. Any tailor five dollar."

" Too much — too much," she declared. " You spoil my cloth too! " But she paid the money to him grudgingly, and he took it from her, delicately careful not to touch her hand.

" Thank you, missy," he said gently.

He dropped to his heels and began to tie up his bundle, his fingers trembling. He must ask her now. But how could he? What would he do if she refused? He gathered his courage together desperately.

" Missy," he said looking up humbly but avoiding her eyes. " You have more dress I can do? "

He waited, hanging on her answer, staring into the shining garden. But she had already turned to go into the house again to take off the dress. She called back at him carelessly,

" No — no more! You makee too muchee trouble. You spoil my cloth — plenty more tailor more cheap and not so muchee trouble! "

The next day at the garden party she met little Mrs. Newman, sitting languidly in a wicker chair, watching white figures move about the lawn intent upon a game of croquet. Mrs. Newman's faded blue eyes brightened somewhat at the sight of the new dress.

" You really did get your dress after all," she said with faint interest. " I didn't think you really would. He did that frill nicely, didn't he? "

Mrs. Lowe looked down upon her large bosom. There the frill lay, beautifully pleated, perfectly ironed. She said with satisfaction, " Yes, it is nice, isn't it? I am glad I decided to have the frill, after all. And so cheap! My dear, with all this frill the dress cost only five dollars to be made — that's less than two dollars at home! What's that? Oh, yes, he brought it punctually at twelve, as I told him he must. It's as I said — you simply have to be firm with these native tailors! "

### QUESTIONS

1. What is the situation at the opening of the story?
2. What type of woman was Mrs. Lowe?
3. What was her chief pride?
4. Why did she survey the dress with hostility?
5. From where did Mrs. Lowe get her ideas about style?
6. How did the tailor receive her criticism?

7. Why didn't she want the flat collar?
8. Why did the tailor ask for the money in advance?
9. Where did he go first after he left Mrs. Lowe?
10. What impelled him to work hard and long to finish the dress?
11. When Mrs. Lowe referred to home in the conversation at the garden party where did she mean?
12. Was she justified in her attitude of firmness? Explain.
13. What contrast do you note between the life of the natives and the foreigners?

## SUBJECTS FOR COMPOSITION

1. The tailor fails to get the dress to Mrs. Lowe at the promised time. Describe his interview with her when he does bring it.
2. Suppose Mrs. Lowe finds out what has really happened to the tailor and goes to his home to make amends. Describe the scene.

## VOLUMES OF SHORT STORIES BY PEARL S. BUCK

*The First Wife and Other Stories*

## BEN AMES WILLIAMS
(1889-    )

BEN AMES WILLIAMS was born in Macon, Mississippi, March 7, 1889. He graduated from Dartmouth College in 1910 and entered the field of journalism, in which he continued until 1916. He worked on newspapers in New York, and in Boston where he still resides. But his real interest lay in the writing of fiction, both novels and short stories. His first books, *All the Brothers Were Valiant* and *The Sea Bride,* were published in 1919. His short stories have appeared and continue to appear in many of the popular magazines.

Ben Ames Williams belongs to that group of writers whose work is profoundly indebted to the journalistic methods of O. Henry, without, however, the humorous slant which is so characteristic of the earlier writer.

" They Grind Exceeding Small " here reprinted was originally published in *The Saturday Evening Post* in 1919 and is now included in the volume *Thrifty Stock,* which contains the best of his short stories up to date. These stories are typical of his favorite themes — the pathos of narrow and stunted experience. Often there is also the surprise ending. His stories are seldom very long but into their few pages he compresses the experiences of a lifetime. Despite their compactness, however, one never has a feeling of sketchiness, the author achieving his effect by an economy of phrasing that is almost terse at times.

The following story admirably illustrates the typical Ben Ames Williams technique. The whole personality and background of Hazen Kinch are conveyed to the reader, not by direct narration, but rather by a clever use of suggestion and a few revealing bits of conversation among the characters. At no place in the story is the reader told, in so many words, that Kinch is a hard, mean man, but he reveals himself to be such by his every act and word. There is never an unnecessary speech or descriptive phrase. The story pushes onward surely and inevitably to produce a simple and single effect quite in the manner of Edgar Allan Poe. A feeling of mystery and the imminence of tragedy permeate the narrative, no small element in the establishment of which is the emphasis upon the weather which ultimately plays such an important part in the outcome of the story.

# "THEY GRIND EXCEEDING SMALL" *

I TELEPHONED down the hill to Hazen Kinch. "Hazen," I asked, "are you going to town today?"

"Yes, yes," he said abruptly in his quick, harsh fashion. "Of course I'm going to town."

"I've a matter of business," I suggested.

"Come along," he invited brusquely. "Come along."

There was not another man within forty miles to whom he would have given that invitation.

"I'll be down in ten minutes," I promised him; and I went to put on my Pontiacs [1] and heavy half boots over them and started downhill through the sandy snow. It was bitterly cold; it had been a cold winter. The bay — I could see it from my window — was frozen over for a dozen miles east and west and thirty north and south; and that had not happened in close to a score of years. Men were freighting across to the islands with heavy teams. Automobiles had beaten a rough road along the course the steamers took in summer. A man who had ventured to stock one of the lower islands with foxes for the sake of their fur, counting on the water to hold them prisoners, had gone bankrupt when his stock in trade escaped across the ice. Bitterly cold and steadily cold, and deep snow lay upon the hills, blue-white in the distance. The evergreens were blue-black blotches on this whiteness. The birches, almost indistinguishable, were like trees in camouflage. To me the hills are never so grand as in this winter coat they wear. It is easy to believe that a brooding God dwells upon them. I wondered as I plowed my way down to Hazen Kinch's farm whether God did indeed dwell among these hills; and I wondered what he thought of Hazen Kinch.

This was no new matter of thought with me. I had given some thought to Hazen in the past. I was interested in the man and in that which should come to him. He was, it seemed

\* The title of the story is taken from a line of "Retribution" by the German poet Friedrich von Logau (1604–1655):

"Though the mills of God grind slowly, yet they grind
  exceeding small."

to me, a problem in fundamental ethics; he was, as matters stood, a demonstration of the essential uprightness of things as they are. The biologist would have called him a sport,[2] a deviation from type, a violation of all the proper laws of life. That such a man should live and grow great and prosper was not fitting; in a well-regulated world it should not be. Yet Hazen Kinch did live; he had grown — in his small way — great; and, by our lights, he had prospered. Therefore I watched him. There was about the man the fascination which clothes a tight-rope walker above Niagara; an aëronaut in the midst of the nose dive. The spectator stares with half-caught breath, afraid to see and afraid to miss seeing the ultimate catastrophe. Sometimes I wondered whether Hazen Kinch suspected this attitude on my part. It was not impossible. There was a cynical courage in the man; it might have amused him. Certainly I was the only man who had in any degree his confidence.

I have said there was not another within forty miles whom he would have given a lift to town; I doubt if there was another man anywhere for whom he would have done this small favor. He seemed to find a mocking sort of pleasure in my company.

When I came to his house he was in the barn harnessing his mare to the sleigh. The mare was a good animal, fast and strong. She feared and she hated Hazen. I could see her roll her eyes backward at him as he adjusted the traces. He called to me without turning, " Shut the door! Shut the door! "

I slid the door shut behind me. There was within the barn the curious chill warmth which housed animals generate to protect themselves against our winters.

" It will snow," I told Hazen. " I was not sure you would go."

He laughed crookedly, jerking at the trace.

" Snow! " he exclaimed. " A man would think you were personal manager of the weather. Why do you say it will snow? "

" The drift of the clouds — and it's warmer," I told him.

" I'll not have it snowing," he said, and looked at me and cackled. He was a little, thin, old man with meager whiskers and a curious precision of speech; and I think he got some enjoyment out of watching my expression at such remarks as this. He elaborated his assumption that the universe was conducted for his benefit, in order to see my silent revolt at the suggestion. "I'll not have it snowing," he said. "Open the door."

He led the mare out and stopped by the kitchen door.

"Come in," he said. "A hot drink."

I went with him into the kitchen. His wife was there, and their child. The woman was lean and frail; and she was afraid of him. The countryside said he had taken her in payment of a bad debt. Her father had owed him money which he could not pay.

"I decided it was time I had a wife," Hazen used to say to me.

The child was on the floor. The woman had a drink of milk and egg and rum, hot and ready for us. We drank, and Hazen knelt beside the child. A boy baby, not yet two years old. It is an ugly thing to say, but I hated this child. There was evil malevolence in his baby eyes. Also, he was deformed — a twisted leg. The women of the neighborhood sometimes said he would be better dead. But Hazen Kinch loved him. He lifted him in his arms now with a curious passion in his movement, and the child stared at him sullenly. When his mother came near, the baby squalled at her, and Hazen said roughly, "Stand away! Leave him alone!"

She moved back furtively; and Hazen asked me, displaying the child, "A fine boy, eh?"

I said nothing, and in his cracked old voice he mumbled endearments to the baby. I had often wondered whether his love for the child redeemed the man; or merely made him vulnerable. Certainly any harm that might come to the baby would be a crushing blow to Hazen.

He put the child down on the floor again and he said to the woman curtly, "Tend him well." She nodded. There was a dumb submission in her eyes; but through this blank veil I had seen now and then a blaze of pain.

Hazen went out of the door without further word to her, and I followed him. We got into the sleigh, bundling ourselves into the robes for the six-mile drive along the drifted road to town. There was a feeling of storm in the air. I looked at the sky; so did Hazen Kinch. He guessed what I would have said and he answered me before I could speak.

"I'll not have it snowing," he said, and leered at me.

Nevertheless, I knew the storm would come. The mare turned out of the barnyard and plowed through the drift and struck hard-packed road. Her hoofs beat a swift tattoo; our runners sang beneath us. We dropped to the little bridge and across, and began the mile-long climb to the top of Rayborn Hill. The road from Hazen's house to town is compounded of such ups and downs.

At the top of the hill we paused for a moment to breathe the mare; paused just in front of the big old Rayborn house, that has stood there for more years than most of us remember. It was closed and shuttered and deserted; and Hazen dipped his whip toward it and said meanly: " An ugly, improvident lot, the Rayborns were."

I had known only one of them — the eldest son. A fine man, I had thought him. Picking apples in his orchard, he fell one October and broke his neck. His widow tried to make a go of the place, but she borrowed of Hazen and he had evicted her this three months back. It was one of the lesser evils he had done. I looked at the house and at him, and he clucked to the mare, and we dipped into the steep valley below the hill.

The wind had a sweep in that valley and there was a drift of snow across it and across the road. This drift was well packed by the wind, but when we drove over its top our left-hand runner broke through the coaming and we tumbled into the snow, Hazen and I. We were well entangled in the rugs. The mare gave a frightened start, but Hazen had held the reins and the whip so that she could not break away. We got up together, he and I, and we righted the sleigh and set it upon the road again. I remember that it was becoming bitter cold and the sun was no longer shining. There was a steel-gray veil drawn across the bay.

When the sleigh was upright Hazen went forward and stood beside the mare. Some men, blaming the beast without reason, would have beaten her. They would have cursed, cried out upon her. That was not the cut of Hazen Kinch. But I could see that he was angry and I was not surprised when he reached up and gripped the horse's ear. He pulled the mare's head down and twisted the ear viciously. All in a silence that was deadly.

The mare snorted and tried to rear back, and Hazen clapped

the butt of his whip across her knees. She stood still, quivering, and he wrenched at her ear again.

"Now," he said softly, "keep the road."

And he returned and climbed to his place beside me in the sleigh. I said nothing. I might have interfered, but something had always impelled me to keep back my hand from Hazen Kinch.

We drove on and the mare was lame. Though Hazen pushed her, we were slow in coming to town; before we reached Hazen's office the snow was whirling down — a pressure of driving, swirling flakes like a heavy white hand.

I left Hazen at the stair that led to his office and I went about my business of the day. He said as I turned away, "Be here at three."

I nodded. But I did not think we should drive home that afternoon. I had some knowledge of storms.

That which brought me to town was not engrossing. I found time to go to the stable and see Hazen's mare. There was an ugly welt across her knees and some blood had flowed. The stableman had tended the welt, and cursed Hazen in my hearing. It was still snowing, and the stable boss, looking out at the driving flakes, spat upon the ground and said to me, "Them legs'll go stiff. That mare won't go home tonight."

"I think you are right," I agreed.

"The white-whiskered skunk!" he said, and I knew he spoke of Hazen.

At a quarter of three I took myself to Hazen Kinch's office. It was not much of an office; not that Hazen could not have afforded a better. But it was up two flights — an attic room ill lighted. A small air-tight stove kept the room stifling hot. The room also was air-tight. Hazen had a table and two chairs, and an iron safe in the corner. He put a pathetic trust in that safe. I believe I could have opened it with a screw-driver. I met him as I climbed the stairs. He said harshly, "I'm going to telephone. They say the road's impassable."

He had no telephone in his office; he used one in the store below — a small economy fairly typical of Hazen.

"I'll wait in the office," I told him.

"Go ahead," he agreed, halfway down the stairs.

I went up to his office and closed the drafts of the stove —

it was red hot — and tried to open the one window, but it was nailed fast. Then Hazen came back up the stairs grumbling.

"Damn the snow," he said. "The wire is down."

"Where to?" I asked.

"My house, man! To my house!"

"You wanted to telephone home that you ——"

"I can't get home tonight. You'll have to go to the hotel."

I nodded good-naturedly.

"All right. You, too, I suppose."

"I'll sleep here," he said.

"I looked around. There was no bed, no cot, nothing but the two stiff chairs. He saw my glance and said angrily: "I've slept on the floor before."

I was always interested in the man's mental processes.

"You wanted to telephone Mrs. Kinch not to worry?" I suggested.

"Pshaw; let her fret!" said Hazen. "I wanted to ask after my boy." His eyes expanded; he rubbed his hands a little, cackling: "A fine boy, sir! A fine boy!"

It was then we heard Doan Marshey coming up the stairs. We heard his stumbling steps as he began the last flight, and Hazen seemed to cock his ears as he listened. Then he sat still and watched the door. The steps climbed nearer; they stopped in the dim little hall outside the door, and someone fumbled with the knob. When the door opened we saw who it was. I knew Marshey. He lived a little beyond Hazen on the same road. Lived in a little two-room cabin — it was little more — with his wife and his five children; lived meanly and pitiably, groveling in the soil for daily bread, sweating life out of the earth — life and no more. A thin man, racking thin; a forward-thrusting neck and a bony face and a sad and drooping mustache about his mouth. His eyes were meek and weary.

He stood in the doorway blinking at us; and with his gloved hands — they were stiff and awkward with the cold — he unwound the ragged muffler that was about his neck and he brushed weakly at the snow upon his head and shoulders. Hazen said angrily, "Come in! Do you want my stove to heat the town?"

Doan shuffled in and he shut the door behind him. He said:

## "They Grind Exceeding Small" 341

"Howdy, Mr. Kinch." And he smiled in a humble and placating way.

Hazen said, "What's your business? Your interest is due."

Doan nodded.

"Yeah, I know, Mr. Kinch. I cain't pay it all."

Kinch exclaimed impatiently, "An old story! How much can you pay?"

"Eleven dollars and fifty cents," said Doan.

"You owe twenty."

"I aim to pay it when the hens begin to lay."

Hazen laughed scornfully.

"You aim to pay! Marshey, if your old farm was worth taking, I'd have you out in this snow, you old scamp!"

Doan pleaded dully, "Don't do that, Mr. Kinch! I aim to pay."

Hazen clapped his hands on the table.

"Rats! Come! Give me what you've got! And, Marshey, you'll have to get the rest. I'm sick of waiting on you."

Marshey came shuffling toward the table. Hazen was sitting with the table between him and the man, and I was a little behind Hazen at one side. Marshey blinked as he came nearer, and his weak, near-sighted eyes turned from Hazen to me. I could see that the man was stiff with the cold.

When he came to the table in front of Hazen, he took off his thick gloves. His hands were blue. Laying the gloves on the table, he reached into an inner pocket of his torn coat and drew out a little cloth pouch. He fumbled into this and I heard the clink of coins. He drew out two quarters and laid them on the table before Hazen, and Hazen picked them up. Then he reached into the pouch again.

Something dropped out of the mouth of the little cloth bag and fell soundlessly on the table. It looked to me like a bill, a piece of paper currency. I was about to speak, but Hazen, without an instant's hesitation, had dropped his hand on the thing and drawn it unostentatiously toward him. When he lifted his hand the money — if it was money — was gone.

Marshey drew out a little roll of worn bills. Hazen took them out of his hand and counted them swiftly.

"All right," he said. "Eleven-fifty. I'll give you a receipt. But you mind me, Doan Marshey, you get the rest before the month's out. I've been too slack with you."

Marshey, his dull eyes watching Hazen write the receipt,

was folding the little pouch and putting it away. Hazen tore off the bit of paper and gave it to him. Doan took it and he said humbly: " Thank'e, sir."

Hazen nodded, " Mind now! " he exclaimed, and Marshey said, " I'll do my best, Mr. Kinch."

Then he turned and shuffled across the room and out into the hall. We heard him descending the stairs.

When he was gone I asked Hazen casually: " What was that he dropped upon the table? "

" A dollar," said Hazen promptly. " A dollar bill. The miserable fool! "

" You mean to give it back to him? " I asked.

He stared at me and he laughed. " No! If he can't take care of his own money — that's why he is what he is."

" Still it is his money."

" He owes me more than that."

" Going to give him credit for it? "

" Am I a fool? " Hazen asked me. " Do I look like so much of a fool? "

" He may charge you with finding it."

" He loses a dollar; I find one. Can he prove ownership? Pshaw! " Hazen laughed again.

" If there is any spine in him he will lay the thing to you as a theft," I suggested. I was not afraid of angering Hazen. He allowed me open speech; he seemed to find a grim pleasure in my distaste for him and for his way of life.

" If there were any backbone in the man he would not be paying me eighty dollars a year on a five-hundred dollar loan — discounted."

Hazen grinned at me triumphantly.

" I wonder if he will ever come back," I said.

" Besides," Hazen continued, " he lied to me. He told me the eleven-fifty was all he had."

" Yes," I agreed. " There is no doubt he lied to you."

Hazen had a letter to write and he bent to it. I sat by the stove and watched him and considered. He had not yet finished the letter when we heard Marshey returning. His dragging feet on the stair were unmistakable. At the sound of his weary feet some tide of indignation surged up in me. I was minded to do violence to Hazen Kinch. But a deeper impulse held my hand from the man.

Marshey came in and his weary eyes wandered about the room. They inspected the floor; they inspected me; they inspected Hazen Kinch's table, and they rose at last humbly to Hazen Kinch.

"Well?" said Hazen.

"I lost a dollar," Marshey told him. "I 'lowed I might have dropped it here."

Hazen frowned.

"You told me eleven-fifty was all you had."

"This here dollar wa'n't mine."

The money-lender laughed.

"Likely! Who would give you a dollar? You lied to me, or you're lying now. I don't believe you lost a dollar."

Marshey reiterated weakly, "I lost a dollar."

"Well," said Hazen, "there's no dollar of yours here."

"It was to git medicine," Marshey said. "It wa'n't mine."

Hazen Kinch exclaimed, "By God, I believe you're accusing me!"

Marshey lifted both hands placatingly.

"No, Mr. Kinch. No, sir." His eyes once more wandered about the room. "Mebbe I dropped it in the snow," he said.

He turned to the door. Even in his slow shuffle there was a hint of trembling eagerness to escape. He went out and down the stairs. Hazen looked at me, his old face wrinkling mirthfully.

"You see?" he said.

I left him a little later and went out into the street. On the way to the hotel I stopped for a cigar at the drug store. Marshy was there, talking with the druggist.

I heard the druggist say, "No, Marshey, I'm sorry. I've been stung too often."

Marshey nodded humbly.

"I didn't 'low you'd figure to trust me," he agreed. "It's all right. I didn't 'low you would."

It was my impulse to give him the dollar he needed, but I did not do it. An overpowering compulsion bade me keep my hands off this matter. I did not know what I expected, but I felt the imminence of the fates. When I went out into the snow it seemed to me the groan of the gale was like the slow grind of millstones, one upon the other.

I thought long upon the matter of Hazen Kinch before sleep came that night.

Toward morning the snow must have stopped; but the wind increased and carved the drifts till sunrise; then abruptly died. I met Hazen at the post office at ten and he said, "I'm starting home."

I asked, "Can you get through?"

He laughed. "I will get through," he told me.

"You're in haste."

"I want to see that boy of mine," said Hazen Kinch. "A fine boy, man!"

"I'm ready," I said.

When we took the road the mare was limping. But she seemed to work out the stiffness in her knees, and after a mile or so of the hard going she was moving smoothly enough. We made good time.

The day, as so often happens after a storm, was full of blinding sunlight. The glare of the sun upon the snow was almost unbearable. I kept my eyes all but closed, but there was so much beauty abroad in the land that I could not bear to close them altogether. The snow clung to twigs and to fences and to wires, and a thousand flames glinted from every crystal when the sun struck down upon the drifts. The pine wood upon the eastern slope of Rayborn Hill was a checkerboard of rich color — green and blue and black and white, indescribably brilliant. When we crossed the bridge at the foot of the hill we could hear the brook playing beneath the ice that sheathed it. On the white pages of the snow wild things had writ here and there the fine-traced tale of their morning's adventuring. We saw once where a fox had pinned a big snowshoe rabbit in a drift.

Hazen talked much of that child of his on the homeward way. I said little. From the top of Rayborn Hill we sighted his house and he laid the whip along the mare and we went down that long last descent at a speed that left me breathless. I shut my eyes and huddled low in the robes for protection against the bitter wind, and I did not open them again until we turned into Hazen's barnyard, plowing through the unpacked snow. When we stopped Hazen laughed.

"Ha!!" he said. "Now, come in, man, and warm yourself and see the baby!"

## "They Grind Exceeding Small"

He was ahead of me at the door; I went in upon his heels. We came into the kitchen together.

In the cold of winter Hazen's kitchen was also living-room and bedroom. The arrangement saved firewood. There was a bed against the wall opposite the door. As we came in a woman got up stiffly from the bed and I saw that this woman was Hazen's wife. But there was a change in her. She was bleak as cold iron and she was somehow strong.

Hazen rasped at this woman impatiently, "Well, I'm home! Where is the boy?"

She looked at him and her lips moved soundlessly. She closed them, opened them again. This time she was able to speak.

"The boy?" she said to Hazen. "The boy is dead!"

The dim-lit kitchen was very quiet for a little time. I felt myself breathe deeply, almost with relief. The thing for which I had waited — it had come. And I looked at Hazen Kinch.

He had always been a little, thin man. He was shrunken now and very white and very still. Only his face twitched. A muscle in one cheek jerked and jerked and jerked at his mouth. It was as though he controlled a desire to smile. That jerking, suppressed smile upon his white and tortured countenance was terrible. I could see the blood drain down from his forehead, down from his cheeks. He became white as death itself.

After a little he tried to speak. I do not know what he meant to say. But what he did was to repeat — as though he had not heard her words — the question which he had flung at her in the beginning. He said huskily, "Where is the boy?"

She looked toward the bed and Hazen looked that way; and then he went across to the bed with uncertain little steps. I followed him. I saw the little twisted body there. The woman had been keeping it warm with her own body. It must have been in her arms when we came in. The tumbled coverings, the crushed pillows, spoke mutely of a ferocious intensity of grief.

Hazen looked down at the little body. He made no move to touch it, but I heard him whisper to himself, "Fine boy!"

After a while he looked at the woman. She seemed to feel an accusation in his eyes. She said, "I did all I could."

He asked, "What was it?"

I had it in me — though I had reason enough to despise the little man — to pity Hazen Kinch.

"He coughed," said the woman. "I knew it was croup. You know I asked you to get the medicine — ipecac. You said no matter — no need — and you had gone."

She looked out of the window.

"I went for help — to Annie Marshey. Her babies had had it. Her husband was going to town and she said he would get the medicine for me. She did not tell it was for me. He would not have done it for you. He did not know. So I gave her a dollar to give him — to bring it out to me.

"He came home in the snow last night. Baby was bad by that time, so I was watching for Doan. I stopped him in the road and I asked him for the medicine. When he understood he told me. He had not brought it."

The woman was speaking dully, without emotion.

"It would have been in time, even then," she said. "But after a while, after that, baby died!"

I understood in that moment the working of the mills. And when I looked at Hazen Kinch I saw that he, too, was beginning to understand. There is a just mercilessness in an aroused God. Hazen Kinch was driven to questions.

"Why — didn't Marshey fetch it?" he asked.

She said slowly: "They would not trust him — at the store."

His mouth twitched, he raised his hands.

"The money!" he cried. "The money! What did he do with that?"

"He said," the woman answered, "that he lost it — in your office — lost the money there."

After a little the old money-lender leaned far back like a man wrenched with agony. His body was contorted; his face was terrible. His dry mouth opened wide.

He screamed!

Halfway up the hill to my house I stopped to look back and all around. The vast hills in their snowy garments looked down upon the land, upon the house of Hazen Kinch — still and silent and inscrutable.

I knew now that a just and brooding God dwelt among these hills.

## NOTES FOR *THEY GRIND EXCEEDING SMALL*

1. *Pontiacs,* felt stockings.
2. *Sport,* in biology, a new and unusual plant or flower differing from its parent stock — as a pink phlox springs from a bed of white-blossoming phloxes.

## QUESTIONS

1. From the opening remarks, select the words that point to Kinch's character.
2. List the words and phrases that indicate the weather.
3. Why did Hazen say " Of course I'm going to town "?
4. How does the mare's reaction to Kinch further indicate his character?
5. Describe Kinch's and his wife's feelings for each other.
6. Account for the narrator's feeling about the child.
7. Was Kinch's attitude toward the child a redeeming trait?
8. Where do you first get an idea of how Kinch made his money?
9. Why was Hazen's method of punishing his horse more in keeping with his character than the usual methods of punishing a horse?
10. Why had the narrator always kept his hands from Hazen?
11. What prevented the men from going home the same day? How does that affect the outcome of the story?
12. Why did Kinch, a farmer, happen to have an office in town? What type of man was Marshey? Contrast him and his circumstances with Kinch.
13. How does Hazen justify his keeping of Marshey's dollar?
14. Why did the narrator not give Marshey the dollar as he was at first tempted to do? Show how it would have changed the story if he had done so.
15. What preparation for tragedy do you find in the description of Mrs. Kinch when the two men return?
16. What made the death of Hazen's son more tragic than it would otherwise have been? Was he sufficiently punished for his selfishness?
17. State briefly what you consider the theme of the story.
18. Give the significance of the title of the story.

## SUBJECTS FOR COMPOSITION

1. Write an imaginary conversation between Mrs. Kinch and Marshey in which he explains why he didn't bring the medicine.
2. Suppose that Kinch and the narrator had started back on the night they originally planned and were lost in the snow storm. Write a description of their experiences.
3. Write about a possible change of relations between Kinch and Marshey, had Marshey been able to get the medicine and save the child's life.

## VOLUMES OF STORIES BY BEN AMES WILLIAMS
*Thrifty Stock and Other Stories*

## I. V. MORRIS

(1903–    )

I. V. MORRIS was born in Chicago, November 11, 1903. He was educated at Harvard and later studied at Heidelberg University. After Heidelberg he returned to America where he worked on a newspaper for a few months. Not liking newspaper work particularly, he next tried the publishing business in London. Morris worked at this for three years during which time he says he acquired an even stronger dislike of office work than he had had previously. Hence he abandoned routine work and went to France to live and devote himself entirely to writing.

Mr. Morris has published magazine short stories and a novel, *Covering Two Years,* published in England. He has also been honored by having his work included in O'Brien's *Best American Short Stories.* "The Sampler," which follows, is an example of the "short short" story, which has come into popularity in the last few years. Few "short shorts" run to more than 1500 words, or one-third the average length of regular short stories.

## THE SAMPLER

IN a certain store where they sell plum puddings, a number of these delicious articles are laid out in a row during the Christmas season. Here you may select the one which is most to your taste, and you are even allowed to sample the various qualities before coming to a decision.

I have often wondered whether this privilege was not imposed on by people who had no intention of making a purchase, and one day when my curiosity drove me to ask this question of the shop girl, I learned it was indeed the case.

"Now there's one old gentleman, for instance," she told me, "who comes here almost every week and samples each one of the puddings, though he never buys anything and I suspect he never will. I remember him from last year and the year before that too. Well, let him come if he wants it that bad, say I, and welcome to it. And what's more, I hope there are a lot more stores where he can go and get his share. He looks as if he needed it all right, and I suppose they can afford it."

She was still speaking when an elderly gentleman limped up to the counter and began scrutinizing the row of puddings with great interest.

"Why that there's the very party I've been telling you about," whispered the shop girl. "Just you watch him now." And then turning to him: "Would you like to sample them, sir? Here's a spoon for you to use."

The elderly gentleman, who, as the novelists say, was poorly but neatly dressed, accepted the spoon and began eagerly to sample one after another of the puddings, only breaking off occasionally to wipe his red eyes with a large torn handkerchief which he drew from the breast pocket of his shoddy overcoat.

"This is quite good," he declared of one variety, and when he came to the next, "This is not bad either, but a trifle too heavy." All the time it was quite evident that he sincerely believed that he might eventually buy one of these puddings, and I am positive that he did not for a moment feel that he was in any way cheating the store. Poor old chap! Probably he had come down in the world and this sampling was all that was left him from the time when he could afford to come and select his favorite pudding, which he would later carry home under his arm.

Amidst the throng of happy, prosperous looking Christmas shoppers, the little black figure of the old man seemed incongruous and pathetic, and in a burst of benevolence, one of those bursts which so often bring pain instead of joy, I went up to him and said:

"Pardon me, sir, will you do me a favor? Let me purchase you one of these puddings. It would give me such pleasure."

He jumped back as if he had been stung, and the blood rushed into his wrinkled face.

"Excuse me," he said, with more dignity than I would have thought possible considering his appearance, "I do not believe I have the pleasure of knowing you. Undoubtedly you have mistaken me for someone else." And with a quick decision he turned to the shop girl and said in a loud voice: "Kindly pack me up this one here. I will take it with me." He pointed at one of the largest and most expensive of the puddings.

In surprise, the girl took down the pudding from its stand

and proceeded to make a parcel of it, while he extracted a worn little black pocketbook and began counting out shillings and sixpenny pieces on to the counter. To save his "honour" he had been forced into a purchase which he could not possibly afford and which probably meant many bitter privations in other things. How I longed for the power to unsay my tactless words! It was too late though, and I felt that the kindest thing I could do now would be to walk away.

"You pay at the desk," the shop girl was telling him, but he did not seem to understand and kept trying to put the coins into her hand. And that was the last I saw or heard of the old man. Now he can never come there to sample plum puddings any more.

## QUESTIONS

1. Was the question of the narrator a natural one to ask of the shop girl? Give your reasons.
2. Was the entrance of the old man expected by you? Why?
3. What makes the narrator suspect that the old man had come down in the world?
4. Why do bursts of generosity often bring pain instead of joy?
5. Did the old gentleman tactfully refuse the offer? Explain.
6. How did he save his "honor" by buying the pudding?
7. Why couldn't he ever come back again to sample the puddings?
8. Have you read other "short shorts"? Find at least one other "short short" and come to class prepared to discuss it.

## SUBJECTS FOR COMPOSITION

1. Tell of an experience that you know of some one who resented charity.
2. Tell how the old man explained the purchase of the pudding to his wife when he got home.

## ARTHUR CONAN DOYLE
### (1859–1929)

IN TALKING about stories it is often customary to refer to a " Poe " story, or an " O. Henry " story, to indicate a certain type of short fiction. In the same way we speak of a " Sherlock Holmes " story when we really mean a " Conan Doyle " story, so thoroughly has the famous detective taken hold of the reading public. Nothing can dislodge him from his pinnacle of fame. He is the supreme sleuth in fiction. In vain do we Americans cry out that Poe was the inventor of the detective story, and that to him should be given first place. That he was the inventor no one denies, least of all Sir Arthur Conan Doyle himself. The fact simply remains that by sheer skill Conan Doyle has popularized the detective story through the methods invented by Poe. In spite of a host of imitators and followers, many exceedingly clever, the Sherlock Holmes story still tops them all.

Not only that; the literary fame of Conan Doyle rests primarily on the group of stories written around this one character, although he is the author of numerous volumes of novels, short stories, plays, and non-fiction books on the Boer War and the more recent Great War in Europe.

Conan Doyle's life has been both active and varied. Born in 1859, in Edinburgh, he went through the local schools, including the University, from which he graduated as a physician in 1885. Occasionally he practiced this profession, on land and on sea, but he owes his fame entirely to what at first he considered a side line by which he could make some easy but necessary money — the writing of detective stories. These soon attracted attention, and when he published his first volume, *The Adventures of Sherlock Holmes,* in 1891, he became internationally famous. Since that time Sherlock Holmes and Conan Doyle have been linked together. When the author at one time decided that the detective had served long enough he had him die, but so clamorous was the reading public for more Sherlock Holmes stories that his creator revived him. The overwhelming popularity of this one character has somewhat obscured Conan Doyle's other stories of romantic adventure, such as *The Adventures of the Brigadier Gerard,* swashbuckling stories of a type that seem never to lose their interest.

Throughout the Boer War in Africa, and after, there was much criticism of the English both at home and abroad. Conan Doyle, who had served with the British soldiers as a doctor, wrote two books on that war in which he tried to explain and justify England's position. For this service to his country he was knighted in 1902. During the Great War of 1914 he was engaged in propaganda work. He has several times visited the United States, giving lectures from one end of the country to the other; after his return to England he wrote books on his experiences.

His later interests have been concerned entirely with the study of psychical phenomena, sometimes erroneously called *spiritualism*. In his writings on this subject he tried to retain the logical methods employed in his detective stories. His aim is to make the mystic seem practical rather than mysterious, but whatever interest the general public takes in this phase of his work rises from the old descriptive phrase, " by the author of ' Sherlock Holmes.' " In 1924 he published *Memories and Adventures,* an autobiography.

# THE ADVENTURE OF THE SPECKLED BAND

IN GLANCING over my notes of the seventy-odd cases in which I have during the last eight years studied the methods of my friend Sherlock Holmes, I find many tragic, some comic, a large number merely strange, but none commonplace; for, working as he did rather for the love of his art than for the acquirement of wealth, he refused to associate himself with any investigation which did not tend toward the unusual, and even the fantastic. Of all these varied cases, however, I cannot recall any which presented more singular features than that which was associated with the well-known Surrey family of the Roylotts of Stoke Moran. The events in question occurred in the early days of my association with Holmes, when we were sharing rooms as bachelors in Baker Street. It is possible that I might have placed them upon record before, but a promise of secrecy was made at the time, from which I have only been freed during the last month by the untimely death of the lady to whom the pledge was given. It is perhaps as well that the facts should now come to light, for I have reasons to know that there are widespread rumors as to the death of Dr. Grimesby Roylott which tend to make the matter even more terrible than the truth.

It was early in April in the year '83 that I woke one morning to find Sherlock Holmes standing, fully dressed, by the side of my bed. He was a late riser as a rule, and as the clock on the mantelpiece showed me that it was only a quarter past seven, I blinked up at him in some surprise, and perhaps just a little resentment, for I was myself regular in my habits.

"Very sorry to knock you up, Watson," said he, "but it's the common lot this morning. Mrs. Hudson has been knocked up, she retorted upon me, and I on you."

"What is it, then — a fire?"

"No; a client. It seems that a young lady has arrived in a considerable state of excitement, who insists upon seeing me. She is waiting now in the sitting-room. Now, when young ladies wander about the metropolis at this hour of the morning, and knock sleepy people up out of their beds, I presume that it is something very pressing which they have to communicate. Should it prove to be an interesting case, you would, I am sure, wish to follow it from the outset. I thought, at any rate, that I should call you and give you the chance."

"My dear fellow, I would not miss it for anything."

I had no keener pleasure than in following Holmes in his professional investigations, and in admiring the rapid deductions, as swift as intuitions, and yet always founded on a logical basis, with which he unravelled the problems which were submitted to him. I rapidly threw on my clothes, and was ready in a few minutes to accompany my friend down to the sitting-room. A lady dressed in black and heavily veiled, who had been sitting in the window, rose as we entered.

"Good-morning, madam," said Holmes, cheerily. "My name is Sherlock Holmes. This is my intimate friend and associate, Dr. Watson, before whom you can speak as freely as before myself. Ha! I am glad to see that Mrs. Hudson has had the good sense to light the fire. Pray draw up to it, and I shall order you a cup of hot coffee, for I observe that you are shivering."

"It is not cold which makes me shiver," said the woman, in a low voice, changing her seat as requested.

"What, then?"

"It is fear, Mr. Holmes. It is terror." She raised her veil as she spoke, and we could see that she was indeed in a pitiable state of agitation, her face all drawn and gray, with restless, frightened eyes, like those of some hunted animal. Her features and figure were those of a woman of thirty, but her hair was shot with premature gray, and her expression was weary and haggard. Sherlock Holmes ran her over with one of his quick, all-comprehensive glances.

"You must not fear," said he, soothingly, bending forward and patting her forearm. "We shall soon set matters right, I have no doubt. You have come in by train this morning, I see."

"You know me, then?"

"No, but I observe the second half of a return ticket in the palm of your left glove. You must have started early, and yet you had a good drive in a dog-cart, along heavy roads, before you reached the station."

The lady gave a violent start, and stared in bewilderment at my companion.

"There is no mystery, my dear madam," said he, smiling. "The left arm of your jacket is spattered with mud in no less than seven places. The marks are perfectly fresh. There is no vehicle save a dog-cart which throws up mud in that way, and then only when you sit on the left-hand side of the driver."

"Whatever your reasons may be, you are perfectly correct," said she. "I started from home before six, reached Leatherhead at twenty past, and came in by the first train to Waterloo. Sir, I can stand this strain no longer; I shall go mad if it continues. I have no one to turn to — none, save only one, who cares for me, and he, poor fellow, can be of little aid. I have heard of you, Mr. Holmes; I have heard of you from Mrs. Farintosh, whom you helped in the hour of her sore need. It was from her that I had your address. Oh, sir, do you not think that you could help me, too, and at least throw a little light through the dense darkness which surrounds me? At present it is out of my power to reward you for your services, but in a month or six weeks I shall be married, with the control of my own income, and then at least you shall not find me ungrateful."

Holmes turned to his desk, and unlocking it, drew out a small case-book, which he consulted.

"Farintosh," said he. "Ah yes, I recall the case; it was concerned with an opal tiara. I think it was before your time, Watson. I can only say, madam, that I shall be happy to devote the same care to your case as I did to that of your friend. As to reward, my profession is its own reward; but you are at liberty to defray whatever expenses I may be put to, at the time which suits you best. And now I beg that you will lay before us everything that may help us in forming an opinion upon the matter."

"Alas!" replied our visitor, "the very horror of my situation lies in the fact that my fears are so vague, and my suspicions depend so entirely upon small points, which might seem trivial to another, that even he to whom of all others I have a right to look for help and advice looks upon all that I tell him about it as the fancies of a nervous woman. He does not say so, but I can read it from his soothing answers and averted eyes. But I have heard, Mr. Holmes, that you can see deeply into the manifold wickedness of the human heart. You may advise me how to walk amid the dangers which encompass me."

"I am all attention, madam."

"My name is Helen Stoner, and I am living with my stepfather, who is the last survivor of one of the oldest Saxon families in England, the Roylotts of Stoke Moran, on the western border of Surrey."

Holmes nodded his head. "The name is familiar to me," said he.

"The family was at one time among the richest in England, and the estates extended over the borders into Berkshire in the north and Hampshire in the west. In the last century, however, four successive heirs were of a dissolute and wasteful disposition, and the family ruin was eventually completed by a gambler in the days of the Regency. Nothing was left save a few acres of ground, and the two-hundred-year-old house, which is itself crushed under a heavy mortgage. The last squire dragged out his existence there, living the horrible life of an aristocratic pauper; but his only son, my stepfather, seeing that he must adapt himself to the new conditions, obtained an advance from a relative, which enabled him to take a medical degree, and went out to Calcutta, where, by his professional skill and his force of character, he established a large practice. In a fit of anger, however, caused by some robberies which had been perpetrated in the house, he beat his native butler to death, and narrowly escaped a capital sentence. As it was, he suffered a long term of imprisonment, and afterward returned to England a morose and disappointed man.

"When Dr. Roylott was in India he married my mother,

Mrs. Stoner, the young widow of Major-General Stoner, of the Bengal Artillery. My sister Julia and I were twins, and we were only two years old at the time of my mother's remarriage. She had a considerable sum of money — not less than £1000 a year — and this she bequeathed to Dr. Roylott entirely while we resided with him, with a provision that a certain annual sum should be allowed to each of us in the event of our marriage. Shortly after our return to England my mother died — she was killed eight years ago in a railway accident near Crewe. Dr. Roylott then abandoned his attempts to establish himself in practice in London, and took us to live with him in the old ancestral house at Stoke Moran. The money which my mother had left was enough for all our wants, and there seemed to be no obstacle to our happiness.

"But a terrible change came over our stepfather about this time. Instead of making friends and exchanging visits with our neighbors, who had at first been overjoyed to see a Roylott of Stoke Moran back in the old family seat, he shut himself up in his house, and seldom came out save to indulge in ferocious quarrels with whoever might cross his path. Violence of temper approaching to mania has been hereditary in the men of the family, and in my stepfather's case it had, I believe, been intensified by his long residence in the tropics. A series of disgraceful brawls took place, two of which ended in the police-court, until at last he became the terror of the village, and the folks would fly at his approach, for he is a man of immense strength, and absolutely uncontrollable in his anger.

"Last week he hurled the local blacksmith over a parapet into a stream, and it was only by paying over all the money which I could gather together that I was able to avert another public exposure. He had no friends at all save the wandering gypsies, and he would give these vagabonds leave to encamp upon the few acres of bramble-covered land which represent the family estate, and would accept in return the hospitality of their tents, wandering away with them sometimes for weeks on end. He has a passion also for Indian animals, which are sent over to him by a correspondent, and he has at this moment a cheetah and a baboon, which wander freely over his grounds, and are feared by the villagers almost as much as their master.

## The Speckled Band

"You can imagine from what I say that my poor sister Julia and I had no great pleasure in our lives. No servant would stay with us, and for a long time we did all the work of the house. She was but thirty at the time of her death, and yet her hair had already begun to whiten, even as mine has."

"Your sister is dead, then?"

"She died just two years ago, and it is of her death that I wish to speak to you. You can understand that, living the life which I have described, we were little likely to see any one of our own age and position. We had, however, an aunt, my mother's maiden sister, Miss Honoria Westphail, who lives near Harrow, and we were occasionally allowed to pay short visits at this lady's house. Julia went there at Christmas two years ago, and met there a half-pay major of marines, to whom she became engaged. My stepfather learned of the engagement when my sister returned, and offered no objection to the marriage; but within a fortnight of the day which had been fixed for the wedding, the terrible event occurred which has deprived me of my only companion."

Sherlock Holmes had been leaning back in his chair with his eyes closed and his head sunk in a cushion, but he half opened his lids now and glanced across at his visitor.

"Pray be precise as to details," said he.

"It is easy for me to be so, for every event of that dreadful time is seared into my memory. The manor-house is, as I have already said, very old, and only one wing is now inhabited. The bedrooms in this wing are on the ground floor, the sitting-rooms being in the central block of the buildings. Of these bedrooms the first is Dr. Roylott's, the second my sister's, and the third my own. There is no communication between them, but they all open out into the same corridor. Do I make myself plain?"

"Perfectly so."

"The windows of the three rooms open out upon the lawn. That fatal night Dr. Roylott had gone to his room early, though we knew that he had not retired to rest, for my sister was troubled by the smell of the strong Indian cigars which it was his custom to smoke. She left her room, therefore, and came into mine, where she sat for some time, chatting about her approaching wedding. At eleven o'clock she rose to leave me, but she paused at the door and looked back.

"'Tell me, Helen,' said she, 'have you ever heard any one whistle in the dead of the night?'

"'Never,' said I.

"'I suppose that you could not possibly whistle, yourself, in your sleep?'

"'Certainly not. But why?'

"'Because during the last few nights I have always, about three in the morning, heard a low, clear whistle. I am a light sleeper, and it has awakened me. I cannot tell where it came from — perhaps from the next room, perhaps from the lawn. I thought that I would just ask you whether you had heard it.'

"'No, I have not. It must be those wretched gypsies in the plantation.'

"'Very likely. And yet if it were on the lawn, I wonder that you did not hear it also.'

"'Ah, but I sleep more heavily than you.'

"'Well, it is of no great consequence, at any rate.' She smiled back at me, closed my door, and a few moments later I heard her key turn in the lock."

"Indeed," said Holmes. "Was it your custom always to lock yourselves in at night?"

"Always."

"And why?"

"I think that I mentioned to you that the doctor kept a cheetah and a baboon. We had no feeling of security unless our doors were locked."

"Quite so. Pray proceed with your statement."

"I could not sleep that night. A vague feeling of impending misfortune impressed me. My sister and I, you will recollect, were twins, and you know how subtle are the links which bind two souls which are so closely allied. It was a wild night. The wind was howling outside, and the rain was beating and splashing against the windows. Suddenly, amid all the hubbub of the gale, there burst forth the wild scream of a terrified woman. I knew that it was my sister's voice. I sprang from my bed, wrapped a shawl round me, and rushed into the corridor. As I opened my door I seemed to hear a low whistle, such as my sister described, and a few moments later a clanging sound, as if a mass of metal had fallen. As I ran down the passage my sister's door was unlocked, and revolved slowly upon its hinges. I stared at it horror-stricken, not knowing what was about to issue from it. By the light of the corridor-lamp I saw my sister appear at the opening, her face blanched with terror, her hands groping for help, her whole figure swaying to and fro like that of a drunkard. I ran to her and threw my arms round her, but at that moment her knees seemed to give way and she fell to the ground. She writhed as one who is in terrible pain, and her limbs were dreadfully convulsed. At first I thought that she had not recognized me, but as I bent over her she suddenly shrieked out, in a voice which I shall never forget: ' Oh, my God! Helen! It was the band! The speckled band! ' There was something else which she would fain have said, and she stabbed with her finger into the air in the direction of the doctor's room, but a fresh convulsion seized her and choked her words. I rushed out, calling loudly for my stepfather, and I met him hastening from his room in his dressing-gown. When he reached my sister's side she was unconscious, and though he poured brandy down her throat and sent for medical aid from the village, all efforts were in vain, for she slowly sank and died without having recovered her consciousness. Such was the dreadful end of my beloved sister."

" One moment," said Holmes; " are you sure about this whistle and metallic sound? Could you swear to it? "

" That was what the county coroner asked me at the inquiry. It is my strong impression that I heard it, and yet, among the crash of the gale and the creaking of an old house, I may possibly have been deceived."

" Was your sister dressed? "

" No, she was in her night-dress. In her right hand was found the charred stump of a match, and in her left a match-box."

" Showing that she had struck a light and looked about her when the alarm took place. That is important. And what conclusions did the coroner come to? "

" He investigated the case with great care, for Dr. Roylott's conduct had long been notorious in the county, but he was unable to find any satisfactory cause of death. My evidence showed that the door had been fastened upon the inner side, and the windows were blocked by old-fashioned shutters with broad iron bars, which were secured every night. The walls were carefully sounded, and were shown to be quite solid all round, and the flooring was also thoroughly examined, with the same result. The chimney is wide, but is barred up by four large staples. It is certain, therefore, that my sister was quite alone when she met her end. Besides, there were no marks of any violence upon her."

"How about poison?"

"The doctors examined her for it, but without success."

"What do you think that this unfortunate lady died of, then?"

"It is my belief that she died of pure fear and nervous shock, though what it was that frightened her I cannot imagine."

"Were there gypsies in the plantation at the time?"

"Yes, there are nearly always some there."

"Ah, and what did you gather from this allusion to a band — a speckled band?"

"Sometimes I have thought that it was merely the wild talk of delirium, sometimes that it may have referred to some band of people, perhaps to these very gypsies in the plantation. I do not know whether the spotted handkerchiefs which so many of them wear over their heads might have suggested the strange adjective which she used."

Holmes shook his head like a man who is far from being satisfied.

"These are very deep waters," said he; "pray go on with your narrative."

"Two years have passed since then, and my life has been until lately lonelier than ever. A month ago, however, a dear friend, whom I have known for many years, has done me the honor to ask my hand in marriage. His name is Armitage — Percy Armitage — the second son of Mr. Armitage, of Crane Water, near Reading. My stepfather has offered no opposition to the match, and we are to be married in the course of the spring. Two days ago some repairs were started in the west wing of the building, and my bedroom wall has been pierced, so that I have had to move into the chamber in which my sister died, and to sleep in the very bed in which she slept. Imagine, then, my thrill of terror when last night, as I lay awake, thinking over her terrible fate, I suddenly heard in the silence of the night the low whistle which had been the herald of her own death. I sprang up and lit the lamp, but nothing was to be seen in the room. I was too shaken to go to bed again, however, so I dressed, and as soon as it was daylight I slipped down, got a dog-cart at the 'Crown Inn,' which is opposite, and drove to Leatherhead, from whence I have come on this morning with the one object of seeing you and asking your advice."

"You have done wisely," said my friend. "But have you told me all?"

"Yes, all."

"Miss Roylott, you have not. You are screening your stepfather."

"Why, what do you mean?"

For answer Holmes pushed back the frill of black lace which fringed the hand that lay upon our visitor's knee. Five little livid spots, the marks of four fingers and a thumb, were printed upon the white wrist.

"You have been cruelly used," said Holmes.

The lady colored deeply and covered over her injured wrist. "He is a hard man," she said, "and perhaps he hardly knows his own strength."

There was a long silence, during which Holmes leaned his chin upon his hands and stared into the crackling fire.

"This is a very deep business," he said, at last. "There are a thousand details which I should desire to know before I decide upon our course of action. Yet we have not a moment to lose. If we were to come to Stoke Moran today, would it be possible for us to see over these rooms without the knowledge of your stepfather?"

"As it happens, he spoke of coming into town today upon some most important business. It is probable that he will be away all day, and that there would be nothing to disturb you. We have a housekeeper now, but she is old and foolish, and I could easily get her out of the way."

"Excellent. You are not averse to this trip, Watson?"

"By no means."

"Then we shall both come. What are you going to do yourself?"

"I have one or two things which I would wish to do now that I am in town. But I shall return by the twelve-o'clock train, so as to be there in time for your coming."

"And you may expect us early in the afternoon. I have myself some small business matters to attend to. Will you not wait and breakfast?"

"No, I must go. My heart is lightened already since I have confided my trouble to you. I shall look forward to seeing you again this afternoon." She dropped her thick black veil over her face and glided from the room.

"And what do you think of it all, Watson?" asked Sherlock Holmes, leaning back in his chair.

"It seems to me to be a most dark and sinister business."

"Dark enough and sinister enough."

"Yet if the lady is correct in saying that the flooring and walls are sound, and that the door, window, and chimney are impassable, then her sister must have been undoubtedly alone when she met her mysterious end."

"What becomes, then, of these nocturnal whistles, and what of the very peculiar words of the dying woman?"

"I cannot think."

"When you combine the ideas of whistles at night, the presence of a band of gypsies who are on intimate terms with this old doctor, the fact that we have every reason to believe that the doctor has an interest in preventing his stepdaughter's marriage, the dying allusion to a band, and, finally, the fact that Miss Helen Stoner heard a metallic clang, which might have been caused by one of those metal bars which secured the shutters falling back into its place, I think that there is good ground to think that the mystery may be cleared along those lines."

"But what, then, did the gypsies do?"

"I cannot imagine."

"I see many objections to any such theory."

"And so do I. It is precisely for that reason that we are going to Stoke Moran this day. I want to see whether the objections are fatal, or if they may be explained away. But what in the name of the devil!"

The ejaculation had been drawn from my companion by the fact that our door had been suddenly dashed open, and that a huge man had framed himself in the aperture. His costume was a peculiar mixture of the professional and of the agricultural, having a black top-hat, a long frock-coat, and a pair of high gaiters, with a hunting-crop swinging in his hand. So tall was he that his hat actually brushed the cross-bar of the doorway, and his breadth seemed to span it across from side to side. A large face, seared with a thousand wrinkles, burned yellow with the sun, and marked with every evil passion, was turned from one to the other of us, while his deep-set, bile-shot eyes, and his high, thin, fleshless nose, gave him somewhat the resemblance to a fierce old bird of prey.

"Which of you is Holmes?" asked this apparition.

"My name, sir; but you have the advantage of me," said my companion, quietly.

"I am Dr. Grimesby Roylott, of Stoke Moran."

"Indeed, doctor," said Holmes, blandly. "Pray take a seat."

"I will do nothing of the kind. My stepdaughter has been here. I have traced her. What has she been saying to you?"

"It is a little cold for the time of the year," said Holmes.

"What has she been saying to you?" screamed the old man, furiously.

"But I have heard that the crocuses promise well," continued my companion, imperturbably.

"Ha! You put me off, do you?" said our new visitor, taking a step forward and shaking his hunting-crop. "I know you, you scoundrel! I have heard of you before. You are Holmes, the meddler."

My friend smiled.

"Holmes, the busybody!"

His smile broadened.

"Holmes, the Scotland Yard Jack-in-office!"

Holmes chuckled heartily. "Your conversation is most entertaining," said he. "When you go out close the door, for there is a decided draught."

"I will go when I have said my say. Don't you dare to meddle with my affairs. I know that Miss Stoner has been here. I traced her! I am a dangerous man to fall foul of! See here." He stepped swiftly forward, seized the poker, and bent it into a curve with his huge brown hands.

"See that you keep yourself out of my grip," he snarled; and hurling the twisted poker into the fireplace, he strode out of the room.

"He seems a very amiable person," said Holmes, laughing.

"I am not quite so bulky, but if he had remained I might have shown him that my grip was not much more feeble than his own." As he spoke he picked up the steel poker, and with a sudden effort straightened it out again.

"Fancy his having the insolence to confound me with the official detective force! This incident gives zest to our investigation, however, and I only trust that our little friend will not suffer from her imprudence in allowing this brute to trace her. And now, Watson, we shall order breakfast, and afterward I shall walk down to Doctors' Commons, where I hope to get some data which may help us in this matter."

It was nearly one o'clock when Sherlock Holmes returned from his excursion. He held in his hand a sheet of blue paper, scrawled over with notes and figures.

"I have seen the will of the deceased wife," said he. "To determine its exact meaning I have been obliged to work out the present prices of the investments with which it is concerned. The total income, which at the time of the wife's death was little short of £1100, is now, through the fall in agricultural prices, not more than £750. Each daughter can claim an income of £250, in case of marriage. It is evident, therefore, that if both girls had married, this beauty would have had a mere pittance, while even one of them would cripple him to a very serious extent. My morning's work has not been wasted, since it has proved that he has the very strongest motives for standing in the way of anything of the sort. And now, Watson, this is too serious for dawdling, especially as the old man is aware that we are interesting ourselves in his affairs; so if you are ready, we shall call a cab and drive to Waterloo. I should be very much obliged if you would slip your revolver into your pocket. An Eley's No. 2 is an excellent argument with gentlemen who can twist steel pokers into knots. That and a tooth-brush are, I think, all that we need."

At Waterloo we were fortunate in catching a train for Leatherhead, where we hired a trap at the station inn, and drove for four or five miles through the lovely Surrey lanes. It was a perfect day, with a bright sun and a few fleecy clouds in the heavens. The trees and wayside hedges were just throwing out their first green shoots, and the air was full of the pleasant smell of the moist earth. To me at least there was a strange contrast between the sweet promise of spring and this sinister quest upon which we were engaged. My companion sat in front of the trap, his arms folded, his hat pulled down over his eyes, and his chin sunk upon his breast, buried in the deepest thought. Suddenly, however, he started, tapped me on the shoulder, and pointed over the meadows.

"Look there!" said he.

A heavily timbered park stretched up in a gentle slope, thickening into a grove at the highest point. From amid the branches there jutted out the gray gables and high roof-tree of a very old mansion.

"Stoke Moran?" said he.

"Yes, sir, that be the house of Dr. Grimesby Roylott," remarked the driver.

"There is some building going on there," said Holmes; "that is where we are going."

"There's the village," said the driver, pointing to a cluster of roofs some distance to the left; "but if you want to get to the house, you'll find it shorter to get over this stile, and so by the foot-path over the fields. There it is, where the lady is walking."

"And the lady, I fancy, is Miss Stoner," observed Holmes, shading his eyes. "Yes, I think we had better do as you suggest."

We got off, paid our fare, and the trap rattled back on its way to Leatherhead.

"I thought it as well," said Holmes, as we climbed the stile, "that this fellow should think we had come here as architects or on some definite business. It may stop his gossip Good-afternoon, Miss Stoner. You see that we have been as good as our word."

Our client of the morning had hurried forward to meet us with a face which spoke her joy. "I have been waiting so eagerly for you!" she cried, shaking hands with us warmly. "All has turned out splendidly. Dr. Roylott has gone to town, and it is unlikely that he will be back before evening."

"We have had the pleasure of making the doctor's acquaintance," said Holmes, and in a few words he sketched out what had occurred. Miss Stoner turned white to the lips as she listened.

"Good heavens!" she cried. "He has followed me, then."

"So it appears."

"He is so cunning that I never know when I am safe from him. What will he say when he returns?"

"He must guard himself, for he may find that there is some one more cunning than himself upon his track. You must lock yourself up from him tonight. If he is violent, we shall take you away to your aunt's at Harrow. Now, we must make the best use of our time, so kindly take us at once to the rooms which we are to examine."

The building was of gray, lichen-blotched stone, with a high central portion, and two curving wings, like the claws of a crab, thrown out on each side. In one of these wings the windows were broken, and blocked with wooden boards, while the roof was partly caved in, a picture of ruin. The central portion was in little better repair, but the right-hand block was comparatively modern, and the blinds in the windows, with the blue smoke curling up from the chimneys, showed that this was where the family resided. Some scaffolding had been erected against the end wall, and the stonework had been broken into, but there were no signs of any workmen at the moment of our visit. Holmes walked slowly up and down the ill-trimmed lawn, and examined with deep attention the outsides of the windows.

"This, I take it, belongs to the room in which you used to sleep, the center one to your sister's, and the one next to the main building to Dr. Roylott's chamber?"

"Exactly so. But I am now sleeping in the middle one."

"Pending the alterations, as I understand. By the way, there does not seem to be any very pressing need for repairs at that end wall."

"There were none. I believe that it was an excuse to move me from my room."

"Ah! that is suggestive. Now, on the other side of this narrow wing runs the corridor from which these three rooms open. There are windows in it, of course?"

"Yes, but very small ones. Too narrow for any one to pass through."

"As you both locked your doors at night, your rooms were unapproachable from that side. Now, would you have the kindness to go into your room and bar your shutters."

Miss Stoner did so, and Holmes, after a careful examination

through the open window, endeavored in every way to force the shutter open, but without success. There was no slit through which a knife could be passed to raise the bar. Then with his lens he tested the hinges, but they were of solid iron, built firmly into the massive masonry. "Hum!" said he, scratching his chin in some perplexity; "my theory certainly presents some difficulties. No one could pass these shutters if they were bolted. Well, we shall see if the inside throws any light upon the matter."

A small side door led into the whitewashed corridor from which the three bedrooms opened. Holmes refused to examine the third chamber, so we passed at once to the second, that in which Miss Stoner was now sleeping, and in which her sister had met with her fate. It was a homely little room, with a low ceiling and a gaping fireplace, after the fashion of old country-houses. A brown chest of drawers stood in one corner, a narrow white-counterpaned bed in another, and a dressing-table on the left-hand side of the window. These articles, with two small wicker-work chairs, made up all the furniture in the room, save for a square of Wilton carpet in the center. The boards round and the paneling of the walls were of brown, worm-eaten oak, so old and discolored that it may have dated from the original building of the house. Holmes drew one of the chairs into a corner and sat silent, while his eyes traveled round and round and up and down, taking in every detail of the apartment.

"Where does that bell communicate with?" he asked, at last, pointing to a thick bell-rope which hung down beside the bed, the tassel actually lying upon the pillow.

"It goes to the housekeeper's room."

"It looks newer than the other things?"

"Yes, it was only put there a couple of years ago."

"Your sister asked for it, I suppose?"

"No, I never heard of her using it. We used always to get what we wanted for ourselves."

"Indeed, it seemed unnecessary to put so nice a bell-pull there. You will excuse me for a few minutes while I satisfy myself as to this floor." He threw himself down upon his face with his lens in his hand, and crawled swiftly backward and forward, examining minutely the cracks between the boards. Then he did the same with the woodwork with which the chamber was paneled. Finally he walked over to the bed, and spent some time in staring at it, and in running his eye up and down the wall. Finally he took the bell-rope in his hand and gave it a brisk tug.

"Why, it's a dummy," said he.

"Won't it ring?"

"No, it is not even attached to a wire. This is very interesting. You can see now that it is fastened to a hook just above where the little opening for the ventilator is."

"How very absurd! I never noticed that before."

"Very strange!" muttered Holmes, pulling at the rope. "There are one or two very singular points about this room. For example, what a fool a builder must be to open a ventilator into another room, when, with the same trouble, he might have communicated with the outside air!"

"That is also quite modern," said the lady.

"Done about the same time as the bell-rope?" remarked Holmes.

"Yes, there were several little changes carried out about that time."

"They seem to have been of a most interesting character — dummy bell-ropes, and ventilators which do not ventilate. With your permission, Miss Stoner, we shall now carry our researches into the inner apartment."

Dr. Grimesby Roylott's chamber was larger than that of his stepdaughter, but was as plainly furnished. A camp-bed, a small wooden shelf full of books, mostly of a technical character, an arm-chair beside the bed, a plain wooden chair against the wall, a round table, and a large iron safe were the principal things which met the eye. Holmes walked slowly round and examined each and all of them with the keenest interest.

"What's in here?" he asked, tapping the safe.

"My stepfather's business papers."

"Oh! you have seen inside, then?"

"Only once, some years ago. I remember that it was full of papers."

"There isn't a cat in it, for example?"

"No. What a strange idea!"

"Well, look at this!" He took up a small saucer of milk which stood on the top of it.

# The Speckled Band

"No; we don't keep a cat. But there is a cheetah and a baboon."

"Ah, yes, of course! Well, a cheetah is just a big cat, and yet a saucer of milk does not go very far in satisfying its wants, I dare say. There is one point which I should wish to determine." He squatted down in front of the wooden chair, and examined the seat of it with the greatest attention.

"Thank you. That is quite settled," said he, rising and putting his lens in his pocket. "Hello! Here is something interesting!"

The object which had caught his eye was a small dog-lash hung on one corner of the bed. The lash, however, was curled upon itself, and tied so as to make a loop of whip-cord.

"What do you make of that, Watson?"

"It's a common enough lash. But I don't know why it should be tied."

"That is not quite so common, is it? Ah, me! it's a wicked world, and when a clever man turns his brains to crime it is the worst of all. I think that I have seen enough now, Miss Stoner, and with your permission we shall walk out upon the lawn."

I had never seen my friend's face so grim or his brow so dark as it was when we turned from the scene of this investigation. We had walked several times up and down the lawn, neither Miss Stoner nor myself liking to break in upon his thoughts before he roused himself from his reverie.

"It is very essential, Miss Stoner," said he, "that you should absolutely follow my advice in every respect."

"I shall most certainly do so."

"The matter is too serious for any hesitation. Your life may depend upon your compliance."

"I assure you that I am in your hands."

"In the first place, both my friend and I must spend the night in your room."

Both Miss Stoner and I gazed at him in astonishment.

"Yes, it must be so. Let me explain. I believe that that is the village inn over there?"

"Yes, that is the 'Crown.'"

"Very good. Your windows would be visible from there?"

"Certainly."

"You must confine yourself to your room, on pretence of a headache, when your stepfather comes back. Then when you hear him retire for the night, you must open the shutters of your window, undo the hasp, put your lamp there as a signal to us, and then withdraw quietly with everything which you are likely to want into the room which you used to occupy. I have no doubt that, in spite of the repairs, you could manage there for one night."

"Oh yes, easily."

"The rest you will leave in our hands."

"But what will you do?"

"We shall spend the night in your room, and we shall investigate the cause of this noise which has disturbed you."

"I believe, Mr. Holmes, that you have already made up your mind," said Miss Stoner, laying her hand upon my companion's sleeve.

"Perhaps I have."

"Then, for pity's sake, tell me what was the cause of my sister's death."

"I should prefer to have clearer proofs before I speak."

"You can at least tell me whether my own thought is correct, and if she died from some sudden fright."

"No, I do not think so. I think that there was probably some more tangible cause. And now, Miss Stoner, we must leave you, for if Dr. Roylott returned and saw us, our journey would be in vain. Good-bye, and be brave, for if you will do what I have told you, you may rest assured that we shall soon drive away the dangers that threaten you."

Sherlock Holmes and I had no difficulty in engaging a bedroom and sitting-room at the "Crown Inn." They were on the upper floor, and from our window we could command a view of the avenue gate, and of the inhabited wing of Stoke Moran Manor-House. At dusk we saw Dr. Grimesby Roylott drive past, his huge form looming up beside the little figure of the lad who drove him. The boy had some slight difficulty in undoing the heavy iron gates, and we heard the hoarse roar of the doctor's voice, and saw the fury with which he shook his clinched fists at him. The trap drove on, and a few minutes later we saw a sudden light spring up among the trees as the lamp was lit in one of the sitting-rooms.

"Do you know, Watson," said Holmes, as we sat together

in the gathering darkness, " I have really some scruples as to taking you tonight. There is a distinct element of danger."

" Can I be of assistance? "

" Your presence might be invaluable."

" Then I shall certainly come."

" It is very kind of you."

" You speak of danger. You have evidently seen more in these rooms than was visible to me."

" No, but I fancy that I may have deduced a little more. I imagine that you saw all that I did."

" I saw nothing remarkable save the bell-rope, and what purpose that could answer I confess is more than I can imagine."

" You saw the ventilator, too? "

" Yes, but I do not think that it is such a very unusual thing to have a small opening between two rooms. It was so small that a rat could hardly pass through."

" I knew that we should find a ventilator before ever we came to Stoke Moran."

" My dear Holmes! "

" Oh yes, I did. You remember in her statement she said that her sister could smell Dr. Roylott's cigar. Now, of course that suggested at once that there must be a communication between the two rooms. It could only be a small one, or it would have been remarked upon at the coroner's inquiry. I deduced a ventilator."

" But what harm can there be in that? "

" Well, there is at least a curious coincidence of dates. A ventilator is made, a cord is hung, and a lady who sleeps in the bed dies. Does not that strike you? "

" I cannot as yet see any connection."

" Did you observe anything very peculiar about that bed? "

" No."

" It was clamped to the floor. Did you ever see a bed fastened like that before? "

" I cannot say that I have."

" The lady could not move her bed. It must always be in the same relative position to the ventilator and to the rope — for so we may call it, since it was clearly never meant for a bell-pull."

" Holmes," I cried, " I seem to see dimly what you are

hinting at! We are only just in time to prevent some subtle and horrible crime."

"Subtle enough and horrible enough. When a doctor does go wrong, he is the first of criminals. He has nerve and he has knowledge. Palmer and Pritchard were among the heads of their profession. This man strikes even deeper; but I think, Watson, that we shall be able to strike deeper still. But we shall have horrors enough before the night is over; for goodness' sake let us have a quiet pipe, and turn our minds for a few hours to something more cheerful."

About nine o'clock the light among the trees was extinguished, and all was dark in the direction of the Manor-House. Two hours passed slowly away, and then, suddenly, just at the stroke of eleven, a single bright light shone out in front of us.

"That is our signal," said Holmes, springing to his feet; "it comes from the middle window."

As we passed out he exchanged a few words with the landlord, explaining that we were going on a late visit to an acquaintance, and that it was possible that we might spend the night there. A moment later we were out on the dark road, a chill wind blowing in our faces, and one yellow light twinkling in front of us through the gloom to guide us on our somber errand.

There was little difficulty in entering the grounds, for unrepaired breaches gaped in the old park wall. Making our way among the trees, we reached the lawn, crossed it, and were about to enter through the window, when out from a clump of laurel-bushes there darted what seemed to be a hideous and distorted child, who threw itself upon the grass with writhing limbs, and then ran swiftly across the lawn into the darkness.

"My God!" I whispered; "did you see it?"

Holmes was for the moment as startled as I. His hand closed like a vise upon my wrist in his agitation. Then he broke into a low laugh, and put his lips to my ear.

"It is a nice household," he murmured. "That is the baboon."

I had forgotten the strange pets which the doctor affected. There was a cheetah, too; perhaps we might find it upon our shoulders at any moment. I confess that I felt easier in my mind when, after following Holmes's example and slipping off my shoes, I found myself inside the bedroom. My companion noiselessly closed the shutters, moved the lamp onto the table, and cast his eyes round the room. All was as we had seen it in the daytime. Then creeping up to me and making a trumpet of his hand, he whispered into my ear again so gently that it was all that I could do to distinguish the words:

" The least sound would be fatal to our plans."

I nodded to show that I had heard.

" We must sit without light. He would see it through the ventilator."

I nodded again.

" Do not go asleep; your very life may depend upon it. Have your pistol ready in case we should need it. I will sit on the side of the bed, and you in that chair."

I took out my revolver and laid it on the corner of the table.

Holmes had brought up a long, thin cane, and this he placed upon the bed beside him. By it he laid the box of matches and the stump of a candle. Then he turned down the lamp, and we were left in darkness.

How shall I ever forget that dreadful vigil? I could not hear a sound, not even the drawing of a breath, and yet I knew that my companion sat open-eyed, within a few feet of me, in the same state of nervous tension in which I was myself. The shutters cut off the least ray of light, and we waited in absolute darkness. From outside came the occasional cry of a night-bird, and once at our very window a long-drawn, cat-like whine, which told us that the cheetah was indeed at liberty. Far away we could hear the deep tones of the parish clock, which boomed out every quarter of an hour. How long they seemed, those quarters! Twelve struck, and one and two and three, and still we sat waiting silently for whatever might befall.

Suddenly there was the momentary gleam of a light up in the direction of the ventilator, which vanished immediately, but was succeeded by a strong smell of burning oil and heated metal. Some one in the next room had lit a dark-lantern. I heard a gentle sound of movement, and then all was silent once more, though the smell grew stronger. For half an hour I sat with straining ears. Then suddenly another sound became audible — a very gentle, soothing sound, like that of a small jet of steam escaping continually from a kettle. The instant that we heard it, Holmes sprang from the bed, struck a match, and lashed furiously with his cane at the bell-pull.

"You see it, Watson?" he yelled. "You see it?"

But I saw nothing. At the moment when Holmes struck the light I heard a low, clear whistle, but the sudden glare flashing into my weary eyes made it impossible for me to tell what it was at which my friend lashed so savagely. I could, however, see that his face was deadly pale, and filled with horror and loathing.

He had ceased to strike, and was gazing up at the ventilator, when suddenly there broke from the silence of the night the most horrible cry to which I have ever listened. It swelled up louder and louder, a hoarse yell of pain and fear and anger all mingled in the one dreadful shriek. They say that away down in the village, and even in the distant parsonage, that cry raised the sleepers from their beds. It struck cold to our hearts, and I stood gazing at Holmes, and he at me, until the last echoes of it had died away into the silence from which it rose.

"What can it mean?" I gasped.

"It means that it is all over," Holmes answered. "And perhaps, after all, it is for the best. Take your pistol, and we will enter Dr. Roylott's room."

With a grave face he lit the lamp and led the way down the corridor. Twice he struck at the chamber door without any reply from within. Then he turned the handle and entered, I at his heels, with the cocked pistol in my hand.

It was a singular sight which met our eyes. On the table stood a dark-lantern with the shutter half open, throwing a brilliant beam of light upon the iron safe, the door of which was ajar. Beside this table, on the wooden chair, sat Dr. Grimesby Roylott, clad in a long gray dressing-gown, his bare ankles protruding beneath, and his feet thrust into red heelless Turkish slippers. Across his lap lay the short stock with the long lash which we had noticed during the day. His chin was cocked upward and his eyes were fixed in a dreadful, rigid stare at the corner of the ceiling. Round his brow he had a peculiar yellow band, with brownish speckles, which seemed to be bound tightly round his head. As we entered he made neither sound nor motion.

"The band! the speckled band!" whispered Holmes.

I took a step forward. In an instant his strange head-gear began to move, and there reared itself from among his hair the squat diamond-shaped head and puffed neck of a loathsome serpent.

"It is a swamp adder!" cried Holmes; "the deadliest snake in India. He has died within ten seconds of being bitten. Violence does, in truth, recoil upon the violent, and the schemer falls into the pit which he digs for another. Let us thrust this creature back into its den, and we can then remove Miss Stoner to some place of shelter, and let the county police know what has happened."

As he spoke he drew the dog-whip swiftly from the dead man's lap, and throwing the noose round the reptile's neck, he drew it from its horrid perch, and carrying it at arm's-length, threw it into the iron safe, which he closed upon it.

Such are the true facts of the death of Dr. Grimesby Roylott, of Stoke Moran. It is not necessary that I should prolong a narrative which has already run to too great a length, by telling how we broke the sad news to the terrified girl, how we conveyed her by the morning train to the care of her good aunt at Harrow, of how the slow process of official inquiry came to the conclusion that the doctor met his fate while indiscreetly playing with a dangerous pet. The little which I had yet to learn of the case was told me by Sherlock Holmes as we traveled back next day.

"I had," said he, "come to an entirely erroneous conclusion, which shows, my dear Watson, how dangerous it always is to reason from insufficient data. The presence of the gypsies, and the use of the word 'band,' which was used by the poor girl, no doubt to explain the appearance which she had caught a hurried glimpse of by the light of her match, were sufficient to put me upon an entirely wrong scent. I can only claim the merit that I instantly reconsidered my position when, however, it became clear to me that whatever danger threatened an occupant of the room could not come either from the window or the door. My attention was speedily drawn, as I have already remarked to you, to this ventilator, and to the bell-rope which hung down to the bed. The discovery that this was a dummy, and that the bed was clamped to the floor, instantly gave rise to the suspicion that the rope was there as bridge for something passing through the hole and coming to the bed. The idea of a snake instantly occurred to me, and when I coupled it with my knowledge that the doctor was furnished with a supply of creatures from India, I felt that I was probably on the right track. The idea of using a form of poison which could not possibly be discovered by any chemical test was just such a one as would occur to a clever and ruthless man who had had an Eastern training. The rapidity with which such a poison would take effect would also, from his point of view, be an advantage. It would be a sharp-eyed coroner, indeed, who could distinguish the two little dark punctures which would show where the poison fangs had done their work. Then I thought of the whistle. Of course he must recall the snake before the morning light revealed it to the victim. He had trained it, probably by the use of the milk which we saw, to return to him when summoned. He would put it through this ventilator at the hour that he thought best, with the certainty that it would crawl down the rope and land on the bed. It might or might not bite the occupant, perhaps she might escape every night for a week, but sooner or later she must fall a victim.

"I had come to these conclusions before ever I had entered his room. An inspection of his chair showed me that he had been in the habit of standing on it, which of course would be necessary in order that he should reach the ventilator. The sight of the safe, the saucer of milk, and the loop of whipcord were enough to finally dispel any doubts which may have remained. The metallic clang heard by Miss Stoner was obviously caused by her stepfather hastily closing the door of his safe upon its terrible occupant. Having once made up my mind, you know the steps which I took in order to put the matter to the proof. I heard the creature hiss, as I have no doubt that you did also, and I instantly lit the light and attacked it."

"With the result of driving it through the ventilator."

"And also with the result of causing it to turn upon its master at the other side. Some of the blows of my cane came home, and roused its snakish temper, so that it flew upon the first person it saw. In this way I am no doubt indirectly responsible for Dr. Grimesby Roylott's death, and I cannot say that it is likely to weigh very heavily upon my conscience."

## QUESTIONS

1. What are the main essentials of all detective stories?
2. Does this story conform to the type?
3. Does it gain by being told indirectly, by Watson?
4. How does the appearance of the woman arouse interest?
5. Jot down the significant facts of Miss Stoner's story.
6. Which is most important?
7. Did you expect the villain to appear so early in the story?
8. Why was it necessary for him to be introduced?
9. Does anything at all ruffle the calmness of Holmes? Explain.
10. Note the details and methods of examining the house.
11. In a detective story there must be suspense. How is it kept up here?
12. Is mystery more mysterious at night?
13. What details within the room prepare for the climax?
14. What was the climax?
15. Had you expected the "band" to be something like what it really was?
16. How far had Holmes deduced the facts before entering the doctor's room?
17. Do they all seem simple enough, from his own explanation to Watson?
18. What makes them appear simple?
19. Should more have been told about Miss Stoner's love affair? Explain.
20. Why do you like detective stories?
21. Read one in a current magazine, and compare with this story.

## FOR COMPOSITION

1. Mysterious crimes are common. Take an account of one from the daily paper and apply Sherlock Holmes methods to its solution.
2. To do this, begin with the climax and work back. Be logical.

## OTHER STORIES BY A. CONAN DOYLE

A Study in Scarlet
The Sign of the Four
How the Brigadier Gerard Captured Saragossa

A Scandal in Bohemia
The Red-Headed League

## VOLUMES OF STORIES BY A. CONAN DOYLE

*Complete Sherlock Holmes* (one volume)

# ARTHUR MORRISON
## (1863– )

NEARLY every large city has its East Side, or East End, as it is called in London, uniformly used to denote the poorer section, or more often the actual slums. These sections teem with life in the raw, and consequently offer rich soil for writers. Among English writers Dickens was the first to depict the humor and the pathos of London's poor, but that was in the middle of the last century, and the types that he portrayed are now as obsolete as Cooper's Indians. Nevertheless, any writer who today undertakes to work in that field risks comparison with Dickens. Such was the fate of George Gissing, who gave a much more realistic picture of the slums than Dickens ever thought of giving. When the first stories of Mr. Arthur Morrison began to appear they at once met with the same comparison.

Mr. Morrison came to London from the county of Kent, where he was born in 1863. He is thus an exact contemporary of Mr. W. W. Jacobs, whose choice of subject matter is not unlike that of Mr. Morrison. As secretary of a charity trust Mr. Morrison spent much time in the East End, and from his experiences and observation wrote the stories collected in *Tales of Mean Streets,* of which "That Brute Simmons" is one. His work was at once recognized as exceptional, but the dwellers in the more fashionable parts of London accused the author of being too cynically brutal. Such things could not be in London, they said, but the little controversy that arose was settled by *The East London Chronicle,* a church paper, which bluntly declared that Mr. Morrison's portrayal was only too true.

His best stories are those that deal with the hopelessly squalid life of the East End tenements, still the worst tenements in the world. People are born there, live there, and die there without ever a chance at anything better. To such districts vagabonds, loafers, crooks, and the poverty-stricken flock in overwhelming numbers. Life there is lived amid indescribable dirt and filth. It is small wonder that a writer should have a strong note of pessimism in his work after having lived and worked in that odorous district. And such a note is characteristic of the stories in *Tales of Mean Streets.* "That Brute Simmons" is the lightest story in the volume.

Mr. Morrison has written many books since 1890, when these stories were published in an English magazine. Like Mr. Jacobs, he lives in seclusion, shunning all publicity. Several of his stories have been dramatized, including the one here given.

# THAT BRUTE SIMMONS

SIMMONS'S infamous behavior toward his wife is still matter for profound wonderment among the neighbors. The other women had all along regarded him as a model husband, and certainly Mrs. Simmons was a most conscientious wife. She toiled and slaved for that man, as any woman in the whole street would have maintained, far more than any husband had a right to expect. And now this was what she got for it. Perhaps he had suddenly gone mad.

Before she married Simmons, Mrs. Simmons had been the widowed Mrs. Ford. Ford had got a berth as donkey-man on a tramp steamer, and that steamer had gone down with all hands off the cape — a judgment, the widow woman feared, for long years of contumacy which had culminated in the wickedness of taking to the sea, and taking to it as a donkey-man, an immeasurable fall for a capable engine-fitter. Twelve years as Mrs. Ford had left her still childless, and childless she remained as Mrs. Simmons.

As for Simmons, he, it was held, was fortunate in that capable wife. He was a moderately good carpenter and joiner, but no man of the world, and he wanted to be one. Nobody could tell what might not have happened to Tommy Simmons if there had been no Mrs. Simmons to take care of him. He was a meek and quiet man, with a boyish face and sparse, limp whiskers. He had no vices (even his pipe departed him after his marriage), and Mrs. Simmons had ingrafted on him divers exotic virtues. He went solemnly to chapel every Sunday, under a tall hat, and put a penny — one returned to him for the purpose out of his week's wages — in the plate. Then, Mrs. Simmons overseeing, he took off his best clothes and brushed them with solicitude and pains. On Saturday afternoons he cleaned the knives, the forks, the boots, the kettles, and the windows, patiently and conscientiously. On Tuesday evenings he took the clothes to the mangling. And on Saturday nights he attended Mrs. Simmons in her marketing, to carry the parcels.

Mrs. Simmons's own virtues were native and numerous. She was a wonderful manager. Every penny of Tommy's thirty-six or thirty-eight shillings a week was bestowed to the greatest advantage, and Tommy never ventured to guess how much of it she saved. Her cleanliness in housewifery was distracting to behold. She met Simmons at the front door whenever he came home, and then and there he changed his boots for slippers, balancing himself painfully on alternate feet on the cold flags. This was because she scrubbed the passage and doorstep turn about with the wife of the downstairs family, and because the stair-carpet was her own. She vigilantly supervised her husband all through the process of "cleaning himself" after work, so as to come between her walls and the possibility of random splashes; and if, in spite of her diligence, a spot remained to tell the tale, she was at pains to impress the fact on Simmons's memory, and to set forth at length all the circumstances of his ungrateful selfishness. In the beginning she had always escorted him to the ready-made clothes shop, and had selected and paid for his clothes — for the reason that men are such perfect fools, and shopkeepers do as they like with them. But she presently improved on that. She found a man selling cheap remnants at a street corner, and straightway she conceived the idea of making Simmons's clothes herself. Decision was one of her virtues, and a suit of uproarious check tweeds was begun that afternoon from the pattern furnished by an old one. More: it was finished by Sunday, when Simmons, overcome by astonishment at the feat, was indued in it, and pushed off to chapel ere he could recover his senses. The things were not altogether comfortable, he found; the trousers clung tight against his shins, but hung loose behind his heels; and when he sat, it was on a wilderness of hard folds and seams. Also his waistcoat collar tickled his nape, but his coat collar went straining across from shoulder to shoulder, while the main garment bagged generously below his waist. Use made a habit of his discomfort, but it never reconciled him to the chaff of his shopmates; for as Mrs. Simmons elaborated successive suits, each one modeled on the last, the primal accidents of her design developed into principles, and grew even bolder and more hideously pronounced. It was vain for Simmons to hint — as hint he did — that he shouldn't like her to overwork herself, tailoring being bad for the eyes, and there was a new tailor's in the Mile End Road, very cheap, where . . . "Ho yus," she retorted, "you're very consid'rit I dessay sittin' there actin' a livin' lie before your own wife Thomas Simmons as though I couldn't see through you like a book a lot you care about overworkin' me as long as *your* turn's served throwin' away money like dirt in the street on a lot o' swindlin' tailors an' me workin' an' slavin' 'ere to save a 'apenny an' this is my return for it any one ud think you could pick up money in the 'orseroad an' I b'lieve I'd be thought better of if I laid in bed all day like some would that I do." So that Thomas Simmons avoided the subject, nor even murmured when she resolved to cut his hair.

So his placid fortune endured for years. Then there came a golden summer evening when Mrs. Simmons betook herself with a basket to do some small shopping, and Simmons was left at home. He washed and put away the tea-things, and then he fell to meditating on a new pair of trousers, finished that day and hanging behind the parlor door. There they hung, in all their decent innocence of shape in the seat, and they were shorter of leg, longer of waist, and wilder of pattern than he had ever worn before. And as he looked on them the small devil of original sin awoke and clamored in his breast. He was ashamed of it, of course, for well he knew the gratitude he owed his wife for those same trousers, among other blessings. Still, there the small devil was, and the small devil was fertile in base suggestions, and could not be kept from hinting at the new crop of workshop gibes that would spring at Tommy's first public appearance in such things.

"Pitch 'em in the dust-bin!" said the small devil, at last; "it's all they're fit for."

Simmons turned away in sheer horror of his wicked self, and for a moment thought of washing the tea-things over again by way of discipline. Then he made for the back room, but saw from the landing that the front door was standing open, probably by the fault of the child downstairs. Now, a front door standing open was a thing that Mrs. Simmons would *not* abide; it looked low. So Simmons went down, that she might not be wroth with him for the thing when she came back; and, as he shut the door, he looked forth into the street.

A man was loitering on the pavement, and prying curiously

about the door. His face was tanned, his hands were deep in the pockets of his unbraced blue trousers, and well back on his head he wore the high-crowned peaked cap topped with a knob of wool, which is affected by Jack ashore about the docks. He lurched a step nearer to the door, and: "Mrs. Ford ain't in, is she?" he said.

Simmons stared at him for a matter of five seconds, and then said: "Eh?"

"Mrs. Ford as was, then — Simmons now, ain't it?"

He said this with a furtive leer that Simmons neither liked nor understood.

"No," said Simmons, "she ain't in now."

"You ain't her 'usband, are ye?"

"Yus."

The man took his pipe from his mouth, and grinned silently and long. "Blimy," he said, at length, "you look the sort o' bloke she'd like." And with that he grinned again. Then, seeing that Simmons made ready to shut the door, he put a foot on the sill and a hand against the panel. "Don't be in a 'urry, matey," he said; "I come 'ere t'ave a little talk with you, man to man, d'ye see?" And he frowned fiercely.

Tommy Simmons felt uncomfortable, but the door would not shut, so he parleyed. "Wotjer want?" he asked. "I dunno you."

"Then if you'll excuse the liberty, I'll interdooce meself, in a manner of speaking." He touched his cap with a bob of mock humility. "I'm Bob Ford," he said, "come back out o' kingdom-come, so to say. Me as went down with the *Mooltan* — safe dead five years gone. I come to see my wife."

During this speech Thomas Simmons's jaw was dropping lower and lower. At the end of it he poked his fingers up through his hair, looked down at the mat, then up at the fanlight, then out into the street, then hard at his visitor. But he found nothing to say.

"Come to see my wife," the man repeated. "So now we can talk it over — as man to man."

Simmons slowly shut his mouth, and led the way upstairs mechanically, his fingers still in his hair. A sense of the state of affairs sunk gradually into his brain, and the small devil woke again. Suppose this man *was* Ford? Suppose he did claim his wife? Would it be a knockdown blow? Would it hit him out? — or not? He thought of the trousers, the tea-things, the mangling, the knives, the kettles, and the window; and he thought of them in the way of a backslider.

On the landing Ford clutched at his arm, and asked, in a horse whisper: " 'Ow long 'fore she's back? "

" 'Bout a hour, I expect," Simmons replied, having first of all repeated the question in his own mind. And then he opened the parlor door.

" Ah," said Ford, looking about him " you've bin pretty comf'table. Them chairs an' things " — jerking his pipe toward them — " was hers — mine, that is to say, speaking straight, and man to man." He sat down, puffing meditatively at his pipe, and presently: " Well," he continued, " 'ere I am ag'in, ol' Bob Ford dead an' done for — gawn down in the *Mooltan*. On'y I *ain't* done for, see? " — and he pointed the stem of his pipe at Simmons's waistcoat — " I ain't done for, 'cause why? Cons'kence o' bein' picked up by a ol' German sailin'-'utch an' took to 'Frisco 'fore the mast. I've 'ad a few years o' knockin' about since then, an' now " — looking hard at Simmons — " I've come back to see my wife."

" She — she don't like smoke in 'ere," said Simmons, as it were, at random.

" No, I bet she don't," Ford answered, taking his pipe from his mouth, and holding it low in his hand. " I know 'Anner. 'Ow d'you find 'er? Do she make ye clean the windows? "

" Well," Simmons admitted, uneasily, " I — I do 'elp 'er sometimes, o' course."

" Ah! An' the knives too, I bet, an' the bloomin' kittles. I know. W'y " — he rose and bent to look behind Simmons's head — " s'elp me, I b'lieve she cuts yer 'air! Well, I'm damned! Jes' wot she would do, too."

He inspected the blushing Simmons from divers points of vantage. Then he lifted a leg of the trousers hanging behind the door. " I'd bet a trifle," he said, " she made these 'ere trucks. Nobody else ud do 'em like that. They're wuss'n wot you've got on."

The small devil began to have the argument all its own way. If this man took his wife back, perhaps he'd have to wear those trousers.

" Ah! " Ford pursued, " she ain't got no milder. An' my davy, wot a jore! "

Simmons began to feel that this was no longer his business.

Plainly, 'Anner was this other man's wife, and he was bound in honor to acknowledge the fact. The small devil put it to him as a matter of duty.

"Well," said Ford, suddenly, "time's short, an' this ain't business. I won't be 'ard on you, matey. I ought prop'ly to stand on my rights, but seein' as you're a well-meanin' young man, so to speak, an' all settled an' a-livin' 'ere quiet an' matrimonual, I'll " — this with a burst of generosity — "damme, yus, I'll compound the felony, an' take me 'ook. Come, I'll name a figure, as man to man, fust an' last, no less an' no more. Five pound does it."

Simmons hadn't five pounds — he hadn't even five pence — and he said so. "An' I wouldn't think for to come between a man an' 'is wife," he added, "not on no account. It may be rough on me, but it's a dooty. *I'll* 'ook it."

"No," said Ford, hastily, clutching Simmons by the arm, "don't do that. I'll make it a bit cheaper. Say three quid — come, that's reasonable, ain't it? Three quid ain't much compensation for me goin' away forever — where the stormy winds do blow, so to say — an' never as much as seein' me own wife ag'in for better nor wuss. Between man an' man now — three quid; an' I'll shunt. That's fair, ain't it?"

"Of course it's fair," Simmons replied, effusively. "It's more'n fair; it's noble — downright noble, *I* call it. But I ain't goin' to take a mean advantage o' your good-'artedness, Mr. Ford. She's your wife, an' I oughtn't to 'a' come between you. I apologize. You stop an' 'ave yer proper rights. It's me as ought to shunt, an' I will." And he made a step toward the door.

"'Old on," quoth Ford, and got between Simmons and the door; "don't do things rash. Look wot a loss it'll be to you with no 'ome to go to, an' nobody to look after ye, an' all that. It'll be dreadful. Say a couple — there, we won't quarrel, jest a single quid, between man an' man, an' I'll stand a pot o' the money. You can easy raise a quid — the clock ud pretty nigh do it. A quid does it; an' I'll —— "

There was a loud double-knock at the front door. In the East End a double-knock is always for the upstairs lodgers.

"Oo's that?" asked Bob Ford, apprehensively.

"I'll see," said Thomas Simmons in reply, and he made a rush for the staircase.

## That Brute Simmons

Bob Ford heard him open the front door. Then he went to the window, and just below him, he saw the crown of a bonnet. It vanished, and borne to him from within the door there fell upon his ear the sound of a well-remembered female voice.

"Where ye goin' now with no 'at?" asked the voice, sharply.

"Awright, 'Anner — there's — there's somebody upstairs to see you," Simmons answered. And, as Bob Ford could see, a man went scuttling down the street in the gathering dusk. And behold, it was Thomas Simmons.

Ford reached the landing in three strides. His wife was still at the front door, staring after Simmons. He flung into the back room, threw open the window, dropped from the wash-house roof into the back yard, scrambled desperately over the fence, and disappeared into the gloom. He was seen by no living soul. And that is why Simmons's base desertion — under his wife's very eyes, too — is still an astonishment to the neighbors.

### QUESTIONS

1. Tell what type of man Simmons was.
2. What do you think of Mrs. Simmons's domestic "virtues"?
3. Write out a scene in which she is "at pains to impress the fact on him."
4. Where does the story begin?
5. What is implied by the word "Jack"?
6. Does it give you a hint of what is coming? Explain.
7. Had "'Anner" ever been different? Explain.
8. How much was "five pound"? "Three quid"? Try to understand the English slang.
9. What does Ford mean by standing "a pot o' the money"?
10. Why should Ford be apprehensive?
11. What finally determined Simmons "to 'ook it"?
12. Why didn't "'Anner" try to stop him?
13. Why should the neighbors have been astonished?
14. Of what famous poem does this story remind you?

### SUBJECTS FOR COMPOSITION

1. Simmons at church in his new suit.
2. Write a story in which a henpecked husband turns the tables.
3. Tell orally the plot of the poem referred to in Question 14.

## OTHER STORIES BY ARTHUR MORRISON

On the Stairs  
Lizerunt

Without Visible Means  
Behind the Shade

## VOLUMES OF STORIES BY ARTHUR MORRISON

*Tales of Mean Streets*  
*Green Ginger*

*The Red Triangle*  
*Chronicles of Martin Hewitt*

## WILLIAM WYMARK JACOBS
(1863–    )

It is difficult to believe that a humorous writer can ever be serious; more difficult still, to believe that he can write a tragic story successfully. So insistent is the human appetite for humor that when Mark Twain wrote a serious book, *Joan of Arc,* he was severely handled by the critics for trying to do something so far out of his line. Whether Mr. W. W. Jacobs had a similar experience is not on record, but it is a fact that this popular English humorist writes tragic stories of greater literary merit than his funny ones. It is for that reason that "The Monkey's Paw" is printed in this book.

Like many of our best modern short story writers, Mr. Jacobs has chosen a definite locale for the setting of his stories, but, as in all local color stories, it is the human interest that makes them endure. He is often erroneously called a writer of sea stories; it would be nearer the truth to say that his characters are persons who follow the sea, or have followed the sea. These people he shows on shore, especially along the London docks. Many of the best are sailors only by courtesy, their "sailing" being confined to the barges that swing sluggishly up and down the black tide of the Thames between London and the sea. Sometimes he does take his reader to the ocean, but usually only on a coast-wise trader. The interest is always in the characters and the strange situations which Mr. Jacobs invents for them. Many of the stories are related by the Night Watchman, whose racy dialect of the docks adds much to the humor. A favorite type of story is one in which a bold bad sailor is tamed by an angry wife, usually only for the moment. There is much reveling in low saloons, or "pubs," as the English call them. There is gambling and fighting. There is contact with the officers of the law. But always there is a humorous slant to these yarns, never any nastiness, and the author makes his reader like the characters in the complications created for them.

Mr. Jacobs's reputation was built up on his humorous stories, the first of which were written while he was still in the civil service in London, where he was born in 1863. His schooling was limited to a few private schools, but preparation for his real life work took place on the docks, which he knew intimately because his father was a dock manager. For the last twenty-five years Mr. Jacobs has given most of his time to writing. It is doubtful whether any living writer has produced so many consistently good stories as this modest Englishman.

In "The Monkey's Paw" the author's interest in the supernatural is apparent — rather a novelty in a humorist. It is not an easy task to convince the modern skeptic of the "reality of the supernatural," and it is to the credit of Mr. Jacobs that he has emphatically succeeded.

# THE MONKEY'S PAW

WITHOUT, the night was cold and wet, but in the small parlor of Lakesnam Villa the blinds were drawn and the fire burned brightly. Father and son were at chess, the former, who possessed ideas about the game involving radical changes, putting his king into such sharp and unnecessary perils that it even provoked comment from the white-haired old lady knitting placidly by the fire.

"Hark at the wind," said Mr. White, who, having seen a fatal mistake after it was too late, was amiably desirous of preventing his son from seeing it.

"I'm listening," said the latter, grimly surveying the board as he stretched out his hand. "Check."

"I should hardly think that he'd come tonight," said his father, with his hand poised over the board.

"Mate," replied the son.

"That's the worst of living so far out," bawled Mr. White, with sudden and unlooked-for violence; "of all the beastly, slushy, out-of-the-way places to live in, this is the worst. Pathway's a bog, and the road's a torrent. I don't know what people are thinking about. I suppose because only two houses on the road are let, they think it doesn't matter."

"Never mind, dear," said his wife soothingly; "perhaps you'll win the next one."

Mr. White looked up sharply, just in time to intercept a knowing glance between mother and son. The words died away on his lips, and he hid a guilty grin in his thin gray beard.

"There he is," said Herbert White, as the gate banged to loudly and heavy footsteps came toward the door.

The old man rose with hospitable haste, and opening the door, was heard condoling with the new arrival. The new arrival also condoled with himself, so that Mrs. White said, "Tut, tut!" and coughed gently as her husband entered the room, followed by a tall burly man, beady of eye and rubicund of visage.

"Sergeant-Major Morris," he said, introducing him.

# The Monkey's Paw

The sergeant-major shook hands, and taking the proffered seat by the fire, watched contentedly while his host got out whisky and tumblers and stood a small copper kettle on the fire.

At the third glass his eyes got brighter, and he began to talk, the little family circle regarding with eager interest this visitor from distant parts, as he squared his broad shoulders in the chair and spoke of strange scenes and doughty deeds, of wars and plagues and strange peoples.

"Twenty-one years of it," said Mr. White, nodding at his wife and son. "When he went away he was a slip of a youth in the warehouse. Now look at him."

"He don't look to have taken much harm," said Mrs. White politely.

"I'd like to go to India myself," said the old man, "just to look round a bit, you know."

"Better where you are," said the sergeant-major, shaking his head. He put down the empty glass and, sighing softly, shook it again.

"I should like to see those old temples and fakirs and jugglers," said the old man. "What was that you started telling me the other day about a monkey's paw or something, Morris?"

"Nothing," said the soldier hastily. "Leastways, nothing worth hearing."

"Monkey's paw?" said Mrs. White curiously.

"Well, it's just a bit of what you might call magic, perhaps," said the sergeant-major off-handedly.

His three listeners leaned forward eagerly. The visitor absent-mindedly put his empty glass to his lips and then set it down again. His host filled it for him.

"To look at," said the sergeant-major, fumbling in his pocket, "it's just an ordinary little paw, dried to a mummy."

He took something out of his pocket and proffered it. Mrs. White drew back with a grimace, but her son, taking it, examined it curiously.

"And what is there special about it?" inquired Mr. White, as he took it from his son and, having examined it, placed it upon the table.

"It had a spell put on it by an old fakir," said the sergeant-major, "a very holy man. He wanted to show that fate ruled people's lives, and that those who interfered with it did so to their sorrow. He put a spell on it so that three separate men could each have three wishes from it."

His manner was so impressive that his hearers were conscious that their light laughter jarred somewhat.

"Well, why don't you have three, sir?" said Herbert White cleverly.

The soldier regarded him in the way that middle age is wont to regard presumptuous youth. "I have," he said quietly, and his blotchy face whitened.

"And did you really have the three wishes granted?" asked Mrs. White.

"I did," said the sergeant-major, and his glass tapped against his strong teeth.

"And has anybody else wished?" inquired the old lady.

"The first man had his three wishes, yes," was the reply. "I don't know what the first two were, but the third was for death. That's how I got the paw."

His tones were so grave that a hush fell upon the group.

"If you've had your three wishes, it's no good to you now, then, Morris," said the old man at last. "What do you keep it for?"

The soldier shook his head. "Fancy, I suppose," he said slowly. "I did have some idea of selling it, but I don't think I will. It has caused enough mischief already. Besides, people won't buy. They think it's a fairy tale, some of them, and those who do think anything of it want to try it first and pay me afterward."

"If you could have another three wishes," said the old man, eyeing him keenly, "would you have them?"

"I don't know," said the other. "I don't know."

He took the paw, and dangling it between his front finger and thumb, suddenly threw it upon the fire. White, with a slight cry, stooped down and snatched it off.

"Better let it burn," said the soldier solemnly.

"If you don't want it, Morris," said the old man, "give it to me."

"I won't," said his friend doggedly. "I threw it on the fire. If you keep it, don't blame me for what happens. Pitch it on the fire again, like a sensible man."

The other shook his head and examined his new possession closely. "How do you do it?" he inquired.

"Hold it up in your right hand and wish aloud," said the sergeant-major, "but I warn you of the consequences."

"Sounds like the *Arabian Nights*," said Mrs. White, as she rose and began to set the supper. "Don't you think you might wish for four pairs of hands for me?"

Her husband drew the talisman from his pocket and then all three burst into laughter as the sergeant-major, with a look of alarm on his face, caught him by the arm.

"If you must wish," he said gruffly, "wish for something sensible."

Mr. White dropped it back into his pocket, and placing chairs, motioned his friend to the table. In the business of supper the talisman was partly forgotten, and afterward the three sat listening in an enthralled fashion to a second installment of the soldier's adventures in India.

"If the tale about the monkey paw is not more truthful than those he has been telling us," said Herbert, as the door closed behind their guest, just in time for him to catch the last train, "we shan't make much out of it."

"Did you give him anything for it, father?" inquired Mrs. White, regarding her husband closely.

"A trifle," said he, coloring slightly. "He didn't want it, but I made him take it. And he pressed me again to throw it away."

"Likely," said Herbert, with pretended horror. "Why, we're going to be rich, and famous, and happy. Wish to be an emperor, father, to begin with; then you can't be henpecked."

He darted round the table, pursued by the maligned Mrs. White armed with an antimacassar.

Mr. White took the paw from his pocket and eyed it dubiously. "I don't know what to wish for, and that's a fact," he said slowly. "It seems to me I've got all I want."

"If you only cleared the house, you'd be quite happy, wouldn't you?" said Herbert, with his hand on his shoulder. "Well, wish for two hundred pounds, then; that'll just do it."

His father, smiling shamefacedly at his own credulity, held up the talisman, as his son, with a solemn face somewhat marred by a wink at his mother, sat down at the piano and struck a few impressive chords.

"I wish for two hundred pounds," said the old man distinctly.

A fine crash from the piano greeted the words, interrupted by a shuddering cry from the old man. His wife and son ran toward him.

"It moved," he cried, with a glance of disgust at the object as it lay on the floor. "As I wished it twisted in my hands like a snake."

"Well, I don't see the money," said his son, as he picked it up and placed it on the table, "and I bet I never shall."

"It must have been your fancy, father," said his wife, regarding him anxiously.

He shook his head. "Never mind, though; there's no harm done, but it gave me a shock all the same."

They sat down by the fire again while the two men finished their pipes. Outside, the wind was higher than ever, and the old man started nervously at the sound of a door banging upstairs. A silence unusual and depressing settled upon all three, which lasted until the old couple rose to retire for the night.

"I expect you'll find the cash tied up in a big bag in the middle of your bed," said Herbert, as he bade them good night, "and something horrible squatting up on top of the wardrobe watching you as you pocket your ill-gotten gains."

## II

In the brightness of the wintry sun next morning as it streamed over the breakfast table Herbert laughed at his fears. There was an air of prosaic wholesomeness about the room which it had lacked on the previous night, and the dirty, shriveled little paw was pitched on the sideboard with a carelessness which betokened no great belief in its virtues.

"I suppose all old soldiers are the same," said Mrs. White. "The idea of our listening to such nonsense! How could wishes be granted in these days? And if they could, how could two hundred pounds hurt you, father?"

"Might drop on his head from the sky," said the frivolous Herbert.

"Morris said the things happened so naturally," said his father, "that you might if you so wished attribute it to coincidence."

"Well, don't break into the money before I come back," said Herbert, as he rose from the table. "I'm afraid it'll turn you into a mean, avaricious man, and we shall have to disown you."

His mother laughed, and following him to the door, watched him down the road, and returning to the breakfast table, was very happy at the expense of her husband's credulity. All of which did not prevent her from scurrying to the door at the postman's knock, nor prevent her from referring somewhat shortly to retired sergeant-majors of bibulous habits when she found that the post brought a tailor's bill.

"Herbert will have some more of his funny remarks, I expect, when he comes home," she said, as they sat at dinner.

"I dare say," said Mr. White, pouring himself out some beer; "but for all that, the thing moved in my hand; that I'll swear to."

"You thought it did," said the old lady soothingly.

"I say it did," replied the other. "There was no thought about it; I had just — What's the matter?"

His wife made no reply. She was watching the mysterious movements of a man outside, who, peering in an undecided fashion at the house, appeared to be trying to make up his mind to enter. In mental connection with the two hundred pounds, she noticed that the stranger was well dressed and wore a silk hat of glossy newness. Three times he paused at the gate, and then walked on again. The fourth time he stood with his hand upon it, and then with sudden resolution flung it open and walked up the path. Mrs. White at the same moment placed her hands behind her, and hurriedly unfastening the strings of her apron, put that useful article of apparel beneath the cushion of her chair.

She brought the stranger, who seemed ill at ease, into the room. He gazed furtively at Mrs. White, and listened in a preoccupied fashion as the old lady apologized for the appearance of the room, and her husband's coat, a garment which he usually reserved for the garden. She then waited as patiently as her sex would permit for him to broach his business, but he was at first strangely silent.

"I — was asked to call," he said at last, and stooped and picked a piece of cotton from his trousers. "I come from Maw and Meggins."

The old lady started. " Is anything the matter? " she asked breathlessly. " Has anything happened to Herbert? What is it? What is it? "

Her husband interposed. " There, there, mother," he said hastily. " Sit down, and don't jump to conclusions. You've not brought bad news, I'm sure, sir," and he eyed the other wistfully.

" I'm sorry —— " began the visitor.

" Is he hurt? " demanded the mother.

The visitor bowed in assent. " Badly hurt," he said quietly, " but he is not in any pain."

" Oh, thank God! " said the old woman, clasping her hands. " Thank God for that! Thank —— "

She broke off suddenly as the sinister meaning of the assurance dawned upon her and she saw the awful confirmation of her fears in the other's averted face. She caught her breath, and turning to her slower-witted husband, laid her trembling old hand upon his. There was a long silence.

" He was caught in the machinery," said the visitor at length, in a low voice.

" Caught in the machinery," repeated Mr. White, in a dazed fashion, " yes."

He sat staring blankly out at the window, and taking his wife's hand between his own, pressed it as he had been wont to do in their old courting days nearly forty years before.

" He was the only one left to us," he said, turning gently to the visitor. " It is hard."

The other coughed, and rising, walked slowly to the window. " The firm wished me to convey their sincere sympathy with you in your great loss," he said, without looking round. " I beg that you will understand I am only their servant and merely obeying orders."

There was no reply; the old woman's face was white, her eyes staring, and her breath inaudible; on the husband's face was a look such as his friend the sergeant might have carried into his first action.

" I was to say that Maw and Meggins disclaim all responsibility," continued the other. " They admit no liability at all, but in consideration of your son's services they wish to present you with a certain sum as compensation."

Mr. White dropped his wife's hand, and rising to his feet,

gazed with a look of horror at his visitor. His dry lips shaped the words, "How much?"

"Two hundred pounds," was the answer.

Unconscious of his wife's shriek, the old man smiled faintly, put out his hands like a sightless man, and dropped, a senseless heap, to the floor.

III

In the huge new cemetery, some two miles distant, the old people buried their dead, and came back to a house steeped in shadow and silence. It was all over so quickly that at first they could hardly realize it, and remained in a state of expectation as though something else to happen — something else which was to lighten this load, too heavy for old hearts to bear. But the days passed, and expectation gave place to resignation — the hopeless resignation of the old, sometimes miscalled apathy. Sometimes they hardly exchanged a word, for now they had nothing to talk about, and their days were long to weariness.

It was about a week after that that the old man, waking suddenly in the night, stretched out his hand and found himself alone. The room was in darkness, and the sound of subdued weeping came from the window. He raised himself in bed and listened.

"Come back," he said tenderly. "You will be cold."

"It is colder for my son," said the old woman, and wept afresh.

The sound of her sobs died away on his ears. The bed was warm, and his eyes heavy with sleep. He dozed fitfully, and then slept until a sudden wild cry from his wife awoke him with a start.

"The monkey's paw!" she cried wildly. "The monkey's paw!"

He started up in alarm. "Where? Where is it? What's the matter?"

She came stumbling across the room toward him. "I want it," she said quietly. "You've not destroyed it?"

"It's in the parlor, on the bracket," he replied, marveling. "Why?"

She cried and laughed together, and bending over, kissed his cheek.

"I only just thought of it," she said hysterically. "Why didn't I think of it before? Why didn't you think of it?"

"Think of what?" he questioned.

"The other two wishes," she replied rapidly. "We've only had one."

"Was not that enough?" he demanded fiercely.

"No," she cried triumphantly; "we'll have one more. Go down and get it quickly, and wish our boy alive again."

The man sat up in bed and flung the bedclothes from his quaking limbs. "Good God, you are mad!" he cried, aghast.

"Get it," she panted; "get it quickly, and wish — Oh, my boy, my boy!"

Her husband struck a match and lit the candle. "Get back to bed," he said unsteadily. "You don't know what you are saying."

"We had the first wish granted," said the old woman feverishly; "why not the second?"

"A coincidence," stammered the old man.

"Go and get it and wish," cried the old woman, and dragged him toward the door.

He went down in the darkness, and felt his way to the parlor, and then to the mantelpiece. The talisman was in its place, and a horrible fear that the unspoken wish might bring his mutilated son before him ere he could escape from the room seized upon him, and he caught his breath as he found that he had lost the direction of the door. His brow cold with sweat, he felt his way round the table, and groped along the wall until he found himself in the small passage with the unwholesome thing in his hand.

Even his wife's face seemed changed as he entered the room. It was white and expectant, and to his fears seemed to have an unnatural look upon it. He was afraid of her.

"Wish!" she cried, in a strong voice.

"It is foolish and wicked," he faltered.

"Wish!" repeated his wife.

He raised his hand. "I wish my son alive again."

The talisman fell to the floor, and he regarded it shudderingly. Then he sank trembling into a chair as the old woman, with burning eyes, walked to the window and raised the blind.

He sat until he was chilled with the cold, glancing occasionally at the figure of the old woman peering through the window. The candle end, which had burnt below the rim of the china candlestick, was throwing pulsating shadows on the ceiling and walls, until, with a flicker larger than the rest, it expired. The old man, with an unspeakable sense of relief at the failure of the talisman, crept back to his bed, and a minute or two afterward the old woman came silently and apathetically beside him.

Neither spoke, but both lay silently listening to the ticking of the clock. A stair creaked, and a squeaky mouse scurried noisily through the wall. The darkness was oppressive, and after lying for some time screwing up his courage, the husband took the box of matches, and striking one, went downstairs for a candle.

At the foot of the stairs the match went out, and he paused to strike another, and at the same moment a knock, so quiet and stealthy as to be scarcely audible, sounded on the front door.

The matches fell from his hand. He stood motionless, his breath suspended until the knock was repeated. Then he turned and fled swiftly back to his room, and closed the door behind him. A third knock sounded through the house.

"*What's that?*" cried the old woman, starting up.

"A rat," said the old man, in shaking tones — "a rat. It passed me on the stairs."

His wife sat up in bed listening. A loud knock resounded through the house.

"It's Herbert!" she screamed. "It's Herbert!"

She ran to the door, but her husband was before her, and catching her by the arm, held her tightly.

"What are you going to do?" he whispered hoarsely.

"It's my boy; it's Herbert!" she cried, struggling mechanically. "I forgot it was two miles away. What are you holding me for? Let go. I must open the door."

"For God's sake don't let it in," cried the old man, trembling.

"You're afraid of your own son," she cried, struggling. "Let me go. I'm coming, Herbert; I'm coming."

There was another knock, and another. The old woman with a sudden wrench broke free and ran from the room. Her husband followed to the landing, and called after her appealingly as she hurried downstairs. He heard the chain rattle back and the bottom bolt drawn slowly and stiffly from the socket. Then the old woman's voice, strained and panting.

"The bolt," she cried loudly. "Come down. I can't reach it."

But her husband was on his hands and knees groping wildly on the floor in search of the paw. If he could only find it before the thing outside got in. A perfect fusillade of knocks reverberated through the house, and he heard the scraping of a chair as his wife put it down in the passage against the door. He heard the creaking of the bolt as it came slowly back, and at the same moment he found the monkey's paw, and frantically breathed his third and last wish.

The knocking ceased suddenly, although the echoes of it were still in the house. He heard the chair drawn back and the door opened. A cold wind rushed up the staircase, and a long loud wail of disappointment and misery from his wife gave him courage to run down to her side, and then to the gate beyond. The street lamp flickering opposite shone on a quiet and deserted road.

## QUESTIONS

1. Contrast the opening with that of "The Three Strangers" and "The Ambitious Guest."
2. What impression of the family do you get from the first paragraphs?
3. Are they portrayed as normal?
4. Does anything about the father suggest Young Man Axelbrod?
5. What other story in this book has an emblem?
6. Why did the sergeant-major's face whiten?
7. Why was his face ordinarily "rubicund"?
8. Might it have any connection with the story? Explain.
9. Make up his three probable wishes.
10. What are the first signs of the unusual?
11. How is the suspense kept up in the beginning of Part II?
12. What did you think the postman brought? Why?
13. Is the crisis at the end of Part II well managed? Explain.
14. Did you suspect the message of the man in the tall hat?
15. Under the circumstances, was the second wish natural?
16. Why do they continue to refer to the son as "it"?
17. What was the old man's third wish?
18. Were you prepared for it? Explain.

19. Why should he have made it?
20. How might "coincidence" have explained the answer to the second wish? the third?
21. Is the atmosphere of weirdness well balanced with the normal?
22. Does anybody today believe in the power of tokens?

## SUBJECTS FOR COMPOSITION

1. You have heard of the "rabbit's foot," the "lucky penny," or some similar object. Write an episode about any one.
2. Write out in some detail the answer to Question 20.
3. Events that seem fantastic are often chronicled in the papers. Watch for one, and use it as the basis for a story.

## OTHER STORIES BY W. W. JACOBS

The Well
The Toll House
In the Library
A Change of Treatment

The Skipper's Wooing
A Black Affair
Good Intentions
Easy Money

## VOLUMES OF STORIES BY W. W. JACOBS

*Many Cargoes*
*The Lady of the Barge*
*Captains All*
*Sailors' Knots*

*Night Watches*
*More Cargoes*
*Snug Harbor*
*Sea Whispers*

# THOMAS HARDY
## (1840–1929)

In no other part of England is there so great a wealth of historic, literary, and legendary tradition as may be found in the southwestern counties, of which Dorset is one. Mysterious Stonehenge, King Arthur and his heroic deeds, marvelous cathedrals — these are but a few of the past glories of this section. More recently, Salisbury Plain quartered many American soldiers before they crossed to France.

To readers the County of Dorset is known today as the "Hardy country," called Wessex in the author's stories. Here Thomas Hardy was born in 1840. After preliminary schooling he went to London, where he attended night classes in King's College. Having determined to be an architect, he apprenticed himself to one who specialized in church architecture, not so much in building new churches as in repairing and preserving the old ones, many of which were falling into ruins through neglect. For some years Hardy worked diligently, and in his novels many scenes and incidents reflect this early interest.

His first literary efforts were in poetry, which attracted little attention. In 1871 his first novel was published, *Desperate Remedies*. From that time until 1895 he wrote fifteen novels, the last one being *Jude the Obscure*. During these years he also published volumes of verse and short stories, including *Wessex Tales,* from which "The Three Strangers" is taken. Since 1895 there have been no more novels, although another volume of short stories was published in 1913, all of them probably written before 1895. In later years Hardy has confined himself to poetry and the drama. As recently as 1923 he wrote a play in the manner of the old English Miracle plays, successfully produced in England.

But to the world at large Thomas Hardy is one of the greatest modern novelists. All his novels and stories are laid in his native Wessex, to which he retired many years ago, and where he has continued to live a secluded life. His best characters are the native peasants. It is their life and their simple human problems which he portrays. But these problems are simple only in the sense that they are elemental and universal. In their native fields, bare hills, dark woods, and barren heaths his characters live, love, and die. His strongest themes are passionate love and the overwhelming of that love in tragic climaxes brought on by inevitable forces over which mortals have no control. To that note he has steadily adhered in spite of much adverse comment. Because readers nowadays demand a "happy ending" they often condemn Hardy as an incorrigible pessimist who has a blind spot for all the brighter phases of life. What he really does is to show that life is other than "one sweet song," that there are such things as sorrow, thwarted love, final disappointment and death.

"The Three Strangers" shows Hardy at his best, both in theme and in style, without, however, the tragic climax. But even that is hovering just around the corner, and only the deliberate art of the author saves the situation by making the hangman a cheerful person. The opening description of the barren hill, at night, in a blinding rainstorm, is typical of Hardy's power. So are the characters. The so-called pessimism is present in this story only by suggestion, such as the reference to the gloomy Timon of Athens, and the delicate thrust at those who "conceive and meditate of pleasant things."

## THE THREE STRANGERS

AMONG the few features of agricultural England which retain an appearance but little modified by the lapse of centuries, may be reckoned the high, grassy and furzy downs, coombs, or ewe-leases, as they are indifferently called, that fill a large area of certain counties in the south and southwest. If any mark of human occupation is met with hereon, it usually takes the form of the solitary cottage of some shepherd.

Fifty years ago such a lonely cottage stood on such a down, and may possibly be standing there now. In spite of its loneliness, however, the spot, by actual measurement, was not more than five miles from a county-town. Yet that affected it little. Five miles of irregular upland, during the long inimical seasons, with their sleets, snows, rains, and mists, afford withdrawing space enough to isolate a Timon or a Nebuchadnezzar; much less, in fair weather, to please that less repellent tribe, the poets, philosophers, artists, and others who "conceive and meditate of pleasant things."

Some old earthen camp or barrow, some clump of trees, at least some starved fragment of ancient hedge is usually taken advantage of in the erection of these forlorn dwellings. But, in the present case, such a kind of shelter had been disregarded. Higher Crowstairs, as the house was called, stood quite detached and undefended. The only reason for its precise situation seemed to be the crossing of two footpaths at right angles hard by, which may have crossed there and thus for a good five hundred years. Hence the house was exposed to the elements on all sides. But, though the wind up here blew unmistakably when it did blow, and the rain hit hard whenever it fell, the various weathers of the winter season were not quite so formidable on the coomb as they were imagined to be by dwellers on low ground. The raw rimes were not so pernicious as in the hollows, and the frosts were scarcely so severe. When the shepherd and his family who tenanted the house were pitied for their sufferings from the exposure, they said that upon the whole they were less inconvenienced by "wuzzes and flames" (hoarses and phlegms) than when they had lived by the stream of a snug neighboring valley.

The night of March 28, 182–, was precisely one of the nights that were wont to call forth these expressions of commiseration. The level rainstorm smote walls, slopes, and hedges like the clothyard shafts of Senlac and Crecy. Such sheep and outdoor animals as had no shelter stood with their buttocks to the winds; while the tails of little birds trying to roost on some scraggy thorn were blown inside-out like umbrellas. The gable-end of the cottage was stained with wet, and the eavesdroppings flapped against the wall. Yet never was commiseration for the shepherd more misplaced. For that cheerful rustic was entertaining a large party in glorification of the christening of his second girl.

The guests had arrived before the rain began to fall, and they were all now assembled in the chief or living room of the dwelling. A glance into the apartment at eight o'clock on this eventful evening would have resulted in the opinion that it was as cozy and comfortable a nook as could be wished for in boisterous weather. The calling of its inhabitant was proclaimed by a number of highly-polished sheep-crooks without stems that were hung ornamentally over the fireplace, the curl of each shining crook varying from the antiquated type engraved in the patriarchal pictures of old family Bibles to the most approved fashion of the last local sheep-fair. The room was lighted by half-a-dozen candles, having wicks only a trifle smaller than the grease which enveloped them, in candlesticks that were never used but at high-days, holy-days, and family feasts. The lights were scattered about the room, two of them standing on the chimney-piece. This position of candles was in itself significant. Candles on the chimney-piece always meant a party.

On the hearth, in front of a back-brand to give substance, blazed a fire of thorns, that crackled "like the laughter of the fool."

Nineteen persons were gathered here. Of these, five women, wearing gowns of various bright hues, sat in chairs along the wall; girls shy and not shy filled the window-bench; four men, including Charley Jake the hedge-carpenter, Elijah New the parish-clerk, and John Pitcher, a neighboring dairyman, the shepherd's father-in-law, lolled in the settle; a young man and maid, who were blushing over tentative *pourparlers* on a life-companionship, sat beneath the corner-cupboard; and an elderly engaged man of fifty or upward moved restlessly about from spots where his betrothed was not to the spot where she was. Enjoyment was pretty general, and so much the more prevailed in being unhampered by conventional restrictions. Absolute confidence in each other's good opinion begat perfect ease, while the finishing stroke of manner, amounting to a truly princely serenity, was lent to the majority by the absence of any expression or trait denoting that they wished to get on in the world, enlarge their minds, or do any eclipsing thing whatever — which nowadays so generally nips the bloom and *bonhomie* of all except the two extremes of the social scale.

Shepherd Fennel had married well, his wife being a dairyman's daughter from a vale at a distance, who brought fifty guineas in her pocket — and kept them there, till they should be required for ministering to the needs of a coming family. This frugal woman had been somewhat exercised as to the character that should be given to the gathering. A sit-still party had its advantages; but an undisturbed position of ease in chairs and settles was apt to lead on the men to such an unconscionable deal of toping that they would sometimes fairly drink the house dry. A dancing-party was the alternative; but this, while avoiding the foregoing objection on the score of good drink, had a counterbalancing disadvantage in the matter of good victuals, the ravenous appetites engendered by the exercise causing immense havoc in the buttery. Shepherdess Fennel fell back upon the intermediate plan of mingling short dances with short periods of talk and singing, so as to hinder any ungovernable rage in either. But this scheme was entirely confined to her own gentle mind: the shepherd himself was in the mood to exhibit the most reckless phases of hospitality.

The fiddler was a boy of those parts, about twelve years of age, who had a wonderful dexterity in jigs and reels, though his fingers were so small and short as to necessitate a constant shifting for the high notes, from which he scrambled back to the first position with sounds not of unmixed purity of tone. At seven the shrill tweedle-dee of this youngster had begun, accompanied by a booming ground-bass from Elijah New, the parish-clerk, who had thoughtfully brought with him his favorite musical instrument, the serpent. Dancing was instantaneous, Mrs. Fennel privately enjoining the players on no account to let the dance exceed the length of a quarter of an hour.

But Elijah and the boy, in the excitement of their position, quite forgot the injunction. Moreover, Oliver Giles, a man of seventeen, one of the dancers, who was enamored of his partner, a fair girl of thirty-three rolling years, had recklessly handed a new crown-piece to the musicians, as a bribe to keep going as long as they had muscle and wind. Mrs. Fennel, seeing the steam begin to generate on the countenances of her guests, crossed over and touched the fiddler's elbow and put her hand on the serpent's mouth. But they took no notice, and fearing she might lose her character of genial hostess if she were to interfere too markedly, she retired and sat down helpless. And so the dance whizzed on with cumulative fury, the performers moving in their planet-like courses, direct and retrograde, from apogee to perigee, till the hand of the well-kicked clock at the bottom of the room had traveled over the circumference of an hour.

While these cheerful events were in course of enactment within Fennel's pastoral dwelling, an incident having considerable bearing on the party had occurred in the gloomy night without. Mrs. Fennel's concern about the growing fierceness of the dance corresponded in point of time with the ascent of a human figure to the solitary hill of Higher Crowstairs from the direction of the distant town. This personage strode on through the rain without a pause, following the little-worn path which, further on in its course, skirted the shepherd's cottage.

It was nearly the time of full moon, and on this account, though the sky was lined with a uniform sheet of dripping cloud, ordinary objects out of doors were readily visible. The sad wan light revealed the lonely pedestrian to be a man of supple frame; his gait suggested that he had somewhat passed the period of perfect and instinctive agility, though not so far as to be otherwise than rapid of motion when occasion required. At a rough guess, he might have been about forty years of age. He appeared tall, but a recruiting sergeant, or other person accustomed to the judging of men's heights by the eye, would have discerned that this was chiefly owing to his gauntness, and that he was not more than five-feet-eight or nine.

Notwithstanding the regularity of his tread, there was caution in it, as in that of one who mentally feels his way; and despite the fact that it was not a black coat nor a dark garment of any sort that he wore, there was something about him which suggested that he naturally belonged to the black-coated tribes of men. His clothes were of fustian, and his boots hobnailed, yet in his progress he showed not the mud-accustomed bearing of hobnailed and fustianed peasantry.

By the time that he had arrived abreast of the shepherd's premises the rain came down, or rather came along, with yet more determined violence. The outskirts of the little settlement partially broke the force of wind and rain, and this induced him to stand still. The most salient of the shepherd's domestic erections was an empty sty at the forward corner of his hedgeless garden, for in these latitudes the principle of masking the homelier features of your establishment by a conventional frontage was unknown. The traveler's eye was attracted to this small building by the pallid shine of the wet slates that covered it. He turned aside, and, finding it empty, stood under the pent-roof for shelter.

While he stood, the boom of the serpent within the adjacent house, and the lesser strains of the fiddler, reached the spot as an accompaniment to the surging hiss of the flying rain on the sod, its louder beating on the cabbage-leaves of the garden, on the eight or ten beehives just discernible by the path, and its dripping from the eaves into a row of buckets and pans that had been placed under the walls of the cottage. For at Higher Crowstairs, as at all such elevated domiciles, the grand difficulty of housekeeping was an insufficiency of water; and a casual rainfall was utilized by turning out, as catchers, every utensil that the house contained. Some queer stories might be told of the contrivances for economy in suds and dish-waters that are absolutely necessitated in upland habitations during the droughts of summer. But at this season there were no such exigencies; a mere acceptance of what the skies bestowed was sufficient for an abundant store.

At last the notes of the serpent ceased and the house was silent. This cessation of activity aroused the solitary pedestrian from the reverie into which he had lapsed, and, emerging from the shed, with an apparently new intention, he walked up the path to the house-door. Arrived here, his first act was to kneel down on a large stone beside the row of vessels, and to drink a copious draught from one of them. Having quenched his thirst he rose and lifted his hand to knock, but paused with his eye upon the panel. Since the dark surface of the wood revealed absolutely nothing, it was evident that he must be mentally looking through the door, as if he wished to measure thereby all the possibilities that a house of this sort might include, and how they might bear upon the question of his entry.

In his indecision he turned and surveyed the scene around. Not a soul was anywhere visible. The garden-path stretched downward from his feet, gleaming like the track of a snail; the roof of the little well (mostly dry), the well-cover, the top rail of the garden-gate, were varnished with the same dull liquid glaze; while, far away in the vale, a faint whiteness of more than usual extent showed that the rivers were high in the meads. Beyond all this winked a few bleared lamplights through the beating drops — lights that denoted the situation of the county-town from which he had appeared to come. The absence of all notes of life in that direction seemed to clinch his intentions, and he knocked at the door.

Within, a desultory chat had taken the place of movement and musical sound. The hedge-carpenter was suggesting a song to the company, which nobody just then was inclined to undertake, so that the knock afforded a not unwelcome diversion.

"Walk in!" said the shepherd promptly.

The latch clicked upward, and out of the night our pedestrian appeared upon the door-mat. The shepherd arose, snuffed two of the nearest candles, and turned to look at him.

Their light disclosed that the stranger was dark in complexion and not unprepossessing as to feature. His hat, which for a moment he did not remove, hung low over his eyes,

## The Three Strangers

without concealing that they were large, open, and determined, moving with a flash rather than a glance round the room. He seemed pleased with his survey, and, baring his shaggy head, said, in a rich deep voice, " The rain is so heavy, friends, that I ask leave to come in and rest awhile."

" To be sure, stranger," said the shepherd. " And faith, you've been lucky in choosing your time, for we are having a bit of a fling for a glad cause — though, to be sure, a man could hardly wish that glad cause to happen more than once a year."

" Nor less," spoke up a woman. " For 'tis best to get your family over and done with, as soon as you can, so as to be all the earlier out of the fag o't."

" And what may be this glad cause? " asked the stranger.

" A birth and christening," said the shepherd.

The stranger hoped his host might not be made unhappy either by too many or too few of such episodes, and being invited by a gesture to a pull at the mug, he readily acquiesced. His manner, which, before entering, had been so dubious, was now altogether that of a careless and candid man.

" Late to be traipsing athwart this coomb — hey? " said the engaged man of fifty.

" Late it is, master, as you say. — I'll take a seat in the chimney-corner, if you have nothing to urge against it, ma'am; for I am a little moist on the side that was next the rain."

Mrs. Shepherd Fennel assented, and made room for the self-invited comer, who, having got completely inside the chimney-corner, stretched out his legs and his arms with the expansiveness of a person quite at home.

" Yes, I am rather cracked in the vamp," he said freely, seeing that the eyes of the shepherd's wife fell upon his boots, " and I am not well fitted either. I have had some rough times lately, and have been forced to pick up what I can get in the way of wearing, but I must find a suit better fit for working-days when I reach home."

" One of hereabouts? " she inquired.

" Not quite that — further up the country."

" I thought so. And so be I; and by your tongue you come from my neighborhood."

" But you would hardly have heard of me," he said quickly. " My time would be long before yours, ma'am, you see."

This testimony to the youthfulness of his hostess had the effect of stopping her cross-examination.

"There is only one thing more wanted to make me happy," continued the new-comer. "And that is a little baccy, which I am sorry to say I am out of."

"I'll fill your pipe," said the shepherd.

"I must ask you to lend me a pipe likewise."

"A smoker, and no pipe about 'ee?"

"I have dropped it somewhere on the road."

The shepherd filled and handed him a new clay pipe, saying, as he did so, "Hand me your baccy-box — I'll fill that too, now I am about it."

The man went through the movement of searching his pockets.

"Lost that too?" said his entertainer, with some surprise.

"I am afraid so," said the man with some confusion. "Give it to me in a screw of paper." Lighting his pipe at the candle with a suction that drew the whole flame into the bowl, he resettled himself in the corner and bent his looks upon the faint steam from his damp legs, as if he wished to say no more.

Meanwhile the general body of guests had been taking little notice of this visitor by reason of an absorbing discussion in which they were engaged with the band about a tune for the next dance. The matter being settled, they were about to stand up when an interruption came in the shape of another knock at the door.

At sound of the same the man in the chimney-corner took up the poker and began stirring the brands as if doing it thoroughly were the one aim of his existence; and a second time the shepherd said, "Walk in!" In a moment another man stood upon the straw-woven door-mat. He too was a stranger.

This individual was one of a type radically different from the first. There was more of the commonplace in his manner, and a certain jovial cosmopolitanism sat upon his features. He was several years older than the first arrival, his hair being slightly frosted, his eyebrows bristly, and his whiskers cut back from his cheeks. His face was rather full and flabby, and yet it was not altogether a face without power. A few grog-blossoms marked the neighborhood of his nose. He flung back his long drab greatcoat, revealing that beneath it he wore a suit of cinder-gray shade throughout, large heavy seals, of some metal or other that would take a polish, dangling from his fob as his only personal ornament. Shaking the water-drops from his low-crowned glazed hat, he said, " I must ask for a few minutes' shelter, comrades, or I shall be wetted to my skin before I get to Casterbridge."

" Make yourself at home, master," said the shepherd, perhaps a trifle less heartily than on the first occasion. Not that Fennel had the least tinge of niggardliness in his composition; but the room was far from large, spare chairs were not numerous, and damp companions were not altogether desirable at close quarters for the women and girls in their bright-colored gowns.

However, the second comer, after taking off his greatcoat, and hanging his hat on a nail in one of the ceiling-beams as if he had been specially invited to put it there, advanced and sat down at the table. This had been pushed so closely into the chimney-corner, to give all available room to the dancers, that its inner edge grazed the elbow of the man who had ensconced himself by the fire; and thus the two strangers were brought into close companionship. They nodded to each other by way of breaking the ice of unacquaintance, and the first stranger handed his neighbor the family mug — a huge vessel of brown ware, having its upper edge worn away like a threshold by the rub of whole generations of thirsty lips that had gone the way of all flesh, and bearing the following inscription burnt upon its rotund side in yellow letters: —

THERE IS NO FUN

UNTILL i CUM.

The other man, nothing loath, raised the mug to his lips, and drank on, and on, and on — till a curious blueness overspread the countenance of the shepherd's wife, who had regarded with no little surprise the first stranger's free offer to the second of what did not belong to him to dispense.

" I knew it! " said the toper to the shepherd with much satisfaction. " When I walked up your garden before coming in, and saw the hives all of a row, I said to myself, ' Where there's bees there's honey, and where there's honey there's mead.' But mead of such a truly comfortable sort as this I really didn't expect to meet in my older days." He took yet another pull at the mug, till it assumed an ominous elevation.

"Glad you enjoy it!" said the shepherd warmly.

"It is goodish mead," assented Mrs. Fennel, with an absence of enthusiasm which seemed to say that it was possible to buy praise for one's cellar at too heavy a price. "It is trouble enough to make — and really I hardly think we shall make any more. For honey sells well, and we ourselves can make shift with a drop o' small mead and metheglin for common use from the comb-washings."

"Oh, but you'll never have the heart!" reproachfully cried the stranger in cinder-gray, after taking up the mug a third time and setting it down empty. "I love mead, when 'tis old like this, as I love to go to church o' Sundays, or to relieve the needy any day of the week."

"Ha, ha, ha!" said the man in the chimney-corner, who in spite of the taciturnity induced by the pipe of tobacco, could not or would not refrain from this slight testimony to his comrade's humor.

Now the old mead of those days, brewed of the purest first-year or maiden honey, four pounds to the gallon — with its due complement of white of eggs, cinnamon, ginger, cloves, mace, rosemary, yeast, and processes of working, bottling, and cellaring — tasted remarkably strong; but it did not taste so strong as it actually was. Hence, presently, the stranger in cinder-gray at the table, moved by its creeping influence, unbuttoned his waistcoat, threw himself back in his chair, spread his legs, and made his presence felt in various ways.

"Well, well, as I say," he resumed, "I am going to Casterbridge, and to Casterbridge I must go. I should have been almost there by this time; but the rain drove me into your dwelling, and I'm not sorry for it."

"You don't live in Casterbridge?" said the shepherd.

"Not as yet; though I shortly mean to move there."

"Going to set up in trade, perhaps?"

"No, no," said the shepherd's wife. "It is easy to see that the gentleman is rich, and don't want to work at anything."

The cinder-gray stranger paused, as if to consider whether he would accept that definition of himself. He presently rejected it by answering, "Rich is not quite the word for me, dame. I do work, and I must work. And even if I only get to Casterbridge by midnight I must begin work there at eight tomorrow morning. Yes, het or wet, blow or snow, famine or sword, my day's work tomorrow must be done."

"Poor man! Then, in spite o' seeming, you be worse off than we?" replied the shepherd's wife.

"'Tis the nature of my trade, men and maidens. 'Tis the nature of my trade more than my poverty. . . . But really and truly I must up and off, or I shan't get a lodging in the town." However, the speaker did not move, and directly added, "There's time for one more draught of friendship before I go; and I'd perform it at once if the mug were not dry."

"Here's a mug o' small," said Mrs. Fennel. "Small, we call it, though to be sure 'tis only the first wash o' the combs."

"No," said the stranger disdainfully. "I won't spoil your first kindness by partaking o' your second."

"Certainly not," broke in Fennel. "We don't increase and multiply every day, and I'll fill the mug again." He went away to the dark place under the stairs where the barrel stood. The shepherdess followed him.

"Why should you do this?" she said reproachfully, as soon as they were alone. "He's emptied it once, though it held enough for ten people; and now he's not contented wi' the small, but must needs call for more o' the strong! And a stranger unbeknown to any of us. For my part, I don't like the look o' the man at all."

"But he's in the house, my honey; and 'tis a wet night, and a christening. Daze it, what's a cup of mead more or less? There'll be plenty more next bee-burning."

"Very well — this time, then," she answered, looking wistfully at the barrel. "But what is the man's calling, and where is he one of, that he should come in and join us like this?"

"I don't know. I'll ask him again."

The catastrophe of having the mug drained dry at one pull by the stranger in cinder-gray was effectually guarded against this time by Mrs. Fennel. She poured out his allowance in a small cup, keeping the large one at a discreet distance from him. When he had tossed off his portion the shepherd renewed his inquiry about the stranger's occupation.

The latter did not immediately reply, and the man in the

chimney-corner, with sudden demonstrativeness, said, "Anybody may know my trade — I'm a wheelwright."

"A very good trade for these parts," said the shepherd.

"And anybody may know mine — if they've the sense to find it out," said the stranger in cinder-gray.

"You may generally tell what a man is by his claws," observed the hedge-carpenter, looking at his own hands. "My fingers be as full of thorns as an old pin-cushion is of pins."

The hands of the man in the chimney-corner instinctively sought the shade, and he gazed into the fire as he resumed his pipe. The man at the table took up the hedge-carpenter's remark, and added smartly, "True; but the oddity of my trade is that, instead of setting a mark upon me, it sets a mark upon my customers."

No observation being offered by anybody in elucidation of this enigma, the shepherd's wife once more called for a song. The same obstacles presented themselves as at the former time — one had no voice, another had forgotten the first verse. The stranger at the table, whose soul had now risen to a good working temperature, relieved the difficulty by exclaiming that, to start the company, he would sing himself. Thrusting one thumb into the arm-hole of his waistcoat, he waved the other hand in the air, and, with an extemporizing gaze at the shining sheep-crooks above the mantelpiece, began: —

> "O my trade it is the rarest one,
>     Simple shepherds all —
>   My trade is a sight to see;
> For my customers I tie, and take them up on high,
>     And waft 'em to a far countree!"

The room was silent when he had finished the verse — with one exception, that of the man in the chimney-corner, who, at the singer's word, "Chorus!" joined him in a deep bass voice of musical relish —

> "And waft 'em to a far countree!"

Oliver Giles, John Pitcher the dairyman, the parish-clerk, the engaged man of fifty, the row of young women against the wall, seemed lost in thought not of the gayest kind. The shepherd looked meditatively on the ground, the shepherdess gazed keenly at the singer, and with some suspicion; she was doubting whether this stranger were merely singing an old song from recollection, or was composing one there and then for the occasion. All were as perplexed at the obscure revelation as the guests at Belshazzar's Feast, except the man in the chimney-corner, who quietly said, "Second verse, stranger," and smoked on.

The singer thoroughly moistened himself from his lips inwards, and went on with the next stanza as requested: —

> " My tools are but common ones,
>     Simple shepherds all —
> My tools are no sight to see:
> A little hempen string, and a post whereon to swing,
>     Are implements enough for me! "

Shepherd Fennel glanced round. There was no longer any doubt that the stranger was answering his question rhythmically. The guests one and all started back with suppressed exclamations. The young woman engaged to the man of fifty fainted half-way, and would have proceeded, but finding him wanting in alacrity for catching her she sat down trembling.

"Oh, he's the — ! " whispered the people in the background, mentioning the name of an ominous public officer. "He's come to do it! 'Tis to be at Casterbridge jail tomorrow — the man for sheep-stealing — the poor clock-maker we heard of, who used to live away at Shottsford and had no work to do — Timothy Summers, whose family were a-starving, and so he went out of Shottsford by the high road, and took a sheep in open daylight defying the farmer and the farmer's wife and the farmer's lad, and every man jack among 'em. He " (and they nodded towards the stranger of the deadly trade) " is come from up the country to do it because there's not enough to do in his own county-town, and he's got the place here now our own county man's dead; he's going to live in the same cottage under the prison wall."

The stranger in cinder-gray took no notice of this whispered string of observations, but again wetted his lips. Seeing that his friend in the chimney-corner was the only one who reciprocated his joviality in any way, he held out his cup towards that appreciative comrade, who also held out his own.

They clinked together, the eyes of the rest of the room hanging upon the singer's actions. He parted his lips for the third verse; but at that moment another knock was audible upon the door. This time the knock was faint and hesitating.

The company seemed scared; the shepherd looked with consternation towards the entrance, and it was with some effort that he resisted his alarmed wife's deprecatory glance, and uttered for the third time the welcoming words "Walk in!"

The door was gently opened, and another man stood upon the mat. He, like those who had preceded him, was a stranger. This time it was a short, small personage, of fair complexion, and dressed in a decent suit of dark clothes.

"Can you tell me the way to ———" he began: when, gazing round the room to observe the nature of the company amongst whom he had fallen, his eyes lighted on the stranger in cinder-gray. It was just at the instant when the latter, who had thrown his mind into his song with such a will that he scarcely heeded the interruption, silenced all whispers and inquiries by bursting into his third verse: —

"Tomorrow is my working day,
    Simple shepherds all —
Tomorrow is a working day for me:
For the farmer's sheep is slain, and the lad who did it ta'en,
    And on his soul may God ha' merc-y!"

The stranger in the chimney-corner, waving cups with the singer so heartily that his mead splashed over on the hearth, repeated in his bass voice as before: —

"And on his soul may God ha' merc-y!"

All this time the third stranger had been standing in the doorway. Finding now that he did not come forward or go on speaking, the guests particularly regarded him. They noticed to their surprise that he stood before them the picture of abject terror — his knees trembling, his hand shaking so violently that the door-latch by which he supported himself rattled audibly: his white lips were parted, and his eyes fixed on the merry officer of justice in the middle of the room. A moment more and he had turned, closed the door, and fled.

"What a man can it be?" said the shepherd.

The rest, between the awfulness of their late discovery and the odd conduct of this third visitor, looked as if they knew not what to think, and said nothing. Instinctively they withdrew further and further from the grim gentleman in their midst, whom some of them seemed to take for the Prince of Darkness himself, till they formed a remote circle, an empty space of floor being left between them and him —

". . . circulus, cujus centrum diabolus."

The room was so silent — though there were more than twenty people in it — that nothing could be heard but the patter of the rain against the window-shutters, accompanied by the occasional hiss of a stray drop that fell down the chimney into the fire, and the steady puffing of the man in the corner, who had now resumed his long pipe of clay.

The stillness was unexpectedly broken. The distant sound of a gun reverberated through the air — apparently from the direction of the county-town.

" Be jiggered! " cried the stranger who had sung the song, jumping up.

" What does that mean? " asked several.

" A prisoner escaped from the jail — that's what it means."

All listened. The sound was repeated, and none of them spoke but the man in the chimney-corner, who said quietly, " I've often been told that in this county they fire a gun at such times; but I never heard it till now."

" I wonder if it is *my* man? " murmured the personage in cinder-gray.

" Surely it is! " said the shepherd involuntarily. " And surely we've zeed him! That little man who looked in at the door by now, and quivered like a leaf when he zeed ye and heard your song! "

" His teeth chattered, and the breath went out of his body," said the dairyman.

" And his heart seemed to sink within him like a stone," said Oliver Giles.

" And he bolted as if he'd been shot at," said the hedge-carpenter.

" True — his teeth chattered, and his heart seemed to sink; and he bolted as if he'd been shot at," slowly summed up the man in the chimney-corner.

"I didn't notice it," remarked the hangman.

"We were all a-wondering what made him run off in such a fright," faltered one of the women against the wall, "and now 'tis explained!"

The firing of the alarm-gun went on at intervals, low and sullenly, and their suspicions became a certainty. The sinister gentleman in cinder-gray roused himself. "Is there a constable here?" he asked, in thick tones. "If so, let him step forward."

The engaged man of fifty stepped quavering out from the wall, his betrothed beginning to sob on the back of the chair.

"You are a sworn constable?"

"I be, sir."

"Then pursue the criminal at once, with assistance, and bring him back here. He can't have gone far."

"I will, sir, I will — when I've got my staff. I'll go home and get it, and come sharp here, and start in a body."

"Staff! — never mind your staff; the man'll be gone!"

"But I can't do nothing without my staff — can I, William, and John, and Charles Jake? No; for there's the king's royal crown a painted on en in yaller and gold, and the lion and the unicorn, so as when I raise en up and hit my prisoner, 'tis made a lawful blow thereby. I wouldn't 'tempt to take up a man without my staff — no, not I. If I hadn't the law to gie me courage, why, instead o' my taking up him he might take up me!"

"Now, I'm a king's man myself, and can give you authority enough for this," said the formidable officer in gray. "Now then, all of ye, be ready. Have ye any lanterns?"

"Yes — have ye any lanterns? — I demand it!" said the constable.

"And the rest of you able-bodied ———"

"Able-bodied men — yes — the rest of ye!" said the constable.

"Have you some good stout staves and pitchforks ———"

"Staves and pitchforks — in the name o' the law! And take 'em in yer hands and go in quest, and do as we in authority tell ye!"

Thus aroused, the men prepared to give chase. The evidence was, indeed, though circumstantial, so convincing, that but little argument was needed to show the shepherd's guests that after what they had seen it would look very much like connivance if they did not instantly pursue the unhappy third stranger, who could not as yet have gone more than a few hundred yards over such uneven country.

A shepherd is always well provided with lanterns; and, lighting these hastily, and with hurdle-staves in their hands, they poured out of the door, taking a direction along the crest of the hill, away from the town, the rain having fortunately a little abated.

Disturbed by the noise, or possibly by unpleasant dreams of her baptism, the child who had been christened began to cry heart-brokenly in the room overhead. These notes of grief came down through the chinks of the floor to the ears of the women below, who jumped up one by one, and seemed glad of the excuse to ascend and comfort the baby, for the incidents of the last half-hour greatly oppressed them. Thus in the space of two or three minutes the room on the ground-floor was deserted quite.

But it was not for long. Hardly had the sound of footsteps died away when a man returned round the corner of the house from the direction the pursuers had taken. Peeping in at the door, and seeing nobody there, he entered leisurely. It was the stranger of the chimney-corner, who had gone out with the rest. The motive of his return was shown by his helping himself to a cut piece of skimmer-cake that lay on a ledge beside where he had sat, and which he had apparently forgotten to take with him. He also poured out half a cup more mead from the quantity that remained, ravenously eating and drinking these as he stood. He had not finished when another figure came in just as quietly — his friend in cinder-gray.

"Oh — you here?" said the latter, smiling. "I thought you had gone to help in the capture." And this speaker also revealed the object of his return by looking solicitously round for the fascinating mug of old mead.

"And I thought you had gone," said the other, continuing his skimmer-cake with some effort.

"Well, on second thoughts, I felt there were enough without me," said the first confidentially, "and such a night as it is, too. Besides, 'tis the business o' the Government to take care of its criminals — not mine."

"True; so it is. And I felt as you did, that there were enough without me."

"I don't want to break my limbs running over the humps and hollows of this wild country."

"Nor I neither, between you and me."

"These shepherd-people are used to it — simple-minded souls, you know, stirred up to anything in a moment. They'll have him ready for me before the morning, and no trouble to me at all."

"They'll have him, and we shall have saved ourselves all labor in the matter."

"True, true. Well, my way is to Casterbridge; and 'tis as much as my legs will do to take me that far. Going the same way?"

"No, I am sorry to say! I have to get home over there" (he nodded indefinitely to the right), "and I feel as you do, that it is quite enough for my legs to do before bedtime."

The other had by this time finished the mead in the mug, after which, shaking hands heartily at the door, and wishing each other well, they went their several ways.

In the meantime the company of pursuers had reached the end of the hog's-back elevation which dominated this part of the down. They had decided on no particular plan of action; and, finding that the man of the baleful trade was no longer in their company, they seemed quite unable to form any such plan now. They descended in all directions down the hill, and straightway several of the party fell into the snare set by Nature for all misguided midnight ramblers over this part of the cretaceous formation. The "lanchets," or flint slopes, which belted the escarpment at intervals of a dozen yards, took the less cautious ones unawares, and losing their footing on the rubbly steep they slid sharply downwards, the lanterns rolling from their hands to the bottom, and there lying on their sides till the horn was scorched through.

When they had again gathered themselves together, the shepherd, as the man who knew the country best, took the lead, and guided them round these treacherous inclines. The lanterns, which seemed rather to dazzle their eyes and warn the fugitive than to assist them in the exploration, were extinguished, due silence was observed; and in this more rational order they plunged into the vale. It was a grassy, briery, moist defile, affording some shelter to any person who had sought it; but the party perambulated it in vain, and ascended on the other side. Here they wandered apart, and after an interval closed together again to report progress. At the second time of closing in they found themselves near a lonely ash, the single tree on this part of the coomb, probably sown there by a passing bird some fifty years before. And here, standing a little to one side of the trunk, as motionless as the trunk itself, appeared the man they were in quest of, his outline being well defined against the sky beyond. The band noiselessly drew up and faced him.

"Your money or your life!" said the constable sternly to the still figure.

"No, no," whispered John Pitcher. "'Tisn't our side ought to say that. That's the doctrine of vagabonds like him, and we be on the side of the law."

"Well, well," replied the constable impatiently; "I must say something, mustn't I? and if you had all the weight o' this undertaking upon your mind, perhaps you'd say the wrong thing too! — Prisoner at the bar, surrender, in the name of the Father — the Crown, I mane!"

The man under the tree seemed now to notice them for the first time, and, giving them no opportunity whatever for exhibiting their courage, he strolled slowly towards them. He was, indeed, the little man, the third stranger; but his trepidation had in a great measure gone.

"Well, travelers," he said, "did I hear ye speak to me?"

"You did: you've got to come and be our prisoner at once!" said the constable. "We arrest 'ee on the charge of not biding in Casterbridge jail in a decent proper manner to be hung tomorrow morning. Neighbors, do your duty, and seize the culpet!"

On hearing the charge, the man seemed enlightened, and, saying not another word, resigned himself with preternatural civility to the search-party, who, with their staves in their hands, surrounded him on all sides, and marched him back towards the shepherd's cottage.

It was eleven o'clock by the time they arrived. The light

shining from the open door, a sound of men's voices within, proclaimed to them as they approached the house that some new events had arisen in their absence. On entering they discovered the shepherd's living room to be invaded by two officers from Casterbridge jail, and a well-known magistrate who lived at the nearest country-seat, intelligence of the escape having become generally circulated.

"Gentlemen," said the constable, "I have brought back your man — not without risk and danger; but every one must do his duty! He is inside this circle of able-bodied persons, who have lent me useful aid, considering their ignorance of Crown work. Men, bring forward your prisoner!" And the third stranger was led to the light.

"Who is this?" said one of the officials.

"The man," said the constable.

"Certainly not," said the turnkey; and the first corroborated his statement.

"But how can it be otherwise?" asked the constable. "Or why was he so terrified at sight o' the singing instrument of the law who sat there?" Here he related the strange behavior of the third stranger on entering the house during the hangman's song.

"Can't understand it," said the officer coolly. "All I know is that it is not the condemned man. He's quite a different character from this one; a gauntish fellow, with dark hair and eyes, rather good-looking, and with a musical bass voice that if you heard it once you'd never mistake as long as you lived."

"Why, souls — 'twas the man in the chimney-corner!"

"Hey — what?" said the magistrate, coming forward after inquiring particulars from the shepherd in the background. "Haven't you got the man after all?"

"Well, sir," said the constable, "he's the man we were in search of, that's true; and yet he's not the man we were in search of. For the man we were in search of was not the man we wanted, sir, if you understand my every-day way; for 'twas the man in the chimney-corner!"

"A pretty kettle of fish altogether!" said the magistrate. "You had better start for the other man at once."

The prisoner now spoke for the first time. The mention of the man in the chimney-corner seemed to have moved him as nothing else could do. " Sir," he said, stepping forward to the magistrate, " take no more trouble about me. The time is come when I may as well speak. I have done nothing; my crime is that the condemned man is my brother. Early this afternoon I left home at Shottsford to tramp it all the way to Casterbridge jail to bid him farewell. I was benighted, and called here to rest and ask the way. When I opened the door I saw before me the very man, my brother, that I thought to see in the condemned cell at Casterbridge. He was in this chimney-corner; and jammed close to him, so that he could not have got out if he had tried, was the executioner who'd come to take his life, singing a song about it and not knowing that it was his victim who was close by, joining in to save appearances. My brother looked a glance of agony at me, and I knew he meant, ' Don't reveal what you see; my life depends on it.' I was so terror-struck that I could hardly stand, and, not knowing what I did, I turned and hurried away."

The narrator's manner and tone had the stamp of truth, and his story made a great impression on all around. " And do you know where your brother is at the present time? " asked the magistrate.

" I do not. I have never seen him since I closed this door."

" I can testify to that, for we've been between ye ever since," said the constable.

" Where does he think to fly to? — what is his occupation? "

" He's a watch-and-clock-maker, sir."

" 'A said 'a was a wheelwright — a wicked rogue," said the constable.

" The wheels of clocks and watches he meant, no doubt," said Shepherd Fennel. " I thought his hands were palish for's trade."

" Well, it appears to me that nothing can be gained by retaining this poor man in custody," said the magistrate; " your business lies with the other, unquestionably."

And so the little man was released off-hand; but he looked nothing the less sad on that account, it being beyond the power of magistrate or constable to raze out the written troubles in his brain, for they concerned another whom he regarded with more solicitude than himself. When this was done, and the man had gone his way, the night was found to be so far advanced that it was deemed useless to renew the search before the next morning.

Next day, accordingly, the quest for the clever sheep-stealer became general and keen, to all appearance at least. But the intended punishment was cruelly disproportioned to the transgression, and the sympathy of a great many country-folk in that district was strongly on the side of the fugitive. Moreover, his marvelous coolness and daring in hob-and-nobbing with the hangman, under the unprecedented circumstances of the shepherd's party, won their admiration. So that it may be questioned if all those who ostensibly made themselves so busy in exploring woods and fields and lanes were quite so thorough when it came to the private examination of their own lofts and outhouses. Stories were afloat of a mysterious figure being occasionally seen in some old overgrown trackway or other, remote from turnpike roads; but when a search was instituted in any of these suspected quarters nobody was found. Thus the days and weeks passed without tidings.

In brief, the bass-voiced man of the chimney-corner was never recaptured. Some said that he went across the sea, others that he did not, but buried himself in the depths of a populous city. At any rate, the gentleman in cinder-gray never did his morning's work at Casterbridge, nor met anywhere at all, for business purposes, the genial comrade with whom he had passed an hour of relaxation in the lonely house on the coomb.

The grass has long been green on the graves of Shepherd Fennel and his frugal wife; the guests who made up the christening party have mainly followed their entertainers to the tomb; the baby in whose honor they all had met is a matron in the sere and yellow leaf. But the arrival of the three strangers at the shepherd's that night, and the details connected therewith, is a story as well known as ever in the country about Higher Crowstairs.


## QUESTIONS

1. What bearing does the opening description have on the story later?
2. Does the contrast between the outside and the inside make for effectiveness?

3. Briefly characterize Shepherdess Fennel.
4. Why did she want the dances limited to fifteen minutes?
5. Where does the story really begin?
6. Select details that make the first stranger seem " queer."
7. Under other conditions would he have seemed a suspicious character?
8. Why does he busy himself with the fire at the second knock?
9. What do the " few grog-blossoms " tell about the second stranger?
10. Is it of any consequence for the story? Explain.
11. What bit of " humor " in the second stranger made the first one laugh?
12. Does the first stranger recognize the second before the song?
13. Of what importance is the whispered conversation?
14. Is the third knock a surprise to the reader as well as to the gathering? If so, give reasons.
15. How does the sound of the gun break the tenseness of the situation?
16. Were there good reasons for suspecting the third stranger?
17. Has the reader by this time an inkling of the real facts?
18. What may have been the first stranger's thought when the second also returned? Give reason for your answer.
19. Does the stupid constable add anything to the story?
20. What in the first stranger won the admiration of the country folk?
21. Were they justified?
22. For the story, was it necessary that the third stranger be caught?
23. Does the author write as if he were familiar with his material?

## SUBJECTS FOR COMPOSITION

1. Perhaps you know some lone house on a hill. Write a description as it appears in midsummer sunshine.
2. Describe it in a dripping autumn gloom.
3. People it with fitting characters, a few only.
4. Imagine some tragic circumstance in their life.
5. Surround this with a complication that leads to the tragic climax.
6. In this exercise adhere rigidly to your plot, making the descriptive feature serve as necessary background only.

## VOLUMES OF STORIES BY THOMAS HARDY

*Wessex Tales*              *A Changed Man*
*Life's Little Ironies*     *A Group of Noble Dames*

## ABOUT THOMAS HARDY AND THE HARDY COUNTRY

*The Art of Thomas Hardy,* Lionel Johnson
   (A remarkable book, essential to an understanding of Hardy)
*Thomas Hardy's Wessex,* Herman Lea

## JOSEPH CONRAD
(1857-1924)

It is no small distinction to be considered one of the two greatest living writers of fiction in English. That enviable position Joseph Conrad had achieved at the time of his death in 1924, his single rival being Thomas Hardy, but it was reached after many years of neglect by an indifferent public. Fortunately he lived long enough to enjoy some of the fruits of success, not merely in matters financial, but in the universal esteem of the critics and of his fellow craftsmen. It had been a difficult voyage, the longest ever made by this captain of the seas. No writer of English ever faced handicaps so overwhelming as those overcome by Joseph Conrad, and the story of Conrad the man is almost as fascinating as the story of any of his heroes.

This life story may be divided into three chapters. The first tells how Teodor Jozef Konrad Korzeniowski became plain Joseph Conrad. He was born of Polish parents, in 1857, in the Ukraine, at that time a part of Russia. At the death of his parents the boy was placed under the care of an uncle who employed tutors to prepare him for the University of Cracow. He was to become a cultured Polish gentleman, like his father. But Teodor Jozef had an incomprehensible ambition. He wanted to become a sailor, an English sailor, this boy who came from a country untouched by the sea, and who knew not a word of English. Overcoming all objections, he shipped before the mast when he was not yet twenty. At first he chose the French Mediterranean service because he knew French almost as well as his native Polish, but in a few years he was serving on an English ship in the North Sea.

The second chapter deals with Conrad the sailor, the English sailor, for he learned the language of the country he served, eventually obtained a master's certificate, and became an English sea captain. For twenty years he sailed the seas, mainly those of the East and the tropics. At this point there should be a lyrical outburst over Conrad's love for the sea, but the truth is that sailors do not love the sea. They love the ships in which they sail, and their fascinating adventure consists of the way in which, through sheer human skill, their ships are made to buffet one of the great forces in nature. It is this human side that had the strongest appeal for Conrad, amply proved by such books as *Youth, Typhoon,* and *The Nigger of the Narcissus*. In his spare time he read much both in French and in English, his favorites being the French Flaubert and Maupassant, the English Dickens and Trollope, and the American Henry James. After twenty years the fevers of the tropics had laid such a heavy hold upon him that he was compelled to retire from the sea, but not before he had written parts of several stories. One of these was *Almayer's Folly*. This he completed after settling down on shore. It was published in 1895.

The final chapter concerns Conrad the literary man. He married an Englishwoman, made his home in Kent after a short residence in France, and devoted himself to writing. It would be pleasant to record that an eager public kept the presses running day and night by an insistent demand for his stories. The facts are otherwise, but Conrad was not accustomed to have things come to him easily. He struggled on. Novel followed novel, short stories appeared at infrequent intervals, but the reading public remained inattentive. Discerning English critics and friends, and far-sighted American publishers encouraged him to continue, with the result that twenty-seven years after his first novel was published an American magazine paid $45,000 for the serial rights to his last story, *The Rover,* printed in book form in 1923.

Conrad is usually called a writer of sea stories. That statement is true enough, but his real interests did not lie in the mere adventure of the sea. The stories already enumerated are sea stories in the literal sense, but in many of his tales the sea merely provides the atmosphere and the characters are men who have followed the sea. He has a special fondness for the human derelicts found in distant ports. Their wasted lives he probes to the depths, and the story becomes a profound analysis of human character. Usually the theme is the sad futility of human struggle. Conventional happy endings are rare in the work of Conrad.

"The Inn of the Two Witches," selected for this volume, has less of the sea than most of the author's stories. The chief characters, aside from those living in the inn, are sailors, but the story can not be called a sea story. Yet it is typical of Conrad. The setting is remote because little known; the witches and the "man with the mule" are of the derelict type already mentioned; and the heroes are strong men of the sea caught in an adventure on land. The indirect manner of narration as well as the style are characteristic of the author's best work. "The Inn of the Two Witches" was written in 1913, and is taken from the volume *Within the Tides.*

# THE INN OF THE TWO WITCHES

## A Find

THIS tale, episode, experience — call it how you will — was related in the fifties of the last century by a man who, by his own confession, was sixty years old at the time. Sixty is not a bad age — unless in perspective, when no doubt it is contemplated by the majority of us with mixed feelings. It is a calm age; the game is practically over by then; and standing aside one begins to remember with a certain vividness what a fine fellow one used to be. I have observed that, by an amiable attention of Providence, most people at sixty begin to take a romantic view of themselves. Their very failures exhale a charm of peculiar potency. And indeed the hopes of the future are a fine company to live with, exquisite forms, fascinating if you like, but — so to speak — naked, stripped for a run. The robes of glamour are luckily the property of the immovable past which, without them, would sit, a shivery sort of thing, under the gathering shadows.

I suppose it was the romanticism of growing age which set our man to relate his experience for his own satisfaction or for the wonder of his posterity. It could not have been for his glory, because the experience was simply that of an abominable fright — terror he calls it. You would have guessed that the relation alluded to in the very first lines was in writing.

This writing constitutes the Find declared in the subtitle. The title itself is my own contrivance (can't call it invention), and has the merit of veracity. We will be concerned with an inn here. As to the witches that's merely a conventional expression, and we must take our man's word for it that it fits the case.

The Find was made in a box of books bought in London, in a street which no longer exists, from a second-hand bookseller in the last stage of decay. As to the books themselves they were at least twentieth-hand, and on inspection turned out not worth the very small sum of money I disbursed. It might have been some premonition of the fact which made me say: "But I must have the box too." The decayed bookseller assented by the careless, tragic gesture of a man already doomed to extinction.

A litter of loose pages at the bottom of the box excited my curiosity but faintly. The close, neat, regular handwriting was not attractive at first sight. But in one place the statement that in A.D. 1813 the writer was twenty-two years old caught my eye. Two and twenty is an interesting age in which one is easily reckless and easily frightened; the faculty of reflection being weak and the power of imagination strong.

In another place the phrase: "At night we stood in again," arrested my languid attention, because it was a sea phrase. "Let's see what it is all about," I thought, without excitement.

Oh! but it was a dull-faced MS., each line resembling every other line in their close-set and regular order. It was like the drone of a monotonous voice. A treatise on sugar-refining (the dreariest subject I can think of) could have been given a more lively appearance. " In A.D. 1813 I was twenty-two years old," he begins earnestly, and goes on with every appearance of calm, horrible industry. Don't imagine, however, that there is anything archaic in my find. Diabolic ingenuity in invention though as old as the world is by no means a lost art. Look at the telephones for shattering the little peace of mind given to us in this world, or at the machine guns for letting with dispatch life out of our bodies. Nowadays any blear-eyed old witch if only strong enough to turn an insignificant little handle could lay low a hundred young men of twenty in the twinkling of an eye.

If this isn't progress! . . . Why, immense! We have moved on, and so you must expect to meet here a certain naïveness of contrivance and simplicity of aim appertaining to the remote epoch. And of course no motoring tourist can hope to find such an inn anywhere, now. This one, the one of the title, was situated in Spain. That much I discovered only from internal evidence, because a good many pages of that relation were missing — perhaps not a great misfortune after all. The writer seemed to have entered into a most elaborate detail of the why and wherefore of his presence on that coast — presumably the north coast of Spain. His experience has nothing to do with the sea, though. As far as I can make it out, he was an officer on board a sloop-of-war. There's nothing strange in that. At all stages of the long Peninsular campaign many of our men-of-war of the smaller kind were cruising off the north coast of Spain — as risky and disagreeable a station as can well be imagined.

It looks as though that ship of his had had some special service to perform. A careful explanation of all the circumstances was to be expected from our man, only, as I've said, some of his pages (good tough paper too) were missing: gone in covers for jampots or in wadding for the fowling-pieces of his irreverent posterity. But it is to be seen clearly that communication with the shore and even the sending of messages inland was part of her service, either to obtain intelligence from or to transmit orders or advice to patriotic Spaniards, guerilleros, or secret juntas of the province. Something of the sort. All this can be only inferred from the preserved scraps of his conscientious writing.

Next we come upon the panegyric of a very fine sailor, a member of the ship's company, having the rating of the captain's coxswain. He was known on board as Cuba Tom; not because he was Cuban however; he was indeed the best type of a genuine British tar of that time, and a man-of-war's man for years. He came by the name on account of some wonderful adventures he had in that island in his young days, adventures which were the favorite subject of the yarns he was in the habit of spinning to his shipmates of an evening on the forecastle head. He was intelligent, very strong, and of proved courage. Incidentally we are told, so exact is our narrator, that Tom had the finest pigtail for thickness and length of any man in the Navy. This appendage, much cared for and sheathed tightly in a porpoise skin, hung half-way down his broad back to the great admiration of all beholders and to the great envy of some.

Our young officer dwells on the manly qualities of Cuba Tom with something like affection. This sort of relation between officer and man was not then very rare. A youngster on joining the service was put under the charge of a trustworthy seaman, who slung his first hammock for him and often later on became a sort of humble friend to the junior officer. The narrator on joining the sloop had found this man on board after some years of separation. There is something touching in the warm pleasure he remembers and records at this meeting with the professional mentor of his boyhood.

We discover then that, no Spaniard being forthcoming for the service, this worthy seaman with the unique pigtail and a very high character for courage and steadiness had been selected as messenger for one of these missions inland which have been mentioned. His preparations were not elaborate. One gloomy autumn morning the sloop ran close to a shallow cove where a landing could be made on that iron-bound shore. A boat was lowered, and pulled in with Tom Corbin (Cuba Tom) perched in the bow, and our young man (Mr. Edgar Byrne was his name on this earth which knows him no more) sitting in the stern sheets.

A few inhabitants of a hamlet, whose gray stone houses could be seen a hundred yards or so up a deep ravine, had

## The Inn of the Two Witches

come down to the shore and watched the approach of the boat. The two Englishmen leaped ashore. Either from dullness or astonishment the peasants gave no greeting, and only fell back in silence.

Mr. Byrne had made up his mind to see Tom Corbin started fairly on his way. He looked round at the heavy surprised faces.

"There isn't much to get out of them," he said. "Let us walk up to the village. There will be a wine-shop for sure where we may find somebody more promising to talk to and get some information from."

"Aye, aye, sir," said Tom, falling into step behind his officer. "A bit of palaver as to courses and distances can do no harm; I crossed the broadest part of Cuba by the help of my tongue though knowing far less Spanish than I do now. As they say it themselves it was 'four words and no more' with me, that time when I got left behind on shore by the *Blanche,* frigate."

He made light of what was before him, which was but a day's journey into the mountains. It is true that there was a full day's journey before striking the mountain path, but that was nothing for a man who had crossed the island of Cuba on his two legs, and with no more than four words of the language to begin with.

The officer and the man were walking now on a thick sodden bed of dead leaves, which the peasants thereabouts accumulate in the streets of their villages to rot during the winter for field manure. Turning his head Mr. Byrne perceived that the whole male population of the hamlet was following them on the noiseless springy carpet. Women stared from the doors of the houses and the children had apparently gone into hiding. The village knew the ship by sight, afar off, but no stranger had landed on that spot perhaps for a hundred years or more. The cocked hat of Mr. Byrne, the bushy whiskers and the enormous pigtail of the sailor, filled them with mute wonder. They pressed behind the two Englishmen staring like those islanders discovered by Captain Cook in the South Seas.

It was then that Byrne had his first glimpse of the little cloaked man in a yellow hat. Faded and dingy as it was, this covering for his head made him noticeable.

The entrance to the wine-shop was like a rough hole in a

wall of flints. The owner was the only person who was not in the street, for he came out from the darkness at the back where the inflated forms of wine skins hung on nails could be vaguely distinguished. He was a tall, one-eyed Asturian with scrubby, hollow cheeks; a grave expression of countenance contrasted enigmatically with the roaming restlessness of his solitary eye. On learning that the matter in hand was the sending on his way of that English mariner toward a certain Gonzales in the mountains, he closed his good eye for a moment as if in meditation. Then opened it, very lively again.

"Possibly, possibly. It could be done."

A friendly murmur arose in the group in the doorway at the name of Gonzales, the local leader against the French. Inquiring as to the safety of the road Byrne was glad to learn that no troops of that nation had been seen in the neighborhood for months. Not the smallest little detachment of these impious *polizones*. While giving these answers the owner of the wine-shop busied himself in drawing into an earthenware jug some wine which he set before the heretic English, pocketing with grave abstraction the small piece of money the officer threw upon the table in recognition of the unwritten law that none may enter a wine-shop without buying drink. His eye was in constant motion as if it were trying to do the work of the two; but when Byrne made inquiries as to the possibility of hiring a mule, it became immovably fixed in the direction of the door which was closely besieged by the curious. In front of them, just within the threshold, the little man in the large cloak and yellow hat had taken his stand. He was a diminutive person, a mere homunculus, Byrne describes him, in a ridiculously mysterious yet assertive attitude, a corner of his cloak thrown cavalierly over his left shoulder, muffling his chin and mouth; while the broad-brimmed yellow hat hung on a corner of his square little head. He stood there taking snuff, repeatedly.

"A mule," repeated the wine-seller, his eyes fixed on that quaint and snuffy figure.... "No, señor officer! Decidedly no mule is to be got in this poor place."

The coxswain, who stood by with the true sailor's air of unconcern in strange surroundings, struck in quietly:

"If your honor will believe me, Shank's pony's the best

for this job. I would have to leave the beast somewhere, anyhow, since the captain has told me that half my way will be along paths fit only for goats."

The diminutive man made a step forward, and speaking through the folds of the cloak which seemed to muffle a sarcastic intention——

"*Sí, señor.* They are too honest in this village to have a single mule amongst them for your worship's service. To that I can bear testimony. In these times it's only rogues or very clever men who can manage to have mules or any other four-footed beasts and the wherewithal to keep them. But what this valiant mariner wants is a guide; and here, señor, behold my brother-in-law, Bernardino, wine-seller, and alcalde of this most Christian and hospitable village, who will find you one."

This, Mr. Byrne says in his relation, was the only thing to do. A youth in a ragged coat and goatskin breeches was produced after some more talk. The English officer stood treat to the whole village, and while the peasants drank he and Cuba Tom took their departure accompanied by the guide. The diminutive man in the cloak had disappeared.

Byrne went along with the coxswain out of the village. He wanted to see him fairly on his way; and he would have gone a greater distance, if the seaman had not suggested respectfully the advisability of return so as not to keep the ship a moment longer than necessary so close in with the shore on such an unpromising looking morning. A wild gloomy sky hung over their heads when they took leave of each other, and their surroundings of rank bushes and stony fields were dreary.

"In four days' time," were Byrne's last words, "the ship will stand in and send a boat on shore if the weather permits. If not you'll have to make it out on shore the best you can till we come along to take you off."

"Right you are, sir," answered Tom, and strode on. Byrne watched him step out on a narrow path. In a thick peajacket with a pair of pistols in his belt, a cutlass by his side, and a stout cudgel in his hand, he looked a sturdy figure and well able to take care of himself. He turned round for a moment to wave his hand, giving to Byrne one more view of his honest bronzed face with bushy whiskers. The lad in goatskin breeches looking, Byrne says, like a faun or a young satyr leaping ahead, stopped to wait for him, and then went off at a bound. Both disappeared.

Byrne turned back. The hamlet was hidden in a fold of the ground, and the spot seemed the most lonely corner of the earth and as if accursed in its uninhabited desolate barrenness. Before he had walked many yards, there appeared very suddenly from behind a bush the muffled up diminutive Spaniard. Naturally Byrne stopped short.

The other made a mysterious gesture with a tiny hand peeping from under his cloak. His hat hung very much at the side of his head. "Señor," he said without any preliminaries. "Caution! It is a positive fact that one-eyed Bernardino, my brother-in-law, has at this moment a mule in his stable. And why he who is not clever has a mule there? Because he is a rogue; a man without conscience. Because I had to give up the *macho* to him to secure for myself a roof to sleep under and a mouthful of *olla* to keep my soul in this insignificant body of mine. Yet, señor, it contains a heart many times bigger than the mean thing which beats in the breast of that brute connection of mine of which I am ashamed, though I opposed that marriage with all my power. Well, the misguided woman suffered enough. She had her purgatory on this earth — God rest her soul."

Byrne says he was so astonished by the sudden appearance of that sprite-like being, and by the sardonic bitterness of the speech, that he was unable to disentangle the significant fact from what seemed but a piece of family history fired out at him without rhyme or reason. Not at first. He was confounded and at the same time he was impressed by the rapid forcible delivery, quite different from the frothy excited loquacity of an Italian. So he stared while the homunculus, letting his cloak fall about him, aspired an immense quantity of snuff out of the hollow of his palm.

"A mule," exclaimed Byrne, seizing at last the real aspect of the discourse. "You say he has got a mule? That's queer! Why did he refuse to let me have it?"

The diminutive Spaniard muffled himself up again with great dignity.

"*Quién sabe?*" he said coldly, with a shrug of his draped shoulders. "He is a great *politico* in everything he does.

But one thing your worship may be certain of — that his intentions are always rascally. This husband of my *defunta* sister ought to have been married a long time ago to the widow with the wooden legs."[1]

"I see. But remember that, whatever your motives, your worship countenanced him in this lie."

The bright unhappy eyes on each side of a predatory nose confronted Byrne without wincing, while with that testiness which lurks so often at the bottom of Spanish dignity ——

"No doubt the señor officer would not lose an ounce of blood if I were stuck under the fifth rib," he retorted. "But what of this poor sinner here?" Then changing his tone: "Señor, by the necessities of the times I live here in exile, a Castilian and an old Christian, existing miserably in the midst of these brute Asturians, and dependent on the worst of them all, who has less conscience and scruples than a wolf. And being a man of intelligence I govern myself accordingly. Yet I can hardly contain my scorn. You have heard the way I spoke. A caballero of parts like your worship might have guessed that there was a cat in there."

"What cat?" said Byrne uneasily. "Oh, I see. Something suspicious. No, señor. I guessed nothing. My nation are not good guessers at that sort of thing; and, therefore, I ask you plainly whether that wine-seller has spoken the truth in other particulars?"

"There are certainly no Frenchmen anywhere about," said the little man with a return to his indifferent manner.

"Or robbers — *ladrones?*"

"*Ladrones en grande* — no! Assuredly not," was the answer in a cold philosophical tone. "What is there left for them to do after the French? And nobody travels in these times. But who can say! Opportunity makes the robber. Still that mariner of yours has a fierce aspect, and with the son of a cat rats will have no play. But there is a saying, too, that where honey is there will soon be flies."

This oracular discourse exasperated Byrne. "In the name of God," he cried, "tell me plainly if you think my man is reasonably safe on his journey."

The homunculus, undergoing one of his rapid changes,

---

[1] The gallows, supposed to be widowed of the last executed criminal and waiting for another.

seized the officer's arm. The grip of his little hand was astonishing.

"Señor! Bernardino had taken notice of him. What more do you want? And listen — men have disappeared on this road — on a certain portion of this road, when Bernardino kept a *meson,* an inn, and I, his brother-in-law, had coaches and mules for hire. Now there are no travelers, no coaches. The French have ruined me. Bernardino has retired here for reasons of his own after my sister died. They were three to torment the life out of her, he and Erminia and Lucilla, two aunts of his — all affiliated to the devil. And now he has robbed me of my last mule. You are an armed man. Demand the *macho* from him, with a pistol to his head, señor — it is not his, I tell you — and ride after your man who is so precious to you. And then you shall both be safe, for no two travelers have been ever known to disappear together in those days. As to the beast, I, its owner, I confide it to your honor."

They were staring hard at each other, and Byrne nearly burst into a laugh at the ingenuity and transparency of the little man's plot to regain possession of his mule. But he had no difficulty to keep a straight face because he felt deep within himself a strange inclination to do that very extraordinary thing. He did not laugh but his lip quivered, at which the diminutive Spaniard, detaching his black glittering eyes from Byrne's face, turned his back on him brusquely with a gesture and a fling of the cloak which somehow expressed contempt, bitterness, and discouragement all at once. He turned away and stood still, his hat aslant, muffled up to the ears. But he was not offended to the point of refusing the silver *duro* which Byrne offered him with a non-committal speech as if nothing extraordinary had passed between them.

"I must make haste on board now," said Byrne, then.

"*Vaya usted con Dios,*" muttered the gnome. And this interview ended with a sarcastic low sweep of the hat which was replaced at the same perilous angle as before.

Directly the boat had been hoisted the ship's sails were filled on the offshore tack, and Byrne imparted the whole story to his captain, who was but a very few years older than himself. There was some amused indignation at it — but while they laughed they looked gravely at each other. A Spanish

## The Inn of the Two Witches

dwarf trying to beguile an officer of His Majesty's navy into stealing a mule for him — that was too funny, too ridiculous, too incredible. Those were the exclamations of the captain. He couldn't get over the grotesqueness of it.

"Incredible. That's just it," murmured Byrne at last in a significant tone.

They exchanged a long stare. "It's as clear as daylight," affirmed the captain impatiently, because in his heart he was not certain. And Tom, the best seaman in the ship for one, the good-humoredly deferential friend of his boyhood for the other, was becoming endowed with a compelling fascination, like a symbolic figure of loyalty appealing to their feelings and their conscience, so that they could not detach their thoughts from his safety. Several times they went up on deck, only to look at the coast, as if it could tell them something of his fate. It stretched away, lengthening in the distance, mute, naked, and savage, veiled now and then by the slanting cold shafts of rain. The westerly swell rolled its interminable angry lines of foam and big dark clouds flew over the ship in a sinister procession.

"I wish to goodness you had done what your little friend in the yellow hat wanted you to do," said the commander of the sloop late in the afternoon with visible exasperation.

"Do you, sir?" answered Byrne, bitter with positive anguish. "I wonder what you would have said afterward? Why! I might have been kicked out of the service for looting a mule from a nation in alliance with His Majesty. Or I might have been battered to a pulp with flails and pitchforks — a pretty tale to get abroad about one of your officers — while trying to steal a mule. Or chased ignominiously to the boat — for you would not have expected me to shoot down unoffending people for the sake of a mangy mule. . . . And yet," he added in a low voice, "I almost wished myself I had done it."

Before dark those two young men had worked themselves up into a highly complex psychological state of scornful skepticism and alarmed credulity. It tormented them exceedingly; and the thought that it would have to last for six days at least, and possibly be prolonged further for an indefinite time, was not to be borne. The ship was therefore put on the inshore tack at dark. All through the gusty dark night she went toward the land to look for her man, at times lying over in the heavy puffs, at others rolling idle in the swell, nearly stationary, as if she too had a mind of her own to swing perplexed between cool reason and warm impulse.

Then just at daybreak a boat put off from her and went on tossed by the seas toward the shallow cove where, with considerable difficulty, an officer in a thick coat and a round hat managed to land on a strip of shingle.

"It was my wish," writes Mr. Byrne, "a wish of which my captain approved, to land secretly if possible. I did not want to be seen either by my aggrieved friend in the yellow hat, whose motives were not clear, or by the one-eyed wine-seller, who may or may not have been affiliated to the devil, or indeed by any other dweller in that primitive village. But unfortunately the cove was the only possible landing place for miles; and from the steepness of the ravine I couldn't make a circuit to avoid the houses."

"Fortunately," he goes on, "all the people were yet in their beds. It was barely daylight when I found myself walking on the thick layer of sodden leaves filling the only street. No soul was stirring abroad, no dog barked. The silence was profound, and I had concluded with some wonder that apparently no dogs were kept in the hamlet, when I heard a low snarl, and from a noisome alley between two hovels emerged a vile cur with its tail between its legs. He slunk off silently showing me his teeth as he ran before me, and he disappeared so suddenly that he might have been the unclean incarnation of the Evil One. There was, too, something so weird in the manner of its coming and vanishing, that my spirits, already by no means very high, became further depressed by the revolting sight of this creature as if by an unlucky presage."

He got away from the coast unobserved, as far as he knew, then struggled manfully to the west against wind and rain, on a barren dark upland, under a sky of ashes. Far away the harsh and desolate mountains raising their scarped and denuded ridges seemed to wait for him menacingly. The evening found him fairly near to them, but, in sailor language, uncertain of his position, hungry, wet, and tired out by a day of steady tramping over broken ground during which he had seen very few people, and had been unable to obtain the slightest intelligence of Tom Corbin's passage. "On! on!

I must push on," he had been saying to himself through the hours of solitary effort, spurred more by incertitude than by any definite fear or definite hope.

The lowering daylight died out quickly, leaving him faced by a broken bridge. He descended into the ravine, forded a narrow stream by the last gleam of rapid water, and clambering out on the other side was met by the night which fell like a bandage over his eyes. The wind sweeping in the darkness the broadside of the sierra worried his ears by a continuous roaring noise as of a maddened sea. He suspected that he had lost the road. Even in daylight, with its ruts and mudholes and ledges of outcropping stone, it was difficult to distinguish from the dreary waste of the moor interspersed with boulders and clumps of naked bushes. But, as he says, " he steered his course by the feel of the wind," his hat rammed low on his brow, his head down, stopping now and again from mere weariness of mind rather than of body — as if not his strength but his resolution were being overtaxed by the strain of endeavor half suspected to be vain, and by the unrest of his feelings.

In one of these pauses borne in the wind faintly as if from very far away he heard a sound of knocking, just knocking on wood. He noticed that the wind had lulled suddenly.

His heart started beating tumultuously because in himself he carried the impression of the desert solitudes he had been traversing for the last six hours — the oppressive sense of an uninhabited world. When he raised his head a gleam of light, illusory as it often happens in dense darkness, swam before his eyes. While he peered, the sound of feeble knocking was repeated — and suddenly he felt rather than saw the existence of a massive obstacle in his path. What was it? The spur of a hill? Or was it a house! Yes. It was a house right close, as though it had risen from the ground or had come gliding to meet him, dumb and pallid, from some dark recess of the night. It towered loftily. He had come up under its lee; another three steps and he could have touched the wall with his hand. It was no doubt a *posada* and some other traveler was trying for admittance. He heard again the sound of cautious knocking.

Next moment a broad band of light fell into the night through the opened door. Byrne stepped eagerly into it, whereupon the person outside leaped with a stifled cry away into the night. An exclamation of surprise was heard too, from within. Byrne, flinging himself against the half-closed door, forced his way in against some considerable resistance.

A miserable candle, a mere rushlight, burned at the end of a long deal table. And in its light Byrne saw, staggering yet, the girl he had driven from the door. She had a short black skirt, an orange shawl, a dark complexion — and the escaped single hairs from the mass, somber and thick like a forest and held up by a comb, made a black mist about her low forehead. A shrill lamentable howl of: " Misericordia! " came in two voices from the further end of the long room, where the fire-light of an open hearth played between heavy shadows. The girl recovering herself drew a hissing breath through her set teeth.

It is unnecessary to report the long process of questions and answers by which he soothed the fears of two old women who sat on each side of the fire, on which stood a large earthenware pot. Byrne thought at once of two witches watching the brewing of some deadly potion. But all the same, when one of them raising forward painfully her broken form lifted the cover of the pot, the escaping steam had an appetizing smell. The other did not budge, but sat hunched up, her head trembling all the time.

They were horrible. There was something grotesque in their decrepitude. Their toothless mouths, their hooked noses, the meagerness of the active one, and the hanging yellow cheeks of the other (the still one, whose head trembled) would have been laughable if the sight of their dreadful physical degradation had not been appalling to one's eyes, had not gripped one's heart with poignant amazement at the unspeakable misery of age, at the awful persistency of life becoming at last an object of disgust and dread.

To get over it Byrne began to talk, saying that he was an Englishman, and that he was in search of a countryman who ought to have passed this way. Directly he had spoken the recollection of his parting with Tom came up in his mind with amazing vividness: the silent villagers, the angry gnome, the one-eyed wine-seller, Bernardino. Why! These two unspeakable frights must be that man's aunts — affiliated to the devil.

Whatever they had been once it was impossible to imagine

what use such feeble creatures could be to the devil, now, in the world of the living. Which was Lucilla and which was Erminia? They were now things without a name. A moment of suspended animation followed Byrne's words. The sorceress with the spoon ceased stirring the mess in the iron pot, the very trembling of the other's head stopped for the space of breath. In this infinitesimal fraction of a second Byrne had the sense of being really on his quest, of having reached the turn of the path, almost within hail of Tom.

"They have seen him," he thought with conviction. Here was at last somebody who had seen him. He made sure they would deny all knowledge of the Inglés; but on the contrary they were eager to tell him that he had eaten and slept the night in the house. They both started talking together, describing his appearance and behavior. An excitement quite fierce in its feebleness possessed them. The doubled-up sorceress flourished aloft her wooden spoon, the puffy monster got off her stool and screeched, stepping from one foot to the other, while the trembling of her head was accelerated to positive vibration. Byrne was quite disconcerted by their excited behavior. . . . Yes! The big, fierce Inglés went away in the morning, after eating a piece of bread and drinking some wine. And if the caballero wished to follow the same path nothing could be easier — in the morning.

"You will give me somebody to show me the way?" said Byrne.

"*Sí, señor.* A proper youth. The man the caballero saw going out."

"But he was knocking at the door," protested Byrne. "He only bolted when he saw me. He was coming in."

"No! No!" the two horrid witches screamed out together. "Going out. Going out!"

After all it may have been true. The sound of knocking had been faint, elusive, reflected Byrne. Perhaps only the effect of his fancy. He asked:

"Who is that man?"

"Her *novio*." They screamed pointing to the girl. "He is gone home to a village far away from here. But he will return in the morning. Her *novio!* And she is an orphan — the child of poor Christian people. She lives with us for the love of God, for the love of God."

The orphan crouching on the corner of the hearth had

been looking at Byrne. He thought that she was more like a child of Satan kept there by these two weird harridans for the love of the Devil. Her eyes were a little oblique, her mouth rather thick, but admirably formed; her dark face had a wild beauty, voluptuous and untamed. As to the character of her steadfast gaze attached upon him with a sensuously savage attention, "to know what it was like," says Mr. Byrne, "you have only to observe a hungry cat watching a bird in a cage or a mouse inside a trap."

It was she who served him the food, of which he was glad; though with those big slanting black eyes examining him at close range, as if he had something curious written on his face, she gave him an uncomfortable sensation. But anything was better than being approached by these blear-eyed nightmarish witches. His apprehensions somehow had been soothed; perhaps by the sensation of warmth after severe exposure and the ease of resting after the exertion of fighting the gale inch by inch all the way. He had no doubt of Tom's safety. He was now sleeping in the mountain camp having been met by Gonzales' men.

Byrne rose, filled a tin goblet with wine out of a skin hanging on the wall, and sat down again. The witch with the mummy face began to talk to him, rambling of old times; she boasted of the inn's fame in those better days. Great people in their own coaches stopped there. An archbishop slept once in the *casa*, a long, long time ago.

The witch with the puffy face seemed to be listening from her stool, motionless, except for the trembling of her head. The girl (Byrne was certain she was a casual gypsy admitted there for some reason or other) sat on the hearthstone in the glow of the embers. She hummed a tune to herself, rattling a pair of castanets slightly now and then. At the mention of the archbishop she chuckled impiously and turned her head to look at Byrne, so that the red glow of the fire flashed in her black eyes and on her white teeth under the dark cowl of the enormous overmantel. And he smiled at her.

He rested now in the ease of security. His advent not having been expected there could be no plot against him in existence. Drowsiness stole upon his senses. He enjoyed it, but keeping a hold, so he thought at least, on his wits; but he must have been gone further than he thought because he was startled beyond measure by a fiendish uproar. He had never heard anything so pitilessly strident in his life. The witches had started a fierce quarrel about something or other. Whatever its origin they were now only abusing each other violently, without arguments; their senile screams expressed nothing but wicked anger and ferocious dismay. The gypsy girl's black eyes flew from one to the other. Never before had Byrne felt himself so removed from fellowship with human beings. Before he had really time to understand the subject of the quarrel, the girl jumped up rattling her castanets loudly. A silence fell. She came up to the table and bending over, her eyes in his:

"Señor," she said with decision, "you shall sleep in the archbishop's room."

Neither of the witches objected. The dried up one bent double was propped on a stick. The puffy faced one had now a crutch.

Byrne got up, walked to the door, and turning the key in the enormous lock put it coolly in his pocket. This was clearly the only entrance, and he did not mean to be taken unawares by whatever danger there might have been lurking outside. When he turned from the door he saw the two witches "affiliated to the Devil" and the Satanic girl looking at him in silence. He wondered if Tom Corbin took the same precaution last night. And thinking of him he had again that queer impression of his nearness. The world was perfectly dumb. And in this stillness he heard the blood beating in his ears with a confused rushing noise, in which there seemed to be a voice uttering the words: "Mr. Byrne, look out, sir." Tom's voice. He shuddered; for the delusions of the sense of hearing are the most vivid of all, and from their nature have a compelling character.

It seemed impossible that Tom should not be there. Again a slight chill as of stealthy draught penetrated through his very clothes and passed over all his body. He shook off the impression with an effort.

It was the girl who preceded him upstairs carrying an iron lamp from the naked flame of which ascended a thin thread of smoke. Her soiled white stockings were full of holes.

With the same quiet resolution with which he had locked

the door below, Byrne threw open one after another the doors in the corridor. All the rooms were empty except for some nondescript lumber in one or two. And the girl seeing what he would be at stopped every time, raising the smoky light in each doorway patiently. Meantime she observed him with sustained attention. The last door of all she threw open herself.

"You sleep here, señor," she murmured in a voice light like a child's breath, offering him the lamp.

"*Buenas noches, señorita,*" he said politely, taking it from her.

She didn't return the wish audibly, though her lips did move a little, while her gaze black like a starless night never for a moment wavered before him. He stepped in, and as he turned to close the door she was still there motionless and disturbing, with her voluptuous mouth and slanting eyes, with the expression of expectant sensual ferocity of a baffled cat. He hesitated for a moment, and in the dumb house he heard again the blood pulsating ponderously in his ears, while once more the illusion of Tom's voice speaking earnestly somewhere near by was specially terrifying, because this time he could not make out the words.

He slammed the door in the girl's face at last, leaving her in the dark; and he opened it again almost on the instant. Nobody. She had vanished without the slightest sound. He closed the door quickly and bolted it with two heavy bolts.

A profound mistrust possessed him suddenly. Why did the witches quarrel about letting him sleep here? And what meant that stare of the girl as if she wanted to impress his features forever in her mind? His own nervousness alarmed him. He seemed to himself to be removed very far from mankind.

He examined his room. It was not very high, just high enough to take the bed which stood under an enormous baldachin-like canopy from which fell heavy curtains at foot and head; a bed certainly worthy of an archbishop. There was a heavy table carved all round the edges, some arm-chairs of enormous weight like the spoils of a grandee's palace; a tall shallow wardrobe placed against the wall and with double doors. He tried them. Locked. A suspicion came into his mind. and he snatched the lamp to make a closer examination.

No, it was not a disguised entrance. That heavy, tall piece of furniture stood clear of the wall by quite an inch. He glanced at the bolts of his room door. No! No one could get at him treacherously while he slept. But would he be able to sleep? he asked himself anxiously. If only he had Tom there — the trusty seaman who had fought at his right hand in a cutting out affair or two, and had always preached to him the necessity to take care of himself. "For it's no great trick," he used to say, "to get yourself killed in a hot fight. Any fool can do that. The proper pastime is to fight the Frenchies and then live to fight another day."

Byrne found it a hard matter not to fall into listening to the silence. Somehow he had the conviction that nothing would break it unless he heard again the haunting sound of Tom's voice. He had heard it twice before. Odd! And yet no wonder, he argued with himself reasonably, since he had been thinking of the man for over thirty hours continuously and, what's more, inconclusively. For his anxiety for Tom had never taken a definite shape. "Disappear" was the only word connected with the idea of Tom's danger. It was very vague and awful. "Disappear!" What did that mean?

Byrne shuddered, and then said to himself that he must be a little feverish. But Tom had not disappeared. Byrne had just heard of him. And again the young man felt the blood beating in his ears. He sat still expecting every moment to hear through the pulsating strokes the sound of Tom's voice. He waited straining his ears, but nothing came. Suddenly the thought occurred to him: "He has not disappeared, but ne cannot make himself heard."

He jumped up from the arm-chair. How absurd! Laying his pistol and his hanger on the table he took off his boots and, feeling suddenly too tired to stand, flung himself on the bed which he found soft and comfortable beyond his hopes.

He had felt very wakeful, but he must have dozed off after all, because the next thing he knew he was sitting up in bed and trying to recollect what it was that Tom's voice had said. Oh! He remembered it now. It had said: "Mr. Byrne! Look out, sir!" A warning this. But against what?

He landed with one leap in the middle of the floor, gasped once, then looked all round the room. The window was shuttered and barred with an iron bar. Again he ran his eyes slowly all round the bare walls, and even looked up at the ceiling, which was rather high. Afterward he went to the door to examine the fastenings. They consisted of two enormous iron bolts sliding into holes made in the wall; and as the corridor outside was too narrow to admit of any battering arrangement or even to permit an axe to be swung, nothing could burst the door open — unless gunpowder. But while he was still making sure that the lower bolt was pushed well home, he received the impression of somebody's presence in the room. It was so strong that he spun round quicker than lightning. There was no one. Who could there be? And yet . . .

It was then that he lost the decorum and restraint a man keeps up for his own sake. He got down on his hands and knees, with the lamp on the floor, to look under the bed, like a silly girl. He saw a lot of dust and nothing else. He got up, his cheeks burning, and walked about discontented with his own behavior and unreasonably angry with Tom for not leaving him alone. The words: "Mr. Byrne! Look out, sir," kept on repeating themselves in his head in a tone of warning.

"Hadn't I better just throw myself on the bed and try to go to sleep?" he asked himself. But his eyes fell on the tall wardrobe, and he went toward it feeling irritated with himself and yet unable to desist. How he could explain tomorrow the burglarious misdeed to the two odious witches he had no idea. Nevertheless he inserted the point of his hanger between the two halves of the door and tried to prize them open. They resisted. He swore, sticking now hotly to his purpose. His mutter: "I hope you will be satisfied, confound you," was addressed to the absent Tom. Just then the doors gave way and flew open.

He was there.

He — the trusty, sagacious, and courageous Tom was there, drawn up shadowy and stiff, in prudent silence, which his wide-open eyes by their fixed gleam seemed to command Byrne to respect. But Byrne was too startled to make a sound. Amazed, he stepped back a little — and on the instant the seaman flung himself forward headlong as if to clasp his officer round the neck. Instinctively Byrne put out his faltering arms; he felt the horrible rigidity of the body and then the coldness of death as their heads knocked together and their faces came into contact. They reeled, Byrne hugging Tom close to his breast in order not to let him fall with a crash. He had just strength enough to lower the awful burden gently to the floor — then his head swam, his legs gave way, and he sank on his knees, leaning over the body with his hands resting on the breast of that man once full of generous life, and now as insensible as a stone.

"Dead! my poor Tom, dead," he repeated mentally. The light of the lamp standing near the edge of the table fell from above straight on the stony empty stare of these eyes which naturally had a mobile and merry expression. Byrne turned his own away from them. Tom's black silk neckerchief was not knotted on his breast. It was gone. The murderers had also taken off his shoes and stockings. And noticing this spoliation, the exposed throat, the bare upturned feet, Byrne felt his eyes run full of tears. In other respects the seaman was fully dressed; neither was his clothing disarranged as it must have been in a violent struggle. Only his checked shirt had been pulled a little out the waistband in one place, just enough to ascertain whether he had a money belt fastened round his body. Byrne began to sob into his handkerchief.

It was a nervous outburst which passed off quickly. Remaining on his knees he contemplated sadly the athletic body of as fine a seaman as ever had drawn a cutlass, laid a gun, or passed the weather earring in a gale, lying stiff and cold, his cheery, fearless spirit departed — perhaps turning to him, his boy chum, to his ship out there rolling on the gray seas off an iron-bound coast, at the very moment of its flight. He perceived that the six brass buttons of Tom's jacket had been cut off. He shuddered at the notion of the two miserable and repulsive witches busying themselves ghoulishly about the defenceless body of his friend. Cut off. Perhaps with the same knife which . . . The head of one trembled; the other was bent double, and their eyes were red and bleared, their infamous claws unsteady. . . . It must have been in this very room too, for Tom could not have been killed in the open and brought in here afterward. Of that Byrne was certain. Yet those devilish crones could not have killed him themselves even by taking him unawares

— and Tom would be always on his guard of course. Tom was a very wide-awake wary man when engaged on any service. . . . And in fact how did they murder him? Who did? In what way?

Byrne jumped up, snatched the lamp off the table, and stooped swiftly over the body. The light revealed on the clothing no stain, no trace, no spot of blood anywhere. Byrne's hands began to shake so that he had to set the lamp on the floor and turn away his head in order to recover from this agitation.

Then he began to explore that cold, still, and rigid body for a stab, a gunshot wound, for the trace of some killing blow. He felt all over the skull anxiously. It was whole. He slipped his hand under the neck. It was unbroken. With terrified eyes he peered close under the chin and saw no marks of strangulation on the throat.

There were no signs anywhere. He was just dead.

Impulsively Byrne got away from the body as if the mystery of an incomprehensible death had changed his pity into suspicion and dread. The lamp on the floor near the set, still face of the seaman showed it staring at the ceiling as if despairingly. In the circle of light Byrne saw by the undisturbed patches of thick dust on the floor that there had been no struggle in that room. "He has died outside," he thought. Yes, outside in that narrow corridor, where there was hardly room to turn, the mysterious death had come to his poor dear Tom. The impulse of snatching up his pistols and rushing out of the room abandoned Byrne suddenly. For Tom, too, had been armed — with just such powerless weapons as he himself possessed — pistols, a cutlass! And Tom had died a nameless death, by incomprehensible means.

A new thought came to Byrne. That stranger knocking at the door and fleeing so swiftly at his appearance had come there to remove the body. Aha! That was the guide the withered witch had promised would show the English officer the shortest way of rejoining his man. A promise, he saw it now, of dreadful import. He who had knocked would have two bodies to deal with. Man and officer would go forth from the house together. For Byrne was certain now that he would have to die before the morning — and in the same mysterious manner, leaving behind him an unmarked body.

The sight of a smashed head, of a cut throat, of a gaping gunshot wound, would have been an inexpressible relief. It would have soothed all his fears. His soul cried within him to that dead man whom he had never found wanting in danger. " Why don't you tell me what I am to look for, Tom? Why don't you? " But in rigid immobility, extended on his back, he seemed to preserve an austere silence, as if disdaining in the finality of his awful knowledge to hold converse with the living.

Suddenly Byrne flung himself on his knees by the side of the body, and dry-eyed, fierce, opened the shirt wide on the breast, as if to tear the secret forcibly from that cold heart which had been so loyal to him in life! Nothing! Nothing! He raised the lamp, and all the sign vouchsafed to him by that face which used to be so kindly in expression was a small bruise on the forehead — the least thing, a mere mark. The skin even was not broken. He stared at it a long time as if lost in a dreadful dream. Then he observed that Tom's hands were clenched as though he had fallen facing somebody in a fight with fists. His knuckles, on closer view, appeared somewhat abraded. Both hands.

The discovery of these slight signs was more appalling to Byrne than the absolute absence of every mark would have been. So Tom had died striking against something which could be hit, and yet could kill one without leaving a wound — by a breath.

Terror, hot terror, began to play about Byrne's heart like a tongue of flame that touches and withdraws before it turns a thing to ashes. He backed away from the body as far as he could, then came forward stealthily casting fearful glances to steal another look at the bruised forehead. There would perhaps be such a faint bruise on his own forehead — before the morning.

" I can't bear it," he whispered to himself. Tom was for him now an object of horror, a sight at once tempting and revolting to his fear. He couldn't bear to look at him.

At last, desperation getting the better of his increasing horror, he stepped forward from the wall against which he had been leaning, seized the corpse under the armpits, and began to lug it over to the bed. The bare heels of the seaman trailed on the floor noiselessly. He was heavy with the dead weight of inanimate objects. With a last effort Byrne landed him face downward on the edge of the bed, rolled him over, snatched from under this stiff passive thing a sheet with which he covered it over. Then he spread the curtains at head and foot so that joining together as he shook their folds they hid the bed altogether from his sight.

He stumbled toward a chair, and fell on it. The perspiration poured from his face for a moment, and then his veins seemed to carry for a while a thin stream of half-frozen blood. Complete terror had possession of him now, a nameless terror which had turned his heart to ashes.

He sat upright in the straight-backed chair, the lamp burning at his feet, his pistols and his hanger at his left elbow on the end of the table, his eyes turning incessantly in their sockets round the walls, over the ceiling, over the floor, in the expectation of a mysterious and appalling vision. The thing which could deal death in a breath was outside that bolted door. But Byrne believed neither in walls nor bolts now. Unreasoning terror turning everything to account, his old-time boyish admiration of the athletic Tom, the undaunted Tom (he had seemed to him invincible), helped to paralyze his faculties, added to his despair.

He was no longer Edgar Byrne. He was a tortured soul suffering more anguish than any sinner's body had ever suffered from rack or boot. The depth of his torment may be measured when I say that this young man, as brave at least as the average of his kind, contemplated seizing a pistol and firing into his own head. But a deadly, chilly languor was spreading over his limbs. It was as if his flesh had been wet plaster stiffening slowly about his ribs. Presently, he thought, the two witches will be coming in, with crutch and stick — horrible, grotesque, monstrous — affiliated to the devil — to put a mark on his forehead, the tiny little bruise of death. And he wouldn't be able to do anything. Tom had struck out at something, but he was not like Tom. His limbs were dead already. He sat still, dying the death over and over again; and the only part of him which moved was his eyes, turning round and round in their sockets, running over the walls, the floor, the ceiling, again and again, till suddenly they became motionless and stony — starting out of his head fixed in the direction of the bed.

## The Inn of the Two Witches

He had seen the heavy curtains stir and shake as if the dead body they concealed had turned over and sat up. Byrne, who thought the world could hold no more terrors in store, felt his hair stir at the roots. He gripped the arms of the chair, his jaw fell, and the sweat broke out on his brow while his dry tongue clove suddenly to the roof of his mouth. Again the curtains stirred, but did not open. "Don't, Tom!" Byrne made effort to shout, but all he heard was a slight moan such as an uneasy sleeper may make. He felt that his brain was going, for, now, it seemed to him that the ceiling over the bed had moved, had slanted, and came level again — and once more the closed curtains swayed gently as if about to part.

Byrne closed his eyes not to see the awful apparition of the seaman's corpse coming out animated by an evil spirit. In the profound silence of the room he endured a moment of frightful agony, then opened his eyes again. And he saw at once that the curtains remained closed still, but that the ceiling over the bed had risen quite a foot. With the last gleam of reason left to him he understood that it was the enormous baldachin over the bed which was coming down, while the curtains attached to it swayed softly, sinking gradually to the floor. His drooping jaw snapped to — and half rising in his chair he watched mutely the noiseless descent of the monstrous canopy. It came down in short smooth rushes till lowered half-way or more, when it took a run and settled swiftly its turtle-back shape with the deep border piece fitting exactly the edge of the bedstead. A slight crack or two of wood were heard, and the overpowering stillness of the room resumed its sway.

Byrne stood up, gasped for breath, and let out a cry of rage and dismay, the first sound which he is perfectly certain did make its way past his lips on this night of terrors. This then was the death he had escaped! This was the devilish artifice of murder poor Tom's soul had perhaps tried from beyond the border to warn him of. For this was how he had died. Byrne was certain he had heard the voice of the seaman, faintly distinct in his familiar phrase, "Mr. Byrne! Look out, sir!" and again uttering words he could not make out. But then the distance separating the living from the dead is so great! Poor Tom had tried. Byrne ran to the bed and attempted to lift up, to push off the horrible lid, smothering the body. It resisted his efforts, heavy as lead, immovable like a tombstone. The rage of vengeance made him desist; his head buzzed with chaotic thoughts of extermination, he turned round the room as if he could find neither his weapons nor the way out; and all the time he stammered awful menaces. . . .

A violent battering at the door of the inn recalled him to his soberer senses. He flew to the window, pulled the shutters open, and looked out. In the faint dawn he saw below him a mob of men. Ha! He would go and face at once this murderous lot collected no doubt for his undoing. After his struggle with nameless terrors he yearned for an open fray with armed enemies. But he must have remained yet bereft of his reason, because forgetting his weapons he rushed downstairs with a wild cry, unbarred the door while blows were raining on it outside, and flinging it open flew with his bare hands at the throat of the first man he saw before him. They rolled over together. Byrne's hazy intention was to break through, to fly up the mountain path, and come back presently with Gonzales' men to exact an exemplary vengeance. He fought furiously till a tree, a house, a mountain, seemed to crash down upon his head — and he knew no more.

Here Mr. Byrne describes in detail the skilful manner in which he found his broken head bandaged, informs us that he had lost a great deal of blood, and ascribes the preservation of his sanity to that circumstance. He sets down Gonzales' profuse apologies in full too. For it was Gonzales who, tired of waiting for news from the English, had come down to the inn with half his band, on his way to the sea. "His excellency," he explained, "rushed out with fierce impetuosity, and, moreover, was not known to us for a friend, and so we . . . etc., etc. When asked what had become of the witches, he only pointed his finger silently to the ground, then voiced calmly a moral reflection: 'The passion for gold is pitiless in the very old, señor,' he said. 'No doubt in former days they have put many a solitary traveler to sleep in the archbishop's bed.'"

"There was also a gypsy girl there," said Byrne feebly from the improvised litter on which he was being carried to the coast by a squad of guerilleros.

# The Inn of the Two Witches

"It was she who winched up that infernal machine, and it was she too who lowered it that night," was the answer.

"But why? Why?" exclaimed Byrne. "Why should she wish for my death?"

"No doubt for the sake of your excellency's coat buttons," said politely the saturnine Gonzales. "We found those of the dead mariner concealed on her person. But your excellency may rest assured that everything that is fitting has been done on this occasion."

Byrne asked no more questions. There was still another death which was considered by Gonzales as "fitting to the occasion." The one-eyed Bernardino stuck against the wall of his wine-shop received the charge of six escopettas into his breast. As the shots rang out the rough bier with Tom's body on it went past carried by a bandit-like gang of Spanish patriots down the ravine to the shore, where two boats from the ship were waiting for what was left on earth of her best seaman.

Mr. Byrne, very pale and weak, stepped into the boat which carried the body of his humble friend. For it was decided that Tom Corbin should rest far out in the Bay of Biscay. The officer took the tiller and, turning his head for the last look at the shore, saw on the gray hillside something moving, which he made out to be a little man in a yellow hat mounted on a mule — that mule without which the fate of Tom Corbin would have remained mysterious forever.

## QUESTIONS

1. Do you like the author's elaborate method of introducing the story?
2. Do you know other writers who do this?
3. What makes Cuba Tom interesting?
4. Note how the author individualizes his characters. Explain.
5. What at once makes the setting promising?
6. What is meant by "Shank's pony"?
7. Where do you find the first hints of a plot complication?
8. Does the Spanish atmosphere help to create interest? Why?
9. Does the dwarf's story sound plausible in spite of its personal motive?
10. In the first twenty pages, do you find hints of impending tragedy?
11. From memory, what did the man Byrne see in the witches' inn?
12. What made him feel that the occupants knew about Tom?

## Joseph Conrad

13. Was Byrne's experience in his room such as to get on one's nerves?
14. Were you prepared for the sudden appearance of Tom? Explain.
15. Under the circumstances, were Byrne's feelings, actions, and terror natural?
16. What was the most terrifying moment in Byrne's experience?
17. Was that the climax of the story?
18. What happened to the witches? How do you know?
19. Are the final explanations satisfactory to you?
20. Why would Tom's fate have remained mysterious but for the mule?

### SUBJECTS FOR COMPOSITION

1. Cuba Tom and the Witches.
2. Write a dramatic incident purporting to come from papers you find in an old trunk.
3. In a brief sketch create an atmosphere of mystery around some old out-of-the-way house.

### VOLUMES OF STORIES BY JOSEPH CONRAD

*Tales of Unrest*             *'Twixt Land and Sea*
*Youth*                       *Within the Tides*
*A Set of Six*

## MARJORIE L. C. PICKTHALL
(1883-1922)

IN SPITE of its unpoetic title, "The Stove" is a story romantic in its setting, strong in theme, and vivid in its suggestion of the chill atmosphere of the Canadian Northwest. Miss Pickthall was born in England but came to Toronto, Canada, while still a child. She went back to England during the war, then returned to Canada and made her home in Victoria, British Columbia. But she preferred to spend her time out in the wilds, especially in the mountains. She admitted that she was "passionately fond" of both. She could not work to her own satisfaction unless she was away from neighbors and sundry other worries of civilization. So she built herself a shack, under a big pine-tree, and there she wrote her stories.

Miss Pickthall also wrote poetry, but the short story was her special forte. She was highly regarded in Canada. From Toronto the editor received this comment: "Canadian critics are all agreed that this collection (*Angels' Shoes*) by Miss Pickthall contains the highest expression of the Canadian short story."

## THE STOVE

"I'LL be back the third day at latest with the doctor. I've left you wood enough for three days and more and you've grub for a month." Garth looked at her anxiously; his strong mouth twitched. Suddenly he leaned forward and brushed her cheek lightly with his yellow beard. "I — hate to leave you, little girl," he said, with a gentleness not common with him, "but I guess it's Derek's only chance."

"Of course you must go. It's Derek's only chance." Dorette faced him steadily. She was pale, slight, sleepy-eyed, but wilderness born and bred, for all that; one guessed a spirit of steel in that fragile sheath. She finished wistfully: "There'll be nothing for me to do — nothing, but — wait."

"Only look after yourself and keep the stove up."

"I'll do it. And you — if you meet Maxime ——"

Rage blazed suddenly in her brother's eyes. The barrel of his rifle gleamed blue as he gripped it. "If I meet Maxime," he said, through his teeth, "it's a finish for him or for me!"

453

He turned about without another word, and swung down the forest trail on his long run to Mandore.

Dorette watched him until he was no more than a dark shadow among the heavy blue shades that hung from spruce to spruce like tangible banners. All life, all sound, all motion seemed to go with him. Mile after mile, she knew, on each side of her was nothing but the same silence, the same stillness, league after league of the desolate fir forest of the North. She went into the cabin and bolted and barred the door behind her, as if the solitude were an enemy which she must keep out.

The cabin was a pleasant place. The walls were sheathed in red cedar, and there were fur rugs on the floor, red curtains at the windows. In the center of the larger of the two rooms into which the cabin was divided stood the great iron stove, in winter the source of their very life.

Its voice filled the cabin with a roar like the forever unsatisfied roaring of the wind and sea — a hungry voice. Dorette swung open the heavy door, wincing from the furnace-glory within, as she flung on more wood. That was her one occupation until Garth came back — feeding the stove.

She went to one of the bunks — like the bunks of a ship — that were built on the wall behind the stove, and looked in.

Derek, her younger brother, lay there without sense or motion, as he had lain ever since the sergeant of police and Garth had carried him in and laid him there. He drowsed between life and death, shot through the body. Now and then he swallowed a little broth, but with no knowledge of the hand that fed him. She dared not touch him. There was nothing she could do for him but keep the cabin warm enough to sustain that flickering lamp of life till the doctor came, for the cold of that country kills like a sword.

Suddenly, clinging to the side of the bunk, she trembled. " If only you could speak to me, Derek," she whispered. " If only I could hear your voice! "

But the only voice was the voice of the great stove.

Her mind painted for her the scene she had not witnessed — the hard men of the mines and the lumber camps, still men with formidable eyes, following Cain's trail from Fort Dismay to Anisette; the end of the trail at a little lonely shack blinded in snow, ringed with watchful men; Derek pleading that Maxime might have " one more chance, boys "; the parley at the door, the shot coming from nowhere; men storming into the shack over Derek's fallen body, and finding it empty; Maxime Dufour escaped again! She saw it all. Heard again Garth's voice in hard-breathed sentences between shut teeth: " But he's not goin' to get away again. He'll have to get food and shelter somewhere; and if it's a thousand miles away, we'll follow and shoot him down like the wolf he is! "

She glanced round, pale and shaken, thinking that still she heard that deep voice of bitter rage. But it was only the undertone of the roaring stove humming its angry song.

She busied herself about such duties as she could find. Twice she fed the stove from the pile of wood on the floor beside it. The fierce heat licked out at her each time, just as a savage beast will strike through the bars of his cage, and each time she shut the door with the sense of prisoning some lion-voiced living thing.

Her work was soon done. Everything in the cabin was tidied and tidied again. She glanced at the clock. Only an hour of the slow time had gone. Garth had only been gone an hour. She turned the clock with its face to the wall, took out a shirt she was making for Garth — red-and-black checked flannel, thick as felt — and stitched resolutely.

Her hearing, accustomed to the sound of the stove, as the ear adjusts itself to the thunder of a waterfall, was acute to catch the faintest noises. She heard the tiny sound of the thread passing through the flannel, the soft thud of snow slipping from the boughs of the forest, the least check and stumble in Derek's shallow breathing. Each time she heard this last, her own heart checked and stumbled in tune with it. She held her own breath till her brother's renewed its weak rhythm.

So the morning passed. In the afternoon, she found a snowshoe that needed re-stringing. Deftly as Montagnais she twisted the gut and wove the net.

It was dark sooner than she could have hoped. She needed no lamp. The stove filled the cabin with its glow. In the dark it became a beautiful and formidable thing, a shape of dull red, with a heart of lambent rose. She glanced at the little windows, sheathed thick with frost-ferns. It would be a cold night. Her thoughts went to Garth, then, with dread, to Maxime Dufour. She dragged her cot from the inner room, set it across the front of the stove, and lay down. The warmth was like a hand pressing on her eyelids.

With the subconscious watchfulness of those who care for the beloved, she was awake five times in the long night to feed the stove. Each time she looked at Derek, and thought, with a pang, that he was deeper sunken among the pillows. His eyes were not quite closed; the silvery line of eyeball reflected the red glow. She would have liked to close them, but her hand shrank from so prophetic an action.

The last time she woke the sun had risen. The gathered crystals on the windows were lit with a glow that paled the stove. Dorette went into the inner room and braided her hair.

That day passed as the first had done. Her brother was weaker. She pleaded with him, passionately tender. "Just a mouthful of soup, Derry. Wake up, Derry dear. Take it for my sake, Derry!" but her voice, which had dimly roused him the day before, could not reach him now. She looked round for something she might do for him.

The diminished heap of logs on the floor showed her work enough. She must bring in a fresh supply from the pile behind the cabin. She ate a hasty breakfast and made herself some coffee. Then, hooded and wrapped against the cold, she opened the door.

She stepped into a world of white, blue, and black; solid, translucent, and motionless as though built from gems. Where the blue sky touched the black trees there seemed to run a setting of gold; where the black trees trailed branches to the snow, was a stain of sapphire shadow. It was fiercely cold. She shut the door behind her, hastily, ran to the snow-buried wood-pile behind the cabin, burdened herself with an armful of small logs, returned, set her load on the threshold, opened the door, and tumbled the wood on the floor. All the morning she worked thus. Her spirits rose; she began to believe that Derek would not die, and soon she might think of Garth's return. The noise of the logs as she flung them on the floor pleased her. It was a change from the one unceasing voice that filled the cabin day and night — the voice of the stove.

The second night she was restless. She dared not sleep at first, for fear she should sleep too well. Wind came up with the electric stars; the great stove sang to a higher, more tremendous note; she could scarcely keep pace with its consuming hunger. The pine knots and bright birch logs fell to ash in a moment. If she slept, she dreamed that the stove was out, and the cold creeping into the cabin in long feathers of frost, that twisted under the door like snakes, until one touched her on the throat and she woke, choking.

Dawn found the sky fleeced with cloud, the cabin warm, and the hurt man yet alive.

Again with the day her heart lightened. Four — five hours from that time, and she might expect Garth with the doctor from the mines at Mandore. She wound the clock, and turned it with its chipped white face to the room, no longer dreading to tell the passage of the hours.

Yet five hours went, and Garth had not come.

She went to the door. Closing it behind her that the cold might not get into the cabin even for a moment, she stared down the trail. It ran in the straight no more than a half-mile; farther than that, she could not see. Yet it was less her eyes than her soul that she thus strained to see beyond the forest.

" Garth! Garth! Garth! "

Who had given that wild cry that rang among the trees? For a moment she wondered, then knew it had come from her own troubled heart.

She must see beyond the first bend of the trail; she must see if, farther than that, the blue-white ribbon between the trees was still empty of her hope.

She built up the fire again, put on coat and hood and snow-shoes, took one glance at Derek, and left the cabin. She sped down the trail. She was panting when she reached the first curve. Almost afraid to look, she saw the long track before her — empty. There was something conscious and deliberate in that emptiness, as if the forest knowingly withheld from her a secret. She dared go no farther. She turned back and fled home.

The clock ticked off another hour — two, three, four. Garth had not come.

Darkness, and he had not come.

Loneliness and suspense were shaking her strong, young nerves. The worst of all was the silence. The voice of the stove became first an annoyance, then a weariness, then an intolerable burden. The voice of its devouring hunger was the very voice of silence, of desolation. She flung the wood in angrily. "If there was only someone to *speak* to," she said, a little wildly—"just someone to give me a word!"

There was no one—then, nor through the endless night, when she feared to sleep, lest, in her dreams, or in reality, that insatiable thing in the stove that kept them alive might escape her, nor with the stormy dawn. Garth did not come.

There was no wood left in the house. Before she did anything else, she wrapped herself and went to the wood-pile.

The wood-pile was heaped against the back of the cabin: it was roofed and sheeted with snow. She pulled at the butt of a log, and the wood came down with a run, mixed with much snow—such dry snow that the wood was not moistened until she held it in her warm hand. The bitter work was a relief to her. She thrust the soft, dark hair out of her eyes and piled herself such a load that she swayed under it. "But it's something to do for Derek," she said, wistfully. "It's all I can do."

She took in enough for the day. But there was the night.

"Garth will be back by then," she muttered, with cold lips, staring at the stove.

"Garth *must* be back by then." The stove sent a screaming rush of flame up the pipe, as if in mockery. She felt an unreasoning hatred for it, as she went wearily out again to gather enough wood for the night too.

Kneeling beside the wood-pile, she groped with numbed hands. She felt nothing but snow.

She thrust in her arm to the shoulder. She met no resistance but that of the snow.

Her heart beat in shuddering throbs. She brought a long pole and prodded the pile, then swung the pole and levelled it. She found nothing but snow.

"How did it happen?" She heard herself asking this over and over. Easily enough. She or Garth or Derek had been drawing supplies from the other side of the pile, and the snow had slipped from the roof and filled the spaces; hardening, it had stretched a roof over emptiness. The pile, which had been taken for good, hardwood logs, fodder for that roaring hungry heat within, was no more than a heap of snow.

Dorette turned slowly, and went into the cabin.

She stood by Derek's bunk, staring at the wood on the floor. It was enough for the day, but what of the night?

Would Garth return before the night?

She looked about the cabin. There were things there, things that would burn. Her sleepy brown eyes widened. There was war in them as she leaned and kissed Derek's cheek. He did not stir from that deepening sleep of his.

"Sleep on, Derry," she whispered, scarcely knowing what she said, "sleep well, Derry. I'll take care of you, I'll fight for you!"

She took Garth's heavy axe, and began on the chairs.

They were heavy and clumsy things, Garth's pride, since he had made them himself. They would feed the stove well; but they were hard for a girl's arm to chop, even though she struck true as a woodman, and Dorette's hands were scorched from the door of the stove. As she toiled, her eyes ranged the cabin, calculating on this box, that shelf, the table. Her heart beat to every sound. As the wind rose higher, the bitter day was full of sounds. A dozen times she ran to the door, crying, "Garth!" A dozen times she saw nothing but the forest and a driven mist of snow, as fine and dry as dust.

By the earliest dusk she had chopped up everything in the cabin. Each stroke sent a jar of pain to her shoulder from her burned and bruised hands, but she did not feel it. And still the stove roared, insatiable. The dried wood of their furnishings, pine for the most part, burned like straw. The great iron horror must be fed, and she had nothing to feed it.

She took the axe and went out.

The gray forest fronted her in a rustling drive of snow and shadow. There must be a hundred fallen boughs within range of the cabin. She found one, dragged it from the snow, and toiled with it into the house. She twisted it apart, desperately, and there was blood on the rough, broken stuff she thrust into the stove.

She went out again. She was growing more desperate as her strength failed. There was a great branch trailing from a spruce, and she tore and wrenched at it, but it would not yield — it was frozen. She swung her weight upon it, sobbing. She struck with all the force remaining in her, but the axe-blade turned in her weary hands. She felt as though the will in her, passionately strong, should sever the bough as by steel. She did not know she was beaten, until she slipped weakly and fell in the snow and lay there, wailing helplessly and softly as a child.

The bitter snow stung her face like heat — like the heat of the stove. If she stayed there, the stove would be out. She lifted herself to her knees, and saw in the growing dark a man, who stood with a rifle on his arm, looking down at her.

"Garth! Oh, Garth!"

But even as the cry left her lips, she knew it was not Garth. A figure, lithe even under the heavy furs, a face hidden in the cowl he had drawn forward above his fur cap, a certain strange immobility that vaguely chilled her, but surely — help? So swift is thought, that in the transitory seconds before she spoke again her brain had shown her a picture, a memory of a wild-cat which she and Garth had vainly tried to corner in the yard — of the creature's utter immobility until it launched itself and struck.

"The stove! Oh, the stove!"

She thought, as her hands went out to that motionless figure in the shadows, that she had spoken all the desperate appeal that was in her heart. But she only repeated: "Oh, the stove, the stove!"

"What stove?"

"The stove. The stove in our cabin. There's — no more wood for it!"

She waited. Surely he understood. But he remained as he was, motionless, staring down at her.

She looked up at him with a burning appeal. She had forgotten to rise from her knees. She kneeled at his feet in the snow. Her breath came in gasps. "There," she repeated, helplessly, "there — in the cabin — the stove! It's going out!"

Still he waited.

"There's a sick man there — my brother! Oh!" she finished, as he did not stir, "help me, if you're a man!"

"Oh, b'gosh, yes, I'm a man!" She fancied that he was laughing in the shadow of the cowl. "But why should I help you?"

She had no more words. Silently she lifted and held out to him her bleeding hands.

After a long minute he stirred slowly. Without a word he laid his gun crosswise on two fir branches that grew above her reach, easily within his own. He lifted the axe from the snow. She watched him. Four sharp cross-cuts, and the trailing branch fell. He set his foot on it, chopped it quickly into four or five pieces. As each piece rolled free, Dorette snatched it as a starving woman might snatch bread.

"That enough?"

Staggering under her load, she stared at him. "No, no!" she stammered. "It's not enough for the night. For the pity of Heaven, cut me some more!"

She turned away and hurried towards the cabin. Halfway there he overtook her. Without a word he lifted the logs from her arms into his own. She was too spent to thank him. Dumbly she moved at his side, conscious only that strength was here, help was here, that she might yet save Derek.

Entering the cabin, there was no glow, no light at all. With a low sound, Dorette swung open the door of the stove. Nothing was there but a handful of red ash ringed with gray.

With trembling hands she gathered a few splinters and thrust them in; she crouched before the gaunt, iron thing, as though she would hold it in her arms and warm it in her bosom. But the man, who had followed her, thrust her aside curtly enough. She watched him as he shaved a stick into delicate ribbons of wood — watched him as he coaxed them into flame. He tickled the appetite of the sullen, devouring thing in the stove with scraps of resinous bark and little twigs. Presently the fire laid hold on the larger logs, and fed upon them, hissing. He shut the door then, and turned to her.

She had lighted a lamp, and in the light stood looking at him, softly bright. Her eyes were stars of gratitude. She said at once: "My brother's still living."

She gestured towards the bunk. His eyes did not follow the gesture, or move from her pale face, as he said, abruptly: "You stay here with him. I'm goin' to get you in some more wood."

Her eyes flashed suddenly with tears. She said, brokenly: "You're *good*. Oh, you're a good man! While you're — cuttin' the wood, I'll — thank God you came!"

He went out into the night without answering her.

He returned in half an hour, loaded mightily. Sitting on the end of her cot, she smiled at him, falteringly. She had been weeping.

He did not speak to her. Light-footed as a cat, he busied himself about the humming stove, then went forth again.

When he came back the second time, she was asleep.

Her face — very pale, very pure, fragile for one of her life and race — was rosed in the glow of the stove. Her hurt hands were curled within one another, like the hands of a child. Moving in his noiseless way, the man went again, and looked down at her.

His furred cowl had fallen back. His face also caught the light of the stove. Dark, keen, predatory, it was the face less of a man than of some embodied passion of hate or revenge, the face of an Ishmael, the face of Cain. It looked strange now, so little was it shaped or accustomed to the gentleness of expression it momentarily wore, as a breath blurs the gleam of steel. Light and silent as all his movements were, they showed no gentleness. But he seemed gentle when he lifted the end of one of Dorette's dark plaits, which had fallen to the soiled floor, and laid it on the cot beside her just because he hesitated and was clumsy.

The plait of dark, silken hair was warm; his hand lingered over it. He leaned above her, and her breath was warm. That strangely unmoving regard of his was on her face. As if it had called her from her dreams, she woke, and lifted to him the clear eyes of a child. " I — did thank God — you came," she whispered, with a child's simplicity. Sleep held her again, almost before she had finished speaking.

The young man drew back, noiselessly lifted the axe, and once more went out.

Sinewy, silent, untiring, he toiled for her all night. And all night she slept.

She had slipped into unconsciousness as a child does, worn out with anxiety and fatigue. She woke a woman, and flushed to her hair, as she realized what she had done.

The man who had helped and guarded her all night, was standing in the doorway. The door was open; there was a frosty freshness in the air, which the roaring stove raised to the warmth of summer. The world outside was a dazzle of sun; silver drops rattled from the eaves; a crow called in the forest. It was the first sun of spring, the year's change. In Dorette's heart was a change also, a quickening, a birth of something new and unknown, that almost brought tears to her eyes. For the first time in her hard life she had rested on another's strength; unconsciously she had found it sweet. That simple heart was in her look as she went to the stranger. She said, softly, "I did not mean to sleep. Why did you let me?"

He said, almost roughly: "You were all tired out."

The tears brimmed over. She did not know if pain or happiness moved her. She went on: "I said — I knew — you were a good man."

"Well," he answered, but not as if he was answering her, "for one night."

His furred hood hid his face. The wakening blush dyed her clear face again, as she said: "Let me see you. Let me see your face."

"Why?"

On the word she faltered, confused. She did not know why. She stammered: "Because of what you have done — of what we owe you."

"We?"

"My brothers and I. Derek's still alive. I almost think he's sleeping better — more natural. When — when Garth comes home, he'll thank you as I'd like to."

She looked up into the shadowed face, wistfully. He had turned from her again, and was gazing down the trail. After a moment, he said: "There's coffee on the back of the stove, and some cornbread. You'd better eat it. I've had some."

She went meekly, shamed that she had slept while her savior served himself. She would have liked to serve him. Something strange and stormy was shaking her; she had no name for it. The food choked her, hungry as she was, but she ate it obediently.

She had scarcely finished, when he called her. She ran and joined him at the door. Something in his voice thrilled her; she saw in him again that strange and threatening immobility of the night before.

He said, swiftly: "You're lookin' for your brother to come back?"

"Yes, yes. Any time."

"With another man?"

"With the doctor. Why?"

He raised his arm and pointed. In the blinding dazzle of sun on snow, she saw two small, dark figures, just rounding the curve of the trail.

Her heart rose and flooded her with a passion of thankfulness. She said, quietly, after a minute: "Yes, yes, it's him and the doctor. Now — now, you'll let him thank you, as you — won't let me."

Her words ended almost in a question, for she saw that, while she had been eating, he had taken his rifle on his arm and put on his snowshoes. Suddenly, she began to tremble a little, aware of something in his silence, his stillness, which vaguely threatened.

He swung upon her suddenly — one would have said, savagely, but that he was laughing. Those two black figures down the trail were sweeping rapidly nearer. All the latent fierceness of the man had flamed into being, at their approach. He laid a hard, slim hand on Dorette's shoulder and turned her, so that, at less than arm's length, she faced him. He said, softly, in the midst of his almost noiseless laughter: "I'll show you how you can thank me."

She looked up at him, her face colorless, her lips parted. In the shadow of the hood his eyes gleamed at her, his face bent nearer. The world fell away from her; there was nothing left in life for a minute but that face, that voice.

She just breathed: "Who are you?"

"You'll know in a minute!" He looked swiftly from her to the two men down the trail. They were coming on fast. He seemed to be measuring his distance from them.

When they were so near that their faces were all but discernible, he caught the girl to him. She was slack in his hold; all her life seemed to be in her dazed eyes; she would have fallen, but that he held her with an arm like a steel bar. And twice and three times he kissed her.

"That's how you can thank me!" He released her laughing still.

She staggered, her hands over her red mouth. With the movement of release he thrust her, rough and swift, within the door of the cabin. A bullet sent a spray of dusty snow over him. She saw, in one reeling instant, Garth on his knee down the trail, rifle leveled for another shot; the other, a laughing shadow, slipping from her hands, from her life, into the shadow of the forest from which he had come.

Another shot, wide of the mark; Garth leaping to his feet again and tearing towards her, followed by the doctor who was to save Derek, and whom he had found at last, thirty miles beyond Mandore. But she had no eyes for them — for a moment, no heart.

Eyes and heart were on that other figure at the edge of the trees, swift, terrible, laughing, calling to her with raised hand:

"Tell him you kissed Maxime Dufour!"

When Garth reached her side, she was on her knees, laughing and sobbing, striving, with her scarred small hands to obliterate his trail in the snow.

## QUESTIONS

1. In the opening paragraphs what possible complications are suggested?
2. Note which, if any, are developed.
3. Can you visualize an old-fashioned wood stove?
4. What had made the shooting of Derek doubly tragic?
5. In that northern country, what type of criminal might Dufour have been?
6. What resolution did Garth make? Does it sound convincing?
7. How does the author keep Dorette's suspense from becoming dull for the reader?
8. How does the exhaustion of the wood prepare for a complication?
9. What was the first real crisis in the story?
10. Were you prepared for the coming of the stranger?
11. Did you suspect his identity? Explain.
12. Why does Dorette fall in love with him so quickly?
13. Did he fall in love with her? Explain.
14. Did he know in whose cottage he was?
15. Why did he laugh after kissing her?
16. Does he have any redeeming traits?
17. Knowing who he was, Dorette covers up his trail. Why?
18. What became of Garth's resolution?
19. Is the title of the story appropriate?
20. What is the climax? State the plot.
21. Is the fate of Derek important to the story?

## SUBJECTS FOR COMPOSITION

1. A character sketch of Maxime Dufour.
2. Derek Pleads for Dufour.
3. Tell orally some other possible ending.

## OTHER STORIES BY MARJORIE L. C. PICKTHALL

Luck
La Blanchisseuse
The Third Generation

White Magic
Saga of Kweetchel

(All in the Volume, *Angels' Shoes*)

## RUDYARD KIPLING
## (1865–    )

No WRITER of the short story in English has attained such universal celebrity as Mr. Rudyard Kipling nor has anyone been more deserving of his fame. He is almost equally famous for his poetry; to many readers more so. His novel *Kim* ranks with the world's foremost. He has traveled the world over, and his impressions are recorded in books that everywhere find favor with readers. He has lived in India, where he was born in 1865. In 1892 he married an American woman and lived four years in Vermont. The Boer War took him to South Africa. At present he lives in England. Everywhere he finds material for books, stories, and poems. The mere bulk of his work is enormous.

Kipling is an embodiment of his ideals as they are represented in his stories, the only part of his writing to be considered here. In them he tells of man at work, especially of the Englishman at the work of empire building. More particularly still, his best known stories deal with the Englishman in India, involved in hard labor under physical conditions almost impossible to believe.

Kipling was educated in England, at the United Services College, Westward Ho, Devon. His writing career began there as a contributor to the school papers. In *Stalky & Company* he tells in story form about this school life. He returned to his family in India and became a newspaper man. While still very young he began to write the stories which eventually made him famous. It is hard to believe that when he brought his first collection to England and America for publication in book form no publisher was willing to assume the risk of printing something so wildly exotic as these tales of India then seemed. The qualities which are now highly exalted were frowned upon in those days, such as the rough robustness of the characters, the strong language of many of them, and a certain arrogance in the author's manner of telling the story. He returned to India and kept on writing.

With a natural gift for telling stories, with a growing consciousness of form, the development of Kipling was rapid. Placed in an environment as raw and untouched as that in which Bret Harte found himself in California a decade before, Kipling had a local color medium ready-made. For creating his effects he used the means taught him by his American predecessor. He chose either a striking situation or an unusual character. Often he combined the two. Like O. Henry and Maupassant, he owes much of his impressionistic manner and compression of style to the fact that most of his earlier stories were contributed to a newspaper. Given characters and situation, he drives the story swiftly and directly to the designed end.

In " In the Matter of a Private," taken from *Plain Tales from the Hills,* Kipling's early manner is apparent. The situation is striking and unusual, the setting equally so, and the introductory analogy of military hysteria to an eruption of silly girls in a convent school only adds to the forcefulness of the presentation. The characters may literally be said to speak for themselves.

Kipling has written many types of stories — of the soldier in India, animal stories, ghost stories, love stories, stories for children. For a while he was obsessed by the idea of glorifying machinery which helps man in his great work of developing the world. " The Ship That Found Herself " and " .007 " belong to this class. Humor and mystery are not uncommon in his tales. Few writers can equal him in horror stories, such as " The Return of Imray " and " The Strange Ride of Morrowbie Jukes." Every form of the short story may be found in Kipling, and in most he excels. There can be no dispute of the claim that he is the greatest modern writer of the short story.

## IN THE MATTER OF A PRIVATE

Hurrah! hurrah! a soldier's life for me!
Shout, boys, shout! for it makes you jolly and free.
*The Ramrod Corps.*

PEOPLE who have seen, say that one of the quaintest spectacles of human frailty is an outbreak of hysterics in a girls' school. It starts without warning, generally on a hot afternoon, among the elder pupils. A girl giggles till the giggle gets beyond control. Then she throws up her head, and cries, "*Honk, honk, honk,*" like a wild goose, and tears mix with the laughter. If the mistress be wise, she will rap out something severe at this point to check matters. If she be tender-hearted, and send for a drink of water, the chances are largely in favor of another girl laughing at the afflicted one and herself collapsing. Thus the trouble spreads, and may end in half of what answers to the Lower Sixth of a boys' school rocking and whooping together. Given a week of warm weather, two stately promenades per diem, a heavy mutton and rice meal in the middle of the day, a certain amount of nagging from the teachers, and a few other things, some amazing effects develop. At least, this is what folk say who have had experience.

Now, the Mother Superior of a Convent and the Colonel of a British Infantry Regiment would be justly shocked at any comparison being made between the respective charges. But it is a fact that, under certain circumstances, Thomas in bulk can be worked up into dithering, rippling hysteria. He does not weep, but he shows his trouble unmistakably, and the consequences get into the newspapers, and all the good people who hardly know a Martini from a Snider say: " Take away the brute's ammunition! "

Thomas isn't a brute, and his business, which is to look after the virtuous people, demands that he shall have his ammunition to his hand. He doesn't wear silk stockings, and he really ought to be supplied with a new Adjective to help him to express his opinions: but, for all that, he is a great man. If you call him " the heroic defender of the national honor " one day, and a " brutal and licentious soldiery " the next, you naturally bewilder him, and he looks upon you with suspicion. There is nobody to speak for Thomas except people who have theories to work off on him; and nobody understands Thomas except Thomas, and he does not always know what is the matter with himself.

That is the prologue. This is the story: —

Corporal Slane was engaged to be married to Miss Jhansi M'Kenna, whose history is well known in the regiment and elsewhere. He had his Colonel's permission, and, being popular with the men, every arrangement had been made to give the wedding what Private Ortheris called "eeklar." It fell in the heart of the hot weather, and, after the wedding, Slane was going up to the Hills with the bride. None the less, Slane's grievance was that the affair would be only a hired-carriage wedding, and he felt that the "eeklar" of that was meager. Miss M'Kenna did not care so much. The Sergeant's wife was helping her to make her wedding-dress, and she was very busy. Slane was, just then, the only moderately contented man in barracks. All the rest were more or less miserable.

And they had so much to make them happy, too. All their work was over at eight in the morning, and for the rest of the day they could lie on their backs and smoke Canteen-plug and swear at the punkah-coolies. They enjoyed a fine, full flesh meal in the middle of the day, and then threw themselves down on their cots and sweated and slept till it was cool enough to go out with their " towny," whose vocabulary contained less than six hundred words, and the Adjective, and whose views on every conceivable question they had heard many times before.

There was the Canteen, of course, and there was the Temperance Room with the second-hand papers in it; but a man of any profession cannot read for eight hours a day in a temperature of 96° or 98° in the shade, running up sometimes to 103° at midnight. Very few men, even though they get a pannikin of flat, stale, muddy beer and hide it under their cots, can continue drinking for six hours a day. One man tried, but he died, and nearly the whole regiment went to his funeral because it gave them something to do. It was too early for the excitement of fever or cholera. The men could only wait and wait and wait, and watch the shadow of the barrack creeping across the blinding white dust. That was a gay life.

They lounged about cantonments — it was too hot for any sort of game, and almost too hot for vice — and fuddled themselves in the evening, and filled themselves to distension with the healthy nitrogeneous food provided for them, and the more they stoked the less exercise they took and more explosive they grew. Then tempers began to wear away, and men fell a-brooding over insults real or imaginary, for they had nothing else to think of. The tone of the repartees changed, and instead of saying light-heartedly: "I'll knock your silly face in," men grew laboriously polite and hinted that the cantonments were not big enough for themselves and their enemy, and that there would be more space for one of the two in another Place.

It may have been the Devil who arranged the thing, but the fact of the case is that Losson had for a long time been worrying Simmons in an aimless way. It gave him occupation. The two had their cots side by side, and would sometimes spend a long afternoon swearing at each other; but Simmons was afraid of Losson and dared not challenge him to a fight. He thought over the words in the hot still nights, and half the hate he felt towards Losson he vented on the wretched punkah-coolie.

Losson bought a parrot in the bazar, and put it into a little cage, and lowered the cage into the cool darkness of a well, and sat on the well-curb, shouting bad language down to the parrot. He taught it to say: "Simmons, ye *so-oor,*" which means swine, and several other things entirely unfit for publication. He was a big gross man, and he shook like a jelly when the parrot had the sentence correctly. Simmons, however, shook with rage, for all the room were laughing at him — the parrot was such a disreputable puff of green feathers and it looked so human when it chattered. Losson used to sit, swinging his fat legs, on the side of the cot, and ask the parrot what it thought of Simmons. The parrot would answer: " Simmons, ye *so-oor*." " Good boy," Losson used to say, scratching the parrot's head; " ye 'ear that, Sim? " And Simmons used to turn over on his stomach and make answer: " I 'ear. Take 'eed *you* don't 'ear something one of these days."

In the restless nights, after he had been asleep all day, fits of blind rage came upon Simmons and held him till he trembled all over, while he thought in how many different ways he would slay Losson. Sometimes he would picture himself trampling the life out of the man, with heavy ammunition-boots, and at others smashing in his face with the butt, and at others jumping on his shoulders and dragging the head back till the neckbone cracked. Then his mouth would feel hot and fevered, and he would reach out for another sup of the beer in the pannikin.

But the fancy that came to him most frequently and stayed with him longest was one connected with the great roll of fat under Losson's right ear. He noticed it first on a moonlight night, and thereafter it was always before his eyes. It was a fascinating roll of fat. A man could get his hand upon it and tear away one side of the neck; or he could place the muzzle of a rifle on it and blow away all the head in a flash. Losson had no right to be sleek and contented and well-to-do, when he, Simmons, was the butt of the room. Some day, perhaps, he would show those who laughed at the " Simmons, ye *so-oor* " joke, that he was as good as the rest, and held a man's life in the crook of his forefinger. When Losson snored, Simmons hated him more bitterly than ever. Why should Losson be able to sleep when Simmons had to stay awake hour after hour, tossing and turning on the tapes, with the dull liver pain gnawing into his right side and his head throbbing and aching after Canteen? He thought over this for many, many nights, and the world became unprofitable to him. He even blunted his naturally fine appetite with beer and tobacco; and all the while the parrot talked at and made a mock of him.

The heat continued and the tempers wore away more quickly than before. A Sergeant's wife died of heat-apoplexy in the night, and the rumor ran abroad that it was cholera. Men rejoiced openly, hoping that it would spread and send them into camp. But that was a false alarm.

It was late on a Tuesday evening, and the men were waiting in the deep double verandas for "Last Posts," when Simmons went to the box at the foot of his bed, took out his pipe, and slammed the lid down with a bang that echoed through the deserted barrack like the crack of a rifle. Ordinarily speaking, the men would have taken no notice; but their nerves were fretted to fiddle-strings. They jumped up, and three or four clattered into the barrack-room only to find Simmons kneeling by his box.

"Ow! It's you, is it?" they said and laughed foolishly. "We thought 'twas ——"

Simmons rose slowly. If the accident had so shaken his fellows, what would not the reality do?

"You thought it was — did you? And what makes you think?" he said, lashing himself into madness as he went on: "to Hell with your thinking, ye dirty spies."

"Simmons, ye *so-oor*," chuckled the parrot in the veranda sleepily, recognizing a well-known voice. Now that was absolutely all.

The tension snapped. Simmons fell back on the arm-rack deliberately — the men were at the far end of the room — and took out his rifle and packet of ammunition. "Don't go playing the goat, Sim!" said Losson. "Put it down," but there was a quaver in his voice. Another man stooped, slipped his boot and hurled it at Simmons's head. The prompt answer was a shot which, fired at random, found its billet in Losson's throat. Losson fell forward without a word, and the others scattered.

"You thought it was!" yelled Simmons. "You're drivin' me to it! I tell you you're drivin' me to it! Get up, Losson, an' don't lie shammin' there — you an' your blasted parrit that druv me to it!"

But there was an unaffected reality about Losson's pose

that showed Simmons what he had done. The men were still clamoring in the veranda. Simmons appropriated two more packets of ammunition and ran into the moonlight, muttering: "I'll make a night of it. Thirty roun's, an' the last for myself. Take you that, you dogs!"

He dropped on one knee and fired into the brown of the men on the veranda, but the bullet flew high, and landed in the brickwork with a vicious *phwit* that made some of the younger ones turn pale. It is, as musketry theorists observe, one thing to fire and another to be fired at.

Then the instinct of the chase flared up. The news spread from barrack to barrack, and the men doubled out intent on the capture of Simmons, the wild beast, who was heading for the Cavalry parade-ground, stopping now and again to send back a shot and a curse in the direction of his pursuers.

"I'll learn you to spy on me!" he shouted; "I'll learn you to give me dorg's names! Come on, the 'ole lot o' you! Colonel John Anthony Deever, C. B.!" — he turned towards the Infantry Mess and shook his rifle — "you think yourself the devil of a man — but I tell you that if you put your ugly old carcass outside o' that door, I'll make you the poorest-lookin' man in the army. Come out, Colonel John Anthony Deever, C. B.! Come out and see me practiss on the rainge. I'm the crack shot of the 'ole bloomin' battalion." In proof of which statement Simmons fired at the lighted windows of the mess-house.

"Private Simmons, E Comp'ny, on the Cavalry p'rade-ground, sir, with thirty rounds," said a Sergeant breathlessly to the Colonel. 'Shootin' right and lef', sir. Shot Private Losson. What's to be done, sir?"

Colonel John Anthony Deever, C. B., sallied out, only to be saluted by a spurt of dust at his feet.

"Pull up!" said the Second in Command; "I don't want my step in that way, Colonel. He's as dangerous as a mad dog."

"Shoot him like one, then," said the Colonel bitterly, "if he won't take his chance. *My* regiment, too! If it had been the Towheads I could have understood."

Private Simmons had occupied a strong position near a well on the edge of the parade-ground, and was defying the regiment to come on. The regiment was not anxious to comply, for there is small honor in being shot by a fellow-private.

Only Corporal Slane, rifle in hand, threw himself down on the ground, and wormed his way towards the well.

"Don't shoot," said he to the men round him; "like as not you'll 'it me. I'll catch the beggar, livin'."

Simmons ceased shouting for a while, and the noise of trap-wheels could be heard across the plain. Major Oldyne, Commanding the Horse Battery, was coming back from a dinner in the Civil Lines; was driving after his usual custom — that is to say, as fast as the horse could go.

"A orf'cer! A blooming spangled orf'cer!" shrieked Simmons; "I'll make a scarecrow of that orf'cer!" The trap stopped.

"What's this?" demanded the Major of Gunners. "You there, drop your rifle."

"Why, it's Jerry Blazes! I ain't got no quarrel with you, Jerry Blazes. Pass frien', an' all's well!"

But Jerry Blazes had not the faintest intention of passing a dangerous murderer. He was, as his adoring Battery swore long and fervently, without knowledge of fear, and they were surely the best judges, for Jerry Blazes, it was notorious, had done his possible to kill a man each time the Battery went out.

He walked towards Simmons, with the intention of rushing him, and knocking him down.

"Don't make me do it, sir," said Simmons; "I ain't got nothing agin you. Ah! you would?" — the Major broke into a run — "Take that then!"

The Major dropped with a bullet through his shoulder, and Simmons stood over him. He had lost the satisfaction of killing Losson in the desired way: but here was a helpless body to his hand. Should he slip in another cartridge, and blow off the head, or with the butt smash in the white face? He stopped to consider, and a cry went up from the far side of the parade-ground: "He's killed Jerry Blazes!" But in the shelter of the well-pillars Simmons was safe, except when he stepped out to fire. "I'll blow yer 'andsome 'ead off, Jerry Blazes," said Simmons reflectively. "Six an' three is nine an' one is ten, an' that leaves me another nineteen, an' one for myself." He tugged at the string of the second packet of ammunition. Corporal Slane crawled out of the shadow of a bank into the moonlight.

"I see you!" said Simmons. "Come a bit furder on an' I'll do for you."

"I'm comin'," said Corporal Slane briefly; "you've done a bad day's work, Sim. Come out 'ere an' come back with me."

"Come to —— ," laughed Simmons, sending a cartridge home with his thumb. "Not before I've settled you an' Jerry Blazes."

The Corporal was lying at full length in the dust of the parade-ground, a rifle under him. Some of the less-cautious men in the distance shouted: "Shoot 'im! Shoot 'im, Slane!"

"You move 'and or foot, Slane," said Simmons, "an' I'll kick Jerry Blazes' 'ead in, and shoot you after."

"I ain't movin'," said the Corporal, raising his head; "you daren't 'it a man on 'is legs. Let go o' Jerry Blazes an' come out o' that with your fistes. Come an' 'it me. You daren't, you bloomin' dog-shooter!"

"I dare."

"You lie, you man-sticker. You sneakin' Sheeny butcher, you lie. See there!" Slane kicked the rifle away, and stood up in the peril of his life. "Come on, now!"

The temptation was more than Simmons could resist, for the Corporal in his white clothes offered a perfect mark.

"Don't misname me," shouted Simmons, firing as he spoke. The shot missed, and the shooter, blind with rage, threw his rifle down and rushed at Slane from the protection of the well. Within striking distance, he kicked savagely at Slane's stomach, but the weedy Corporal knew something of Simmons's weakness, and knew, too, the deadly guard for that kick. Bowing forward and drawing up his right leg till the heel of the right foot was set some three inches above the inside of the left knee-cap, he met the blow standing on one leg — exactly as Gonds stand when they meditate — and ready for the fall that would follow. There was an oath, the Corporal fell over to his own left as shinbone met shinbone, and the Private collapsed, his right leg broken an inch above the ankle.

"Pity you don't know that guard, Sim," said Slane, spitting out the dust as he rose. Then raising his voice — "Come an' take him orf. I've bruk 'is leg." This was not strictly true, for the Private had accomplished his own downfall, since it is the special merit of that leg-guard that the harder the kick the greater the kicker's discomfiture.

Slane walked to Jerry Blazes and hung over him with ostentatious anxiety, while Simmons, weeping with pain, was carried away. " 'Ope you ain't 'urt badly, sir," said Slane. The Major had fainted, and there was an ugly, ragged hole through the top of his arm. Slane knelt down and murmured: " S'elp me, I believe 'e's dead. Well, if that ain't my blooming luck all over! "

But the Major was destined to lead his Battery afield for many a long day with unshaken nerve. He was removed, and nursed and petted into convalescence, while the Battery discussed the wisdom of capturing Simmons, and blowing him from a gun. They idolized their Major, and his reappearance on parade brought about a scene nowhere provided for in the Army Regulations.

Great, too, was the glory that fell to Slane's share. The Gunners would have made him drunk thrice a day for at least a fortnight. Even the Colonel of his own regiment complimented him upon his coolness, and the local paper called him a hero. These things did not puff him up. When the Major offered him money and thanks, the virtuous Corporal took the one and put aside the other. But he had a request to make and prefaced it with many a " Beg y' pardon, sir." Could the Major see his way to letting the Slane-M'Kenna wedding be adorned by the presence of four Battery horses to pull a hired barouche? The Major could, and so could the Battery. Excessively so. It was a gorgeous wedding.

"Wot did I do it for?" said Corporal Slane. "For the 'orses, o' course. Jhansi ain't a beauty to look at, but I wasn't goin' to 'ave a hired turn-out. Jerry Blazes? If I 'adn't 'a' wanted something, Sim might ha' blowed Jerry Blazes' blooming 'ead into Hirish stew for aught I'd 'a' cared."

And they hanged Private Simmons — hanged him as high as Haman in hollow square of the regiment; and the Colonel said it was Drink; and the Chaplain was sure it was the Devil; and Simmons fancied it was both, but he didn't know, and only hoped his fate would be a warning to his companions; and half a dozen "intelligent publicists" wrote six beautiful leading articles on "The Prevalence of Crime in the Army."

But not a soul thought of comparing the "bloody-minded Simmons" to the squawking, gaping schoolgirl with which this story opens.

## QUESTIONS

1. Note the author's device for giving the keynote to the story.
2. What does he mean by "Thomas in bulk"?
3. What is meant by "eeklar"?
4. State what constituted the "gay life" of the barracks.
5. How did this life affect Losson and Simmons?
6. Why should men rejoice openly at a threat of cholera?
7. Under the conditions, do you think the temperament of the cantonment natural?
8. What was the first dramatic crisis?
9. What is the point in the reference to the "Towheads"?
10. To what instinct did Slane appeal when he stood up without his rifle?
11. Why didn't Simmons respond?
12. Just how did Slane accomplish Simmons's downfall?
13. What do you think of Slane's explanation?
14. If true does it add to the interest of the story?
15. With whom are the author's sympathies?
16. How do you know?
17. Is there any humor?
18. Tell whether you liked the story or not, and why.

## SUBJECTS FOR COMPOSITION

1. Tell orally the story of Slane's engagement to Jhansi. (See "The Daughter of the Regiment.")
2. From Kipling stories you have have read, write an appreciative essay along the lines indicated in the sketch.
3. Write a brief "dramatic incident" story of someone who ran amuck.

## OTHER STORIES BY RUDYARD KIPLING

In the Rukh
Rikki-Tikki-Tavi
Without Benefit of Clergy
On Greenhow Hill
The Return of Imray
The Brushwood Boy

The Ship That Found Herself
.007
Moti Guj — Mutineer
The Man Who Was
The Man Who Would Be King

## VOLUMES OF STORIES BY RUDYARD KIPLING

Plain Tales from the Hills
Soldiers Three
Mine Own People
Life's Handicap
The Day's Work
Actions and Reactions

Many Inventions
Traffics and Discoveries
The Jungle Books
Just-So Stories
Puck of Pook's Hill
Limits and Renewals

## BOOKS ABOUT RUDYARD KIPLING

*Rudyard Kipling*, John Palmer
*Rudyard Kipling*, Richard Le Gallienne

## ARNOLD BENNETT
### (1867–1931)

THE name of Arnold Bennett is one of the best known in modern English fiction, but that does not mean that he is generally considered one of the best writers. Yet *The Old Wives' Tale, Clayhanger,* and *Riceyman Steps,* published respectively in 1908, 1912, and 1923, certainly entitle him to a high rank among novelists. The trouble with Mr. Bennett was that he published so much which was trivial that it seems impossible to believe that he was really a novelist of the first water. Following his first published book in 1898 he wrote a prodigious amount, much of it frankly of the pot-boiling class. He was besides irritatingly egotistic, a trait that laid him open to frequent flayings by critics. He probably enjoyed them, for just when a work had been declared hopelessly cheap he proceeded to write one that was quite the contrary, and the critics forthwith had to face about.

What has been said about his novels applies also to his short stories, of which he published several volumes. Many are poor indeed, while others are exceptionally good. "A Letter Home," from *Tales of the Five Towns,* is one of his best. Interestingly enough, it is perhaps his very first short story, and his first published work. It was written in 1893 and published two years later in *The Yellow Book,* a magazine famous in the history of nineteenth century literature.

With the exception of *Riceyman Steps,* all his best work is laid wholly or in part in the Five Towns, the name he gave to a group of small cities in the pottery district of North Staffordshire. In one of them he was born in 1867, and spent a part of his early life there. He studied law, but this he soon abandoned in favor of journalism. Once started on a literary career he determined to be a "successful author." Unfortunately he understood the word "successful" in its most vicious modern sense, but whatever one may say negatively about Mr. Bennett's work in no way detracts from the actual merit of that which is good.

In "A Letter Home" Mr. Bennett exercised a repression in his style that is not common in his work. He has compressed much drama into a short sketch, of which a good part is left to the imagination of the reader. In a few words he presents his characters and creates an atmosphere of impending tragedy. The story is practically nothing more than the dramatic climax. There is no waste of words in descriptive passages, no sentimental wailing over the futilities of life. It is a "hospital case," the focus on the letter being made doubly intense by the befuddled action of Darkey.

Besides novels and short stories, Mr. Bennett wrote a few plays, autobiographical sketches, books on self-improvement, and articles for papers and magazines. His *Journal* has been published (1933).

# A LETTER HOME

## I

RAIN was falling — it had fallen steadily through the night — but the sky showed promise of fairer weather. As the first streaks of dawn appeared, the wind died away, and the young leaves on the trees were almost silent. The birds were insistently clamorous, vociferating times without number that it was a healthy spring morning and good to be alive.

A little, bedraggled crowd stood before the park gates, awaiting the hour named on the notice board when they would be admitted to such lodging and shelter as iron seats and overspreading branches might afford. A weary, patient-eyed, dogged crowd — a dozen men, a boy of thirteen, and a couple of women, both past middle age — which had been gathering slowly since five o'clock. The boy appeared to be the least uncomfortable. His feet were bare, but he had slept well in an area in Grosvenor Place, and was not very damp yet. The women had nodded on many doorsteps, and were soaked. They stood apart from the men, who seemed unconscious of their existence. The men were exactly such as one would have expected to find there — beery and restless as to the eyes, quaintly shod, and with nondescript greenish clothes which for the most part bore traces of the yoke of the sandwich board. Only one amongst them was different.

He was young, and his cap, and manner of wearing it, gave sign of the sea. His face showed the rough outlines of his history. Yet it was a transparently honest face, very pale, but still boyish and fresh enough to make one wonder by what rapid descent he had reached his present level. Perhaps the receding chin, the heavy, pouting lower lip, and the ceaselessly twitching mouth offered a key to the problem.

"Say, Darkey!" he said.

"Well?"

"How much longer?"

"Can't ye see the clock? It's staring ye in the face."

"No. Something queer's come over my eyes."

Darkey was a short, sturdy man, who kept his head down and his hands deep in his pockets. The raindrops clinging to the rim of an ancient hat fell every now and then into his gray beard, which presented a drowned appearance. He was a person of long and varied experiences; he knew that queer feeling in the eyes, and his heart softened.

"Come, lean against the pillar," he said, "if you don't want to tumble. Three of brandy's what you want. There's four minutes to wait yet."

With body flattened to the masonry, legs apart, and head thrown back, Darkey's companion felt more secure, and his mercurial spirits began to revive. He took off his cap, and brushing back his light brown curly hair with the hand which held it, he looked down at Darkey through half-closed eyes, the play of his features divided between a smile and a yawn.

He had a lively sense of humor, and the irony of his situation was not lost on him. He took a grim, ferocious delight in calling up the might-have-beens and the "fatuous ineffectual yesterdays" of life. There is a certain sardonic satisfaction to be gleaned from a frank recognition of the fact that you are the architect of your own misfortune. He felt that satisfaction, and laughed at Darkey, who was one of those who moan about "ill-luck" and "victims of circumstance."

"No doubt," he would say, "you're a very deserving fellow, Darkey, who's been treated badly. I'm not."

To have attained such wisdom at twenty-five is not to have lived altogether in vain.

A park-keeper presently arrived to unlock the gates, and the band of outcasts straggled indolently towards the nearest sheltered seats. Some went to sleep at once, in a sitting posture. Darkey produced a clay pipe, and, charging it with a few shreds of tobacco laboriously gathered from his waistcoat pocket, began to smoke. He was accustomed to this sort of thing, and with a pipe in his mouth could contrive to be moderately philosophical upon occasion. He looked curiously at his companion, who lay stretched at full length on another bench.

"I say, pal," he remarked, "I've known ye two days; ye've never told me yer name, and I don't ask ye to. But I see ye've not slep' in a park before."

"You hit it, Darkey; but how?"

"Well, if the keeper catches ye lying down he'll be on to ye. Lying down's not allowed."

The man raised himself on his elbow.

"Really now," he said; "that's interesting. But I think I'll give the keeper the opportunity of moving me. Why, it's quite fine, the sun's coming out, and the sparrows are hopping round — cheeky little devils! I'm not sure that I don't feel jolly."

"I wish I'd got the price of a pint about me," sighed Darkey, and the other man dropped his head and appeared to sleep. Then Darkey dozed a little, and heard in his waking sleep the heavy, crunching tread of an approaching park-keeper; he started up to warn his companion, but thought better of it, and closed his eyes again.

"Now then, there," the park-keeper shouted to the man with the sailor's cap, "get up! This ain't a fourpenny doss, you know. No lying down."

A rough shake accompanied the words, and the man sat up.

"All right, my friend."

The keeper, who was a good-humored man, passed on without further objurgation.

The face of the younger man had grown whiter.

"Look here, Darkey," he said, "I believe I'm done for."

"Never say die."

"No, just die without speaking."

His head fell forward and his eyes closed.

"At any rate, this is better than some deaths I've seen," he began again with a strange accession of liveliness. "Darkey, did I tell you the story of the five Japanese girls?"

"What, in Suez Bay?" said Darkey, who had heard many sea-stories during the last two days, and recollected them but hazily.

"No, man. This was at Nagasaki. We were taking in a cargo of coal for Hongkong. Hundreds of little Jap girls pass the coal from hand to hand over the ship's side in tiny baskets that hold about a plateful. In that way you can get three thousand tons aboard in two days."

"Talking of platefuls reminds me of sausage and mash," said Darkey.

"Don't interrupt. Well, five of these gay little dolls wanted to go to Hongkong, and they arranged with the Chinese sailors to stow away; I believe their friends paid those cold-blooded fiends something to pass them down food on the voyage, and give them an airing at nights. We had a particularly lively trip, battened everything down tight, and scarcely uncovered till we got into port. Then I and another man found those five girls among the coal."

" Dead, eh? "

" They'd simply torn themselves to pieces. Their bits of frock things were in strips, and they were scratched deep from top to toe. The Chinese had never troubled their heads about them at all, although they must have known it meant death. You may bet there was a row. The Japanese authorities make you search ship before sailing, now."

" Well? "

" Well, I shan't die like that. That's all."

He stretched himself out once more, and for ten minutes neither spoke. The park-keeper strolled up again.

" Get up, there! " he said shortly and gruffly.

" Up ye get, mate," added Darkey, but the man on the bench did not stir. One look at his face sufficed to startle the keeper, and presently two policemen were wheeling an ambulance cart to the hospital. Darkey followed, gave such information as he could, and then went his own ways.

II

In the afternoon the patient regained full consciousness. His eyes wandered vacantly about the illimitable ward, with its rows of beds stretching away on either side of him. A woman with a white cap, a white apron, and white wristbands bent over him, and he felt something gratefully warm passing down his throat. For just one second he was happy. Then his memory returned, and the nurse saw that he was crying. When he caught the nurse's eye he ceased, and looked steadily at the distant ceiling.

" You're better? "

" Yes."

He tried to speak boldly, decisively, nonchalantly. He was filled with a sense of physical shame, the shame which bodily helplessness always experiences in the presence of arrogant, patronizing health. He would have got up and walked briskly away if he could. He hated to be waited on, to be humored, to be examined and theorized about. This woman would be wanting to feel his pulse. She should not; he would turn cantankerous. No doubt they had been saying to each other, " And so young, too! How sad! " Confound them!

" Have you any friends that you would like to send for? "

" No, none."

The girl — she was only a girl — looked at him, and there was that in her eye which overcame him.

" None at all? "

" Not that I want to see."

" Are your parents alive? "

" My mother is, but she lives away in the Five Towns."

" You've not seen her lately, perhaps? "

He did not reply, and the nurse spoke again, but her voice sounded indistinct and far off.

When he awoke it was night. At the other end of the ward was a long table covered with a white cloth, and on this table a lamp.

In the ring of light under the lamp was an open book, an inkstand and a pen. A nurse — not *his* nurse — was standing by the table, her fingers idly drumming the cloth, and near her a man in evening dress. Perhaps a doctor. They were conversing in low tones. In the middle of the ward was an open stove, and the restless flames were reflected in all the brass knobs of the bedsteads and in some shining metal balls which hung from an unlighted chandelier. His part of the ward was almost in darkness. A confused, subdued murmur of little coughs, breathings, rustlings, was continually audible, and sometimes it rose above the conversation at the table. He noticed all these things. He became conscious, too, of a strangely familiar smell. What was it? Ah, yes! Acetic acid; his mother used it for her rheumatics.

Suddenly, magically, a great longing came over him. He must see his mother, or his brothers, or his little sister — someone who knew him, someone who *belonged* to him. He could have cried out in his desire. This one thought consumed all his faculties. If his mother could but walk in just now through that doorway! If only old Spot even could amble up to him, tongue out and tail furiously wagging! He tried to sit up, and he could not move! Then despair settled on him, and weighed him down. He closed his eyes.

The doctor and the nurse came slowly up the ward, pausing

here and there. They stopped before his bed, and he held his breath.

"Not roused up again, I suppose?"

"No."

"H'm! He may flicker on for forty-eight hours. Not more."

They went on, and with a sigh of relief he opened his eyes again. The doctor shook hands with the nurse, who returned to the table and sat down.

Death! The end of all this. Yes, it was coming. He felt it. His had been one of those wasted lives of which he used to read in books. How strange! Almost amusing! He was one of those sons who bring sorrow and shame into a family. Again, how strange! What a coincidence that he — just *he* and not the man in the next bed — should be one of those rare, legendary good-for-nothings who go recklessly to ruin. And yet, he was sure that he was not such a bad fellow after all. Only somehow he had been careless. Yes, careless; that was the word . . . nothing worse. . . . As to death, he was indifferent. Remembering his father's death, he reflected that it was probably less disturbing to die one's self than to watch another pass.

He smelt the acetic acid once more, and his thoughts reverted to his mother. Poor mother! No, great mother! The grandeur of her life's struggle filled him with a sense of awe. Strange that until that moment he had never seen the heroic side of her humdrum, commonplace existence! He must write to her, now, at once, before it was too late. His letter would trouble her, add another wrinkle to her face, but he must write; she must know that he had been thinking of her.

"Nurse!" he cried out, in a thin, weak voice.

"Ssh!"

She was by his side directly, but not before he had lost consciousness again.

The following morning he managed with infinite labor to scrawl a few lines:

"DEAR MAMMA,

"You will be surprised but not glad to get this letter. I'm done for, and you will never see me again. I'm sorry for what I've done, and how I've treated you, but it's no use saying anything now. If Pater had only lived he might have kept me in order. But you were too kind, you know. You've had a hard struggle these last six years, and I hope Arthur and Dick will stand by you better than I did, now they are growing up. Give them my love, and kiss little Fannie for me.

WILLIE."

" *Mrs. Hancock ———* "

He got no further with the address.

### III

By some turn of the wheel, Darkey gathered several shillings during the next day or two, and, feeling both elated and benevolent, he called one afternoon at the hospital, " just to inquire like." They told him the man was dead.

" By the way, he left a letter without an address. Mrs. Hancock — here it is."

" That'll be his mother; he did tell me about her — lived at Knype, Staffordshire," he said. " I'll see to it."

They gave Darkey the letter.

" So his name's Hancock," he soliloquized, when he got into the street. " I knew a girl of that name — once. I'll go and have a pint of four-half."

At nine o'clock that night Darkey was still consuming four-half, and relating certain adventures by sea which, he averred, had happened to himself. He was very drunk.

" Yes," he said, " and them five lil gals was lying there without a stitch on 'em, dead as meat; 's true as I'm 'ere. I've seen a thing or two in my time, I can tell ye."

" Talking about these Anarchists — " said a man who appeared anxious to change the subject.

" An — kists," Darkey interrupted. " I tell ye what I'd do with that muck."

He stopped to light his pipe, looked in vain for a match, felt in his pockets, and pulled out a piece of paper — the letter.

" I tell you what I'd do. I'd —— "

He slowly and meditatively tore the letter in two, dropped one piece on the floor, thrust the other into a convenient gas-jet, and applied it to the tobacco.

"I'd get 'em 'gether in a heap, and I'd— Damn this pipe!"

He picked up the other half of the letter, and relighted the pipe.

"After you, mate," said a man sitting near, who was just biting the end from a cigar.

### QUESTIONS

1. Where had the group spent the previous night?
2. How does the setting help create an atmosphere of drabness?
3. What is meant by the reference to the "sandwich board"?
4. What qualities in the young outcast appeal to the reader's sympathy?
5. How is contrast used to keep up the interest?
6. What is the point in the story about the Jap girls?
7. What made the boy suddenly want to see his mother?
8. Was he right when he says that he "was not such a bad fellow after all"?
9. What may have caused him to leave home?
10. What does he mean by his reference to his father?
11. Is the end of the story made more or less pathetic because of Darkey?
12. Was it just as well that the letter never reached his mother?
13. Do you know any other writer who picked up characters on park benches?

### SUBJECTS FOR COMPOSITION

1. A character sketch of the boy. Avoid sentimentality.
2. Darkey Sobers Up.
3. Write an episode in the life of some waif.

### OTHER STORIES BY ARNOLD BENNETT

Phantom
The Idiot
Mary with the High Hand
(All in *Tales of the Five Towns*)

### VOLUMES OF STORIES BY ARNOLD BENNETT

*Tales of the Five Towns*      *Elsie and the Child*
*The Grim Smile of the Five Towns*   *The Woman Who Stole Everything*
*Matador of the Five Towns*

## ROBERT LOUIS STEVENSON
### (1850–1894)

ROBERT LOUIS STEVENSON'S first published short story was "A Lodging for the Night," purporting to be an episode in the life of François Villon, France's most picturesque literary vagabond. His first published books were *An Inland Voyage* and *Travels with a Donkey*, both dealing with actual experiences in France. These are but a few titles that show how much Stevenson himself was addicted to the habit of wandering.

Almost from the day of his birth, Nov. 13, 1850, he was an invalid, and his travels were usually made in search of health. From the rigorous winters of Edinburgh he took refuge in the south of England and in France. As a boy his education was irregular, but he eventually reached Edinburgh University, where he studied engineering, his father having destined him for the family profession, that of lighthouse construction. When it became clear that he could not pursue that calling the young man turned to the study of law, like his earlier fellow-townsman Scott, and, like that great romancer, he managed to pass the final examinations for the bar.

But his real interests had always been elsewhere. He says:

"All through my boyhood and youth I was known and pointed out for the pattern of an idler; and yet I was always busy on my own private end, which was to learn to write. I kept always two books in my pocket, one to read, one to write in. As I walked, my mind was busy fitting what I saw with appropriate words."

This practical enthusiasm for writing eventually made Stevenson one of the foremost stylists in modern English literature. At first he had but little success with editors. Even *Treasure Island* met with no enthusiasm. The best that happened in these early days was the making of many friendships that later were helpful. One of these was with the editor of the *Cornhill Magazine,* and after a time his work began to appear in that magazine as well as in other English journals.

Stevenson's first visit to America was not for the purpose of selling stories, but to pursue a personal romance of his own. On one of his periodical trips to France he had met Mrs. Osbourne, a lady from California, and had fallen in love with her. She was not free to marry him at that time and returned home. In 1879 Stevenson heard that she was very ill. He followed her. In 1880 marriage became possible and the Stevensons returned to England.

Stevenson now definitely gave himself over to authorship, as much as his fluctuating health allowed. But neither the south of France, nor Switzerland, was of final avail, and in 1887 he left for America where the Adirondacks afforded relief sufficient to enable him to work. In the spring of 1888 a trip to the South Seas was planned and undertaken. He took the keenest joy in adventuring about in those almost uncharted seas, and, as it happened, never again returned permanently to civilization. He settled down on one of the Samoan Islands, where he bought an estate from the natives and built himself a home, giving it the name Vailima, the Samoan for Five Waters. To the natives he became known as Tusitala, the Teller of Tales. His health was such that he was able to work with some regularity. But although he was cheerful and active, full of ideas, and undoubtedly courageous, his frail physique at last gave way, and he died on Dec. 13, 1894. In obedience to his own request, he was buried on a mountain top above his home, having been carried there by his native friends. Over his grave is a stone monument, on one side of which is his own " Requiem ":

> " Under the wide and starry sky,
>   Dig the grave and let me lie.
>   Glad did I live and gladly die,
>       And I laid me down with a will.

> " This be the verse you grave for me:
>   *Here he lies where he longed to be;
>   Home is the sailor, home from the sea,
>       And the hunter home from the hill."*

" Will o' the Mill," however romantic it may be, has two aspects rarely found in Stevenson — a well-defined attempt to portray a woman, and the lack of the ordinary adjuncts of a romance. As characters, women interested Stevenson less than men and boys. Think of all the Stevenson stories you know. Usually you will find the women mere types, necessary for the story, but chiefly to bring out the male characters. Ordinarily we think of romance as a series of dashing deeds, or wild adventures, whether in pursuit of fair lady or in search of buried treasure. One or more of these elements are sure to be found in Stevenson's stories — with the exception of " Will o' the Mill." And yet they are there too, in a way, in the imagination of Will. He feels all the allurements of that wonderful Land of Romance, the Great Unknown that lies beyond his own valley, along the shores of his river, in the bright cities of its banks, and on the rolling seas beyond.

This story embodies Stevenson's own longings; indeed one of the commonest of human traits, the universal desire to know what there is just around the corner. But in " Will o' the Mill " the emphasis lies in the fact that Will *longs,* but does not go forth to seek, as Stevenson himself did, and all his other heroes.

## WILL O' THE MILL

THE Mill where Will lived with his adopted parents stood in a falling valley between pinewoods and great mountains. Above, hill after hill soared upwards until they soared out of the depth of the hardiest timber, and stood naked against the sky. Some way up, a long gray village lay like a seam or a rag of vapor on a wooded hillside; and when the wind was favorable, the sound of the church bells would drop down, thin and silvery, to Will. Below, the valley grew ever steeper and steeper, and at the same time widened out on either hand; and from an eminence beside the mill it was possible to see its whole length and away beyond it over a wide plain, where the river turned and shone, and moved on from city to city on its voyage towards the sea. It chanced that over this valley there lay a pass into a neighboring kingdom, so that, quiet and rural as it was, the road that ran along beside the river was a high thoroughfare between two splendid and powerful societies. All through the summer, traveling carriages came crawling up, or went plunging briskly downwards past the mill; and as it happened that the other side was very much easier of ascent, the path was not much frequented, except by people going in one direction; and of all the carriages that Will saw go by, five-sixths were plunging briskly downwards and only one-sixth crawling up. Much more was this the case with foot-passengers. All the light-footed tourists, all the peddlers laden with strange wares, were tending downward like the river that accompanied their path. Nor was this all; for when Will was yet a child a disastrous war arose over a great part of the world. The newspapers were full of defeats and victories, the earth rang with cavalry hoofs, and often for days together and for miles around the coil of battle terrified good people from their labors in the field. Of all this, nothing was heard for a long time in the valley; but at last one of the commanders pushed an army over the pass by forced marches, and for three days horse and foot, cannon and tumbril, drum and standard, kept pouring downward past the mill. All day the child stood and watched them on their passage — the rhythmical stride, the pale, unshaven faces tanned about the eyes, the discolored regimentals and the tattered flags, filled him with a sense of weariness, pity, and wonder; and all night long, after he was in bed, he could hear the cannon pounding and the feet trampling, and the great armament sweeping onward and downward past the mill. No one in the valley ever heard the fate of the expedition, for they lay out of the way of gossip in those troublous times; but Will saw one thing plainly, that not a man returned. Whither had they all gone? Whither went all the tourists and peddlers with strange wares? whither all the brisk barouches with servants in the dicky? whither the water of the stream, ever coursing downward and ever renewed from above? Even the wind blew oftener down the valley, and carried the dead leaves along with it in the fall. It seemed like a great conspiracy of things animate and inanimate; they all went downward, fleetly and gaily downward, and only he, it seemed, remained behind, like a stock upon the wayside. It sometimes made him glad when he noticed how the fishes kept their heads up stream. They, at least, stood faithfully by him, while all else were posting downward to the unknown world.

One evening he asked the miller where the river went.

"It goes down the valley," answered he, "and turns a power of mills — six score mills, they say, from here to Unterdeck — and it none the wearier after all. And then it goes out into the lowlands and waters the great corn country, and runs through a sight of fine cities (so they say) where kings live all alone in great palaces, with a sentry walking up and down before the door. And it goes under bridges with stone men upon them, looking down and smiling so curious at the water, and living folks leaning their elbows on the wall and looking over too. And then it goes on and on, and down through marshes and sands, until at last it falls into the sea, where the ships are that bring parrots and tobacco from the Indies. Ay, it has a long trot before it as it goes singing over our weir, bless its heart!"

"And what is the sea?" asked Will.

"The sea!" cried the miller. "Lord help us all, it is the greatest thing God made! That is where all the water in the world runs down into a great salt lake. There it lies, as flat

as my hand and as innocent-like as a child; but they do say
when the wind blows it gets up into water-mountains bigger
than any of ours, and swallows down great ships bigger than
our mill, and makes such a roaring that you can hear it miles
away upon the land. There are great fish in it five times
bigger than a bull, and one old serpent as long as our river
and as old as all the world, with whiskers like a man, and a
crown of silver on her head."

Will thought he had never heard anything like this, and he
kept on asking question after question about the world that
lay away down the river, with all its perils and marvels, until
the old miller became quite interested himself, and at last
took him by the hand and led him to the hill-top that overlooks the valley and the plain. The sun was near setting,
and hung low down in a cloudless sky. Everything was defined and glorified in golden light. Will had never seen so
great an expanse of country in his life; he stood and gazed
with all his eyes. He could see the cities, and the woods
and fields, and the bright curves of the river, and far away
to where the rim of the plain trenched along the shining
heavens. An over-mastering emotion seized upon the boy,
soul and body; his heart beat so thickly that he could not
breathe; the scene swam before his eyes; the sun seemed to
wheel round and round, and throw off, as it turned, strange
shapes which disappeared with the rapidity of thought, and
were succeeded by others. Will covered his face with his
hands, and burst into a violent fit of tears; and the poor
miller, sadly disappointed and perplexed, saw nothing better
for it than to take him up in his arms and carry him home in
silence.

From that day forward Will was full of new hopes and longings. Something kept tugging at his heart-strings; the running water carried his desires along with it as he dreamed
over its fleeting surface; the wind, as it ran over innumerable
tree-tops, hailed him with encouraging words; branches beckoned downward; the open road, as it shouldered round the
angles and went turning and vanishing faster and faster down
the valley, tortured him with its solicitations. He spent long
whiles on the eminence, looking down the river-shed and
abroad on the flat lowlands, and watched the clouds that
traveled forth upon the sluggish wind and trailed their purple

shadows on the plain; or he would linger by the wayside, and follow the carriages with his eyes as they rattled downward by the river. It did not matter what it was; everything that went that way, were it cloud or carriage, bird or brown water in the stream, he felt his heart flow out after it in an ecstasy of longing.

We are told by men of science that all the ventures of mariners on the sea, all that counter-marching of tribes and races that confounds old history with its dust and rumor, sprang from nothing more abstruse than the laws of supply and demand, and a certain natural instinct for cheap rations. To any one thinking deeply, this will seem a dull and pitiful explanation. The tribes that came swarming out of the North and East, if they were indeed pressed onward from behind by others, were drawn at the same time by the magnetic influence of the South and West. The fame of other lands had reached them; the name of the eternal city rang in their ears; they were not colonists, but pilgrims; they traveled towards wine and gold and sunshine, but their hearts were set on something higher. That divine unrest, that old stinging trouble of humanity that makes all high achievements and all miserable failure, the same that spread wings with Icarus, the same that sent Columbus into the desolate Atlantic, inspired and supported these barbarians on their perilous march. There is one legend which profoundly represents their spirit, of how a flying party of these wanderers encountered a very old man shod with iron. The old man asked them whither they were going; and they answered with one voice: " To the Eternal City! " He looked upon them gravely. " I have sought it," he said, " over the most part of the world. Three such pairs as I now carry on my feet have I worn out upon this pilgrimage, and now the fourth is growing slender underneath my steps. And all this while I have not found the city." And he turned and went his own way alone, leaving them astonished.

And yet this would scarcely parallel the intensity of Will's feeling for the plain. If he could only go far enough out there, he felt as if his eyesight would be purged and clarified, as if his hearing would grow more delicate, and his very breath would come and go with luxury. He was transplanted and withering where he was; he lay in a strange country and was sick for home. Bit by bit, he pieced together broken notions of the world below: of the river, ever moving and growing until it sailed forth into the majestic ocean; of the cities, full of brisk and beautiful people, playing fountains, bands of music and marble palaces, and lighted up at night from end to end with artificial stars of gold; of the great churches, wise universities, brave armies, and untold money lying stored in vaults; of the high-flying vice that moved in the sunshine, and the stealth and swiftness of midnight murder. I have said he was sick as if for home: the figure halts. He was like some one lying in twilit, formless pre-existence, and stretching out his hands lovingly towards many-colored, many-sounding life. It was no wonder he was unhappy, he would go and tell the fish: they were made for their life, wished for no more than worms and running water, and a hole below a falling bank; but he was differently designed, full of desires and aspirations, itching at the fingers, lusting with the eyes, whom the whole variegated world could not satisfy with aspects. The true life, the true bright sunshine, lay far out upon the plain. And oh! to see this sunlight once before he died! to move with a jocund spirit in a golden land! to hear the trained singers and sweet church bells, and see the holiday gardens! "And O fish!" he would cry, "if you would only turn your noses down stream, you could swim so easily into the fabled waters and see the vast ships passing over your head like clouds, and hear the great water-hills making music over you all day long!" But the fish kept looking patiently in their own direction, until Will hardly knew whether to laugh or cry.

Hitherto the traffic on the road had passed by Will, like something seen in a picture: he had perhaps exchanged salutations with a tourist, or caught sight of an old gentleman in a traveling-cap at a carriage window; but for the most part it had been a mere symbol, which he contemplated from apart and with something of a superstitious feeling. A time came at last when this was to be changed. The miller, who was a greedy man in his way, and never forewent an opportunity of honest profit, turned the mill-house into a little wayside inn, and, several pieces of good fortune falling in opportunely, built stables and got the position of post-master on the road. It now became Will's duty to wait upon people, as they sat to break their fasts in the little arbor at the top of the mill garden; and you may be sure that he kept his ears open, and learned many new things about the outside world as he brought the omelette or the wine. Nay, he would often get into conversation with single guests, and by adroit questions and polite attention, not only gratify his own curiosity, but win the goodwill of the travelers. Many complimented the old couple on their serving-boy; and a professor was eager to take him away with him, and have him properly educated in the plain. The miller and his wife were mightily astonished and even more pleased. They thought it a very good thing that they should have opened their inn. "You see," the old man would remark, "he has a kind of talent for a publican; he never would have made anything else!" And so life wagged on in the valley, with high satisfaction to all concerned but Will. Every carriage that left the inn-door seemed to take a part of him away with it; and when people jestingly offered him a lift, he could with difficulty command his emotion. Night after night he would dream that he was awakened by flustered servants, and that a splendid equipage waited at the door to carry him down into the plain; night after night; until the dream, which had seemed all jollity to him at first, began to take on a color of gravity, and the nocturnal summons and waiting equipage occupied a place in his mind as something to be both feared and hoped for.

One day, when Will was about sixteen, a fat young man arrived at sunset to pass the night. He was a contented-looking fellow, with a jolly eye, and carried a knapsack. While dinner was preparing, he sat in the arbor to read a book; but as soon as he had begun to observe Will, the book was laid aside; he was plainly one of those who prefer living people to people made of ink and paper. Will, on his part, although he had not been much interested in the stranger at first sight, soon began to take a great deal of pleasure in his talk, which was full of good nature and good sense, and at last conceived a great respect for his character and wisdom. They sat far into the night; and about two in the morning Will opened his heart to the young man, and told him how he longed to leave the valley and what bright hopes he had connected with the cities of the plain. The young man whistled, and then broke into a smile.

"My young friend," he remarked, "you are a very curious little fellow to be sure, and wish a great many things which you will never get. Why, you would feel quite ashamed if you knew how the little fellows in these fairy cities of yours are all after the same sort of nonsense, and keep breaking their hearts to get up into the mountains. And let me tell you, those who go down into the plains are a very short while there before they wish themselves heartily back again. The air is not so light nor so pure; nor is the sun any brighter. As for the beautiful men and women, you would see many of them in rags and many of them deformed with horrible disorders; and a city is so hard a place for people who are poor and sensitive that many choose to die by their own hand."

"You must think me very simple," answered Will. "Although I have never been out of this valley, believe me, I have used my eyes. I know how one thing lives on another; for instance, how the fish hangs in the eddy to catch his fellows; and the shepherd, who makes so pretty a picture carrying home the lamb, is only carrying it home for dinner. I do not expect to find all things right in your cities. That is not what troubles me; it might have been that once upon a time; but although I live here always, I have asked many questions and learned a great deal in these last years, and certainly enough to cure me of my old fancies. But you would not have me die like a dog and not see all that is to be seen, and do all that a man can do, let it be good or evil? you would not have me spend all my days between this road here and the river, and not so much as make a motion to be up and live my life? — I would rather die out of hand," he cried, "than linger on as I am doing."

"Thousands of people," said the young man, "live and die like you, and are none the less happy."

"Ah!" said Will, "if there are thousands who would like, why should not one of them have my place?"

It was quite dark; there was a hanging lamp in the arbor which lit up the table and the faces of the speakers; and along the arch, the leaves upon the trellis stood out illuminated against the night sky, a pattern of transparent green upon a dusky purple. The fat young man rose, and, taking Will by the arm, led him out under the open heavens.

"Did you ever look at the stars?" he asked, pointing upwards.

"Often and often," answered Will.

"And do you know what they are?"

"I have fancied many things."

"They are worlds like ours," said the young man. "Some of them less; many of them a million times greater; and some of the least sparkles that you see are not only worlds, but whole clusters of worlds turning about each other in the midst of space. We do not know what there may be in any of them; perhaps the answer to all our difficulties or the cure of all our sufferings: and yet we can never reach them; not all the skill of the craftiest of men can fit out a ship for the nearest of these our neighbors, nor would the life of the most aged suffice for such a journey. When a great battle has been lost or a dear friend is dead, when we are hipped or in high spirits, there they are unweariedly shining overhead. We may stand down here, a whole army of us together, and shout until we break our hearts, and not a whisper reaches them. We may climb the highest mountain, and we are no nearer them. All we can do is to stand down here in the garden and take off our hats; the starshine lights upon our heads, and where mine is a little bald, I dare say you can see it glisten in the darkness. The mountain and the mouse. That is like to be all we shall ever have to do with Arcturus or Aldebaran. Can you apply a parable?" he added, laying his hand upon Will's shoulder. "It is not the same thing as a reason, but usually vastly more convincing."

Will hung his head a little, and then raised it once more to heaven. The stars seem to expand and emit a sharper brilliancy; and as he kept turning his eyes higher and higher, they seemed to increase in multitude under his gaze.

"I see," he said, turning to the young man. "We are in a rat-trap."

"Something of that size. Did you ever see a squirrel turning in a cage? and another squirrel sitting philosophically over his nuts? I needn't ask you which of them looked more of a fool."

### THE PARSON'S MARJORY

After some years the old people died, both in one winter, very carefully tended by their adopted son, and very quietly mourned when they were gone. People who had heard of his roving fancies supposed he would hasten to sell the property, and go down the river to push his fortunes. But there was never any sign of such an intention on the part of Will. On the contrary, he had the inn set on a better footing, and hired a couple of servants to assist him in carrying it on; and there he settled down, a kind, talkative, inscrutable young man, six feet three in his stockings, with an iron constitution and a friendly voice. He soon began to take rank in the district as a bit of an oddity: it was not much to be wondered at from the first, for he was always full of notions, and kept calling the plainest common-sense in question; but what most raised the report upon him was the odd circumstance of his courtship with the parson's Marjory.

The parson's Marjory was a lass about nineteen, when Will would be about thirty; well enough looking, and much better educated than any other girl in that part of the country, as became her parentage. She held her head very high, and had already refused several offers of marriage with a grand air, which had got her hard names among the neighbors. For all that she was a good girl, and one that would have made any man well contented.

Will had never seen much of her; for although the church and parsonage were only two miles from his own door, he was never known to go there but on Sundays. It chanced, however, that the parsonage fell into disrepair, and had to be dismantled; and the parson and his daughter took lodgings for a month or so, on very much reduced terms, at Will's inn. Now, what with the inn, and the mill, and the old miller's savings, our friend was a man of substance; and besides that, he had a name for good temper and shrewdness, which make a capital portion in marriage; and so it was currently gossiped, among their ill-wishers, that the parson and his daughter had not chosen their temporary lodging with their eyes shut. Will was about the last man in the world to be cajoled or frightened into marriage. You had only to look into his eyes, limpid and still like pools of water, and yet with a sort of clear light that seemed to come from within, and you would understand at once that here was one who knew his own mind, and would stand to it immovably. Marjory herself was no weakling by her looks, with strong steady eyes and a resolute and quiet bearing. It might be a question whether she was not Will's match in steadfastness, after all, or which of them would rule the roost in marriage. But Marjory had never given it a thought, and accompanied her father with the most unshaken innocence and unconcern.

The season was still so early that Will's customers were few and far between; but the lilacs were already flowering, and the weather was so mild that the party took dinner under the trellis, with the noise of the river in their ears and the woods ringing about them with the songs of birds. Will soon began to take a particular pleasure in these dinners. The parson was rather a dull companion, with a habit of dozing at table; but nothing rude or cruel ever fell from his lips. And as for the parson's daughter, she suited her surroundings with the best grace imaginable; and whatever she said seemed so pat and pretty that Will conceived a great idea of her talents. He could see her face, as she leaned forward, against a background of rising pine woods; her eyes shone peaceably; the light lay around her hair like a kerchief; something that was hardly a smile rippled her pale cheeks, and Will could not contain himself from gazing on her in an agreeable dismay. She looked, even in her quietest moments, so complete in herself, and so quick with life down to her finger tips and the very skirts of her dress, that the remainder of created things became no more than a blot by comparison; and if Will glanced away from her to her surroundings, the trees looked inanimate and senseless, the clouds hung in heaven like dead things, and even the mountain tops were disenchanted. The whole valley could not compare in looks with this one girl.

Will was always observant in the society of his fellow-creatures; but his observation became almost painfully eager in the case of Marjory. He listened to all she uttered, and read her eyes, at the same time, for the unspoken commentary. Many kind, simple, and sincere speeches found an echo in his heart. He became conscious of a soul beautifully poised upon itself, nothing doubting, nothing desiring, clothed in peace. It was not possible to separate her thoughts from her appearance. The turn of her wrist, the still sound of her voice, the light in her eyes, the lines of her body, fell in tune with her grave and gentle words, like the accompaniment that sustains and harmonizes the voice of the singer. Her influence was one thing, not to be divided or discussed, only to be felt with gratitude and joy. To Will, her presence recalled something of his childhood, and the thought of her took its place in his mind beside that of dawn, of running water, and of the earliest violets and lilacs. It is the property of things seen for the first time, or for the first time after long, like the flowers in spring, to reawaken in us the sharp edge of sense and that impression of mystic strangeness which otherwise passes out of life with the coming of years; but the sight of a loved face is what renews a man's character from the fountain upwards.

One day after dinner Will took a stroll among the firs; a grave beatitude possessed him from top to toe, and he kept smiling to himself and the landscape as he went. The river ran between the stepping-stones with a pretty wimple; a bird sang loudly in the wood; the hill-tops looked immeasurably high, and as he glanced at them from time to time seemed to contemplate his movements with a beneficent but awful curiosity. His way took him to the eminence which overlooked the plain; and there he sat down upon a stone, and fell into deep and pleasant thought. The plain lay abroad with its cities and silver river; everything was asleep, except a great eddy of birds which kept rising and falling and going round and round in the blue air. He repeated Marjory's name aloud, and the sound of it gratified his ear. He shut his eyes, and her image sprang up before him, quietly luminous and attended with good thoughts. The river might run for ever; the birds fly higher and higher till they touched the stars. He saw it was empty bustle after all; for here, without stirring a foot, waiting patiently in his own narrow valley, he also had attained the better sunlight.

The next day Will made a sort of declaration across the dinner-table, while the parson was filling his pipe.

"Miss Marjory," he said, "I never knew any one I liked so well as you. I am mostly a cold, unkindly sort of man; not from want of heart, but out of strangeness in my way of thinking; and people seem far away from me. 'Tis as if there were a circle round me, which kept every one out but you; I can hear the others talking and laughing; but you come quite close. Maybe this is disagreeable to you?" he asked.

Marjory made no answer.

"Speak up, girl," said the parson.

"Nay, now," returned Will, "I wouldn't press her, parson. I feel tongue-tied myself, who am not used to it; and she's a woman, and little more than a child, when all is said. But for my part, as far as I can understand what people mean by it, I fancy I must be what they call in love. I do not wish to be held as committing myself; for I may be wrong; but that is how I believe things are with me. And if Miss Marjory should feel any otherwise on her part, mayhap she would be so kind as shake her head."

Marjory was silent, and gave no sign that she had heard.

"How is that, parson?" asked Will.

"The girl must speak," replied the parson, laying down his pipe. "Here's our neighbor who says he loves you, Madge. Do you love him, ay or no?"

"I think I do," said Marjory faintly.

"Well, then, that's all that could be wished!" cried Will heartily. And he took her hand across the table, and held it a moment in both of his with great satisfaction.

"You must marry," observed the parson, replacing his pipe in his mouth.

"Is that the right thing to do, think you?" demanded Will.

"It is indispensable," said the parson.

"Very well," replied the wooer.

Two or three days passed away with great delight to Will, although a bystander might scarce have found it out. He continued to take his meals opposite Marjory, and to talk with her and gaze upon her in her father's presence; but he made no attempt to see her alone, nor in any other way changed his conduct towards her from what it had been since the beginning. Perhaps the girl was a little disappointed, and perhaps not unjustly; and yet if it had been enough to be always in the thoughts of another person, and so pervade and alter his whole life, she might have been thoroughly contented. For she was never out of Will's mind for an instant. He sat over the stream, and watched the dust of the eddy, and the poised fish, and straining weeds; he wandered out alone into the purple even, with all the blackbirds piping round him in the woods; he rose early in the morning, and saw the sky turn from grey to gold, and the light leap upon the hill-tops; and all the while he kept wondering if he had never seen such things before, or how it was that they should look so different now. The sound of his own mill-wheel, or of the wind among the trees, confounded and charmed his heart. The most enchanting thoughts presented themselves unbidden in his mind. He was so happy that he could not sleep at night, and so restless that he could hardly sit still out of her company. And yet it seemed as if he avoided her rather than sought her out.

One day, as he was coming home from a ramble, Will found Marjory in the garden picking flowers, and as he came up with her, slackened his pace and continued walking by her side.

"You like flowers?" he said.

"Indeed I love them dearly," she replied. "Do you?"

"Why, no," said he, "not so much. They are a very small affair, when all is done. I can fancy people caring for them greatly, but not doing as you are just now."

"How?" she asked, pausing and looking up at him.

"Plucking them," said he. "They are a deal better off where they are, and look a deal prettier, if you go to that."

"I wish to have them for my own," she answered, "to carry them near my heart, and keep them in my room. They tempt me when they grow here; they seem to say, 'Come and do something with us'; but once I have cut them and put them by, the charm is laid, and I can look at them with quite an easy heart."

"You wish to possess them," replied Will, "in order to think no more about them. It's a bit like killing the goose with the golden eggs. It's a bit like what I wished to do when I was a boy. Because I had a fancy for looking out over the plain, I wished to go down there — where I couldn't look out over it any longer. Was not that fine reasoning? Dear, dear, if they only thought of it, all the world would do like me; and you would let your flowers alone, just as I stay up here in the mountains." Suddenly he broke off sharp. "By the Lord!" he cried. And when she asked him what was wrong, he turned the question off, and walked away into the house with rather a humorous expression of face.

He was silent at table; and after the night had fallen and the stars had come out overhead, he walked up and down for hours in the court-yard and garden with an uneven pace. There was still a light in the window of Marjory's room: one little oblong patch of orange in a world of dark blue hills and silver starlight. Will's mind ran a great deal on the window; but his thoughts were not very lover-like. "There she is in her room," he thought, "and there are the stars overhead: — a blessing upon both!" Both were good influences in his life; both soothed and braced him in his profound contentment with the world. And what more should he desire with either? The fat young man and his counsels were so present to his mind that he threw back his head, and, putting his hands before his mouth, shouted aloud to the populous heavens. Whether from the position of his head or the sudden strain of the exertion, he seemed to see a momentary shock among the stars, and a diffusion of frosty light pass from one to another along the sky. At the same instant, a corner of the blind was lifted up and lowered again at once. He laughed a loud ho-ho! "One and another!" thought Will. "The stars tremble, and the blind goes up. Why, before Heaven, what a great magician I must be! Now, if I were only a fool, should not I be in a pretty way?" And he went off to bed, chuckling to himself: "If I were only a fool!"

The next morning, pretty early, he saw her once more in the garden, and sought her out.

"I have been thinking about getting married," he began abruptly; "and after having turned it all over, I have made up my mind it's not worth while."

She turned upon him for a single moment; but his radiant, kindly appearance would, under the circumstances, have disconcerted an angel, and she looked down again upon the ground in silence. He could see her tremble.

"I hope you don't mind," he went on, a little taken aback. "You ought not. I have turned it all over, and upon my soul there's nothing in it. We should never be one whit nearer than we are just now, and, if I am a wise man, nothing like so happy."

"It is unnecessary to go round about with me," she said. "I very well remember that you refused to commit yourself; and now that I see you were mistaken, and in reality have never cared for me, I can only feel sad that I have been so far misled."

"I ask your pardon," said Will stoutly; "you do not understand my meaning. As to whether I have ever loved you or not, I must leave that to others. But for one thing, my feeling is not changed; and for another, you may make it your boast that you have made my whole life and character something different from what they were. I mean what I say; no less I do not think getting married is worth while. I would rather you went on living with your father, so that I could walk over and see you once, or maybe twice a week, as people go to church, and then we should both be all the happier between whiles. That's my notion. But I'll marry you if you will," he added.

"Do you know that you are insulting me?" she broke out.

"Not I, Marjory," said he; "if there is anything in a clear conscience, not I. I offer all my heart's best affections; you can take it or want it, though I suspect it's beyond either your power or mine to change what has once been done, and set me fancy-free I'll marry you, if you like; but I tell you again and again, it's not worth while, and we had best stay friends. Though I am a quiet man I have noticed a heap of things in my life. Trust in me, and take things as I propose; or, if you don't like that, say the word, and I'll marry you out of hand."

There was a considerable pause, and Will, who began to feel uneasy, began to grow angry in consequence.

"It seems you are too proud to say your mind," he said. "Believe me, that's a pity. A clean shrift makes simple living. Can a man be more downright or honorable to a woman than I have been? I have said my say, and given you your choice. Do you want me to marry you? or will you take my friendship, as I think best? or have you had enough of me for good? Speak out for the dear God's sake! You know your father told you a girl should speak her mind in these affairs."

She seemed to recover herself at that, turned without a word, walked rapidly through the garden, and disappeared into the house, leaving Will in some confusion as to the result. He walked up and down the garden, whistling softly to himself. Sometimes he stopped and contemplated the sky and hill-tops; sometimes he went down to the tail of the weir and sat there, looking foolishly in the water. All this dubiety and perturbation was so foreign to his nature and the life which he had resolutely chosen for himself, that he began to regret

Marjory's arrival. "After all," he thought, "I was as happy as a man need be. I could come down here and watch my fishes all day long if I wanted: I was as settled and contented as my old mill."

Marjory came down to dinner, looking very trim and quiet; and no sooner were all three at table than she made her father a speech, with her eyes fixed upon her plate, but showing no other sign of embarrassment or distress.

"Father," she began, "Mr. Will and I have been talking things over. We see that we have each made a mistake about our feelings, and he has agreed, at my request, to give up all idea of marriage, and be no more than my very good friend, as in the past. You see, there is no shadow of a quarrel, and indeed I hope we shall see a great deal of him in the future, for his visits will always be welcome in our house. Of course, father, you will know best, but perhaps we should do better to leave Mr. Will's house for the present. I believe, after what has passed, we should hardly be agreeable inmates for some days."

Will, who had commanded himself with difficulty from the first, broke out upon this into an inarticulate noise, and raised one hand with an appearance of real dismay, as if he were about to interfere and contradict. But she checked him at once, looking up at him with a swift glance and an angry flush upon her cheek.

"You will perhaps have the good grace," she said, "to let me explain these matters for myself."

Will was put entirely out of countenance by her expression and the ring of her voice. He held his peace, concluding that there were some things about this girl beyond his comprehension, in which he was exactly right.

The poor parson was quite crestfallen. He tried to prove that this was no more than a true lovers' tiff, which would pass off before night; and when he was dislodged from that position, he went on to argue that where there was no quarrel there could be no call for a separation; for the good man liked both his entertainment and his host. It was curious to see how the girl managed them, saying little all the time, and that very quietly, and yet twisting them round her finger and insensibly leading them wherever she would by feminine tact and generalship. It scarcely seemed to have been her doing

— it seemed as if things had merely so fallen out — that she and her father took their departure that same afternoon in a farm-cart, and went farther down the valley, to wait, until their own house was ready for them, in another hamlet. But Will had been observing closely, and was well aware of her dexterity and resolution. When he found himself alone he had a great many curious matters to turn over in his mind. He was very sad and solitary, to begin with. All the interest had gone out of his life; and he might look up at the stars as long as he pleased, he somehow failed to find support or consolation. And then he was in such a turmoil of spirit about Marjory. He had been puzzled and irritated at her behavior, and yet he could not keep himself from admiring it. He thought he recognized a fine perverse angel in that still soul which he had never hitherto suspected; and though he saw it was an influence that would fit but ill with his own life of artificial calm, he could not keep himself from ardently desiring to possess it. Like a man who has lived among shadows and now meets the sun, he was both pained and delighted.

As the days went forward he passed from one extreme to another; now pluming himself on the strength of his determination, now despising his timid and silly caution. The former was, perhaps, the true thought of his heart, and represented the regular tenor of the man's reflections; but the latter burst forth from time to time with an unruly violence, and then he would forget all consideration, and go up and down his house and garden or walk among the fir woods like one who is beside himself with remorse. To equable, steady-minded Will this state of matters was intolerable; and he determined, at whatever cost, to bring it to an end. So, one warm summer afternoon he put on his best clothes, took a thorn switch in his hand, and set out down the valley by the river. As soon as he had taken his determination, he had regained at a bound his customary peace of heart, and he enjoyed the bright weather and the variety of the scene without any admixture of alarm or unpleasant eagerness. It was nearly the same to him how the matter turned out. If she accepted him, he would have to marry her this time, which perhaps was all for the best. If she refused him, he would have done his utmost, and might follow his own way in the future with an untroubled conscience. He hoped, on the whole, she would refuse him; and then, again, as he saw the brown roof which sheltered her, peeping through some willows at an angle of the stream, he was half inclined to reverse the wish, and more than half ashamed of himself for this infirmity of purpose.

Marjory seemed glad to see him, and gave him her hand without affectation or delay.

"I have been thinking about this marriage," he began.

"So have I," she answered. "And I respect you more and more for a very wise man. You understood me better than I understood myself; and I am now quite certain that things are all for the best as they are."

"At the same time — " ventured Will.

"You must be tired," she interrupted. "Take a seat and let me fetch you a glass of wine. The afternoon is so warm; and I wish you not to be displeased with your visit. You must come quite often; once a week, if you can spare the time; I am always so glad to see my friends."

"Oh, very well," thought Will to himself. "It appears I was right after all." And he paid a very agreeable visit, walked home again in capital spirits, and gave himself no further concern about the matter.

For nearly three years Will and Marjory continued on these terms, seeing each other once or twice a week without any word of love between them; and for all that time I believe Will was nearly as happy as a man can be. He rather stinted himself the pleasure of seeing her; and he would often walk half-way over to the parsonage, and then back again, as if to whet his appetite. Indeed there was one corner of the road, whence he could see the church-spire wedged into a crevice of the valley between sloping fir woods, with a triangular snatch of plain by way of background, which he greatly affected as a place to sit and moralize in before returning homewards; and the peasants got so much into the habit of finding him there in the twilight that they gave it the name of "Will o' the Mill's Corner."

At the end of the three years Marjory played him a sad trick by suddenly marrying somebody else. Will kept his countenance bravely, and merely remarked that, for as little as he knew of women, he had acted very prudently in not marrying her himself three years before. She plainly knew very little of her own mind, and, in spite of a deceptive manner, was as fickle and flighty as the rest of them. He had to congratulate himself on an escape, he said, and would take a higher opinion of his own wisdom in consequence. But at heart, he was reasonably displeased, moped a good deal for a month or two, and fell away in flesh, to the astonishment of his serving-lads.

It was perhaps a year after this marriage that Will was awakened late one night by the sound of a horse galloping on the road, followed by precipitate knocking at the inn-door. He opened his window and saw a farm servant, mounted and holding a led horse by the bridle, who told him to make what haste he could and go along with him; for Marjory was dying, and had sent urgently to fetch him to her bedside. Will was no horseman, and made so little speed upon the way that the poor young wife was very near her end before he arrived. But they had some minutes' talk in private, and he was present and wept very bitterly while she breathed her last.

## DEATH

Year after year went away into nothing, with great explosions and outcries in the cities on the plain; red revolt springing up and being suppressed in blood, battle swaying hither and thither, patient astronomers in observatory towers picking out and christening new stars, plays being performed in lighted theaters, people being carried into hospitals on stretchers, and all the usual turmoil and agitation of men's lives in crowded centers. Up in Will's valley only the winds and seasons made an epoch; the fish hung in the swift stream, the birds circled overhead, the pine-tops rustled underneath the stars, the tall hills stood over all; and Will went to and fro, minding his wayside inn, until the snow began to thicken on his head. His heart was young and vigorous and if his pulses kept a sober time, they still beat strong and steady in his wrists. He carried a ruddy stain on either cheek, like a ripe apple; he stooped a little, but his step was still firm; and his sinewy hands were reached out to all men with a friendly pressure. His face was covered with those wrinkles which are got in open air, and which, rightly looked at, are no more than a sort of permanent sunburning; such wrinkles heighten the stupidity of stupid faces; but to a person like Will, with his clear eyes and smiling mouth, only give another charm by testifying to a simple and easy life. His talk was full of wise sayings. He had a taste for other people; and other people had a taste for him. When the valley was full of tourists in the season, there were merry nights in Will's arbor; and his views, which seemed whimsical to his neighbors, were often enough admired by learned people out of towns and colleges. Indeed, he had a very noble old age, and grew daily better known; so that his fame was heard of in the cities of the plain; and young men who had been summer travelers spoke together in cafés of Will o' the Mill and his rough philosophy. Many and many an invitation, you may be sure, he had; but nothing could tempt him from his upland valley. He would shake his head and smile over his tobacco-pipe with a deal of meaning. " You come too late," he would answer. " I am a dead man now: I have lived and died already. Fifty years ago you would have brought my heart into my mouth; and now you do not even tempt me. But that is the object of long living, that man should cease to care about life." And again: " There is only one difference between a long life and a good dinner: that, in the dinner, the sweets come last." Or once more: " When I was a boy, I was a bit puzzled, and hardly knew whether it was myself or the world that was curious and worth looking into. Now, I know it is myself, and stick to that."

He never showed any symptoms of frailty, but kept stalwart and firm to the last; but they say he grew less talkative towards the end, and would listen to other people by the hour in an amused and sympathetic silence. Only, when he did speak, it was more to the point and more charged with old experience. He drank a bottle of wine gladly; above all, at sunset on the hill-top or quite late at night under the stars in the arbor. The sight of something attractive and unattainable seasoned his enjoyment, he would say; and he professed he had lived long enough to admire a candle all the more when he could compare it with a planet.

One night, in his seventy-second year, he awoke in bed, in such uneasiness of body and mind that he arose and dressed himself and went out to meditate in the arbor. It was pitch dark, without a star; the river was swollen, and the wet woods and meadows loaded the air with perfume. It had thundered during the day, and it promised more thunder for the morrow. A murky, stifling night for a man of seventy-two! Whether it was the weather or the wakefulness, or some little touch of fever in his old limbs, Will's mind was besieged by tumultuous and crying memories. His boyhood, the night with the fat young man, the death of his adopted parents, the summer days with Marjory, and many of those small circumstances, which seem nothing to another, and are yet the very gist of a man's own life to himself — things seen, words heard, looks misconstrued — arose from their forgotten corners and usurped his attention. The dead themselves were with him, not merely taking part in this thin show of memory that defiled before his brain, but revisiting his bodily senses as they do in profound and vivid dreams. The fat young man leaned his elbows on the table opposite; Marjory came and went with an apronful of flowers between the garden and the arbor; he could hear the old parson knocking out his pipe or blowing his resonant nose. The tide of his consciousness ebbed and flowed; he was sometimes half asleep and drowned in his recollections of the past; and sometimes he was broad awake, wondering at himself. But about the middle of the night he was startled by the voice of the dead miller calling to him out of the house as he used to do on the arrival of custom. The hallucination was so perfect that Will sprang from his seat and stood listening for the summons to be repeated; and as he listened he became conscious of another noise besides the brawling of the river and the ringing in his feverish ears. It was like the stir of the horses and the creaking of harness, as though a carriage with an impatient team had been brought up upon the road before the court-yard gate. At such an hour, upon this rough and dangerous pass, the supposition was no better than absurd; and Will dismissed it from his mind, and resumed his seat upon the arbor chair; and sleep closed over him again like running water. He was once again awakened by the dead miller's call, thinner and more spectral than before; and once again he heard the noise of an equipage upon the road. And so thrice and four times, the same dream, or the same fancy, presented itself to his senses: until at length, smiling to himself as when one humors a nervous child, he proceeded towards the gate to set his uncertainty at rest.

From the arbor to the gate was no great distance, and yet it took Will some time; it seemed as if the dead thickened around him in the court, and crossed his path at every step. For, first, he was suddenly surprised by an overpowering sweetness of heliotropes; it was as if his garden had been planted with this flower from end to end, and the hot, damp night had drawn forth all their perfumes in a breath. Now the heliotrope had been Marjory's favorite flower, and since her death not one of them had ever been planted in Will's ground.

"I must be going crazy," he thought. "Poor Marjory and her heliotropes!"

And with that he raised his eyes towards the window that had once been hers. If he had been bewildered before, he was now almost terrified; for there was a light in the room; the window was an orange oblong as of yore; and the corner of the blind was lifted and let fall as on the night when he stood and shouted to the stars in his perplexity. The illusion only endured an instant; but it left him somewhat unmanned, rubbing his eyes and staring at the outline of the house and the black night behind it. While he thus stood, and it seemed as if he must have stood there quite a long time, there came a renewal of the noises on the road: and he turned in time to meet a stranger, who was advancing to meet him across the court. There was something like the outline of a great carriage discernible on the road behind the stranger, and, above that, a few black pinetops, like so many plumes.

"Master Will?" asked the new-comer, in brief military fashion.

"That same, sir," answered Will. "Can I do anything to serve you?"

"I have heard you much spoken of, Master Will," returned the other; "much spoken of, and well. And though I have both hands full of business, I wish to drink a bottle of wine with you in your arbor. Before I go, I shall introduce myself."

Will led the way to the trellis, and got a lamp lighted and a bottle uncorked. He was not altogether unused to such complimentary interviews, and hoped little enough from this one, being schooled by many disappointments. A sort of cloud had settled on his wits and prevented him from remembering the strangeness of the hour. He moved like a person in his sleep; and it seemed as if the lamp caught fire and the bottle came uncorked with the facility of thought. Still, he had some curiosity about the appearance of his visitor, and tried in vain to turn the light into his face; either he handled the lamp clumsily, or there was a dimness over his eyes; but he could make out little more than a shadow at table with him. He stared and stared at this shadow, as he wiped out the glasses, and began to feel cold and strange about the heart. The silence weighed upon him, for he could hear nothing now, not even the river, but the drumming of his own arteries in his ears.

"Here's to you," said the stranger roughly.

"Here is my service, sir," replied Will, sipping his wine, which somehow tasted oddly.

"I understand you are a very positive fellow," pursued the stranger.

Will made answer with a smile of some satisfaction and a little nod.

"So am I," continued the other; "and it is the delight of my heart to tramp on people's corns. I will have nobody positive but myself; not one. I have crossed the whims, in my time, of kings and generals and great artists. And what would you say," he went on, "if I had come up here on purpose to cross yours?"

Will had it on his tongue to make a sharp rejoinder; but the politeness of an old innkeeper prevailed; and he held his peace and made answer with a civil gesture of the hand.

"I have," said the stranger. "And if I did not hold you in a particular esteem, I should make no words about the matter. It appears you pride yourself on staying where you are. You mean to stick by your inn. Now I mean you shall come for a turn with me in my barouche; and before this bottle's empty, so you shall."

"That would be an odd thing, to be sure," replied Will, with a chuckle. "Why, sir, I have grown here like an old oak tree; the Devil himself could hardly root me up; and for all I perceive you are a very entertaining old gentleman, I would wager you another bottle you lose your pains with me."

The dimness of Will's eyesight had been increasing all this while; but he was somehow conscious of a sharp and chilling scrutiny which irritated and yet overmastered him.

"You need not think," he broke out suddenly, in an explosive, febrile manner that startled and alarmed himself, "that I am a stay-at-home, because I fear anything under God. God knows I am tired enough of it all; and when the time comes for a longer journey than ever you dream of, I reckon I shall find myself prepared."

The stranger emptied his glass and pushed it away from him. He looked down for a little, and then, leaning over the table, tapped Will three times upon the forearm with a single finger. "The time has come!" he said solemnly.

An ugly thrill spread from the spot he touched. The tones of his voice were dull and startling, and echoed strangely in Will's heart.

"I beg your pardon," he said, with some discomposure. "What do you mean?"

"Look at me, and you will find your eyesight swim. Raise your hand; it is dead-heavy. This is your last bottle of wine, Master Will, and your last night upon the earth."

"You are a doctor?" quavered Will.

"The best that ever was," replied the other; "for I cure both mind and body with the same prescription. I take away all pain and I forgive all sins; and where my patients have gone wrong in life, I smooth out all complications and set them free again upon their feet."

"I have no need of you," said Will.

"A time comes for all men, Master Will," replied the doctor, "when the helm is taken out of their hands. For you, because you were prudent and quiet, it has been long of coming, and you have had long to discipline yourself for its reception. You have seen what is to be seen about your mill; you have sat close all your days like a hare in its form; but now that is at an end; and," added the doctor, getting on his feet, "you must arise and come with me."

"You are a strange physician," said Will, looking steadfastly upon his guest.

"I am a natural law," he replied, "and people call me Death."

"Why did you not tell me so at first?" cried Will. "I have been waiting for you these many years. Give me your hand, and welcome."

"Lean upon my arm," said the stranger, "for already your strength abates. Lean on me heavily as you need; for though I am old, I am very strong. It is but three steps to my carriage, and there all your trouble ends. Why, Will," he added, "I have been yearning for you as if you were my own son; and of all the men that ever I came for in my long days, I have come for you most gladly. I am caustic, and sometimes offend people at first sight; but I am a good friend at heart to such as you."

"Since Marjory was taken," returned Will, "I declare before God you were the only friend I had to look for."

So the pair went arm in arm across the court-yard.

One of the servants awoke about this time and heard the noise of horses pawing before he dropped asleep again; all down the valley that night there was a rushing as of a smooth and steady wind descending towards the plain; and when the world rose next morning, sure enough Will o' the Mill had gone at last upon his travels.

## QUESTIONS

1. From memory, give an oral description of the mill and its location.
2. Are Will's questions about the river and the sea such as a boy might ask?
3. Write down all the important steps in Will's life: his first view from the mountain, etc.
4. How did the "fat young man's" view of life differ from Will's?
5. What does Will mean when he concludes that "we are in a rat-trap"?
6. Was he more contented after his talk with the young man?
7. What type of girl was Marjory? Romantic, designing, or what?
8. Is Will's attitude in harmony with his character? Explain.
9. What was the parson's idea of the match?
10. How and to whom did Will express his ecstasy of love?
11. Did Marjory understand his method of courtship?
12. Contrast Will's idea of plucking flowers with that of the girl.
13. To which do you feel more sympathetic, and why?
14. Just exactly what expression by Will indicates a turn in his love affair?
15. Explain in detail this change and its reasons. It is important in understanding Will's character.

# Will o' the Mill

16. Did Will ever really regret his action?
17. What happened at the bedside of the dying Marjory?
18. Does Will change as he grows older?
19. Has he changed in his inner life? Pick out passages that prove your answer.
20. In the last scene of all, does his character hold up? Or does he cringe at any point?
21. He says, "I have been waiting for you these many years." Does he mean it? Give reasons for your answer.
22. How do you like the author's method of describing death? Contrast it with that of other authors you know.
23. With the whole story in mind, answer frankly: Does the interest keep up even though nothing much happens except the death of all the characters?
24. Would you call it a sad story? Explain.

## SUBJECTS FOR COMPOSITION

1. Describe Will and his manner of life when he was an old man.
2. An old man becomes reminiscent about the dreams of his youth.
3. From the point of view of an observer, write an episode in the life of a person thought by the world to be queer.

## OTHER STORIES BY ROBERT LOUIS STEVENSON

A Lodging for the Night
Sire de Maletroit's Door
Markheim
Providence and the Guitar
The Pavilion on the Links
The Bottle Imp

Dr. Jekyl and Mr. Hyde
Olalla
The Merry Men
The Treasure of Franchard
The Young Man with the Cream Tarts
The Saratoga Trunk

## ABOUT ROBERT LOUIS STEVENSON

*The Life of Robert Louis Stevenson,* David Graham Balfour
*Robert Louis Stevenson,* Rosalie Masson
*Robert Louis Stevenson,* John A. Steuart
*R. L. Stevenson,* Frank Swinnerton

# JAMES MATTHEW BARRIE
## (1860– )

A WRITER who excels in one form of literature when he is young, and then completely abandons that form as he passes into middle age, only to become more famous in another, is sure to be known for what he has done most recently. Since 1904 Mr. J. M. Barrie has been most widely known as the author of *Peter Pan,* a fantastic play made enormously popular through the acting of Miss Maude Adams. In the last years of the nineteenth century *The Little Minister,* in play form, had its vogue. But *The Little Minister* achieved its first popularity as a novel in 1891 — which may serve as a reminder that Barrie's first successes as an author were in fiction.

Barrie first attracted attention for his studies and sketches of village life in Scotland, where he was born in 1860. His native village was Kirriemuir, but this he wisely transformed, for literary purposes, into Thrums. He received his university education in Edinburgh. By 1885 he was a journalist in London, and has made his home there ever since. In 1888 appeared a volume of his sketches, the *Auld Licht Idylls,* followed in 1889 by *A Window in Thrums,* from which the story in this volume is taken. These stories purport to be in the dialect of the common people of the Scotch village and were the beginning of what is called the "Kailyard" school of fiction; that is, dialect stories. This type of the short story was popular for many years, and may still be found in certain magazines. On the whole, however, the American public does not like dialect stories unless they portray types of character and aspects of human nature that are in themselves interesting. This is true of Barrie's stories, all the more because of their pervasive humor.

Since 1913 J. M. Barrie has been Sir James Matthew Barrie, the honor having been conferred entirely for his eminence in literature. In America he remains known as plain J. M. Barrie, novelist, short story writer, and dramatist.

# HOW GAVIN BIRSE PUT IT TO MAG LOWNIE

IN A wet day the rain gathered in blobs on the road that passed our garden. Then it crawled into the cart-tracks until the road was streaked with water. Lastly, the water gathered in heavy yellow pools. If the on-ding still continued, clods of earth toppled from the garden dike into the ditch.

On such a day, when even the dulseman had gone into shelter, and the women scudded by with their wrappers over their heads, came Gavin Birse to our door. Gavin, who was the Glen Quharity post, was still young, but had never been quite the same man since some amateurs in the glen ironed his back for rheumatism. I thought he had called to have a crack with me. He sent his compliments up to the attic, however, by Leeby, and would I come and be a witness?

Gavin came up and explained. He had taken off his scarf and thrust it into his pocket, lest the rain should take the color out of it. His boots cheeped, and his shoulders had risen to his ears. He stood steaming before my fire.

"If it's no' ower muckle to ask ye," he said, "I would like ye for a witness."

"A witness! But for what do you need a witness, Gavin?"

"I want ye," he said, "to come wi' me to Mag's, and be a witness."

Gavin Birse and Mag had been engaged for a year or more. Mag was the daughter of Janet Ogilvy, who was best remembered as the body that took the hill (that is, wandered about it) for twelve hours on the day Mr. Dishart, the Auld Licht minister, accepted a call to another church.

"You don't mean to tell me, Gavin," I asked, "that your marriage is to take place today?"

By the twist of his mouth I saw that he was only deferring a smile.

"Far frae that," he said.

"Ah, then, you have quarreled, and I am to speak up for you?"

"Na, na," he said, "I dinna want ye to do that above all things. It would be a favor if ye could gie me a bad character."

This beat me, and, I dare say, my face showed it.

515

"I'm no' juist what ye would call anxious to marry Mag noo," said Gavin, without a tremor.

I told him to go on.

"There's a lassie oot at Craigiebuckle," he explained, "workin' on the farm — Jeanie Luke by name. Ye may hae seen her?"

"What of her?" I asked, severely.

"Weel," said Gavin, still unabashed, "I'm thinkin' noo 'at I would rather hae her."

Then he stated his case more fully.

"Ay, I thocht I liked Mag oncommon till I saw Jeanie, an' I like her fine yet, but I prefer the other ane. That state o' matters canna gang on forever, so I came into Thrums the day to settle't one wy or another."

"And how," I asked, "do you propose going about it? It is a somewhat delicate business."

"Ou, I see nae great difficulty in't. I'll speir at Mag, blunt oot, if she'll let me aff. Yes, I'll put it to her plain."

"You're sure Jeanie would take you?"

"Ay; oh, there's nae fear o' that."

"But if Mag keeps you to your bargain?"

"Weel in that case there's nae harm done."

"You are in a great hurry, Gavin?"

"Ye may say that; but I want to be married. The wifie I lodge wi' canna last lang, an' I would like to settle doon in some place."

"So you are on your way to Mag's now?"

"Ay, we'll get her in atween twal' and ane."

"Oh, yes; but why do you want me to go with you?"

"I want ye for a witness. If she winna let me aff, weel an' guid; an' if she will, it's better to hae a witness in case she should go back on her word."

Gavin made his proposal briskly, and as coolly as if he were only asking me to go fishing; but I did not accompany him to Mag's. He left the house to look for another witness, and about an hour afterward Jess saw him pass with Tammas Haggart. Tammas cried in during the evening to tell us how the mission prospered.

"Mind ye," said Tammas, a drop of water hanging to the point of his nose, "I disclaim all responsibility in the business. I ken Mag weel for a thrifty, respectable woman, as her mither was afore her, an' so I said to Gavin when he came to speir me."

"Ay, mony a pirn has 'Lisbeth filled to me," said Hendry, settling down to a reminiscence.

"No to be ower hard on Gavin," continued Tammas, forestalling Hendry, "he took what I said in guid part; but aye when I stopped speakin', to draw breath, he says, 'The question is, will ye come wi' me?' He was michty made up in 's mind."

"Weel, ye went wi' him," suggested Jess, who wanted to bring Tammas to the point.

"Ay," said the stone-breaker, "but no in sic a hurry as that."

He worked his mouth round and round, to clear the course as it were for a sarcasm.

"Fowk often say," he continued, "'at 'am quick beyond the ordinar' in seein' the humorous side o' things."

Here Tammas paused and looked at us.

"So ye are, Tammas," said Hendry. "Losh, ye mind hoo ye saw the humorous side o' me wearin' a pair o' boots 'at wisna marrows! No, the ane had a toe-piece on, an' the other hadna."

"Ye juist wore them sometimes when ye was delvin'," broke in Jess; "ye have as guid a pair o' boots as ony in Thrums."

"Ay, but I had worn them," said Hendry, "at odd times for mair than a year, an' I had never seen the humorous side o' them. Weel, as fac as death [here he addressed me], Tammas had juist seen them twa or three times when he saw the humorous side o' them. Syne I saw their humorous side, too, but no till Tammas pointed it oot."

"That was naething," said Tammas, " naething ava to some things I've done."

"But what aboot Mag?" said Leeby.

"We wasna that length, was we?" said Tammas. "Na, we was speakin' aboot the humorous side. Ay, wait a wee, I didna mention the humorous side for naething."

He paused to reflect.

"Oh, yes," he said at last, brightening up. "I was sayin' to ye hoo quick I was to see the humorous side o' onything. Ay, then, what made me say that was 'at in a clink [flash] I saw the humorous side o' Gavin's position."

"Man, man," said Hendry, admiringly, "an' what is 't?"

"Oh, it's this: there's something humorous in speirin' a woman to let ye aff so as ye can be married to another woman."

"I daur say there is," said Hendry, doubtfully.

"Did she let him aff?" asked Jess, taking the words out of Leeby's mouth.

"I'm comin' to that," said Tammas. "Gavin proposes to me after I had ha'en my laugh ——"

"Yes," cried Hendry, banging the table with his fist, "it has a humorous side. Ye're richt again, Tammas."

"I wish ye wadna blatter [beat] the table," said Jess, and then Tammas proceeded:

"Gavin wanted me to tak paper an' ink an' a pen wi' me, to write the proceedin's doon, but I said, 'Na, na, I'll tak paper, but nae ink nor nae pen, for there'll be ink an' a pen there.' That was what I said."

"An' did she let him aff?" asked Leeby.

"Weel," said Tammas, "aff we goes to Mag's hoose, an' sure enough Mag was in. She was alane, too; so Gavin, no to waste time, juist sat doon for politeness' sake, an' sune rises up again; an' says he, 'Marget Lownie, I hae a solemn question to speir at ye, namely this, Will you, Marget Lownie, let me, Gavin Birse, aff?'"

"Mag would start at that?"

"Sal, she was braw an' cool. I thocht she maun hae got wind o' his intentions aforehand, for she juist replies, quietlike, 'Hoo do ye want aff, Gavin?'

"'Because,' says he, like a book, 'my affections has undergone a change.'

"'Ye mean Jean Luke?' says Mag.

"'That is wha I mean,' says Gavin, very straightforrard."

"But she didna let him aff, did she?"

"Na, she wasna the kind. Says she, 'I wonder to hear ye, Gavin, but am no goin' to agree to naething o' that sort.'

"'Think it ower,' says Gavin.

"'Na, my mind's made up,' said she.

"'Ye would sune get anither man,' he says earnestly.

"'Hoo do I ken that?' she speirs, rale sensibly, I thocht, for men's no sae easy to get.

"'Am sure o' 't,' Gavin says, wi' michty conviction in his

## How Gavin Birse Put It to Mag Lownie

voice, ' for ye're bonny to look at, an' weel kent for bein' a guid body.'

"'Ay,' says Mag, 'I'm glad ye like me, Gavin, for ye have to tak me.'"

"That put a clincher on him," interrupted Hendry.

"He was loath to gie in," replied Tammas, so he says: 'Ye think 'am a fine character, Marget Lownie, but ye're very far mista'en. I wouldna wonder but what I was lossin' my place some o' thae days, an' syne whaur would ye be? — Marget Lownie,' he goes on, ''am nat'rally lazy an' fond o' the drink. As sure as ye stand there, 'am a reg'lar deevil!'"

"That was strong language," said Hendry, "but he would be wantin' to fleg [frighten] her?"

"Juist so, but he didna manage 't, for Mag says: 'We a' hae oor faults, Gavin, an' deevil or no deevil, ye're the man for me!'"

"Gavin thocht a bit," continued Tammas, "an' syne he tries her on a new tack. 'Marget Lownie,' he says, 'yer father's an auld man noo, an' he has naebody but yersel' to look after him. I'm thinkin' it would be kind o' cruel o' me to tak' ye awa frae him?'"

"Mag wouldna be ta'en in wi' that; she wasna born on a Sawbath," said Jess, using one of her favorite sayings.

"She wasna," answered Tammas. "Says she, 'Hae nae fear on that score, Gavin; my father's fine willin' to spare me!'"

"An' that ended it?"

"Ay, that ended it."

"Did ye tak it doon in writin'?" asked Hendry.

"There was nae need," said Tammas, handing round his snuff-mull. "No, I never touched paper. When I saw the thing was settled, I left them to their coortin'. They're to tak a look at Snecky Hobart's auld hoose the nicht. It's to let."

### QUESTIONS

1. Note the way the story is told. How is it unusual?
2. Why did Gavin Birse want a witness?
3. Does the bluntness of his request tell something about himself?
4. What is the complication?
5. What do you think about Tammas and his sense of humor?

6. State the two examples of it in the story.
7. From the conversation, what do you learn about the community?
8. What is your impression of Mag Lownie?
9. What is the climax?
10. Most of the dialect words can be understood from the context. Others are given below.

## SCOTCH WORDS AND PHRASES

1. *on-ding,* rain storm.
2. *dulseman,* gatherer of seaweed.
3. *to have a crack,* gossip.
4. *muckle,* much.
5. *speir,* ask.
6. *pirn,* spool to hold yarn.
7. *michty,* mighty.
8. *sic,* such.
9. *losh,* an exclamation.
10. *maun,* must.
11. *sal,* an exclamation.
12. *marrows,* mates.
13. *ou,* oh.

## SUBJECTS FOR COMPOSITION

1. Character Sketch of Mag Lownie.
2. Gavin and Mag Select Their Home.
3. Write a possible different ending for the story.

## OTHER STORIES BY J. M. BARRIE

The Inconsiderate Waiter
Two of Them
The Courting of T'nowhead's Bell
A Humorist on His Calling

# JOHN GALSWORTHY
## (1867–1933)

JOHN GALSWORTHY, the son of a successful London lawyer, was born at Coombe, Surrey, now a suburb of London. At the age of fourteen he was sent to Harrow, one of the best known secondary schools for boys in England. At this school he took an active interest in sports, became captain of the football team, and was also known as a runner and a jumper. From Harrow he went to New College, Oxford, from which he received an honor degree in law in 1889. The following year he was called to the bar but because of a very strong distaste for his profession he practised very little and soon abandoned it altogether. He himself said, " I disliked my profession thoroughly."

Fortunately he had no particular need of money so that he was able to devote several years to travel. On one of his voyages he met Joseph Conrad, then still a sea captain. Despite the dissimilarity of their backgrounds and personalities the two men became friends and because of Galsworthy's marked interest in literature — he had read quantities of English, French and Russian novels — Conrad showed him some of his as yet unpublished work. Galsworthy was sufficiently impressed to urge the seaman to keep on writing.

Galsworthy himself was first urged to write by the lady who later became his wife. His first novel, *Jocelyn,* published in 1898 when Galsworthy was only thirty-one years old, attracted some attention. However, it is quite different from the very specialized type of novel for which Galsworthy has since become famous, and is interesting chiefly in the light of his later development. It is also interesting that from 1898 till 1904 Galsworthy published under the pseudonym of John Sinjohn. In all, three books appeared under this name.

In 1904 *The Island Pharisees* appeared. Published under Galsworthy's own name, this book contains a hint of what he was later to develop into — a social critic and philosopher. But not until two years later, with the publication of *The Man of Property* (1906), did Galsworthy really strike his characteristic note. This book began a sequence of stories now known as *The Forsyte Saga* which gives a detailed picture of upper middle class society of the later Victorian age and that of King Edward VII. This the author accomplished by portraying the history of a single family through three generations. In all, Galsworthy occupied himself for twenty-six years with the Forsytes. In his later novels he has carried on the history of the Forsyte descendants to the present day. His theme is always the same — humanity as it is, with all its weaknesses and strength. On the whole, Galsworthy's attitude was ironic and often he becomes distinctly satiric.

Besides being a novelist of distinction, Galsworthy was also a successful dramatist, having had produced a large number of plays between the years 1906 and 1926. Among the best known are " Old English," " Strife,"

"Justice," and "Loyalties," all of which were popular successes in London and New York. It is interesting to note that "Old English" is based upon one of his short stories called "A Stoic." Following its successful run in this country it was also made into a movie which has proved equally popular.

An unusually versatile man for this twentieth century era of specialization, Galsworthy wrote essays, poems, and short stories in between times, as it were. The most famous collection of his short stories is *Caravan* (1925) which is really his assembled tales. The story reprinted below is included in this volume though it originally appeared in *The Inn of Tranquillity* in 1912.

In all of Galsworthy's work, whether it be novels, short stories, or plays, his realism is so intense that the reader is left with a feeling of pessimism — the feeling that whatever is, is wrong. But Galsworthy is so clever and so accomplished a writer that never at any time does he himself appear to be taking sides. One has the feeling, rather, that the author is saying "Here are the facts; interpret them as you like. I am not interested." This is an art which only the great writer achieves, but Galsworthy does it superbly.

In the story "Quality" most of Galsworthy's best and most individual characteristics are illustrated. The very theme of the story affords an example of a favorite Galsworthy subject — the gross injustice of an impersonal social system to an individual whose only offense is that he cannot fit himself into the new system. Here it happens to be a skilled but ageing German shoemaker who loves his work and has ideals of workmanship that, laudable though they be, have ceased to be practicable in a mechanized and industrialized age which stresses speed and advertising rather than painstaking and dignified workmanship. Through no fault of any particular individual Gessler is finally beaten down, in spite of his valiant efforts to uphold his ideals of craftsmanship, and he goes down dignified and uncomplaining as he has always lived. The reader feels clearly the pathos and the injustice of the situation, though Galsworthy never at any place in the story directly expresses it.

The figure of Gessler reveals the author's skill at its best in the art of portraiture. The man is as real to us at the end of the story as though we had known him personally and in some way we feel that he is more to us than the mere sum of physical characteristics enumerated early in the story. How Galsworthy manages to achieve this is a matter of technique; and his methods are by no means easy to analyze by those less gifted in the art of writing. But since he does manage so to create characters in all of his books and very particularly in *The Forsyte Saga*, it is well to attempt to discover, both in the following story and in whatever other Galsworthy you may read, the secret of his success in portraying characters.

## QUALITY

I KNEW him from the days of my extreme youth, because he made my father's boots; inhabiting with his elder brother two little shops let into one, in a small by-street — now no more, but then most fashionably placed in the West End.

That tenement had a certain quiet distinction; there was no sign upon its face that he made for any of the Royal Family [1] — merely his own German name of Gessler Brothers; and in the window a few pairs of boots. I remember that it always troubled me to account for those unvarying boots in the window, for he made only what was ordered, reaching nothing down, and it seemed so inconceivable that what he made could ever have failed to fit. Had he bought them to put there? That, too, seemed inconceivable. He would never have tolerated in his house leather on which he had not worked himself. Besides, they were too beautiful — the pair of pumps, so inexpressibly slim, the patent leathers with cloth tops, making water come into one's mouth, the tall brown riding-boots with marvelous sooty glow, as if, though new, they had been worn a hundred years. Those pairs could only have been made by one who saw before him the Soul of Boot — so truly were they prototypes, incarnating the very spirit of all footwear. These thoughts, of course, came to me later, though even when I was promoted to him, at the age of perhaps fourteen, some inkling haunted me of the dignity of himself and brother. For to make boots — such boots as he made — seemed to me then, and still seems to me, mysterious and wonderful.

I remember well my shy remark, one day, while stretching out to him my youthful foot:

"Isn't it awfully hard to do, Mr. Gessler?"

And his answer, given with a sudden smile from out of the sardonic redness of his beard: "Id is an Ardt!"

Himself, he was a little as if made of leather, with his yellow crinkly face, and crinkly reddish hair and beard, and neat folds slanting down his cheeks to the corners of his mouth, and his guttural and one-toned voice; for leather is a sardonic substance, and stiff and slow of purpose. And that was the character of his face, save that his eyes, which were gray-blue, had in them the simple gravity of one secretly possessed by the Ideal. His elder brother was so very like him — though watery, paler in every way, with a great industry — that sometimes in early days I was not quite sure of him until the interview was over. Then I knew that it was he, if the words, " I will ask my brudder," had not been spoken, and that, if they had, it was the elder brother.

When one grew old and wild and ran up bills, one somehow never ran them up with Gessler Brothers. It would not have seemed becoming to go in there and stretch out one's foot to that blue iron-spectacled face, owing him for more than — say — two pairs, just the comfortable reassurance that one was still his client.

For it was not possible to go to him very often — his boots lasted terribly, having something beyond the temporary — some, as it were, essence of boot stitched into them.

One went in, not as into most shops, in the mood of: " Please serve me, and let me go! " but restfully, as one enters a church; and, sitting on the single wooden chair, waited — for there was never anybody there. Soon — over the top edge of that sort of well — rather dark, and smelling soothingly of leather — which formed the shop, there would be seen his face, or that of his elder brother, peering down. A guttural sound, and the tip-tap of bast slippers beating the narrow wooden stairs, and he would stand before one without coat, a little bent, in leather apron, with sleeves turned back, blinking — as if awakened from some dream of boots, or like an owl surprised in daylight and annoyed at this interruption.

And I would say: " How do you do, Mr. Gessler? Could you make me a pair of Russia leather boots? "

Without a word he would leave me, retiring whence he came, or into the other portion of the shop, and I would continue to rest in the wooden chair, inhaling the incense of his trade. Soon he would come back, holding in his thin, veined hand a piece of gold-brown leather. With eyes fixed on it, he would remark: " What a beaudiful biece! " When I, too, had admired it, he would speak again. " When do you wand dem? "

And I would answer: "Oh! As soon as you conveniently can." And he would say: "Tomorrow fordnighd?" Or if he were his elder brother: "I will ask my brudder!"

Then I would murmur: "Thank you! Good-morning, Mr. Gessler." "Goot-morning!" he would reply, still looking at the leather in his hand. And as I moved to the door, I would hear the tip-tap of his bast slippers restoring him, up the stairs, to his dream of boots. But if it were some new kind of foot-gear that he had not yet made me, then indeed he would observe ceremony — divesting me of my boot and holding it long in his hand, looking at it with eyes at once critical and loving, as if recalling the glow with which he had created it, and rebuking the way in which one had disorganized this masterpiece. Then, placing my foot on a piece of paper, he would two or three times tickle the outer edges with a pencil and pass his nervous fingers over my toes, feeling himself into the heart of my requirements.

I cannot forget that day on which I had occasion to say to him: "Mr. Gessler, that last pair of town walking-boots creaked, you know."

He looked at me for a time without replying, as if expecting me to withdraw or qualify the statement, then said:

"Id shouldn'd 'ave greaked."

"It did, I'm afraid."

"You goddem wed before dey found demselves?"

"I don't think so."

At that he lowered his eyes, as if hunting for memory of those boots, and I felt sorry I had mentioned this grave thing.

"Zend dem back!" he said; "I will look at dem."

A feeling of compassion for my creaking boots surged up in me, so well could I imagine the sorrowful long curiosity of regard which he would bend on them.

"Zome boods," he said slowly, "are bad from birdt. If I can do noding wid dem, I dake dem off your bill."

Once (once only) I went absent-mindedly into his shop, in a pair of boots bought in an emergency at some large firm's. He took my order without showing me any leather, and I could feel his eyes penetrating the inferior integument of my foot. At last he said:

"Dose are nod my boods."

The tone was not one of anger, nor of sorrow, not even of

contempt, but there was in it something quiet that froze the blood. He put his hand down and pressed a finger on the place where the left boot, endeavoring to be fashionable, was not quite comfortable.

"Id 'urds you dere," he said. "Dose big virms 'ave no self-respect. Drash!" And then, as if something had given way within him, he spoke long and bitterly. It was the only time I ever heard him discuss the conditions and hardships of his trade.

"Dey get id all," he said, "dey get id by adverdisement, nod by work. Dey dake it away from us, who lofe our boods. Id gomes to this — bresently I haf no work. Every year id gets less — you will see." And looking at his lined face I saw things I had never noticed before, bitter things and bitter struggle — and what a lot of gray hairs there seemed suddenly in his red beard!

As best I could, I explained the circumstances of the purchase of those ill-omened boots. But his face and voice made a so deep impression that during the next few minutes I ordered many pairs! Nemesis fell! They lasted more terribly than ever. And I was not able conscientiously to go to him for nearly two years.

When at last I went I was surprised that outside one of the two little windows of his shop another name was painted, also that of a bootmaker — making, of course, for the Royal Family.[1] The old familiar boots, no longer in dignified isolation, were huddled in the single window. Inside, the now contracted well of the one little shop was more scented and darker than ever. And it was longer than usual, too, before a face peered down, and the tip-tap of the bast slippers began. At last he stood before me, and, gazing through those rusty iron spectacles, said:

"Mr. ——, isn'd it?"

"Ah! Mr. Gessler," I stammered, "but your boots are really *too* good, you know! See, these are quite decent still!" And I stretched out to him my foot. He looked at it.

"Yes," he said, "beople do nod wand good boods, id seems."

To get away from his reproachful eyes and voice I hastily remarked: "What have you done to your shop?"

He answered quietly: "Id was too exbensif. Do you wand some boods?"

I ordered three pairs, though I had only wanted two, and quickly left. I had, I know not quite what feeling of being part, in his mind, of a conspiracy against him; or not perhaps so much against him as against his idea of boot. One does not, I suppose, care to feel like that; for it was again many months before my next visit to his shop, paid, I remember, with the feeling: " Oh! well, I can't leave the old boy — so here goes! Perhaps it'll be his elder brother! "

For his elder brother, I knew, had not character enough to reproach me, even dumbly.

And, to my relief, in the shop there did appear to be his elder brother, handling a piece of leather.

" Well, Mr. Gessler," I said, " how are you? "

He came close, and peered at me.

" I am breddy well," he said slowly; " but my elder brudder is dead."

And I saw that it was indeed himself — but how aged and wan! And never before had I heard him mention his brother. Much shocked, I murmured: " Oh! I am sorry! "

" Yes," he answered, " he was a good man, he made a good bood; but he is dead." And he touched the top of his head, where the hair had suddenly gone as thin as it had been on that of his poor brother, to indicate, I suppose, the cause of death. " He could nod ged over losing de oder shop. Do you wand any boods? " And he held up the leather in his hand: " Id's a beaudiful biece."

I ordered several pairs. It was very long before they came — but they were better than ever. One simply could not wear them out. And soon after that I went abroad.

It was over a year before I was again in London. And the first shop I went to was my old friend's. I had left a man of sixty, I came back to find one of seventy-five, pinched and worn and tremulous, who genuinely, this time, did not at first know me.

" Oh! Mr. Gessler," I said, sick at heart; " how splendid your boots are! See, I've been wearing this pair nearly all the time I've been abroad; and they're not half worn out, are they? "

He looked long at my boots — a pair of Russia leather, and his face seemed to regain its steadiness. Putting his hand on my instep, he said:

"Do dey vid you here? I 'ad drouble wid dat bair, I remember."

I assured him that they had fitted beautifully.

"Do you wand any boods?" he said. "I can make dem quickly; id is a slack dime."

I answered: "Please, please! I want boots all round — every kind!"

"I vill make a vresh model. Your food must be bigger." And with utter slowness, he traced round my foot, and felt my toes, only once looking up to say:

"Did I dell you my brudder was dead?"

To watch him was quite painful, so feeble had he grown; I was glad to get away.

I had given those boots up, when one evening they came. Opening the parcel, I set the four pairs out in a row. Then one by one I tried them on. There was no doubt about it. In shape and fit, in finish and quality of leather, they were the best he had ever made me. And in the mouth of one of the town walking-boots I found his bill. The amount was the same as usual, but it gave me quite a shock. He had never before sent it in until quarter day. I flew downstairs and wrote a check, and posted it at once with my own hand.

A week later, passing the little street, I thought I would go in and tell him how splendidly the new boots fitted. But when I came to where his shop had been, his name was gone. Still there, in the window, were the slim pumps, the patent leathers with cloth tops, the sooty riding-boots.

I went in, very much disturbed. In the two little shops — again made into one — was a young man with an English face.

"Mr. Gessler in?" I said.

He gave me a strange, ingratiating look.

"No, sir," he said, "no. But we can attend to anything with pleasure. We've taken the shop over. You've seen our name, no doubt, next door. We make for some very good people."

"Yes, yes," I said, "but Mr. Gessler?"

"Oh!" he answered; "dead."

"Dead! But I only received these boots from him last Wednesday week."

"Ah!" he said; "a shockin' go. Poor old man starved 'imself."

"Good God!"

# Quality

"Slow starvation, the doctor called it! You see he went to work in such a way! Would keep the shop on; wouldn't have a soul touch his boots except himself. When he got an order, it took him such a time. People won't wait. He lost everybody. And there he'd sit, goin' on and on — I will say that for him — not a man in London made a better boot! But look at the competition! He never advertised! Would 'ave the best leather, too, and do it all 'imself. Well, there it is. What could you expect with his ideas?"

"But starvation — !"

"That may be a bit flowery, as the sayin' is — but I know myself he was sittin' over his boots day and night, to the very last. You see, I used to watch him. Never gave 'imself time to eat; never had a penny in the house. All went in rent and leather. How he lived so long I don't know. He regular let his fire go out. He was a character. But he made good boots."

"Yes," I said, "he made good boots."

### NOTES FOR *QUALITY*

1. A reference to a common English custom that shops which supply members of the Royal Family are permitted to use that fact as advertising.

### QUESTIONS

1. Does the story gain or lose by being told in the first person? Give reasons.
2. To what social class did the narrator belong? How do you know?
3. Where is the theme of the story first indicated?
4. How did the shop differ from an ordinary shoe store?
5. Show how his craft reflects itself in his personal appearance.
6. Do you think that there is any reason other than kinship why the brothers are so much alike? Explain.
7. How did the young customer know to which of the brothers he had spoken?
8. Why was it inconceivable to run up bills with Gessler Brothers?
9. Find five different sentences which show that Gessler loved his work.
10. Had Gessler been an ordinary shoemaker would it have seemed so unkind for the customer to have complained about his creaking boots? Why?
11. Was the customer's embarrassment at having worn factory-made shoes into Gessler's warranted? Give reasons for your answer.
12. Where do we first find Gessler expressing his feelings about factory competition?
13. When Gessler says "Dey get id all" what is meant?
14. What is meant by "Nemesis fell!"?

15. Do you think the customer liked the fact that the shoes wore so well?
16. Note how carefully the reader is led to the tragic aspects of the story. Where do we get our first hint of the tragedy that is to overtake Gessler?
17. Was Gessler's sorrow for more than the mere death of his brother? Find a sentence which seems to indicate this.
18. Why was the customer surprised to find the bill when his last order was filled? What did it indicate about Gessler's financial condition?
19. Why do you think Gessler aged so rapidly toward the end? Pick out all the things that you can find that indicate the rapidity with which he aged.
20. How did the customer learn of the death of Mr. Gessler?
21. How did the new proprietor account for the apparently sudden death?
22. Was the new proprietor able to understand the ideas and ideals of Gessler? Explain. In what way does this make Gessler's death even more tragic?
23. What final tribute did they pay to the old shoemaker?

## SUBJECTS FOR COMPOSITION

1. Rewrite the story from the point of view of Gessler's competitor.
2. Imagine this as a play and write the lines and stage directions for it. Remember that Galsworthy was a dramatist as well as a story writer.
3. Pretend that the young customer engineered an advertising campaign among his friends in favor of handmade boots which resulted in the failure of Gessler's competitor and describe Gessler's reactions to his unexpected good fortune.

## VOLUMES OF SHORT STORIES BY JOHN GALSWORTHY

*From the Four Winds*  *Captures*
*Five Tales*  *Caravan*
*Tatterdemalion*  *The Inn of Tranquillity*

# KATHERINE MANSFIELD
## (1888–1923)

KATHLEEN BEAUCHAMP was born in Wellington, New Zealand October 14, 1888. Her father was a prosperous business man who was knighted and is today Sir Harold Beauchamp. Katherine, as she later preferred to be called, spent her early childhood in a small township called Karori, a few miles from Wellington. There she attended the village school. She was early interested in writing stories and had her first story accepted at the age of nine. Its title was " The Lone Hand." At about the same time she won first prize for English composition in her school, the subject being a sea voyage. When she was thirteen she was sent to England to complete her education. She entered Queen's College where she remained for five years. There she edited the college magazine and read widely among the authors then popular with the younger generation. Besides her deep interest in literature she was also interested in music, especially the violoncello on which she became a proficient performer.

At eighteen, much against her will, she returned to New Zealand where she found herself in constant rebellion against what she considered the narrowness and provincialism of the remote colony in which she lived. For a while, however, she found some solace in association with a family of musicians living in Wellington. When they left for England, Katherine was in despair and eventually persuaded her father to permit her to return to London on a small allowance.

Once more in England, she hoped to make a career in music and for a short time traveled with opera companies but she soon abandoned music for literature. Like most young writers, she sent her early manuscripts to editors of periodicals without success. But the quality of her writing at last appealed to the editor of *The New Age* and for two years, 1909–1911, her work appeared frequently in that magazine. These stories were based upon her experiences in Germany where she had gone to convalesce from an illness and were later collected into a volume called *In a German Pension*. This collection received favorable notice from the press and quickly passed through three editions. Then the publisher failed. Miss Mansfield had received an advance of fifteen pounds on publication of her book, which was all, since the failure of the publisher precluded payment of the royalties due her.

In 1911 she met J. Middleton Murry, then an undergraduate at Oxford where he was interested in a youthful literary magazine called *Rhythm*. After meeting Murry, Katherine Mansfield began to write regularly for *Rhythm*. For its last three numbers this magazine became known as *The Blue Review*, its entire life lasting some eighteen months during which time Katherine Mansfield and J. Middleton Murry were co-editors. When *The Blue Review* passed out of existence in 1913, Miss Mansfield once again had no place for her stories.

531

In 1915 D. H. Lawrence, Katherine Mansfield and Middleton Murry, who had become her husband, published a magazine called *The Signature*. They were the editors, publishers, and sole contributors. Only three numbers appeared. Miss Mansfield had, however, begun to contribute book reviews and essays to *The Athenaeum* and *The Nation*. Mr. Murry became editor of *The Athenaeum* and so once more a medium of publication was provided for Katherine Mansfield, although a few of her stories appeared in other English magazines.

She had by now achieved recognition as a writer of unusual talent, both as a critic and as a writer of stories. The Great War brought confusion into her life as it did into the lives of many other young writers of the day. She received a great spiritual shock which for a time disrupted her work. In 1915 a dearly loved younger brother visited her in England on his way to the front as an officer. During this visit they had several long conversations about their old life in New Zealand. After his death in France about a month later Katherine Mansfield determined to dedicate her talents to the writing of stories based on recollections of her own country and of the people that she and her brother had loved there. In her Journal she speaks of this as a sacred debt that she owes to her country because she and her brother were born there. She also seems to have felt that by doing this she was perpetuating the memory of her dead brother.

In order to escape the trying climate of England, shortly after her brother's death she went to Bandol in the south of France where she began to work on a long story called at first " The Aloe " but which was called " Prelude " when it later appeared in shorter form. It was published by itself in what was known at the time as a " blue-paper " volume. It was sent to the reviews and was practically ignored by all of them. However, Mr. Murry recalls that Miss Mansfield had her moment of triumph when she heard that the printer who set up the work exclaimed, " My! but these kids are real! " She felt, as a result, that she had succeeded in doing what she had set out to do — to write so that her stories should appeal to the unliterary class as well as to the more cultured classes. This characteristic became even more marked later on, especially after the publication of her book called *Bliss* when she received many letters from simple people who loved her work. She felt that to them she must tell the truth and nothing but the truth about life as she saw it. This preoccupation with truth became the devouring passion of her later years. She turned away from modern literature, so little of contemporary work seemed to her to be true. " The writers are not humble," she used to say.

In December, 1917, after she had finished revising " Prelude " Miss Mansfield had a serious attack of pleurisy and found it necessary to return to Bandol in order to escape the rigors of a London winter. She left England at the beginning of January, 1918 and this was the beginning of an almost nomadic life in search of health, for by spring Katherine Mansfield realized that she had a fairly well advanced case of tuberculosis. Condemned to an eternal quest for sunshine and mild climate her dreams of a permanent home of which she speaks so often in her letters and her Journal were shattered and she spent her winters in Italy, Switzerland, and southern France, usually returning to England for the summer months. During some of this time it was possible for her husband to be with her, but during a great deal of it she was absolutely alone except for a faithful traveling companion.

But these years of illness did not interrupt her work. Although often desperately ill she forced herself to write. She contributed regularly to her husband's magazine, *The Athenaeum,* and her reputation had now become great enough to have publishers ask her to collect her stories for volume publication. In 1920 the volume, *Bliss,* appeared. She learned of its success while ill at Mentone. By the autumn of 1921 she had completed a new book of short stories, *The Garden Party and Other Stories.* It was published in 1922.

In the meantime she had gone to Paris for special treatment and while there in spite of her almost impossible struggle against disease she became obsessed with an inward conviction that she could not successfully accomplish her aims in story writing because she lacked the necessary inward purification. For only then could one express the complete truth to life. Accordingly, shortly after finishing her last story, "The Canary," she determined to abandon writing and went into retirement at Fontainebleau where she died suddenly and unexpectedly the night of January 9, 1923 only a few hours after her husband had arrived from England to pay her a visit.

With the publication of *The Garden Party* and *Bliss* Katherine Mansfield's position as one of the foremost contemporary writers was fully and finally established. The influence of her work was widespread and continues to be so at the present time.

Katherine Mansfield's short life seems sad and tragic, all the more so because she was so thoroughly in love with life and so desirous of making her work worth while. In her Journal and her Letters, both published since her death, it is possible to find many fascinating details about her daily routine of life, as well as her ambitions as a human being and an author. One entry in her Journal for November 21, 1921 contains a prayer written when she had one of her bad spells, as she called them, " I know how it must be done. May I be found worthy to do it! Lord make me crystal clear for the light to shine through." From this passage it is evident that she was never satisfied with her achievement. This dissatisfaction is also evidenced by many other passages in the Journal and Letters. This is but one of the tragic elements in her life. She often forced herself to work when she should have been resting, for she was always full of ideas for stories and feared that she might not live long enough to leave behind a sufficient quantity of work to insure her the place in literature she hoped to attain. It is, however, interesting to note that many of the prominent critics of today assert that her work was the most notable of her generation.

Katherine Mansfield's stories are based on direct observation. Usually she took a situation and by deep concentration tried to create something of almost perfect beauty. She was little concerned with action but she had a genius for catching the exact significance of little touches in life as well as the little worries and comedies of which it is made up. Her method of approach was direct and objective; always she tried to say things in the simplest and clearest way. In this she was eminently successful. In reading her stories the reader is delightfully conscious of seeing the details exactly as the author conceived them. Her manner is often called expository, a term frequently used in describing the method of the Russian, Chekhov, whose work Miss Mansfield greatly admired, but by no means imitated. They both saw life from a similar angle but each expressed what he saw in his own particular manner.

The story reprinted in this volume to represent Miss Mansfield's work is taken from *The Dove's Nest*. In her Journal she records on the day of January 11, 1921, " Wrote and finished ' A Cup of Tea.' It took 4–5 hours."

If you were to read Katherine Mansfield's Journal and Letters before reading this story so that you came to know and feel the author's personality and all the gay delightful little things that she loved to do, you would feel that when she describes Rosemary Fell and her mode of life that she is describing life as she would have liked to live it. For instance, in almost every entry in her Journal and in most of her letters there are references to her love of flowers. With this in mind, note that she devotes a fairly long paragraph to describing how Rosemary Fell buys flowers. The purchase of the little box in the shop in Curzon street is another almost personal touch, for Katherine makes several references to her delight in pretty boxes and bottles and she was always extremely fastidious about her personal surroundings. And the description of the picture on the box is typical of the Mansfield way of thinking outside of stories as well as in. In a letter to her husband dated December 23, 1915 Katherine Mansfield speaks of their sitting under a rhubarb leaf and showing each other what they have in their pockets. In another, dated December 25, she says she is putting a little nut shell in her letter for a hat and in still another letter dated October 1, 1919 she says that in the evening the cicada shakes his tiny tambourine. These are only a few of the almost innumerable examples of whimsical phrasing which make Miss Mansfield's Letters and Journal such delightful reading but they serve to show that when they appear in her stories they are spontaneous phrasings, and not studied and stilted strivings after effect.

# A CUP OF TEA

ROSEMARY FELL was not exactly beautiful. No, you couldn't have called her beautiful. Pretty? Well, if you took her to pieces . . . But why be so cruel as to take anyone to pieces? She was young, brilliant, extremely modern, exquisitely well dressed, amazingly well read in the newest of the new books, and her parties were the most delicious mixture of the really important people and . . . artists — quaint creatures, discoveries of hers, some of them too terrifying for words, but others quite presentable and amusing.

Rosemary had been married two years. She had a duck of

a boy. No, not Peter — Michael. And her husband absolutely adored her. They were rich, really rich, not just comfortably well off, which is odious and stuffy and sounds like one's grandparents. But if Rosemary wanted to shop she would go to Paris as you and I would go to Bond [1] Street. If she wanted to buy flowers, the car pulled up at that perfect shop in Regent [1] Street, and Rosemary inside the shop just gazed in her dazzled, rather exotic way, and said: " I want those and those and those. Give me four bunches of those. And that jar of roses. Yes, I'll have all the roses in the jar. No, no lilac. I hate lilac. It's got no shape." The attendant bowed and put the lilac out of sight, as though this was only too true; lilac was dreadfully shapeless. " Give me those stumpy little tulips. Those red and white ones." And she was followed to the car by a thin shopgirl staggering under an immense white paper armful that looked like a baby in long clothes. . . .

One winter afternoon she had been buying something in a little antique shop in Curzon [1] Street. It was a shop she liked. For one thing, one usually had it to oneself. And then the man who kept it was ridiculously fond of serving her. He beamed whenever she came in. He clasped his hands; he was so gratified he could scarcely speak. Flattery, of course. All the same, there was something . . .

" You see, madam," he would explain in his low respectful tones, " I love my things. I would rather not part with them than sell them to someone who does not appreciate them, who has not that fine feeling which is so rare. . . ." And, breathing deeply he unrolled a tiny square of blue velvet and pressed it on the glass counter with his pale finger-tips.

Today it was a little box. He had been keeping it for her. He had shown it to nobody as yet. An exquisite little enamel box with a glaze so fine it looked as though it had been baked in cream. On the lid a minute creature stood under a flowery tree, and a more minute creature still had her arms around his neck. Her hat, really no bigger than a geranium petal, hung from a branch; it had green ribbons. And there was a pink cloud like a watchful cherub floating above their heads. Rosemary took her hands out of her long gloves. She always took off her gloves to examine such things. Yes, she liked it very much. She loved it; it was a great duck. She must have it. And, turning the creamy box, opening and shutting it, she couldn't help noticing how charming her hands were against the blue velvet. The shopman, in some dim cavern of his mind, may have dared to think so too. For he took a pencil, leant over the counter, and his pale bloodless fingers crept timidly towards those rosy, flashing ones, as he murmured gently: " If I may venture to point out to madam, the flowers on the little lady's bodice."

" Charming! " Rosemary admired the flowers. But what was the price? For a moment the shopman did not seem to hear. Then a murmur reached her. " Twenty-eight guineas, madame."

" Twenty-eight guineas." Rosemary gave no sign. She laid the little box down; she buttoned her gloves again. Twenty-eight guineas.[2] Even if one is rich . . . She looked vague. She stared at a plump tea-kettle like a plump hen above the shopman's head, and her voice was dreamy as she answered: " Well, keep it for me — will you? I'll . . ."

But the shopman had already bowed as though keeping it for her was all any human being could ask. He would be willing, of course, to keep it for her forever.

The discreet door shut with a click. She was outside on the step, gazing at the winter afternoon. Rain was falling, and with the rain it seemed the dark came too, spinning down like ashes. There was a cold bitter taste in the air, and the new-lighted lamps looked sad. Sad were the lights in the houses opposite. Dimly they burned as if regretting something. And people hurried by, hidden under their hateful umbrellas. Rosemary felt a strange pang. She pressed her muff to her breast; she wished she had the little box, too, to cling to. Of course, the car was there. She'd only to cross the pavement. But still she waited. There are moments, horrible moments in life, when one emerges from shelter and looks out, and it's awful. One oughtn't to give way to them. One ought to go home and have an extra-special tea. But at the very instant of thinking that, a young girl, thin, dark, shadowy — where had she come from? — was standing at Rosemary's elbow and a voice like a sigh, almost like a sob, breathed: " Madame, may I speak to you a moment? "

" Speak to me? " Rosemary turned. She saw a little battered creature with enormous eyes, someone quite young, no older than herself, who clutched at her coat-collar with reddened hands, and shivered as though she had just come out of the water.

"M-madame," stammered the voice. "Would you let me have the price of a cup of tea?"

"A cup of tea?" There was something simple, sincere in that voice; it wasn't in the least the voice of a beggar. "Then have you no money at all?" asked Rosemary.

"None, madam," came the answer.

"How extraordinary!" Rosemary peered through the dusk, and the girl gazed back at her. How more than extraordinary! And suddenly it seemed to Rosemary such an adventure. It was like something out of a novel by Dostoevsky, this meeting in the dusk. Supposing she took the girl home? Supposing she did do one of those things she was always reading about or seeing on the stage, what would happen? It would be thrilling. And she heard herself saying afterwards to the amazement of her friends: "I simply took her home with me," as she stepped forward and said to that dim person beside her: "Come home to tea with me."

The girl drew back startled. She even stopped shivering for a moment. Rosemary put out a hand and touched her arm. "I mean it," she said, smiling. And she felt how simple and kind her smile was. "Why won't you? Do. Come home with me now in my car and have tea."

"You — you don't mean it, madam," said the girl, and there was pain in her voice.

"But I do," cried Rosemary. "I want you to. To please me. Come along."

The girl put her fingers to her lips and her eyes devoured Rosemary. "You're — you're not taking me to the police station?" she stammered.

"The police station!" Rosemary laughed out. "Why should I be so cruel? No, I only want to make you warm and to hear — anything you care to tell me."

Hungry people are easily led. The footman held the door of the car open, and a moment later they were skimming through the dusk.

"There!" said Rosemary. She had a feeling of triumph as she slipped her hand through the velvet strap. She could have said, "Now I've got you," as she gazed at the little captive she had netted. But of course she meant it kindly.

Oh, more than kindly. She was going to prove to this girl that — wonderful things did happen in life, that — fairy godmothers were real, that — rich people had hearts, and that women *were* sisters. She turned impulsively, saying: " Don't be frightened. After all, why shouldn't you come back with me? We're both women. If I'm the more fortunate, you ought to expect . . ."

But happily at that moment, for she didn't know how the sentence was going to end, the car stopped. The bell was rung, the door opened, and with a charming, protecting, almost embracing movement, Rosemary drew the other into the hall. Warmth, softness, light, a sweet scent, all those things so familiar to her she never even thought about them, she watched that other receive. It was fascinating. She was like the little rich girl in her nursery with all the cupboards to open, all the boxes to unpack.

" Come, come upstairs," said Rosemary, longing to begin to be generous. " Come up to my room." And, besides, she wanted to spare this poor little thing from being stared at by the servants; she decided as they mounted the stairs she would not even ring for Jeanne, but take off her things by herself. The great thing was to be natural!

And " There! " cried Rosemary again, as they reached her beautiful big bedroom with the curtains drawn, the fire leaping on her wonderful lacquer furniture, her gold cushions and the primrose and blue rugs.

The girl stood just inside the door; she seemed dazed. But Rosemary didn't mind that.

" Come and sit down," she cried, dragging her big chair up to the fire, " in this comfy chair. Come and get warm. You look so dreadfully cold."

" I daren't, madam," said the girl, and she edged backwards.

" Oh, please," — Rosemary ran forward — " you mustn't be frightened, you mustn't, really. Sit down, and when I've taken off my things we shall go into the next room and have tea and be cosy. Why are you afraid? " And gently she half pushed the thin figure into its deep cradle.

But there was no answer. The girl stayed just as she had been put, with her hands by her sides and her mouth slightly open. To be quite sincere, she looked rather stupid. But

Rosemary wouldn't acknowledge it. She leant over her, saying: " Won't you take off your hat? Your pretty hair is all wet. And one is so much more comfortable without a hat, isn't one? "

There was a whisper that sounded like " Very good madam," and the crushed hat was taken off.

" Let me help you off with your coat, too," said Rosemary.

The girl stood up. But she held on to the chair with one hand and let Rosemary pull. It was quite an effort. The other scarcely helped her at all. She seemed to stagger like a child, and the thought came and went through Rosemary's mind, that if people wanted helping they must respond a little, just a little, otherwise it became very difficult indeed. And what was she to do with the coat now? She left it on the floor, and the hat too. She was just going to take a cigarette off the mantelpiece when the girl said quickly, but so lightly and strangely: " I'm very sorry, madam, but I'm going to faint. I shall go off, madam, if I don't have something."

" Good heavens, how thoughtless I am! " Rosemary rushed to the bell.

" Tea! Tea at once! And some brandy immediately! "

The maid was gone again, but the girl almost cried out. " No, I don't want no brandy. I never drink brandy. It's a cup of tea I want, madam." And she burst into tears.

It was a terrible and fascinating moment. Rosemary knelt beside her chair.

" Don't cry, poor little thing," she said. " Don't cry." And she gave the other her lace handkerchief. She really was touched beyond words. She put her arm around those thin, bird-like shoulders.

Now at last the other forgot to be shy, forgot everything except that they were both women, and gasped out: " I can't go on no longer like this. I can't bear it. I shall do away with myself. I can't bear no more."

" You shan't have to. I'll look after you. Don't cry any more. Don't you see what a good thing it was that you met me? We'll have tea and you'll tell me everything. And I shall arrange something. I promise. *Do* stop crying. It's so exhausting. Please! "

The other did stop just in time for Rosemary to get up before the tea came. She had the table placed between them. She plied the poor little creature with everything, all the sandwiches, all the bread and butter, and every time her cup was empty she filled it with tea, cream and sugar. People always said sugar was so nourishing. As for herself she didn't eat; she smoked and looked away tactfully so that the other should not be shy.

And really the effect of that slight meal was marvellous. When the tea-table was carried away a new being, a light, frail creature with tangled hair, dark lips, deep, lighted eyes, lay back in the big chair in a kind of sweet languor, looking at the blaze. Rosemary lit a fresh cigarette; it was time to begin.

"And when did you have your last meal?" she asked softly.

But at that moment the door-handle turned.

"Rosemary, may I come in?" It was Philip.

"Of course."

He came in. "Oh, I'm sorry," he said, and stopped and stared.

"It's quite all right," said Rosemary smiling. "This is my friend, Miss ——"

"Smith, madam," said the languid figure, who was strangely still and unafraid.

"Smith," said Rosemary. "We are going to have a little talk."

"Oh, yes," said Philip. "Quite," and his eye caught sight of the coat and hat on the floor. He came over to the fire and turned his back to it. "It's a beastly afternoon," he said curiously, still looking at that listless figure, looking at its hands and boots, and then at Rosemary again.

"Yes, isn't it?" said Rosemary enthusiastically. "Vile."

Philip smiled his charming smile. "As a matter of fact," said he, "I wanted you to come into the library for a moment. Would you? Will Miss Smith excuse us?"

The big eyes were raised to him, but Rosemary answered for her. "Of course she will." And they went out of the room together.

"I say," said Philip, when they were alone. "Explain. Who is she? What does it all mean?"

Rosemary, laughing, leaned against the door and said: "I

picked her up in Curzon Street. Really. She's a real pick-up. She asked me for the price of a cup of tea, and I brought her home with me."

"But what on earth are you going to do with her?" cried Philip.

"Be nice to her," said Rosemary quickly. "Be frightfully nice to her. Look after her. I don't know how. We haven't talked yet. But show her — treat her — make her feel ——"

"My darling girl," said Philip, "you're quite mad, you know. It simply can't be done."

"I knew you'd say that," retorted Rosemary. "Why not? I want to. Isn't that a reason? And besides, one's always reading about these things. I decided ——"

"But," said Philip slowly, and he cut the end of a cigar, "she's so astonishingly pretty."

"Pretty?" Rosemary was so surprised that she blushed. "Do you think so? I — I hadn't thought about it."

"Good Lord!" Philip struck a match. "She's absolutely lovely. Look again, my child. I was bowled over when I came into your room just now. However . . . I think you're making a ghastly mistake. Sorry, darling, if I'm crude and all that. But let me know if Miss Smith is going to dine with us in time for me to look up *The Milliner's Gazette*."

"You absurd creature!" said Rosemary, and she went out of the library, but not back to her bedroom. She went to her writing-room and sat down at her desk. Pretty! Absolutely lovely! Bowled over! Her heart beat like a heavy bell. Pretty! Lovely! She drew her cheque book towards her. But no, cheques would be no use, of course. She opened a drawer and took out five pound[3] notes, looked at them, put two back, and holding the three squeezed in her hand, she went back to her bedroom.

Half an hour later Philip was still in the library, when Rosemary came in.

"I only wanted to tell you," said she, and she leaned against the door and again looked at him with her dazzled exotic gaze, "Miss Smith won't dine with us tonight."

Philip put down the paper. "Oh, what's happened? Previous engagement?"

Rosemary came over and sat down on his knee. "She insisted on going," said she, "So I gave the poor little thing a present of money. I couldn't keep her against her will, could I? " she added softly.

Rosemary had just done her hair, darkened her eyes a little, and put on her pearls. She put up her hands and touched Philip's cheeks.

" Do you like me? " said she, and her tone, sweet, husky, troubled him.

" I like you awfully," he said, and he held her tighter. " Kiss me."

There was a pause.

Then Rosemary said dreamily, " I saw a fascinating little box today. It cost twenty-eight guineas. May I have it? "

Philip jumped her on his knee. " You may, little wasteful one," said he.

But that was not really what Rosemary wanted to say.

" Philip," she whispered, and she pressed his head against her bosom, " am I *pretty?* "

## NOTES FOR *A CUP OF TEA*

1. The streets mentioned are famous as fashionable shopping streets in London.
2. A guinea is a little more than five dollars.
3. An English pound is equivalent to about five dollars.

## QUESTIONS

1. In your own words, describe Rosemary.
2. How were her parties different from other people's?
3. Why were shopmen so subservient when Rosemary bought things? Give three instance of this subserviency.
4. Approximately how much was the box worth in American money? Did Rosemary buy it?
5. Where is the first hint of the idea of the story as suggested by the title?
6. What prompted Rosemary to invite the strange girl to her home?
7. Why was the girl startled?
8. What do you think Rosemary was going to say when she stopped with the word " expect " ? Why did she stop?
9. Why did the girl feel frightened upon entering Rosemary's room?
10. Was the girl really about to faint or was she only bluffing?
11. Did Philip realize the exact state of things when he came in?
12. How was he impressed with his wife's idea of what she intended to do for the stranger?
13. Do you think that Philip was really impressed by the beauty of the girl? If not, what was his motive for pretending to be?
14. What did Philip mean by his reference to *The Milliner's Gazette?*

15. Why didn't Rosemary write a check?
16. How much did she finally give the girl?
17. What is the real point in Rosemary's last question?

## SUBJECTS FOR COMPOSITION

1. Write about an episode in your own life where you have been asked for help and what you did.
2. Write an imaginary conversation in which Rosemary tells one of her friends about her adventure.

## VOLUMES OF SHORT STORIES BY KATHERINE MANSFIELD

*Bliss and Other Stories*                          *The Dove's Nest*
*The Garden Party*

## GUY DE MAUPASSANT
### (1850–1893)

THE life and career of Maupassant has many parallels with that of his Russian contemporary Chekhov. Among the French writers of the short story, if not among those of the whole world, Maupassant easily ranks first, as does Chekhov among the Russians. Both are noted for their short stories primarily, although Maupassant wrote four novels and Chekhov several plays that are still produced. Their outlook on life was essentially similar — pessimistic, and often bitter. Both found their best story material in the lives of the common people, the tragedy that eternally lurks in the commonplace. As to style, each is a master in his own language. Both died in early middle age, and under exceptional circumstances.

Maupassant wrote over two hundred short stories, most of them very short, of less than two thousand words. This extraordinary compression came in part from his being limited to a column in a daily paper, but he had been taught by his literary master, Gustave Flaubert, not to waste his words. Careful observation, accurate and terse expression, with no complexity, are the essentials of his style. The range of his situations is extensive, but they may roughly be put into three groups: those dealing with the peasant life of Normandy, where he was born in 1850; those in which he portrays life in Paris, where he held a position in the Ministry of Marine; and those based on his travels, especially in the south of France. His characters he found in every phase of life, on the farms, in the shops, among the government clerks, on the docks in seaports, and among the grandees of the salons. In addition to these types he at times chose subjects that were mystic or fantastic, the most startling of which is "The Horla," written when his mind was about to give way finally to a chronic nervous disorder from which he died, hopelessly insane, in 1893.

The story presented in this volume belongs to a group that is less harsh in both its subject and its manner of treatment, but it is nevertheless a typical Maupassant story. The happiness described in the story is hardly the kind that American readers demand in their stories, but the sad wistfulness with which the author presents his tale, together with the incomparable style in which it is written, can not help startling the reader into a throb of sympathy for the two old people. It is the sort of thing that Maupassant could do best; that is, surround a drab situation with an entrancingly beautiful atmosphere that serves, after all, to accentuate the cruelty and the bitterness of human life.

# HAPPINESS

IT WAS tea-time before the appearance of the lamps. The villa commanded the sea; the sun, which had disappeared, had left the sky all rosy from his passing — rubbed, as it were, with gold-dust; and the Mediterranean, without a ripple, without a shudder, smooth, still shining under the dying day, seemed like a huge and polished metal plate.

Far off to the right the jagged mountains outlined their black profile on the paled purple of the west.

We talked of love, we discussed that old subject, we said again the things which we had said already very often. The sweet melancholy of the twilight made our words slower, caused a tenderness to waver in our souls; and that word, "love," which came back ceaselessly, now pronounced by a strong man's voice, now uttered by the frail-toned voice of a woman, seemed to fill the little *salon,* to flutter there like a bird, to hover there like a spirit.

Can one remain in love for several years in succession?

"Yes," maintained some.

"No," affirmed others.

We distinguished cases, we established limitations, we cited examples; and all, men and women, filled with rising and troubling memories, which they could not quote, and which mounted to their lips, seemed moved, and talked of that common, that sovereign thing, the tender and mysterious union of two beings, with a profound emotion and an ardent interest.

But all of a sudden some one, whose eyes had been fixed upon the distance, cried out:

"Oh! Look down there; what is it?"

On the sea, at the bottom of the horizon, loomed up a mass, gray, enormous, and confused.

The women had risen from their seats, and without understanding, looked at this surprising thing which they had never seen before.

Some one said:

"It is Corsica! You see it so two or three times a year, in certain exceptional conditions of the atmosphere, when the air is perfectly clear, and it is not concealed by those mists of sea-fog which always veil the distances."

We distinguished vaguely the mountain ridges, we thought we recognized the snow of their summits. And every one remained surprised, troubled, almost terrified, by this sudden apparition of a world, by this phantom risen from the sea. Maybe that those who, like Columbus, went away across undiscovered oceans had such strange visions as this.

Then said an old gentleman who had not yet spoken:

" See here: I knew in that island which raises itself before us, as if in person to answer what we said, and to recall to me a singular memory — I knew, I say, an admirable case of love which was true, of love which, improbably enough, was happy.

" Here it is.

" Five years ago I made a journey in Corsica. That savage island is more unknown and more distant from us than America, even though you see it sometimes from the very coasts of France, as we have done today.

" Imagine a world which is still chaos, imagine a storm of mountains separated by narrow ravines where torrents roll; not a single plain, but immense waves of granite, and giant undulations of earth covered with brushwood or with high forests of chestnut-trees and pines. It is a virgin soil, uncultivated, desert, although you sometimes make out a village like a heap of rocks, on the summit of a mountain. No culture, no industries, no art. One never meets here with a morsel of carved wood, or a bit of sculptured stone, never the least reminder that the ancestors of these people had any taste, whether rude or refined, for gracious and beautiful things. It is this which strikes you the most in their superb and hard country: their hereditary indifference to that search for seductive forms which is called Art.

" Italy, where every palace, full of masterpieces, is a masterpiece itself: Italy, where marble, wood, bronze, iron, metals, and precious stones attest man's genius, where the smallest old things which lie about in the ancient houses reveal that divine care for grace — Italy is for us the sacred country which we love, because she shows to us and proves to us the struggle, the grandeur, the power, and the triumph of the intelligence which creates.

" And, face to face with her, the savage Corsica has remained exactly as in her earliest days. A man lives there in his rude house, indifferent to everything which does not concern his own bare existence or his family feuds. And he has retained the vices and the virtues of savage races; he is violent, malignant, sanguinary without a thought of remorse, but also hospitable, generous, devoted, simple, opening his door to passers-by, and giving his faithful friendship in return for the least sign of sympathy.

" So, for a month, I had been wandering over this magnificent island with the sensation that I was at the end of the world. No more inns, no taverns, no roads. You gain by mule-paths hamlets hanging up, as it were, on a mountain side, and commanding tortuous abysses whence of an evening you hear rising the steady sound, the dull and deep voice, of the torrent. You knock at the doors of the houses. You ask a shelter for the night and something to live on till the morrow. And you sit down at the humble board, and you sleep under the humble roof, and in the morning you press the extended hand of your host, who has guided you as far as the outskirts of the village.

" Now, one night, after ten hours' walking, I reached a little dwelling quite by itself at the bottom of a narrow valley which was about to throw itself into the sea a league farther on. The two steep slopes of the mountain, covered with brush, with fallen rocks, and with great trees, shut in this lamentably sad ravine like two somber walls.

" Around the cottages were some vines, a little garden, and, farther off, several large chestnut-trees — enough to live on; in fact, a fortune for this poor country.

" The woman who received me was old, severe, and neat — exceptionally so. The man, seated on a straw chair, rose to salute me, then sat down again without saying a word. His companion said to me:

" ' Excuse him; he is deaf now. He is eighty-two years old.'

" She spoke the French of France. I was surprised.

" I asked her:

" ' You are not of Corsica? '

" She answered:

" ' No; we are from the Continent. But we have lived here now fifty years.'

" A feeling of anguish and of fear seized me at the thought of those fifty years passed in this gloomy hole, so far from the cities where human beings dwell. An old shepherd returned, and we began to eat the only dish there was for dinner, a thick soup in which potatoes, lard, and cabbages had been boiled together.

"When the short repast was finished, I went and sat down before the door, my heart pinched by the melancholy of the mournful landscape, wrung by that distress which sometimes seizes travelers on certain sad evenings, in certain desolate places. It seems that everything is near its ending — existence, and the universe itself. You perceive sharply the dreadful misery of life, the isolation of every one, the nothingness of all things and the black loneliness of the heart which nurses itself and deceives itself with dreams until the hour of death.

"The old woman rejoined me, and, tortured by that curiosity which ever lies at the bottom of the most resigned of souls:

"'So you come from France?' said she.

"'Yes; I'm traveling for pleasure.'

"'You are from Paris, perhaps?'

"'No, I am from Nancy.'

"It seemed to me that an extraordinary emotion agitated her. How I saw, or rather how I felt it, I do not know.

"She repeated, in a slow voice:

"'You are from Nancy?'

"The man appeared in the door, impassible, like all the deaf.

"She resumed:

"'It doesn't make any difference. He can't hear.'

"Then, at the end of several seconds:

"'So you know people at Nancy?'

"'Oh yes, nearly everybody.'

"'The family of Sainte-Allaize?'

"'Yes, very well; they were friends of my father.'

"'What are you called?'

"I told her my name. She regarded me fixedly, then said, in that low voice which is roused by memories:

"'Yes, yes; I remember well. And the Brisemares, what has become of them?'

"'They are all dead.'

"'Ah! And the Sirmonts, do you know them?'

"'Yes, the last of the family is a general.'

" Then she said, trembling with emotion, with anguish, with I do not know what, feeling confused, powerful, and holy, with I do not know how great a need to confess, to tell all, to talk of those things which she had hitherto kept shut in the bottom of her heart, and to speak of those people whose name distracted her soul:

" ' Yes, Henri de Sirmont. I know him well. He is my brother.'

" And I lifted my eyes at her, aghast with surprise. And all of a sudden my memory of it came back.

" It had caused, once, a great scandal among the nobility of Lorraine. A young girl, beautiful and rich, Suzanne de Sirmont, had run away with an under-officer in the regiment of hussars commanded by her father.

" He was a handsome fellow, the son of a peasant, but he carried his blue dolman very well, this soldier who had captivated his colonel's daughter. She had seen him, noticed him, fallen in love with him, doubtless while watching the squadrons filing by. But how she had got speech of him, how they had managed to see one another, to hear from one another; how she had dared to let him understand she loved him — that was never known.

" Nothing was divined, nothing suspected. One night when the soldier had just finished his time of service, they disappeared together. Her people looked for them in vain. They never received tidings, and they considered her as dead.

" So I found her in this sinister valley.

" Then in my turn I took up the word:

" ' Yes, I remember well. You are Mademoiselle Suzanne.'

" She made the sign ' yes,' with her head. Tears fell from her eyes. Then with a look showing me the old man motionless on the threshold of his hut, she said:

" ' That is he.'

" And I understood that she loved him yet, that she still saw him with her bewitched eyes.

" I asked:

" ' Have you at least been happy? '

" She answered with a voice which came from her heart:

" ' Oh yes! very happy. He has made me very happy. I have never regretted.'

" I looked at her, sad, surprised, astounded by the sovereign strength of love! That rich young lady had followed this man, this peasant. She was become herself a peasant woman. She had made for herself a life without charm, without luxury, without delicacy of any kind, she had stooped to simple customs. And she loved him yet. She was become the wife of a rustic, in a cap, in a cloth skirt. Seated on a straw-bottomed chair, she ate from an earthen-ware dish, at a wooden table, a soup of potatoes and of cabbages with lard. She slept on a mattress by his side.

" She had never thought of anything but of him. She had never regretted her jewels, nor her fine dresses, nor the elegancies of life, nor the perfumed warmth of the chambers hung with tapestry, nor the softness of the down-beds where the body sinks in for repose. She had never had need of anything but him; provided he was there, she desired nothing.

" Still young, she had abandoned life and the world and those who had brought her up, and who had loved her. She had come, alone with him, into this savage valley. And he had been everything to her, all that one desires, all that one dreams of, all that one waits for without ceasing, all that one hopes for without end. He had filled her life with happiness from the one end to the other.

" She could not have been more happy.

" And all the night, listening to the hoarse breathing of the old soldier stretched on his pallet beside her who had followed him so far, I thought of this strange and simple adventure, of this happiness so complete, made of so very little.

" And I went away at sunrise, after having pressed the hands of that aged pair."

The story-teller was silent. A woman said:

" All the same, she had ideals which were too easily satisfied, needs which were too primitive, requirements which were too simple. She could only have been a fool."

Another said, in a low, slow voice, " What matter! she was happy."

And down there at the end of the horizon, Corsica was sinking into the night, returning gently into the sea, blotting out her great shadow, which had appeared as if in person to tell the story of those two humble lovers who were sheltered by her coasts.

# Happiness

## QUESTIONS

1. Explain how the early descriptive passages suggest the atmosphere.
2. To what social class do the people in the villa belong?
3. Does this intensify the interest in the story that follows?
4. In the same connection, why is there emphasis on the culture of Italy?
5. Is Corsica today like that described in the story?
6. Where does the story begin?
7. What language is spoken in Corsica?
8. Why did the narrator have " a feeling of anguish and fear " ?
9. Why did the old woman ask about the Sirmonts last?
10. What is the climax?
11. What is meant by having " just finished his time of service " ?
12. Do you think that the woman's life had been all that the narrator so poetically describes?
13. Which of the two women, at the end, was probably right in her conclusion? Explain.
14. How much of the charm of the story lies in the way it is told?
15. Find illustrations of Maupassant's characteristics as outlined in the sketch.

## SUBJECTS FOR COMPOSITION

1. Write what the narrator might have reported to the brother.
2. Construct a story which tells the old man's side.
3. From your observation, weave a story around some old couple whose past you do not know.

## OTHER STORIES BY GUY DE MAUPASSANT

The Necklace
The Piece of String
The Horla
A Coward
Moonlight
On the Journey

The Two Friends
The Wreck
The Hand
Fright
A Ghost

## ANTON PAVLOVICH CHEKHOV
(1860–1904)

THE Russian short stories best known to English readers were written in the hundred years preceding 1917, the date of the Russian Revolution. It is important to bear this in mind because all writers were both influenced and limited by the two most obnoxious institutions under the old monarchy, strict censorship and fear of exile. In spite of these handicaps authors wrote of the miseries of life in Russia, and especially of the hopelessness that pervaded the life of the poor. The effect on the writers was shown by their general pessimism. That is the chief note in Russian fiction.

Anton Chekhov, who was born in 1860 in Taganrog, southern Russia, at first seemed different from his predecessors and contemporaries. He wrote humorous stories, but their humor was that of satire, and the typical Russian bitterness is often only thinly veiled. The sad circumstances of his own life were at least partially responsible for his later seriousness. His father was an emancipated serf but had prospered sufficiently to give his children a good education. Anton chose medicine as his profession, and after graduating from the medical school at Moscow did some volunteer practicing for a short time, but his interest lay mainly in abnormal cases. This interest led him to a study of how the mind decays under certain physical conditions. The tragedy of that misfortune may easily be discerned in many of his characters. That he was himself afflicted with an incurable disease heightened the tragic impulse and colored much of his later work. He died in 1904.

The story of "The Bet," printed in this volume, is typical of what might be called Chekhov's middle period. It is neither sordidly tragic nor satirically humorous, and yet has elements of both humor and tragedy. The silliness of this bet, made by two men of presumably more than average intelligence, might be considered funny. The mental transformation of the prisoner certainly was not, but the reader is left at the end with some doubt as to what the author's conclusions were. The satire is evident enough.

Chekhov enjoyed great popularity during his short life as an author, and many critics today give him first place among European short story writers. That at once challenges comparisons with Maupassant. The two have many things in common. Both are at their best in the short story; indeed the Russian wrote nothing else in prose fiction, while the Frenchman's novels and poems are negligible. The stories of both are usually very short. Both show keen power of observing men and things, together with an analytic mind that is imaginatively constructive. The gift of style, assiduously cultivated by both, places them in the very front rank of the world's story-writers.

# THE BET

## I

IT WAS a dark autumn night. The old banker was pacing from corner to corner of his study, recalling to his mind the party he gave in the autumn fifteen years before. There were many clever people at the party and much interesting conversation. They talked among other things of capital punishment. The guests, among them not a few scholars and journalists, for the most part disapproved of capital punishment. They found it obsolete as a means of punishment, unfitted to a Christian State and immoral. Some of them thought that capital punishment should be replaced universally by life-imprisonment.

"I don't agree with you," said the host. "I myself have experienced neither capital punishment nor life-imprisonment, but if one may judge *a priori*, then in my opinion capital punishment is more moral and more humane than imprisonment. Execution kills instantly, life-imprisonment kills by degrees. Who is the more humane executioner, one who kills you in a few seconds or one who draws the life out of you incessantly, for years?"

"They're both equally immoral," remarked one of the guests, "because their purpose is the same, to take away life. The State is not God. It has no right to take away that which it cannot give back, if it should so desire."

Among the company was a lawyer, a young man of about twenty-five. On being asked his opinion, he said:

"Capital punishment and life-imprisonment are equally immoral; but if I were offered the choice between them, I would certainly choose the second. It's better to live somehow than not to live at all."

There ensued a lively discussion. The banker, who was then younger and more nervous, suddenly lost his temper, banged his fist on the table, and turning to the young lawyer, cried out:

"It's a lie. I bet you two millions you wouldn't stick in a cell even for five years."

"If you mean it seriously," replied the lawyer, "then I bet I'll stay not five but fifteen."

"Fifteen! Done!" cried the banker. "Gentlemen, I stake two millions."

"Agreed. You stake two millions, I my freedom," said the lawyer.

So this wild, ridiculous bet came to pass. The banker, who at that time had too many millions to count, spoiled and capricious, was beside himself with rapture. During supper he said to the lawyer jokingly:

"Come to your senses, young man, before it's too late. Two millions are nothing to me, but you stand to lose three or four of the best years of your life. I say three or four, because you'll never stick it out any longer. Don't forget either, you unhappy man, that voluntary is much heavier than enforced imprisonment. The idea that you have the right to free yourself at any moment will poison the whole of your life in the cell. I pity you."

And now the banker, pacing from corner to corner, recalled all this and asked himself:

"Why did I make this bet? What's the good? The lawyer loses fifteen years of his life and I throw away two millions. Will it convince people that capital punishment is worse or better than imprisonment for life? No, no! all stuff and rubbish. On my part, it was the caprice of a well-fed man; on the lawyer's pure greed of gold."

He recollected further what happened after the evening party. It was decided that the lawyer must undergo his imprisonment under the strictest observation, in a garden wing of the banker's house. It was agreed that during the period he would be deprived of the right to cross the threshold, to see living people, to hear human voices, and to receive letters and newspapers. He was permitted to have a musical instrument, to read books, to write letters, to drink wine and smoke tobacco. By the agreement he could communicate, but only in silence, with the outside world through a little window specially constructed for this purpose. Everything necessary, books, music, wine, he could receive in any quantity by sending a note through the window. The agreement provided for all the minutest details, which made the confinement strictly solitary, and it obliged the lawyer to remain exactly fifteen years from twelve o'clock of November 14th, 1870, to twelve o'clock of November 14th, 1885. The least attempt on his part to violate the conditions, to escape if only for two minutes before the time, freed the banker from the obligation to pay him the two millions.

During the first year of imprisonment, the lawyer, as far as it was possible to judge from his short notes, suffered terribly from loneliness and boredom. From his wing day and night came the sound of the piano. He rejected wine and tobacco. "Wine," he wrote, "excites desires, and desires are the chief foes of a prisoner; besides, nothing is more boring than to drink good wine alone, and tobacco spoils the air in his room." During the first year the lawyer was sent books of a light character; novels with a complicated love interest, stories of crime and fantasy, comedies, and so on.

In the second year the piano was heard no longer and the lawyer asked only for classics. In the fifth year, music was heard again, and the prisoner asked for wine. Those who watched him said that during the whole of that year he was only eating, drinking, and lying on his bed. He yawned often and talked angrily to himself. Books he did not read. Sometimes at nights he would sit down to write. He would write for a long time and tear it all up in the morning. More than once he was heard to weep.

In the second half of the sixth year, the prisoner began zealously to study languages, philosophy, and history. He fell on these subjects so hungrily that the banker hardly had time to get books enough for him. In the space of four years about six hundred volumes were bought at his request. It was while that passion lasted that the banker received the following letter from the prisoner: " My dear gaoler, I am writing these lines in six languages. Show them to experts. Let them read them. If they do not find one single mistake, I beg you to give orders to have a gun fired off in the garden. By the noise I shall know that my efforts have not been in vain. The geniuses of all ages and countries speak in different languages; but in them all burns the same flame. Oh, if you knew my heavenly happiness now that I can understand them! " The prisoner's desire was fulfilled. Two shots were fired in the garden by the banker's order.

Later on, after the tenth year, the lawyer sat immovable before his table and read only the New Testament. The banker found it strange that a man who in four years had mastered six hundred erudite volumes, should have spent nearly a year in reading one book, easy to understand and by no means thick. The New Testament was then replaced by the history of religions and theology.

During the last two years of his confinement the prisoner read an extraordinary amount, quite haphazard. Now he would apply himself to the natural sciences, then he would read Byron or Shakespeare. Notes used to come from him in which he asked to be sent at the same time a book on chemistry, a textbook of medicine, a novel, and some treatise on philosophy or theology. He read as though he were swimming in the sea among broken pieces of wreckage, and in his desire to save his life was eagerly grasping one piece after another.

II

The banker recalled all this, and thought:

"Tomorrow at twelve o'clock he receives his freedom. Under the agreement, I shall have to pay him two millions. If I pay, it's all over with me. I am ruined forever . . ."

Fifteen years before he had too many millions to count, but now he was afraid to ask himself which he had more of, money or debts. Gambling on the Stock-Exchange, risky speculation, and the recklessness of which he could not rid himself even in old age, had gradually brought his business to decay; and the fearless, self-confident, proud man of business had become an ordinary banker, trembling at every rise and fall in the market.

"That cursed bet," murmured the old man clutching his head in despair. . . . "Why didn't the man die? He's only forty years old. He will take away my last farthing, marry, enjoy life, gamble on the Exchange, and I will look on like an envious beggar and hear the same words from him every day: 'I'm obliged to you for the happiness of my life. Let me help you.' No, it's too much! The only escape from bankruptcy and disgrace — is that the man should die."

The clock had just struck three. The banker was listening. In the house every one was asleep, and one could hear only the frozen trees whining outside the windows. Trying to make no sound, he took out of his safe the key of the door which had not been opened for fifteen years, put on his overcoat, and

## The Bet

went out of the house. The garden was dark and cold. It was raining. A damp, penetrating wind howled in the garden and gave the trees no rest. Though he strained his eyes, the banker could see neither the ground, nor the white statues, nor the garden wing, nor the trees. Approaching the garden wing, he called the watchman twice. There was no answer. Evidently the watchman had taken shelter from the bad weather and was now asleep somewhere in the kitchen or the greenhouse.

"If I have the courage to fulfil my intention," thought the old man, "the suspicion will fall on the watchman first of all."

In the darkness he groped for the steps and the door and entered the hall of the garden-wing, then poked his way into a narrow passage and struck a match. Not a soul was there. Some one's bed, with no bedclothes on it, stood there, and an iron stove loomed dark in the corner. The seals on the door that led into the prisoner's room were unbroken.

When the match went out, the old man, trembling from agitation, peeped into the little window.

In the prisoner's room a candle was burning dimly. The prisoner himself sat by the table. Only his back, the hair on his head and his hands were visible. Open books were strewn about on the table, the two chairs, and on the carpet near the table.

Five minutes passed and the prisoner never once stirred. Fifteen years' confinement had taught him to sit motionless. The banker tapped on the window with his finger, but the prisoner made no movement in reply. Then the banker cautiously tore the seals from the door and put the key into the lock. The rusty lock gave a hoarse groan and the door creaked. The banker expected instantly to hear a cry of surprise and the sound of steps. Three minutes passed and it was as quiet inside as it had been before. He made up his mind to enter.

Before the table sat a man, unlike an ordinary human being. It was a skeleton, with tight-drawn skin, with long curly hair like a woman's, and a shaggy beard. The color of his face was yellow, of an earthy shade; the cheeks were sunken, the back long and narrow, and the hand upon which he leaned his hairy head was so lean and skinny that it was painful to look upon. His hair was already silvering with gray, and no one who glanced at the senile emaciation of the face would have believed that he was only forty years old. On the table, before his bended head, lay a sheet of paper on which something was written in a tiny hand.

"Poor devil," thought the banker, "he's asleep and probably seeing millions in his dreams. I have only to take and throw this half-dead thing on the bed, smother him a moment with the pillow, and the most careful examination will find no trace of unnatural death. But, first, let us read what he has written here."

The banker took the sheet from the table and read:

"Tomorrow at twelve o'clock midnight, I shall obtain my freedom and the right to mix with people. But before I leave this room and see the sun I think it necessary to say a few words to you. On my own clear conscience and before God who sees me I declare to you that I despise freedom, life, health, and all that your books call the blessings of the world.

"For fifteen years I have diligently studied earthly life. True, I saw neither the earth nor the people, but in your books I drank fragrant wine, sang songs, hunted deer and wild boar in the forests, loved women. . . . And beautiful women, like clouds ethereal, created by the magic of your poets' genius, visited me by night and whispered to me wonderful tales, which made my head drunken. In your books I climbed the summits of Elburz and Mont Blanc and saw from there how the sun rose in the morning, and in the evening suffused the sky, the ocean, and the mountain ridges with a purple gold. I saw from there how above me lightnings glimmered cleaving the clouds; I saw green forests, fields, rivers, lakes, cities; I heard sirens singing, and the playing of the pipes of Pan; I touched the wings of beautiful devils who came flying to me to speak of God. . . . In your books I cast myself into bottomless abysses, worked miracles, burned cities to the ground, preached new religions, conquered whole countries. . . .

"Your books gave me wisdom. All that unwearying human thought created in the centuries is compressed to a little lump in my skull. I know that I am cleverer than you all.

"And I despise your books, despise all worldly blessings and wisdom. Everything is void, frail, visionary and delusive as a mirage. Though you be proud and wise and beautiful, yet will death wipe you from the face of the earth like the mice underground; and your posterity, your history, and the immortality of your men of genius will be as frozen slag, burnt down together with the terrestrial globe.

"You are mad, and gone the wrong way. You take falsehood for truth and ugliness for beauty. You would marvel if suddenly apple and orange trees should bear frogs and lizards instead of fruit, and if roses should begin to breathe the odor of a sweating horse. So do I marvel at you, who have bartered heaven for earth. I do not want to understand you.

"That I may show you in deed my contempt for that by which you live, I waive the two millions of which I once dreamed as of paradise, and which I now despise. That I may deprive myself of my right to them, I shall come out from here five minutes before the stipulated term, and thus shall violate the agreement."

When he had read, the banker put the sheet on the table, kissed the head of the strange man, and began to weep. He went out of the wing. Never at any other time, not even after his terrible losses on the Exchange, had he felt such contempt for himself as now. Coming home, he lay down on his bed, but agitation and tears kept him a long time from sleeping. . . .

The next morning the poor watchman came running to him and told him that they had seen the man who lived in the wing climb through the window into the garden. He had gone to the gate and disappeared. The banker instantly went with his servants to the wing and established the escape of his prisoner. To avoid unnecessary rumors he took the paper with the renunciation from the table and, on his return, locked it in his safe.

### QUESTIONS

1. State briefly how the bet was made, and its conditions. The "millions" are rubles, not dollars.
2. Do you think voluntary imprisonment worse than enforced imprisonment? Explain.
3. Account for the prisoner's activities during the first two years.
4. How do you explain his sixth year?
5. Do the same for the tenth year; the last two years. In this co nection see the introductory sketch on Chekhov.
6. What is meant by "desire to save his life"?
7. By the end of fifteen years how had the banker's character deteriorated?
8. Which of the two was in the worse condition? Explain.

9. What do you think of the prisoner's views as expressed in the letter?
10. Were both the richer for their experience?
11. Do you find any satire in this story?
12. Is there a theme? A plot?
13. Why are stories of this type called "psychological"?

## SUBJECTS FOR COMPOSITION

1. Write a possible other ending.
2. Describe what you think might be a life prisoner's state of mind on his being unexpectedly released after twenty years.
3. Tell orally about some silly bet, the kind made at election time.

## OTHER STORIES BY ANTON CHEKHOV

| | |
|---|---|
| A Work of Art | Ward No. 6 |
| The Steppe | The Black Monk |
| Vanka | The Darling |
| In Exile | The Kiss |

## BJÖRNSTJERNE BJÖRNSON
## (1832–1910)

For the average reader in English there are only two outstanding names in Norwegian literature, Björnstjerne Björnson and Henrik Ibsen. As boys they were schoolmates, and they remained lifelong friends. Ibsen is known chiefly as a dramatist, while Björnson practiced nearly every form of writing — he was a poet, playwright, novelist, short story writer; he was also an orator, theatrical manager, and political patriot. Ibsen was more a man of the world, in the sense that he traveled a great deal, but he was always an ardent Norwegian. Until his later years Björnson stayed at home in Norway, always active in his country's welfare, especially in the movement for separating Norway politically from Sweden, a cause that ultimately triumphed. Both Ibsen and Björnson were men of strong physique and striking personal appearance, true descendants of the Vikings of old.

Björnson was born in 1832, and spent his boyhood in remote mountain regions where his father was a country parson in the Lutheran church. As a boy in school he was not a delight to his teachers, who considered him dull. As a student at the University of Christiania he spent more time writing poetry and magazine articles than on the prescribed studies. He had the joy of seeing his first play produced before he was twenty. Throughout the rest of his life he remained intensely active in literary and political affairs. To English readers he is best known as a novelist and story-teller. He died in Paris in 1910.

In his stories Björnson has the same universal themes that characterize the work of Ibsen, but unlike his friend, he writes as a romantic optimist. Norway is a stern rugged country; its men and women reflect this quality in their serious preoccupation with the problems of life and death. The story of "The Father" is therefore not only a good story, but also a fair representation of the Norwegian type of mind and spirit.

The most striking outward feature of the story is its brevity: it has only 931 words. This brevity is emphasized by the simplicity of the language, the shortness of the sentences and paragraphs, and the directness of the statements. No description for background, no analysis of character other than that implied in the action, no wordy explanation of what the author was driving at; and yet everything is there by implication and suggestion. The tone of the story is almost biblical and it may well be read in connection with "The Prodigal Son." However different in motive, both tend in the same direction, that of spiritual content.

# THE FATHER

THE man whose story is here to be told was the wealthiest and most influential person in his parish; his name was Thord Överaas. He appeared in the parson's study one day, tall and earnest.

"I have gotten a son," said he, "and I wish to present him for baptism."

"What shall his name be?"

"Finn — after my father."

"And the sponsors?"

They were mentioned, and proved to be the best men and women of Thord's relations in the parish.

"Is there anything else?" inquired the parson, and looked up. The peasant hesitated a little.

"I should like very much to have him baptized by himself," said he, finally.

"That is to say on a week-day?"

"Next Saturday, at twelve o'clock noon."

"Is there anything else?" inquired the parson.

"There is nothing else;" and the peasant twirled his cap, as though he were about to go.

Then the parson rose. "There is yet this, however," said he, and walking toward Thord, he took him by the hand and looked gravely into his eyes: "God grant that the child may become a blessing to you!"

One day sixteen years later, Thord stood once more in the parson's study.

"Really, you carry your age astonishingly well, Thord," said the parson; for he saw no change whatever in the man.

"That is because I have no troubles," replied Thord.

To this the parson said nothing, but after a while he asked: "What is your pleasure this evening?"

"I have come this evening about that son of mine who is to be confirmed tomorrow."

"He is a bright boy."

"I did not wish to pay the parson until I heard what number the boy would have when he takes his place in the church tomorrow."

"He will stand number one."

562

## The Father

"So I have heard; and here are ten dollars for the parson."

"Is there anything else I can do for you?" inquired the parson, fixing his eyes on Thord.

"There is nothing else."

Thord went out.

Eight years more rolled by, and then one day a noise was heard outside of the parson's study, for many men were approaching, and at their head was Thord, who entered first.

The parson looked up and recognized him.

"You come well attended this evening, Thord," said he.

"I am here to request that the banns may be published for my son: he is about to marry Karen Storliden, daughter of Gudmund, who stands here beside me."

"Why, that is the richest girl in the parish."

"So they say," replied the peasant, stroking back his hair with one hand.

The parson sat awhile as if in deep thought, then entered the names in his book, without making any comments, and the men wrote their signatures underneath. Thord laid three dollars on the table.

"One is all I am to have," said the parson.

"I know that very well; but he is my only child; I want to do it handsomely."

The parson took the money.

"This is now the third time, Thord, that you have come here on your son's account."

"But now I am through with him," said Thord, and folding up his pocket-book he said farewell and walked away.

The men slowly followed him.

A fortnight later, the father and son were rowing across the lake, one calm, still day, to Storliden to make arrangements for the wedding.

"This thwart is not secure," said the son, and stood up to straighten the seat on which he was sitting.

At the same moment the board he was standing on slipped from under him; he threw out his arms, uttered a shriek, and fell overboard.

"Take hold of the oar!" shouted the father, springing to his feet and holding out the oar.

But when the son had made a couple of efforts he grew stiff.

"Wait a moment!" cried the father, and began to row toward his son.

Then the son rolled over on his back, gave his father one long look, and sank.

Thord could scarcely believe it; he held the boat still, and stared at the spot where his son had gone down, as though he must surely come to the surface again. There rose some bubbles, then some more, and finally one large one that burst; and the lake lay there as smooth and bright as a mirror again.

For three days and three nights people saw the father rowing round and round the spot, without taking either food or sleep; he was dragging the lake for the body of his son. And toward morning of the third day he found it, and carried it in his arms up over the hills to his gard.

It might have been about a year from that day, when the parson, late one autumn evening, heard some one in the passage outside of the door, carefully trying to find the latch. The parson opened the door, and in walked a tall, thin man, with bowed form and white hair. The parson looked long at him before he recognized him. It was Thord.

"Are you out walking so late?" said the parson, and stood still in front of him.

"Ah, yes! it is late," said Thord, and took a seat.

The parson sat down also, as though waiting. A long, long silence followed. At last Thord said:

"I have something with me that I should like to give to the poor; I want it to be invested as a legacy in my son's name."

He rose, laid some money on the table, and sat down again. The parson counted it.

"It is a great deal of money," said he.

"It is half the price of my gard. I sold it today."

The parson sat long in silence. At last he asked, but gently:

"What do you propose to do now, Thord?"

"Something better."

They sat there for a while, Thord with downcast eyes, the parson with his eyes fixed on Thord. Presently the parson said, slowly and softly:

"I think your son has at last brought you a true blessing."

"Yes, I think so myself," said Thord, looking up, while two big tears coursed slowly down his cheeks.

## QUESTIONS

1. This is a story of theme. State it clearly and briefly.
2. How is it suggested in the first paragraph?
3. From the first paragraph, what about the father's character?
4. How is the theme emphasized by the choice of sponsors?
5. How are the parson's words connected with the theme?
6. In what respect does the father's second visit resemble the first?
7. How is the theme advanced by the third visit?
8. Why should the parson sit "as if in deep thought"?
9. Would the tragic moment gain in vividness by longer description?
10. What is the "something better" that Thord intends to do?
11. What "true blessing" does the parson mean?
12. In the best imaginative writing more is suggested than told. Is that true here?
13. In what respects does the story resemble the parables in the Bible?
14. What is your feeling about the style? Be explicit.
15. Has the story a dramatic note? Illustrate.
16. Do you see any parallel in "The Ambitious Guest"? Eplain.

## SUBJECTS FOR COMPOSITION

1. Write a father-and-son story. Imitate the simple direct style of Björnson.
2. As an interesting exercise in style, take a story from a popular magazine and cross out useless words and sentences, keeping the story itself intact.

## OTHER STORIES BY BJÖRNSTJERNE BJÖRNSON

A Happy Boy
The Fisher Maiden
The Bear Hunter

Railroad and Churchyard
The Bridal March

## ABOUT BJÖRNSTJERNE BJÖRNSON

*Björnstjerne Björnson,* W. M. Payne

# ALEXANDRE DUMAS
## (1802–1870)

THE elder Dumas has been pompously described as "the greatest French romantic novelist and the most universally read story-teller of the world." One more superlative might be added, that he wrote *more* stories and novels than any other writer. In the French edition they total nearly 300 volumes. These include his plays and all the odds and ends that can possibly be attributed to him, and some that perhaps should not.

Alexandre Dumas had an adventurous ancestry. His father and grandfather were intimately involved in the stirring events that were part of the times in France and her colonies. The grandfather returned from Haiti with a black wife, but that was not regarded in France as it would be in America. France has never been noted for political tranquillity, and alert eager men were constantly involved in intrigues that often made a change of scenery quickly imperative. When to this condition is added the spirit of vagabondage common to the Dumas family it becomes possible to understand somewhat the character of Alexandre.

He was born near Paris in 1802, and from childhood was left pretty much to his own devices. At times he was fortunate in his surroundings, but more often not. When he grew up he secured employment of various kinds through politics, the kinds that change with political conditions. He had many adventures in the Revolution of 1830, and after, but he was always writing, or planning something to write. The result of that phase of his life only is of concern here.

As a writer he had an almost unparalleled creative power, a facility in devising a situation that was interesting, and fitting it with incidents that made it more so. The plot just naturally seems to be there, carried forward by swift action and fascinating dialogue, so that the reader constantly wants to know "what comes next," and how it is going to "turn out." Dumas was a short story writer only incidentally, but what is said of his long stories applies equally to "Zodomirsky's Duel," printed here.

The story of Dumas's life is much too crowded to tell here. He was popular in his own day and earned enormous sums, but spent even more. He was accused of plagiarism and of hiring assistants. As he admitted both of these charges, they need not be discussed. He founded a fiction factory and had as many as ten men at work, generals, as he called them, over whom he was Napoleon. That was the kind of answer that one might expect from the author of *The Three Musketeers* and *The Count of Monte Cristo*.

In his old age he became very poor, and his adventures consisted mainly in fleeing from his creditors. He visited England, Italy, and Russia. In his last years he was cared for by a son whom he had neglected. He died in Puys, December 5, 1870, the day of its occupation by the Prussians.

# ZODOMIRSKY'S DUEL

I

AT THE time of this story our regiment was stationed in the dirty little village of Valins, on the frontier of Austria. It was the fourth of May in the year 182–, and I, with several other officers, had been breakfasting with the Aide-de-Camp in honor of his birthday, and discussing the various topics of the garrison.

"Can you tell us without being indiscreet," asked Sub-Lieutenant Stamm of Andrew Michaelovitch, the Aide-de-Camp, "what the Colonel was so eager to say to you this morning?"

"A new officer," he replied, "is to fill the vacancy of captain."

"His name?" demanded two or three voices.

"Lieutenant Zodomirsky, who is betrothed to the beautiful Mariana Ravensky."

"And when does he arrive?" asked Major Belayef.

"He *has* arrived. I have been presented to him at the Colonel's house. He is very anxious to make your acquaintance, gentlemen, and I have therefore invited him to dine with us. But that reminds me, Captain, you must know him," he continued, turning to me; "you were both in the same regiment at St. Petersburg."

"It is true," I replied. "We studied there together. He was then a brave, handsome youth, adored by his comrades, in every one's good graces, but of a fiery and irritable temper."

"Mademoiselle Ravensky informed me that he was a skilful duelist," said Stamm. "Well, he will do very well here; a duel is a family affair with us. You are welcome, Monsieur Zodomirsky. However quick your temper, you must be careful of it before me, or I shall take upon myself to cool it."

And Stamm pronounced these words with a visible sneer.

"How is it that he leaves the Guards? Is he ruined?" asked Cornet Naletoff.

"I have been informed," replied Stamm, "that he has just inherited from an old aunt about twenty thousand rubles. No, poor devil! he is consumptive."

"Come, gentlemen," said the Aide-de-Camp, rising, "let us pass to the saloon and have a game of cards. Koloff will serve dinner while we play."

We had been seated some time, and Stamm, who was far from rich, was in the act of losing sixty rubles, when Koloff announced:

"Captain Zodomirsky."

"Here you are, at last!" cried Michaelovitch, jumping from his chair. "You are welcome."

Then, turning to us, he continued: "These are your new comrades, Captain Zodomirsky; all good fellows and brave soldiers."

"Gentlemen," said Zodomirsky, "I am proud and happy to have joined your regiment. To do so has been my greatest desire for some time, and if I am welcome, as you courteously say, I shall be the happiest man in the world."

"Ah! good day, Captain," he continued, turning to me and holding out his hand. "We meet again. You have not forgotten an old friend, I hope?"

As he smilingly uttered these words, Stamm, to whom his back was turned, darted at him a glance full of bitter hatred. Stamm was not liked in the regiment; his cold and taciturn nature had formed no friendship with any of us. I could not understand his apparent hostility toward Zodomirsky, whom I believed he had never seen before.

Some one offered Zodomirsky a cigar. He accepted it, lit it at the cigar of an officer near him, and began to talk gaily to his new comrades.

"Do you stay here long?" asked Major Belayef.

"Yes, monsieur," replied Zodomirsky. "I wish to stay with you as long as possible," and as he pronounced these words he saluted us all round with a smile. He continued: "I have taken a house near that of my old friend Ravensky whom I knew at St. Petersburg. I have my horses there, an excellent cook, a passable library, a little garden, and a target; and there I shall be quiet as a hermit, and happy as a king. It is the life that suits me."

"Ha! you practise shooting!" said Stamm, in such a strange voice, accompanied by a smile so sardonic, that Zodomirsky regarded him in astonishment.

"It is my custom every morning to fire twelve balls," he replied.

"You are very fond of that amusement, then?" demanded Stamm, in a voice without any trace of emotion; adding, "I do not understand the use of shooting, unless it is to hunt with."

Zodomirsky's pale face was flushed with a sudden flame. He turned to Stamm, and replied in a quiet but firm voice: "I think, monsieur, that you are wrong in calling it lost time to learn to shoot with a pistol; in our garrison life an imprudent word often leads to a meeting between comrades, in which case he who is known for a good shot inspires respect among those indiscreet persons who amuse themselves in asking useless questions."

"Oh! that is not a reason, Captain. In duels, as in everything else, something should be left to chance. I maintain my first opinion, and say that an honorable man ought not to take too many precautions."

"And why?" asked Zodomirsky.

"I will explain to you," replied Stamm. "Do you play at cards, Captain?"

"Why do you ask that question?"

"I will try to render my explanation clear, so that all will understand it. Every one knows that there are certain players who have an enviable knack, while shuffling the pack, of adroitly making themselves master of the winning card. Now, I see no difference, myself, between the man who robs his neighbor of his money and the one who robs him of his life." Then he added, in a way to take nothing from the insolence of his observation, "I do not say this to you, in particular, Captain; I speak in general terms."

"It is too much as it is, monsieur!" cried Zodomirsky, "I beg Captain Alexis Stephanovitch to terminate this affair with you." Then, turning to me, he said: "You will not refuse me this request?"

"So be it, Captain," replied Stamm quickly. "You have told me yourself you practise shooting every day, while I practise only on the day I fight. We will equalize the chances. I will settle details with Monsieur Stephanovitch."

Then he rose and turned to our host.

"*Au revoir*, Michaelovitch," he said. "I will dine at the Colonel's." And with these words he left the room.

The most profound silence had been kept during this altercation; but, as soon as Stamm disappeared, Captain Pravdine, an old officer, addressed himself to us all.

"We can not let them fight, gentlemen," he said.

Zodomirsky touched him gently on his arm.

"Captain," he said, "I am a newcomer among you; none of you know me. I have yet, as it were, to win my spurs; is impossible for me to let this quarrel pass without fighting. do not know what I have done to annoy this gentleman, but it is evident that he has some spite against me."

"The truth of the matter is that Stamm is jealous of you, Zodomirsky," said Cornet Naletoff. "It is well known that he is in love with Mademoiselle Ravensky."

"That, indeed, explains all," he replied. "However, gentlemen, I thank you for your kind sympathy in this affair from the bottom of my heart."

"And now to dinner, gentlemen!" cried Michaelovitch. "Place yourselves as you choose. The soup, Koloff; the soup!"

Everybody was very animated. Stamm seemed forgotten; only Zodomirsky appeared a little sad. Zodomirsky's health was drunk; he seemed touched with this significant attention, and thanked the officers with a broken voice.

"Stephanovitch," said Zodomirsky to me, when dinner was over, and all had risen, "since Monsieur Stamm knows you are my second and has accepted you as such, see him, and arrange everything with him; accept all his conditions; then meet Captain Pravdine and me at my rooms. The first who arrives will wait for the other. We are now going to Monsieur Ravensky's house."

"You will let us know the hour of combat?" said several voices.

"Certainly, gentlemen. Come and bid a last farewell to one of us."

We all parted at the Ravenskys' door, each officer shaking hands with Zodomirsky as with an old friend.

## II

Stamm was waiting for me when I arrived at his house. His conditions were these: Two sabers were to be planted at a distance of one pace apart; each opponent to extend his arm at full length and fire at the word "*three.*" One pistol alone was to be loaded.

I endeavored in vain to obtain another mode of combat.

"It is not a victim I offer to Monsieur Zodomirsky," said Stamm, "but an adversary. He will fight as I propose, or I will not fight at all; but in that case I shall prove that Monsieur Zodomirsky is brave only when sure of his own safety."

Zodomirsky's orders were imperative. I accepted.

When I entered Zodomirsky's rooms, they were vacant; he had not arrived. I looked round with curiosity. They were furnished in a rich but simple manner, and with evident taste. I drew a chair near the balcony and looked out over the plain. A storm was brewing; some drops of rain fell already, and thunder moaned.

At this instant the door opened, and Zodomirsky and Pravdine entered. I advanced to meet them.

"We are late, Captain," said Zodomirsky, "but it was unavoidable."

"And what says Stamm?" he continued.

I gave him his adversary's conditions. When I had ended, a sad smile passed over his face; he drew his hand across his forehead and his eyes glittered with feverish luster.

"I had foreseen this," he murmured. "You have accepted, I presume?"

"Did you not give me the order yourself?"

"Absolutely," he replied.

Zodomirsky threw himself in a chair by the table, in which position he faced the door. Pravdine placed himself near the window, and I near the fire. A presentiment weighed down our spirits. A mournful silence reigned.

Suddenly the door opened and a woman muffled in a mantle which streamed with water, and with the hood drawn over her face, pushed past the servant, and stood before us. She threw back the hood, and we recognized Mariana Ravensky!

Pravdine and I stood motionless with astonishment. Zodomirsky sprang toward her.

"Great heavens! what has happened, and why are you here?"

"Why am I here, George?" she cried. "Is it *you* who ask me, when this night is perhaps the last of your life? Why am I here? To say farewell to you. It is only two hours since I saw you, and not one word passed between us of to-morrow. Was that well, George?"

"But I am not alone here," said Zodomirsky in a low voice. "Think, Mariana. Your reputation — your fair fame——"

"Are you not all in all to me, George? And in such a time as this, what matters anything else?"

She threw her arm about his neck and pressed her head against his breast.

Pravdine and I made some steps to quit the room.

"Stay, gentlemen," she said lifting her head. "Since you have seen me here, I have nothing more to hide from you, and perhaps you may be able to help me in what I am about to say." Then, suddenly flinging herself at his feet:

"I implore you, I command you, George," she cried, "not to fight this duel with Monsieur Stamm. You will not end two lives by such a useless act! Your life belongs to me; it is no longer yours. George, do you hear? You will not do this."

"Mariana! Mariana! in the name of Heaven do not torture me thus! Can I refuse to fight? I should be dishonored — lost! If I could do so cowardly an act, shame would kill me more surely than Stamm's pistol."

"Captain," she said to Pravdine, "you are esteemed in the regiment as a man of honor; you can, then, judge about affairs of honor. Have pity on me, Captain, and tell him he can refuse such a duel as this. Make him understand that it is not a duel, but an assassination; speak, speak, Captain, and if he will not listen to me, he will to you."

Pravdine was moved. His lips trembled and his eyes were dimmed with tears. He rose, and, approaching Mariana, respectfully kissed her hand, and said with a trembling voice:

"To spare you any sorrow, mademoiselle, I would lay down my life; but to counsel Monsieur Zodomirsky to be unworthy of his uniform by refusing this duel is impossible. Each adversary, your betrothed as well as Stamm, has a right to propose his conditions. But whatever be the conditions, the Captain is in circumstances which render this duel absolutely necessary.

'He is known as a skilful duelist; to refuse Stamm's conditions were to indicate that he counts upon his skill."

"Enough, Mariana, enough," cried George. "Unhappy girl! you do not know what you demand. Do you wish me, then, to fall so low that you yourself would be ashamed of me? I ask you, are you capable of loving a dishonored man?"

Mariana had let herself fall upon a chair. She rose, pale as a corpse, and began to put her mantle on.

"You are right, George, it is not I who would love you no more, but you who would hate me. We must resign ourselves to our fate. Give me your hand, George; perhaps we shall never see each other again. Tomorrow! tomorrow! my love."

She threw herself upon his breast, without tears, without sobs, but with a profound despair.

She wished to depart alone, but Zodomirsky insisted on leading her home.

Midnight was striking when he returned.

"You had better both retire," said Zodomirsky as he entered. "I have several letters to write before sleeping. At five we must be at the rendezvous."

I felt so wearied that I did not want telling twice. Pravdine passed into the saloon, I into Zodomirsky's bedroom, and the master of the house into his study.

The cool air of the morning woke me. I cast my eyes upon the window, where the dawn commenced to appear. I heard Pravdine also stirring. I passed into the saloon, where Zodomirsky immediately joined us. His face was pale but serene.

"Are the horses ready?" he inquired.

I made a sign in the affirmative.

"Then, let us start," he said.

We mounted into the carriage and drove off.

### III

"Ah," said Pravdine all at once, "there is Michaelovitch's carriage. Yes, yes, it is he with one of ours, and there is Naletoff, on his Circassian horse. Good! the others are coming behind. It is well we started so soon."

The carriage had to pass the house of the Ravenskys. I could not refrain from looking up; the poor girl was at her window, motionless as a statue. She did not even nod to us.

"Quicker! quicker!" cried Zodomirsky to the coachman. It was the only sign by which I knew that he had seen Mariana.

Soon we distanced the other carriages, and arrived upon the place of combat — a plain where two great pyramids rose, passing in this district by the name of the "Tomb of the Two Brothers." The first rays of the sun darting through the trees began to dissipate the mists of night.

Michaelovitch arrived immediately after us, and in a few minutes we formed a group of nearly twenty persons. Then we heard the crunch of other steps upon the gravel. They were those of our opponents. Stamm walked first, holding in his hand a box of pistols. He bowed to Zodomirsky and the officers.

"Who gives the word to fire, gentlemen?" he asked.

The two adversaries and the seconds turned toward the officers, who regarded them with perplexity.

No one offered. No one wished to pronounce that terrible "three," which would sign the fate of a comrade.

"Major," said Zodomirsky to Belayef, "will you render me this service?"

Thus asked, the Major could not refuse, and he made a sign that he accepted.

"Be good enough to indicate our places, gentlemen," continued Zodomirsky, giving me his saber and taking off his coat; "then load, if you please."

"That is useless," said Stamm. "I have brought the pistols; one of the two is loaded, the other has only a gun-cap."

"Do you know which is which?" said Pravdine.

"What does it matter?" replied Stamm, "Monsieur Zodomirsky will choose."

"It is well," said Zodomirsky.

Belayef drew his saber and thrust it in the ground midway between the two pyramids. Then he took another saber and planted it before the first. One pace alone separated the two blades. Each adversary was to stand behind a saber, extending his arm at full length. In this way each had the muzzle of his opponent's pistol at six inches from his heart. While Belayef made these preparations Stamm unbuckled his saber and divested himself of his coat. His seconds opened his box of pistols, and Zodomirsky, approaching, took without hesitation the nearest to him. Then he placed himself behind one of the sabers.

Stamm regarded him closely; not a muscle of Zodomirsky's face moved, and there was not about him the least appearance of bravado, but the calmness of courage.

"He is brave," murmured Stamm.

And taking the pistol left by Zodomirsky he took up his position behind the other saber, in front of his adversary.

They were both pale, but while the eyes of Zodomirsky burned with implacable resolution, those of Stamm were uneasy and shifting. I felt my heart beat loudly.

Belayef advanced. All eyes were fixed on him.

"Are you ready, gentlemen?" he asked.

"We are waiting, Major," replied Zodomirsky and Stamm together, and each lifted his pistol before the breast of the other.

A death-like silence reigned. Only the birds sang in the bushes near the place of combat. In the midst of this silence the Major's voice resounding made every one tremble.

"One."

"Two."

"*Three.*"

Then we heard the sound of the hammer falling on the cap of Zodomirsky's pistol. There was a flash, but no sound followed it.

Stamm had not fired, and continued to hold the mouth of his pistol against the breast of his adversary.

"Fire!" said Zodomirsky, in a voice perfectly calm.

"It is not for you to command, monsieur," said Stamm; "it is I who must decide whether to fire or not, and that depends on how you answer what I am about to say."

"Speak, then; but in the name of Heaven speak quickly."

"Never fear, I will not abuse your patience."

We were all ears.

"I have not come to kill you, monsieur," continued Stamm. "I have come with the carelessness of a man to whom life holds nothing, while it has kept none of the promises it has made to him. You, monsieur, are rich, you are beloved, you have a promising future before you: life must be dear to you. But Fate has decided against you: it is you who must die and not I. Well, Monsieur Zodomirsky, give me your word not to be so prompt in the future to fight duels, and I will not fire."

"I have not been prompt to call you out, monsieur," replied Zodomirsky in the same calm voice; "you have wounded me by an outrageous comparison, and I have been compelled to challenge you. Fire, then; I have nothing to say to you."

"My conditions can not wound your honor," insisted Stamm. "Be our judge, Major," he added, turning to Belayef. "I will abide by your opinion; perhaps Monsieur Zodomirsky will follow my example."

"Monsieur Zodomirsky has conducted himself as bravely as possible; if he is not killed, it is not his fault." Then, turning to the officers round, he said:

"Can Monsieur Zodomirsky accept the imposed condition?"

"He can! he can!" they cried, "and without staining his honor in the slightest."

Zodomirsky stood motionless.

"The Captain consents," said old Pravdine, advancing. "Yes, in the future he will be less prompt."

"It is you who speak, Captain, and not Monsieur Zodomirsky," said Stamm.

"Will you affirm my words, Monsieur Zodomirsky?" asked Pravdine, almost supplicating in his eagerness.

"I consent," said Zodomirsky, in a voice scarcely intelligible.

"Hurrah! hurrah!" cried all the officers, enchanted with this termination. Two or three threw up their caps.

"I am more charmed than any one," said Stamm, "that all has ended as I desired. Now, Captain, I have shown you that before a resolute man the art of shooting is nothing in a duel, and that if the chances are equal a good shot is on the same level as a bad one. I did not wish in any case to kill you. Only I had a great desire to see how you would look death in the face. You are a man of courage; accept my compliments. The pistols were not loaded." Stamm, as he said these words, fired off his pistol. There was no report!

Zodomirsky uttered a cry which resembled the roar of a wounded lion.

"By my father's soul!" he cried, "this is a new offense, and more insulting than the first. Ah! it is ended, you say? No, monsieur, it must recommence, and this time the pistols shall be loaded, if I have to load them myself."

"No, Captain," replied Stamm, tranquilly, "I have given you your life, I will not take it back. Insult me if you wish, I will not fight with you."

"Then it is with me whom you will fight, Monsieur Stamm,"

cried Pravdine, pulling off his coat. "You have acted like a scoundrel; you have deceived Zodomirsky and his seconds, and, in five minutes if your dead body is not lying at my feet, there is no such thing as justice."

Stamm was visibly confused. He had not bargained for this.

"And if the Captain does not kill you, I will!" said Naletoff.

"Or I!" "Or I!" cried with one voice all the officers.

"The devil! I can not fight with you all," replied Stamm. "Choose one among you, and I will fight with him, though it will not be a duel, but an assassination."

"Reassure yourself, monsieur," replied Major Belayef; "we will do nothing that the most scrupulous honor can complain of. All our officers are insulted, for under their uniform you have conducted yourself like a rascal. You can not fight with all; it is even probable you will fight with none. Hold yourself in readiness, then. You are to be judged. Gentlemen, will you approach?"

We surrounded the Major, and the fiat went forth without discussion. Every one was of the same opinion.

Then the Major, who had played the rôle of president, approached Stamm, and said to him:

"Monsieur, you are lost to all the laws of honor. Your crime was premeditated in cold blood. You have made M. Zodomirsky pass through all the sensations of a man condemned to death, while you were perfectly at ease, you who knew that the pistols were not loaded. Finally, you have refused to fight with the man whom you have doubly insulted."

"Load the pistols! load them!" cried Stamm, exasperated. "I will fight with any one!"

But the Major shook his head with a smile of contempt.

"No, Monsieur Lieutenant," he said, "you will fight no more with your comrades. You have stained your uniform. We can no longer serve with you. The officers have charged me to say that, not wishing to make your deficiencies known to the Government, they ask you to give in your resignation on the cause of bad health. The surgeon will sign all necessary certificates. Today is the 3d of May: you have from now to the 3d of June to quit the regiment."

"I will quit it, certainly; not because it is your desire, but mine," said Stamm, picking up his saber and putting on his coat.

Then he leaped upon his horse, and galloped off toward the village, casting a last malediction to us all.

We all pressed round Zodomirsky. He was sad; more than sad, gloomy.

"Why did you force me to consent to this scoundrel's conditions, gentlemen?" he said. "Without you, I should never have accepted them."

"My comrades and I," said the Major, "will take all the responsibility. You have acted nobly, and I must tell you in the name of us all, Monsieur Zodomirsky, that you are a man of honor." Then, turning to the officers: "Let us go, gentlemen; we must inform the Colonel of what has passed."

We mounted into the carriages. As we did so we saw Stamm in the distance galloping up the mountainside from the village upon his horse. Zodomirsky's eyes followed him.

"I know not what presentiment torments me," he said, "but I wish his pistol had been loaded, and that he had fired."

He uttered a deep sigh, then shook his head, as if with that he could disperse his gloomy thoughts.

"Home," he called to the driver.

We took the same route that we had come by, and consequently again passed Mariana Ravensky's window. Each of us looked up, but Mariana was no longer there.

"Captain," said Zodomirsky, "will you do me a service?"

"Whatever you wish," I replied.

"I count upon you to tell my poor Mariana the result of this miserable affair."

"I will do so. And when?"

"Now. The sooner the better. Stop!" cried Zodomirsky to the coachman. He stopped, and I descended, and the carriage drove on.

Zodomirsky had hardly entered when he saw me appear in the doorway of the saloon. Without doubt my face was pale, and wore a look of consternation, for Zodomirsky sprang toward me, crying:

"Great heavens, Captain! What has happened?"

I drew him from the saloon.

"My poor friend, haste, if you wish to see Mariana alive.

She was at her window; she saw Stamm gallop past. Stamm being alive, it followed that you were dead. She uttered a cry, and fell. From that moment she has never opened her eyes."

"Oh, my presentiments!" cried Zodomirsky, "my presentiments!" and he rushed hatless and without his saber into the street.

On the staircase of Mademoiselle Ravensky's house he met the doctor, who was coming down.

"Doctor," he cried, stopping him, "she is better, is she not?"

"Yes," he answered, "better, because she suffers no more."

"Dead!" murmured Zodomirsky, growing white, and supporting himself against the wall. "Dead!"

"I always told her, poor girl! that, having a weak heart, she must avoid all emotion ——"

But Zodomirsky had ceased to listen. He sprang up the steps, crossed the hall and the saloon, calling like a madman: "Mariana! Mariana!"

At the door of the sleeping chamber stood Mariana's old nurse, who tried to bar his progress. He pushed by her, and entered the room.

Mariana was lying motionless and pale upon her bed. Her face was calm as if she slept. Zodomirsky threw himself upon his knees by the bedside, and seized her hand. It was cold, and in it was clenched a curl of black hair.

"My hair!" cried Zodomirsky, bursting into sobs. "Yes, yours," said the old nurse, "your hair that she cut off herself on quitting you at St. Petersburg. I have often told her it would bring misfortune to one of you."

If any one desires to learn what became of Zodomirsky, let him inquire for Brother Vassili, at the Monastery of Troitza.

The holy brothers will show the visitor his tomb. They know neither his real name nor the causes which, at twenty-six, had made him take the robe of a monk. Only they say, vaguely, that it was after a great sorrow, caused by the death of a woman whom he loved.

## QUESTIONS

1. What about Zodomirsky suggests lines of complication?
2. What does Stamm mean by saying " a duel is a family affair with us " ?
3. In your own words, how did Stamm insult Zodomirsky?
4. What exactly were the conditions of the duel?
5. On what basis does Mariana make her plea?
6. What " two lives " does she mean?
7. Was Zodomirsky justified in his reasons for not withdrawing?
8. Why did all the officers turn against Stamm after the encounter?
9. How is the ending of the story hinted at?
10. Why did Zodomirsky not go to Mariana himself?
11. Was Mariana's conclusion natural after seeing Stamm?  Explain.
12. What is there peculiar about the nurse's prediction?
13. Is the last paragraph necessary?  Explain.
14. Should something more be said about Stamm?
15. What gives novelty to this duel?

## SUBJECTS FOR COMPOSITION

1. Tell orally of the duel between Aaron Burr and Alexander Hamilton.
2. If possible, read Pushkin's " The Shot," and write a comparison.
3 Write an episode involving a serious struggle that is futile.

## SELMA LAGERLÖF
### (1858–1940)

SELMA LAGERLÖF was born November 20, 1858 in the province of Vermland, Sweden. She was one of a large family of Swedish gentlefolk of the landowner class. Her father was a retired army officer, while her mother came from a long line of clergymen. As a child she was not strong enough to run wild on the farm with the other children, but she was quite content to stay at home reading or listening to the stories about the great and wonderful things which had happened in the world. There was an ample family library in which she was allowed to browse, helped by both her father and mother. While still quite young she began to write, using material at second hand from the books she had read. She went about filling every available scrap of paper with verse, prose, plays, and romances.

At the age of nine Selma Lagerlöf spent the winter in Stockholm with an uncle whose housekeeper often took her to the theatre. On her return home she played theatre with her brothers and sisters. She said that from that time on she longed to write great plays instead of sitting in school and wasting her time on composition and mathematics. At this time she wrote a great deal of verse.

At the age of twenty-two she went to Stockholm again for a year's study in a girls' lyceum, and from there she entered the Royal Women's Superior Training College to prepare herself to teach. One day it suddenly dawned upon her that her own province of Vermland was rich in material for books so she determined to write a story about the local cavaliers.

When she had completed the course at the training school she went to teach in a grammar school for girls at Landskrona. She wrote sonnets and told her pupils endless folk tales after school hours. She then laid definite plans for her first novel, *Gösta Berling*. When she had finished the first five chapters she sent them to a magazine and was awarded a prize. Thus encouraged she finished the story and it was published in 1894. Following the publication of her second book *Invisible Links* in the same year, the royal family of Sweden extended her financial assistance so that she could give up teaching in 1895. She employed her freedom in taking several extended trips, one to the Orient and another to Italy. Both resulted in books. At the request of the Swedish school authorities for a school reader, she produced the two volumes of the *Adventures of Nils* in 1906 and 1907.

In 1907 Miss Lagerlöf was given an honorary doctor's degree by the University of Upsala. In 1909 she was awarded the Nobel prize in literature — the first woman to achieve that distinction.

Her summers she spends at Märbacka where she cultivates a hundred and forty acres of land and looks after her fifty-three tenants. In winter she goes to Falun.

Selma Lagerlöf is intensely racial and national in her literary reflections but in her sympathies and insight into the problems of life she is international. Love of home is one of the primal qualities of her personality and writing. She has kept her imagination young by her delight in hero tales and the national sagas.

She is greatly admired and loved in her own country because no other writer has so faithfully mirrored the Swedish soul. Her work is also popular in all the continental countries and in England. She has never been to America, but has many American friends. She had an uncle who lived in Seattle and on her dining room walls are found many landscapes of western America. Miss Lagerlöf, not very strong physically, is greatly impressed by the energy and vivacity of American women, many of whom she receives in her home in Märbacka.

She reads easily in six languages and is thoroughly familiar with the major interests of all countries.

In her work, Miss Lagerlöf is both a realist and an idealist. Her realism is not the morbid kind so common in much European fiction. Her outstanding characteristics are fully noted in the citation that accompanied the Nobel award: " Given because of the noble idealism, the wealth of fancy and the spiritual quality that characterize her works." These traits apply both to her long novels and to her short stories. It may be noted in addition that she always stresses the meaning of her stories. " The Silver Mine " printed here from the volume, *The Girl from the Marsh Croft,* is a typical Lagerlöf story.

# THE SILVER MINE *

KING GUSTAV the Third [1] was travelling through Dalecarlia. He was pressed for time, and all the way he wanted to drive like lightning. Although they drove with such speed that the horses were extended like stretched rubber bands and the coach cleared the turns on two wheels, the King poked his head out of the window and shouted to the postilion: " Why don't you go ahead? Do you think you are driving over eggs? "

Since they had to drive over poor country roads at such a mad pace, it would have been almost a miracle had the harness and wagon held together! And they didn't, either; for at the foot of a steep hill the pole broke — and there the King sat! The courtiers sprang from the coach and scolded the driver, but this did not lessen the damage done. There

* Translated from the Swedish by Velma Swanston Howard.

was no possibility of continuing the journey until the coach was mended.

When the courtiers looked round to try and find something with which the King could amuse himself while he waited, they noticed a church spire looming high above the trees in a grove a short distance ahead. They intimated to the King that he might step into one of the coaches in which the attendants were riding and drive up to the church. It was a Sunday, and the King might attend service to pass the time until the royal coach was ready.

The King accepted the proposal and drove toward the church. He had been travelling for hours through dark forest regions, but here it looked more cheerful, with fairly large meadows and villages, and with the Dal River gliding on, light and pretty, between thick rows of alder bushes.

But the King had ill-luck to this extent: the bellringer took up the recessional chant just as the King was stepping from the coach on the church knoll and the people were coming out from the service. But when they came walking past him, the King remained standing, with one foot in the wagon and the other on the foot-step. He did not move from the spot — only stared at them. They were the finest lot of folk he had ever seen. All the men were above the average height, with intelligent and earnest faces, and the women were dignified and stately, with an air of Sabbath peace about them.

The whole of the preceding day the King had talked only of the desolate tracts he was passing through, and had said to his courtiers again and again, " Now I am certainly driving through the very poorest part of my kingdom! " But now, when he saw the people, garbed in the picturesque dress of this section of the country, he forgot to think of their poverty; instead his heart warmed, and he remarked to himself: " The King of Sweden is not so badly off as his enemies think. So long as my subjects look like this, I shall probably be able to defend both my faith and my country."

He commanded the courtiers to make known to the people that the stranger who was standing amongst them was their King, and that they should gather around him, so he could talk to them.

And then the King made a speech to the people. He spoke

from the high steps outside the vestry, and the narrow step upon which he stood is there even today.

The King gave an account of the sad plight in which the kingdom was placed. He said that the Swedes were threatened with war, both by Russians and Danes. Under ordinary circumstances it wouldn't be such a serious matter, but now the army was filled with traitors, and he did not dare depend upon it. Therefore there was no other course for him to pursue than to go himself into the country settlements and ask his subjects if they would be loyal to their King and help him with men and money, so he could save the Fatherland.

The peasants stood quietly while the King was speaking, and when he had finished they gave no sign either of approval or disapproval.

The King himself thought that he had spoken very well. The tears had sprung to his eyes several times while he was speaking. But when the peasants stood there all the while, troubled and undecided, and could not make up their minds to answer him, the King frowned and looked displeased.

The peasants understood that it was becoming monotonous for the King to wait, and finally one of them stepped out from the crowd.

"Now, you must know, King Gustaf, that we were not expecting a royal visit in the parish today," said the peasant, "and therefore we are not prepared to answer you at once. I advise you to go into the vestry and speak with our pastor, while we discuss among ourselves this matter which you have laid before us."

The King apprehended that a more satisfactory response was not to be had immediately, so he felt that it would be best for him to follow the peasant's advice.

When he came into the vestry, he found no one there but a man who looked like a peasant. He was tall and rugged, with big hands, toughened by labor, and he wore neither cassock nor collar, but leather breeches and a long white homespun coat, like all the other men.

He arose and bowed to the King when the latter entered.

"I thought I should find the parson in here," said the King.

The man grew somewhat red in the face. He thought it annoying to mention the fact that he was the parson of this parish, when he saw that the King had mistaken him for a peasant. "Yes," said he, "the parson is usually on hand in here."

The King dropped into a large armchair which stood in the vestry at that time, and which stands there today, looking exactly like itself, with this difference: the congregation has had a gilded crown attached to the back of it.

"Have you a good parson in this parish?" asked the King, who wanted to appear interested in the welfare of the peasants.

When the King questioned him in this manner, the parson felt that he couldn't possibly tell who he was. "It's better to let him go on believing that I'm only a peasant," thought he, and replied that the parson was good enough. He preached a pure and clear gospel and tried to live as he taught.

The King thought that this was a good commendation, but he had a sharp ear and marked a certain doubt in the tone. "You sound as if you were not quite satisfied with the parson," said the King.

"He's a bit arbitrary," said the man, thinking that if the King should find out later who he was, he would not think that the parson had been standing here and blowing his own horn, therefore he wished to come out with a little fault-finding also. "There are some, no doubt, who say the parson wants to be the only one to counsel and rule in this parish," he continued.

"Then, at all events, he has led and managed in the best possible way," said the King. He didn't like it that the peasant had complained of one who was placed above him. "To me it appears as though good habits and old-time simplicity were the rule here."

"The people are good enough," said the curate, "but then they live in poverty and isolation. Human beings here would certainly be no better than others if this world's temptations came closer to them."

"But there's no fear of anything of the sort happening," said the King with a shrug.

He said nothing further, but began thrumming on the table with his fingers. He thought he had exchanged a sufficient number of gracious words with this peasant and wondered when the others would be ready with their answer.

"These peasants are not very eager to help their King," thought he. "If I only had my coach, I would drive away from them and their palaver!"

The pastor sat there troubled, debating with himself as to how he should decide an important matter which he must settle. He was beginning to feel happy because he had not told the King who he was. Now he felt that he could speak with him about matters which otherwise he could not have placed before him.

After a while the parson broke the silence and asked the King if it was an actual fact that enemies were upon them and that the kingdom was in danger.

The King thought this man ought to have sense enough not to trouble him further. He simply glared at him and said nothing.

"I ask because I was standing in here and could not hear very well," said the parson. "But if this is really the case, I want to say to you that the pastor of this congregation might perhaps be able to procure for the King as much money as he will need."

"I thought you said just now that every one here was poor," said the King, thinking that the man didn't know what he was talking about.

"Yes, that is true," replied the rector, "and the parson has no more than any of the others. But if the King would condescend to listen to me for a moment, I will explain how the pastor happens to have the power to help him."

"You may speak," said the King. "You seem to find it easier to get the words past your lips than your friends and neighbors out there, who never will be ready with what they have to tell me."

"It is not so easy to reply to the King! I'm afraid that, in the end, it will be the parson who must undertake this on behalf of the others."

The King crossed his legs, folded his arms, and let his head sink down on his breast. "You may begin now," he said in the tone of one already asleep.

"Once upon a time there were five men from this parish who were out on a moose hunt," began the clergyman. "One of them was the parson of whom we are speaking. Two of the others were soldiers, named Olaf and Eric Svärd; the fourth man was the innkeeper in this settlement, and the fifth was a peasant named Israel Per Persson."

"Don't go to the trouble of mentioning so many names," muttered the King, letting his head droop to one side.

"Those men were good hunters," continued the parson, "who usually had luck with them; but that day they had wandered long and far without getting anything. Finally they gave up the hunt altogether and sat down on the ground to talk. They said there was not a spot in the whole forest fit for cultivation; all of it was only mountain and swamp land. 'Our Lord has not done right by us in giving us such a poor land to live in,' said one. 'In other localities people can get riches for themselves in abundance, but here, with all our toil and drudgery, we can scarcely get our daily bread.'"

The pastor paused a moment, as if uncertain that the King heard him, but the latter moved his little finger to show that he was awake.

"Just as the hunters were discussing this matter, the parson saw something that glittered at the base of the mountain, where he had kicked away a moss-tuft. 'This is a queer mountain,' he thought, as he kicked off another moss-tuft. He picked up a shiver of stone that came with the moss and which shone exactly like the other. 'It can't be possible that this stuff is lead,' said he. Then the others sprang up and scraped away the turf with the butt end of their rifles. When they did this, they saw plainly that a broad vein of ore followed the mountain. 'What do you think this might be?' asked the parson. The men chipped off bits of stone and bit into them. 'It must be lead, or zinc at least,' said they. 'And the whole mountain is full of it,' added the innkeeper."

When the parson had got thus far in his narrative, the King's head was seen to straighten up a little and one eye opened. "Do you know if any of those persons knew anything about ore and minerals?" he asked.

"They did not," replied the parson.

Then the King's head sank and both eyes closed.

"The clergyman and his companions were very happy," continued the speaker, without letting himself be disturbed by the King's indifference; "they fancied that now they had found that which would give them and their descendants wealth. 'I'll never have to do any more work,' said one.

'Now I can afford to do nothing at all the whole week through, and on Sundays I shall drive to church in a golden chariot!'
They were otherwise sensible men, but the great find had gone to their heads and they talked like children. Still they had enough presence of mind to put back the moss-tufts and conceal the vein of ore. Then they carefully noted the place where it was, and went home. Before they parted company, they agreed that the parson should travel to Falun and ask the mining expert what kind of ore this was. He was to return as soon as possible, and until then they promised one another on oath not to reveal to a single soul where the ore was to be found."

The King's head was raised again a trifle, but he did not interrupt the speaker with a word. It appeared as though he was beginning to believe that the man actually had something of importance he wished to say to him, since he didn't allow himself to be disturbed by his indifference.

"Then the parson departed with a few samples of ore in his pocket. He was just as happy in the thought of becoming rich as the others were. He was thinking of rebuilding the parsonage, which at present was no better than a peasant's cottage, and then he would marry a dean's daughter whom he liked. He had thought that he might have to wait for her many years! He was poor and obscure and knew that it would be a long while before he should get any post that would enable him to marry.

"The parson drove over to Falun in two days, and there he had to wait another whole day because the mining expert was away. Finally, he ran across him and showed him the bits of ore. The mining expert took them in his hand. He looked at them first, then at the parson. The parson related how he had found them in a mountain at home in his parish, and wondered if it might not be lead.

"'No, it's not lead,' said the mining expert.

"'Perhaps it is zinc, then?' asked the parson.

"'Nor is it zinc,' said the mineralogist.

"The parson thought that all the hope within him sank. He had not been so depressed in many a long day.

"'Have you many stones like these in your parish?' asked the mineralogist.

"'We have a whole mountain full,' said the parson.

"Then the mineralogist came up closer, slapped the parson on the shoulder, and said, 'Let us see that you make such good use of this that it will prove a blessing both to yourselves and to the country, for this is silver.'

"'Indeed?' said the parson, feeling his way. 'So it is silver!'

"The mineralogist began telling him how he should go to work to get legal rights to the mine and gave him many valuable suggestions; but the parson stood there dazed and didn't listen to what he was saying. He was only thinking of how wonderful it was that at home in his poor parish stood a whole mountain of silver ore, waiting for him."

The King raised his head so suddenly that the parson stopped short in his narrative. "It turned out, of course, that when he got home and began working the mine, he saw that the mineralogist had only been stringing him," said the King.

"Oh, no, the mineralogist had not fooled him," said the parson.

"You may continue," said the King, as he settled himself more comfortably in the chair to listen.

"When the parson was at home again and was driving through the parish," continued the clergyman, "he thought that first of all he should inform his partners of the value of their find. And as he drove alongside the Innkeeper Sten Stensson's place, he intended to drive up to the house and tell him they had found silver. But when he stopped outside the gate, he noticed that a broad path of evergreen was strewn all the way up to the doorstep.

"'Who has died in this place?' asked the parson of a boy who stood leaning against the fence.

"'The innkeeper himself,' answered the boy. Then he let the clergyman know that the innkeeper had drunk himself full every day for a week. 'Oh, so much brandy, so much brandy has been drunk here!'

"'How can that be?' asked the parson. 'The innkeeper used never to drink himself full.'

"'Oh,' said the boy, 'he drank because he said he had found a mine. He was very rich. He should never have to do anything now but drink, he said. Last night he drove off, full as he was, and the wagon turned over and he was killed.'

"When the parson heard this, he drove homeward. He was distressed over what he had heard. He had come back so happy, rejoicing because he could tell the great good news.

"When the parson had driven a few paces, he saw Israel Per Persson walking along. He looked about as usual, and the parson thought it was well that fortune had not gone to his head too. Him he would cheer at once with the news that he was a rich man.

"'Good day!' said Per Persson. 'Do you come from Falun now?'

"'I do,' said the parson. 'And now I must tell you that it has turned out even better than we had imagined. The mineralogist said it was silver ore that we had found.'

"That instant Per Persson looked as though the ground under him had opened! 'What are you saying, what are you saying? Is it silver?'

"'Yes,' answered the parson. 'We'll all be rich men now, all of us, and can live like gentlemen.'

"'Oh, is it silver!' said Per Persson once again, looking more and more mournful.

"'Why, of course it is silver,' replied the parson. 'You mustn't think that I want to deceive you. You mustn't be afraid of being happy.'

"'Happy!' said Per Persson. 'Should I be happy? I believed it was only glitter that we had found, so I thought it would be better to take the certain for the uncertain: I have sold my share in the mine to Olaf Svärd for a hundred dollars.' He was desperate, and when the parson drove away from him, he stood on the highway and wept.

"When the clergyman got back to his home, he sent a servant to Olaf Svärd and his brother to tell them that it was silver they had found. He thought that he had had quite enough driving around and spreading the good news.

"But in the evening, when the parson sat alone, his joy asserted itself again. He went out in the darkness and stood on a hillock upon which he contemplated building the new parsonage. It should be imposing, of course, as fine as a bishop's palace. He stood out there long that night; nor did he content himself with rebuilding the parsonage! It occurred to him that, since there were such riches to be found in the parish, throngs of people would pour in and, finally, a whole city would be built around the mine. And then he would have to erect a new church in place of the old one. Towards this object a large portion of his wealth would probably go. And he was not content with this, either, but fancied that when his church was ready, the King and many bishops would come to the dedication. Then the King would be pleased with the church, but he would remark that there was no place where a king might put up, and then he would have to erect a castle in the new city."

Just then one of the King's courtiers opened the door of the vestry and announced that the big royal coach was mended.

At the first moment the King was ready to withdraw, but on second thought he changed his mind. " You may tell your story to the end," he said to the parson. " But you can hurry it a bit. We know all about how the man thought and dreamed. We want to know how he acted."

" But while the parson was still lost in his dreams," continued the clergyman, " word came to him that Israel Per Persson had made away with himself. He had not been able to bear the disappointment of having sold his share in the mine. He had thought, no doubt, that he could not endure to go about every day seeing another enjoying the wealth that might have been his."

The King straightened up a little. He kept both eyes open. " Upon my word," he said, " if I had been that parson, I should have had enough of the mine! "

" The King is a rich man," said the parson. " He has quite enough, at all events. It is not the same thing with a poor curate who possesses nothing. The unhappy wretch thought instead, when he saw that God's blessing was not with his enterprise: ' I will dream no more of bringing glory and profit to myself with these riches; but I can't let the silver lie buried in the earth! I must take it out, for the benefit of the poor and needy. I will work the mine, to put the whole parish on its feet.'

" So one day the parson went out to see Olaf Svärd, to ask him and his brother as to what should be done immediately with the silver mountain. When he came in the vicinity of the barracks, he met a cart surrounded by armed peasants, and in the cart sat a man with his hands tied behind him and a rope around his ankles.

"When the parson passed by, the cart stopped, and he had time to regard the prisoner, whose head was tied up so it wasn't easy to see who he was. But the parson thought he recognized Olaf Svärd. He heard the prisoner beg those who guarded him to let him speak a few words with the parson.

"The parson drew nearer, and the prisoner turned toward him. 'You will soon be the only one who knows where the silver mine is,' said Olaf.

"'What are you saying, Olaf?' asked the parson.

"'Well, you see, parson, since we have learned that it was a silver mine we had found, my brother and I could no longer be as good friends as before. We were continually quarrelling. Last night we got into a controversy over which one of us five it was who first discovered the mine. It ended in strife between us, and we came to blows. I have killed my brother and he has left me with a souvenir across the forehead [2] to remember him by. I must hang now, and then you will be the only one who knows anything about the mine; therefore I wish to ask something of you.'

"'Speak out!' said the parson. 'I'll do what I can for you.'

"'You know that I am leaving several little children behind me,' began the soldier, but the parson interrupted him.

"'As regards this, you can rest easy. That which comes to your share in the mine, they shall have, exactly as if you yourself were living.'

"'No,' said Olaf Svärd, 'it was another thing I wanted to ask you. Don't let them have any portion of that which comes from the mine!'

"The parson staggered back a step. He stood there dumb and could not answer.

"'If you do not promise me this, I cannot die in peace,' said the prisoner.

"'Yes,' said the parson slowly and painfully. 'I promise you what you ask of me.'

"Thereupon the murderer was taken away, and the parson stood on the highway thinking how he should keep the promise he had given him. On the way home he thought of the wealth which he had been so happy over. But if it really were true that the people in this community could not stand riches? — Already four were ruined, who hitherto had been dignified and excellent men. He seemed to see the whole community before him, and he pictured to himself how this silver mine would destroy one after another. Was it befitting that he, who had been appointed to watch over these poor human beings' souls, should let loose upon them that which would be their destruction?"

All of a sudden the King sat bolt upright in his chair. " I declare! " said he, " you'll make me understand that a parson in this isolated settlement must be every inch a man."

" Nor was it enough with what had already happened," continued the parson, " for as soon as the news about the mine spread among the parishioners, they stopped working and went about in idleness, waiting for the time when great riches should pour in on them. All the ne'er-do-wells there were in this section streamed in, and drunkenness and fighting were what the parson heard talked of continually. A lot of people did nothing but tramp round in the forest searching for the mine, and the parson marked that as soon as he left the house people followed him stealthily to find out if he wasn't going to the silver mountain and to steal the secret from him.

" When matters were come to this pass, the parson called the peasants together to vote. To start with, he reminded them of all the misfortunes which the discovery of the mountain had brought upon them, and he asked them if they were going to let themselves be ruined or if they would save themselves. Then he told them that they must not expect him, who was their spiritual adviser, to help on their destruction. Now he had decided not to reveal to any one where the silver mine was, and never would he himself take riches from it. And then he asked the peasants how they would have it henceforth. If they wished to continue their search for the mine and wait upon riches, then he would go so far away that not a hearsay of their misery could reach him; but if they would give up thinking about the silver mine and be as heretofore, he would remain with them. ' Whichever way you may choose,' said the parson, ' remember this, that from me no one shall ever know anything about the silver mountain! ' "

" Well," said the King, " how did they decide? "

" They did as their pastor wished," said the parson. " They understood that he meant well by them when he wanted to remain poor for their sakes. And they commissioned him to go to the forest and conceal the vein of ore with evergreen and stone, so that no one would be able to find it — neither they themselves nor their posterity."

" And ever since the parson has been living here just as poor as the rest? "

" Yes," answered the curate, " he has lived here just as poor as the rest."

" He has married, of course, and built himself a new parsonage? " said the King.

" No, he couldn't afford to marry, and he lives in the old cabin."

" It's a pretty story that you have told me," said the King. After a few seconds he resumed: " Was it of the silver mountain that you were thinking when you said that the parson here would be able to procure for me as much money as I need? "

" Yes," said the other.

" But I can't put the thumb-screws on him," said the King. " Or how would you that I should get such a man to show me the mountain — a man who has renounced his sweetheart and all the allurements of life? "

" Oh, that's a different matter," said the parson. " But if it's the Fatherland that is in need of the fortune, he will probably give in."

" Will you answer for that? " asked the King.

" Yes, that I will answer for," said the clergyman.

" Doesn't he care, then, what becomes of his parishioners? "

" That can rest in God's hand."

The King rose from the chair and walked over to the window. He stood for a moment and looked upon the group of people outside. The longer he looked, the clearer his large eyes shone, and his figure seemed to grow. " You may greet the pastor of this congregation, and say that for Sweden's King there is no sight more beautiful than to see a people such as this! "

Then the King turned from the window and looked at the clergyman. He began to smile. " Is it true that the pastor of this parish is so poor that he removes his black clothes as soon as the service is over and dresses himself like a peasant? " asked the King.

" Yes, so poor is he," said the curate, and a crimson flush leaped into his rough-hewn face.

The King went back to the window. One could see that he was in his best mood. All that was noble and great within him had been quickened into life. "You must let that mine lie in peace," said the King. "Inasmuch as you have labored and starved a lifetime to make this people such as you would have it, you may keep it as it is."

"But if the kingdom is in danger?" said the parson.

"The kingdom is better served with men than with money," remarked the King. When he had said this, he bade the clergyman farewell and went out from the vestry.

Without stood the group of people, as quiet and taciturn as they were when he went in. As the King came down the steps, a peasant stepped up to him.

"Have you had a talk with our pastor?" said the peasant.

"Yes," said the King. "I have talked with him."

"Then of course you have our answer?" said the peasant. "We asked you to go in and talk with our parson, that he might give you an answer from us."

"I have the answer," said the King.

### NOTES FOR *THE SILVER MINE*

1. Gustaf the Third, King of Sweden 1771–1792.
2. A reference to Cain's murder of his brother Abel, *Gen.* iv, 3–15.

### QUESTIONS

1. Why was the King pressed for time?
2. Why did the people not respond immediately to the King's speech?
3. Whom did the King find in the vestry?
4. Why did the parson not at once admit his identity?
5. What account did he give of the people? In the light of later developments in the story do you think his statement was justified? Give reasons.
6. How did the hunters discover the ore?
7. Why did they select the parson as the one to go to the city with the sample?
8. What evidence do you find that at last the king became interested in the story?
9. What were the first reactions of the parson when he thought that he might become wealthy?
10. What was the tragedy of the innkeeper?
11. What local custom is mentioned that told the parson what had happened?
12. What caused Per Persson to be so mournful?
13. How did the parson spend the evening at home?

14. What interrupted the parson's story? What was the King's first inclination? Why did he not yield to it?
15. Explain what had happened to Olaf Svärd. What did he want of the parson?
16. Did the parson have the right idea about the possible effects of the mine upon the community? Discuss the idea fully.
17. What made the King declare that the parson was every inch a man?
18. How had the parson persuaded his people to forget about the mine? Is there any indication that they later regretted their decision?
19. Does the King at last recognize the parson? Explain.
20. What answer did the King get from the people?
21. Do you think this was the right ending for the story? Tell why you believe as you do.

## SUBJECTS FOR COMPOSITION

1. Read Stevenson's *Treasure Island* and then write a comparison of these two stories.
2. Suppose that the King had taken the parson's offer and then write a sequel to this story.
3. Suppose that none of the finders of the mine had died but had lived to enjoy their wealth. Choose any one of the characters and tell what he did with his wealth.

## VOLUMES OF STORIES BY SELMA LAGERLÖF

*Invisible Links*
*From a Swedish Homestead*
*The Adventures of Nils*

*The Girl from the Marsh Croft*
*Men and Trolls*

# READING LISTS ACCORDING TO TYPES

NOTE. — The stories of a particular type printed in this volume come first in each list. Obviously many stories might be classed under more than one type, but in each case the story is listed under the type of predominant emphasis. For instance, "Zenobia's Infidelity" is an animal story, but the element of humor dominates, and it is so listed.

### ATMOSPHERE

*The Fall of the House of Usher*, Edgar Allan Poe
*They Grind Exceeding Small*, Ben Ames Williams
*Moonlight*, Guy de Maupassant
*The Young Man with the Cream Tarts*, Robert Louis Stevenson
*King Solomon of Kentucky*, James Lane Allen
*The Heart of Darkness*, Joseph Conrad
*April 25th as Usual*, Edna Ferber
*They*, Rudyard Kipling
*To Build a Fire*, Jack London
*A Man's a Fool*, Wilbur Daniel Steele

### LOVE

*The Token*, Joseph Hergesheimer
*Ice Water, Pl——!* Fannie Hurst
*Hunger*, Anzia Yezierska
*Happiness*, Guy de Maupassant
*Monsieur Beaucaire*, Booth Tarkington
*A Thread Without a Knot*, Dorothy Canfield
*The Wreck*, Guy de Maupassant
*The Gift of the Magi*, O. Henry
*The Best Seller*, O. Henry
*Madame Bo-Peep of the Ranches*, O. Henry
*The Sire de Malétroit's Door*, Robert Louis Stevenson
*The Love Letters of Smith*, H. C. Bunner
*The Snowstorm*, Alexander Pushkin
*L'Arrabiata*, Paul Heyse
*The Turquoise Cup*, Arthur Coslett Smith
*The Monk and the Dancer*, Arthur Coslett Smith

### LOCAL COLOR

*Turkey Red*, Frances Gilchrist Wood
*The Postmistress of Laurel Run*, Bret Harte

*That Brute Simmons,* Arthur Morrison
*The Stove,* Marjorie L. C. Pickthall
*The Luck of Roaring Camp,* Bret Harte
*Shoes,* Frances Gilchrist Wood
*On the Stairs,* Arthur Morrison
*Luck,* Marjorie L. C. Pickthall
*Namgay Doola,* Rudyard Kipling
*The Tomb of His Ancestors,* Rudyard Kipling
*A Day Off,* Alice Brown
*A New England Nun,* Mary E. Wilkins Freeman
*The Revolt of Mother,* Mary E. Wilkins Freeman
*Ghitza,* Konrad Bercovici
*The Conversion of Elviny,* Helen R. Martin

### WEIRD AND MYSTERY

*The Monkey's Paw,* W. W. Jacobs
*The Well,* W. W. Jacobs
*Wandering Willie's Tale,* Walter Scott
*The Return of Imray,* Rudyard Kipling
*The Diamond Lens,* Fitz-James O'Brien
*What Was It? A Mystery,* Fitz-James O'Brien
*The Bottle Imp,* Robert Louis Stevenson
*The Mummy's Foot,* Théophile Gautier
*White Horse Winter,* Wilbur Daniel Steele

### DETECTIVE

*The Speckled Band,* A. Conan Doyle
*The Red-Headed League,* A. Conan Doyle
*The Purloined Letter,* Edgar Allan Poe
*The Murders in the Rue Morgue,* Edgar Allan Poe
*A Retrieved Reformation,* O. Henry
*Gallegher,* Richard Harding Davis
*The Doomdorf Mystery,* Melville Davisson Post
*Five Thousand Dollars Reward,* Melville Davisson Post
*Room No. 3,* Anna Katharine Green
*The Silent Bullet,* Arthur B. Reeve

### HUMOR

*The Third Ingredient,* O. Henry
*Zenobia's Infidelity,* H. C. Bunner
*The Jumping Frog of Calaveras County,* Mark Twain
*The Stolen White Elephant,* Mark Twain

## Reading Lists According to Types 599

*The Tenor,* H. C. Bunner
*The Pope's Mule,* Alphonse Daudet
*The Courting of T'nowhead's Bell,* J. M. Barrie
*A Change of Treatment,* W. W. Jacobs
*A Black Affair,* W. W. Jacobs
*Goliath,* Thomas Bailey Aldrich

### Child

*Penrod's Busy Day,* Booth Tarkington
*An Overwhelming Saturday,* Booth Tarkington
*A Christmas Present for a Lady,* Myra Kelly
*The Crow Child,* Mary Mapes Dodge
*Sonny's Schoolin',* Ruth McEnery Stuart
*The King of Boyville,* William Allen White
*The Last Class,* Alphonse Daudet
*Valia,* Leonid Andreev
*The Right Promethean Fire,* George Madden Martin
*Not Wanted,* Jesse Lynch Williams

### Dramatic Incident

*The Ambitious Guest,* Nathaniel Hawthorne
*The Inn of the Two Witches,* Joseph Conrad
*In the Matter of a Private,* Rudyard Kipling
*Zodomirsky's Duel,* Alexandre Dumas
*The Gray Champion,* Nathaniel Hawthorne
*The Frill,* Pearl S. Buck
*The Man Who Would Be King,* Rudyard Kipling
*Mateo Falcone,* Prosper Mérimée
*The Cask of Amontillado,* Edgar Allan Poe
*The Red Mark,* John Russell
*The Price of the Head,* John Russell
*Ching, Ching, Chinaman,* Wilbur Daniel Steele
*The Gold Brick,* Brand Whitlock
*The Shot,* Alexander Pushkin
*The Sin of the Bishop of Modenstein,* Anthony Hope
*My Friend Julio,* Charles J. Finger
*Footfalls,* Wilbur Daniel Steele

### Sea

*Making Port,* Richard Matthews Hallet
*Typhoon,* Joseph Conrad
*Youth,* Joseph Conrad

*The Trawler*, James B. Connolly
*The Truth About the Oliver Cromwell*, James B. Connolly
*On the Fever Ship*, Richard Harding Davis
*The Town-Ho's Story*, Herman Melville
*Davy Jones's Gift*, John Masefield
*The Open Boat*, Stephen Crane

### ANIMAL

*The Elephant Remembers*, Edison Marshall
*The Heart of the Little Shikara*, Edison Marshall
*Moti Guj — Mutineer*, Rudyard Kipling
*Rikki-Tikki-Tavi*, Rudyard Kipling
*Bimi*, Rudyard Kipling
*In the Rukh*, Rudyard Kipling
*The Call of the Wild*, Jack London
*A Passion in the Desert*, Honoré de Balzac
*A Dog of Flanders*, Ouida

### PSYCHOLOGICAL

*The Bet*, Anton P. Chekhov
*Markheim*, Robert Louis Stevenson
*A Cup of Tea*, Katherine Mansfield
*In Exile*, Anton P. Chekhov
*A Coward*, Guy de Maupassant
*The Liar*, Henry James
*The White Cowl*, James Lane Allen
*Cain*, Alexander Kuprin
*The Taipan*, W. Somerset Maugham

### CHARACTER

*Will o' the Mill*, Robert Louis Stevenson
*The Heyday of the Blood*, Dorothy Canfield
*Young Man Axelbrod*, Sinclair Lewis
*The Inconsiderate Waiter*, J. M. Barrie
*A Letter Home*, Arnold Bennett
*Meadow Lark*, Edna Ferber
*The Sampler*, Ira V. Morris
*The Captain's Vices*, François Coppée
*The Captive*, Rudyard Kipling
*Humoresque*, Fannie Hurst
*The Game of Life and Death*, Lincoln Colcord
*Boys Will Be Boys*, Irvin Cobb

*The Gay Old Dog*, Edna Ferber
*The Two Friends*, Guy de Maupassant
*A Lodging for the Night*, Robert Louis Stevenson
*The Derelict*, Richard Harding Davis
*The Cloak*, Nicolai Gogol
*The Buckpasser*, Hugh McNair Kahler

### Fantastic

*The Wreck of the Thomas Hyke*, Frank R. Stockton
*A Tale of Negative Gravity*, Frank R. Stockton
*The Strange Ride of Morrowbie Jukes*, Rudyard Kipling
*The Mark of the Beast*, Rudyard Kipling
*Kerfol*, Edith Wharton
*Witch Mary*, Genevieve Larssen
*The Devil's Cross*, Gustavo Becquer

### Theme

*The Father*, Björnstjerne Björnson
*Quality*, John Galsworthy
*The Silver Mine*, Selma Lagerlöf
*Roads of Destiny*, O. Henry
*Bitter-Sweet*, Fannie Hurst
*Love of Life*, Jack London
*The Story of the Other Wise Man*, Henry van Dyke
*The Master of the Inn*, Robert Herrick

### The Tale

*The Legend of Sleepy Hollow*, Washington Irving
*The Three Strangers*, Thomas Hardy
*Rip Van Winkle*, Washington Irving
*Mr. Higginbotham's Catastrophe*, Nathaniel Hawthorne
*The Treasure of Franchard*, Robert Louis Stevenson
*Providence and the Guitar*, Robert Louis Stevenson
*The House of Cobwebs*, George Gissing
*Where Was Wyche Street?* Stacy Aumonier
*A Lear of the Steppes*, Ivan Turgenev
*The Prisoner of the Caucasus*, Leo Tolstoi

# A LIST OF SHORT STORIES

NOTE. — Stories printed in this volume are not listed. Whenever possible, anthologies are preferred in citing volumes. Where library facilities are ample, an author's volumes of stories may readily be found, but school libraries should include some of the more comprehensive anthologies of short stories. Titles of volumes in this list are abbreviated when possible. (Title Story) means that the volume bears the name of the story.

### AMERICAN SHORT STORIES

1. ABDULLAH, ACHMED, A Simple Act of Piety, *The Honorable Gentleman*
2. ALDRICH, THOMAS B., Marjorie Daw, (Title Story)
3. ALLEN, JAMES LANE, The White Cowl, *The Flute and Violin*
4. ANDERSON, SHERWOOD, I'm a Fool, *O'Brien, 1922*
5. BERCOVICI, KONRAD, Ghitza, *O'Brien, 1920*
6. BIERCE, AMBROSE, An Occurrence at Owl Creek Bridge, Jessup's *American Short Stories*
   —— A Horseman in the Sky, Oxford *Selected Short Stories*
7. BROWN, ALICE, A Day Off, *A Country Road*
8. BUNNER, H. C., The Love Letters of Smith, *Short Sixes*
   —— Nice People, *Short Sixes*
   —— The Tenor, *Short Sixes*
9. BURT, STRUTHERS, The Water-Hole, *John O'May*
10. CABLE, GEORGE W., Posson Jone, *Old Creole Days*
11. CANFIELD, DOROTHY, A Thread Without a Knot, *The Real Motive*
12. COBB, IRVIN, The Belled Buzzard, Jessup's *American Short Stories*
    —— Boys Will Be Boys, *O. Henry Mem., 1920*
13. CONNOLLY, J. B., The Truth of the Oliver Cromwell, *The Deep Sea's Toll*
14. CRANE, STEPHEN, The Open Boat, *Men, Women, and Boats*
15. CRAWFORD, F. MARION, The Upper Berth, *Wandering Ghosts*
16. DAVIS, RICHARD HARDING, My Disreputable Friend, Mr. Raegen, *Gallegher and Other Stories*
    —— Gallegher, (Title Story)
    —— The Derelict, *Ranson's Folly*
17. DELAND, MARGARET, Good for the Soul, *Old Chester Tales*
18. DWIGHT, H. G., The Pasha's Garden, *Stamboul Nights*
19. FERBER, EDNA, The Gay Old Dog, *O'Brien, 1917*
    —— Shore Leave, *Cheerful — by Request*
20. FINGER, CHARLES J., My Friend Julio, *In Lawless Lands*
21. FOX, JOHN JR., Christmas Eve on Lonesome, (Title Story)

# A List of Short Stories

22. FREEMAN, MARY E. W., A New England Nun, (Title Story)
    — The Copy Cat, (Title Story)
23. GARLAND, HAMLIN, The Return of a Private, *Main Travelled Roads*
    — Up the Cooly, *Main Travelled Roads*
24. GREENE, FREDERICK S., The Bunker Mouse, *O'Brien, 1917*
    — A Cat of the Cane-Brake, *Thrice Told Tales*
25. HALE, EDWARD EVERETT, The Man Without a Country, *Jessup's American Short Stories*
26. HALLETT, RICHARD M., Making Port, *O'Brien, 1917*
27. HARRIS, JOEL CHANDLER, The Tar Baby, *Uncle Remus*
28. HARTE, BRET, The Luck of Roaring Camp, (Title Story)
    — The Outcasts of Poker Flat, *The Luck of Roaring Camp*
    — Tennessee's Partner, *The Luck of Roaring Camp*
29. HAWTHORNE, NATHANIEL, Dr. Heidegger's Experiment, *Twice Told Tales*
    — The Minister's Black Veil, *Twice Told Tales*
    — Mr. Higginbotham's Catastrophe, *Twice Told Tales*
    — Peter Goldthwaite's Treasure, *Twice Told Tales*
    — David Swan, *Twice Told Tales*
    — The White Old Maid, *Twice Told Tales*
30. HENRY, O., The Gift of the Magi, *The Four Million*
    — The Furnished Room, *The Four Million*
    — An Unfinished Story, *The Four Million*
    — The Best Seller, *Options*
    — The Hiding of Black Bill, *Options*
    — No Story, *Options*
    — A Retrieved Reformation, *Roads of Destiny*
    — Roads of Destiny, (Title Story)
    — The Ransom of Red Chief, *Whirligigs*
    — A Municipal Report, *Strictly Business*
31. HERGESHEIMER, J., Tol'able David, *The Happy End*
    — The Thrush in the Hedge, *The Happy End*
    — Lonely Valleys, *The Happy End*
32. HERRICK, ROBERT, The Master of the Inn, (Title Story)
33. HURST, FANNIE, Humoresque, (Title Story)
    — T—B, *Every Soul Hath Its Song*
    — The Sob Sister, *Every Soul Hath Its Song*
34. IRVING, WASHINGTON, Rip Van Winkle, *The Sketch Book*
    — The Spectre Bridegroom, *The Sketch Book*
    — The Three Beautiful Princesses, *The Alhambra*
35. JAMES, HENRY, The Liar, *The Aspern Papers*
    — The Real Thing, (Title Story)
36. KAHLER, HUGH McN., The Buckpasser, *Babel*
37. KELLY, MYRA, A Christmas Present for a Lady, *Little Citizens*
    — Love Among the Blackboards, *Little Citizens*
38. LARSSEN, GENEVIEVE, Witch Mary, *Thrice Told Tales*

39. LEFEVRE, EDWIN, Woman and Her Bonds, *Wall Street Stories*
40. LEWIS, SINCLAIR, Willow Walk, *O'Brien, 1918*
41. LONDON, JACK, The Call of the Wild, (Title Story)
   —— Love of Life, (Title Story)
   —— Seed of McCoy, Jessup's *American Short Stories*
42. NORRIS, FRANK, A Deal in Wheat, (Title Story)
43. O'BRIEN, FITZ-JAMES, The Diamond Lens, (Title Story)
   —— What Was It? A Mystery, *The Diamond Lens*
44. PAGE, THOMAS NELSON, Marse Chan, *In Ole Virginia*
   —— Meh Lady, *In Ole Virginia*
45. POE, EDGAR ALLAN, The Gold Bug, *Poe's Complete Works*
   —— The Cask of Amontillado, *Poe's Complete Works*
   —— The Purloined Letter, *Poe's Complete Works*
   —— The Pit and the Pendulum, *Poe's Complete Works*
46. POST, MELVILLE DAVISSON, The Doomdorf Mystery, *Uncle Abner*
   —— Five Thousand Dollars Reward, *O. Henry Mem., 1919*
47. REEVE, ARTHUR B., The Silent Bullet, (Title Story)
48. RUSSELL, JOHN, The Price of the Head, *Where the Pavement Ends*
49. SMITH, ARTHUR COSLETT, The Monk and the Dancer, (Title Story)
   —— The Turquoise Cup, (Title Story)
50. SMITH, F. HOPKINSON, The Girl in the Steamer Chair, *The Wood-Fire in No. 3*
   —— A Night Out, *The Other Fellow*
51. STEELE, WILBUR DANIEL, Ching, Ching, Chinaman, *O'Brien, 1917*
   —— The Woman at Seven Brothers, *Land's End*
   —— Footfalls, *O. Henry Mem., 1920*
52. STOCKTON, FRANK R., The Lady or the Tiger? (Title Story)
   —— The Transferred Ghost, Jessup's *American Short Stories*
   —— A Tale of Negative Gravity, *The Christmas Wreck*
   —— The Christmas Wreck, (Title Story)
53. TARKINGTON, BOOTH, *Monsieur Beaucaire*, (Title Story)
   —— Bing, *Penrod*
   —— An Overwhelming Saturday, *Penrod*
54. TAYLOR, BAYARD, Who Was She? *Stories by American Authors*
55. TWAIN, MARK, The Jumping Frog, *Sketches New and Old*
   —— The Man That Corrupted Hadleyburg, (Title Story)
   —— The Stolen White Elephant, *Tom Sawyer Abroad*
56. VAN DYKE, HENRY, The Story of the Other Wise Man, *The Blue Flower*
   —— Spy Rock, *The Ruling Passion*
   —— The Keeper of the Light, *The Ruling Passion*
57. WHARTON, EDITH, The Pelican, *The Greater Inclination*
   —— Xingu, (Title Story)
58. WHITE, WILLIAM ALLEN, The King of Boyville, *The Court of Boyville*
59. WHITLOCK, BRAND, The Gold Brick, (Title Story)

60. WILLIAMS, BEN AMES, Sheener, *O'Brien, 1920*
61. WILLIAMS, JESSE LYNCH, Not Wanted, *O. Henry Mem., 1923*
   —— The Stolen Story, (Title Story)
62. WISTER, OWEN, Philosophy 4, (Title Story)
63. WOOD, FRANCES GILCHRIST, Shoes, *O'Brien, 1924*
64. YEZIERSKA, ANZIA, Wings, *Hungry Hearts*
   —— The Fat of the Land, *Hungry Hearts*

ENGLISH SHORT STORIES

1. ANSTEY, F., The Black Poodle, *Stories by English Authors*
2. AUMONIER, STACY, Where Was Wyche Street? *O'Brien — British, 1923*
3. BARRIE, J. M., Two of Them, (Title Story)
   —— How Gavin Birse Put It to Mag Lownie, *A Window in Thrums*
   —— The Courting of T'nowhead's Bell, *Auld Licht Idylls*
4. BENNETT, ARNOLD, The Idiot, *Tales of the Five Towns*
   —— Mary with the High Hand, *Tales of the Five Towns*
5. BURKE, THOMAS, The Chink and the Child, *Limehouse Nights*
6. CONRAD, JOSEPH, Youth, (Title Story)
   —— The Heart of Darkness, *Youth*
   —— The Lagoon, *Tales of Unrest*
7. COPPARD, A. E., The Black Dog, (Title Story)
   —— The Higgler, *O'Brien — British, 1924*
8. DICKENS, CHARLES, The Boots of the Holly Tree Inn, *Dickens' Complete Works*
   —— The Signal Man, *Dickens' Complete Works*
9. DOYLE, A. CONAN, The Red-Headed League, *The Adventures of Sherlock Holmes*
   —— The Capture of Saragossa, *The Brigadier Gerard*
10. GALSWORTHY, JOHN, Quality, *The Inn of Tranquillity*
11. GISSING, GEORGE, The House of Cobwebs, (Title Story)
    —— Christopherson, *The House of Cobwebs*
12. GRAHAM, KENNETH, The Roman Road, *The Golden Age*
13. GRANT, ROBERT, The Bachelor's Christmas, (Title Story)
14. HARDY, THOMAS, The Withered Arm, *Wessex Tales*
15. HOPE, ANTHONY, The Philosopher in the Apple Orchard, *Comedies of Courtship*
    —— The House Opposite, *The Dolly Dialogues*
    —— The Sin of the Bishop of Modenstein, *The Heart of the Princess Osra*
16. JACOBS, W. W., The Lady of the Barge, (Title Story)
    —— A Black Affair, *Many Cargoes*
    —— A Change of Treatment, *Many Cargoes*
    —— The Toll House, *Sailors' Knots*

17. KIPLING, RUDYARD, Without Benefit of Clergy, *Life's Handicap*
    —— Namgay Doola, *Life's Handicap*
    —— Moti Guj — Mutineer, *Life's Handicap*
    —— The Man Who Was, *Life's Handicap*
    —— The Return of Imray, *Life's Handicap*
    —— The Man Who Would Be King, *Under the Deodars*
    —— The Brushwood Boy, *The Day's Work*
    —— In the Rukh, *Many Inventions*
18. LEACOCK, STEPHEN, A Hero in Homespun, *Nonsense Novels*
19. LEWIS, ANGELO, The Wrong Black Bag, *Stories by English Authors*
20. MAUGHAM, W. SOMERSET, The Taipan, *23 Stories*
21. MERRICK, LEONARD, The Tale That Wouldn't Do, *Whispers About Women*
    —— The Man Who Understood Women, (Title Story)
22. MORRISON, ARTHUR, On the Stairs, *Tales of Mean Streets*
    —— Lizerunt, *Tales of Mean Streets*
23. OUIDA, A Dog of Flanders, *Stories by English Authors*
    —— A Leaf in the Storm, *Stories by English Authors*
24. PARKER, GILBERT, A Prairie Vagabond, *Pierre and His People*
25. PICKTHALL, MARJORIE L. C., Luck, *Angels' Shoes*
26. SCOTT, WALTER, Wandering Willie's Tale, *Redgauntlet*
27. STEVENSON, ROBERT LOUIS, A Lodging for the Night, *Stevenson's Short Stories*
    —— Markheim, *Stevenson's Short Stories*
    —— Sire de Maletroit's Door, *Stevenson's Short Stories*
    —— The Bottle Imp, *Stevenson's Short Stories*
    —— The Young Man with the Cream Tarts, *New Arabian Nights*
28. WELLS, H. G., The Stolen Bacillus, *Thirty Strange Stories*
    —— The Story of the Late Mr. Elvesham, *Thirty Strange Stories*
29. ZANGWILL, ISRAEL, A Rose of the Ghetto, *Ghetto Comedies*
    —— They That Walk in Darkness, *Ghetto Tragedies*

### FRENCH SHORT STORIES

1. BALZAC, HONORÉ DE, La Grande Breteche, *Little French Masterpieces*
   —— A Passion in the Desert, *Little French Masterpieces*
   —— An Episode of the Terror, *French Short Stories*
2. COPPÉE, FRANÇOIS, The Substitute, *Ten Tales from Coppée*
   —— The Captain's Vices, *Ten Tales from Coppée*
   —— The Piece of Bread, *French Short Stories*
3. DAUDET, ALPHONSE, The Last Class, *French Short Stories*
   —— The Pope's Mule, *French Short Stories*
   —— The Death of the Dauphin, *Letters from My Mill*
   —— The Siege of Berlin, *Monday Tales*
4. FRANCE, ANATOLE, The Juggler of Notre Dame, *French Short Stories*

5. MAUPASSANT, GUY DE, The Necklace, *French Short Stories*
    —— The Wreck, *French Short Stories*
    —— Fright, *French Short Stories*
    —— The Hand, *French Short Stories*
    —— The Two Friends, *French Short Stories*
    —— The Piece of String, *The Odd Number*
    —— A Coward, *The Odd Number*
    —— A Ghost, *The Odd Number*
    —— The Journey, *The Odd Number*
    —— The Horla, *Modern Ghosts*
6. MÉRIMÉE, PROSPER, Mateo Falcone, *French Short Stories*
7. SARDOU, VICTORIEN, The Black Pearl, Patten's *Foreign Short Stories*
    —*French*
8. ZOLA, EMILE, The Attack on the Mill, Patten's *Foreign Short Stories*
    —*French*

### RUSSIAN SHORT STORIES

1. ANDREEV, LEONID, Valia, *Russian Short Stories*
    —— The Red Laugh, (Title Story)
    —— Silence, *The Little Angel*
    —— A Grand Slam, *Short Stories from Russian Authors* (Ev. Lib.)
2. CHEKHOV, ANTON P., In Exile, *Russian Short Stories*
    —— The Black Monk, (Title Story)
    —— A Work of Art, *Nine Humorous Tales*
    —— The Kiss, *Short Stories from Russian Authors* (Ev. Lib.)
3. CHIRIKOV, E., Faust, *Short Stories from Russian Authors* (Ev. Lib.)
4. DOSTOEVSKI, FEDOR, The Thief, *Russian Short Stories*
5. GARSHIN, W. M., The Signal, *Russian Short Stories*
    —— Four Days, *The Signal*
6. GOGOL, NICOLAI, The Cloak, *Russian Short Stories*
7. GORKI, MAXIM, Chelkash, *Russian Short Stories*
    —— Comrades, *Russian Short Stories*
    —— One Autumn Night, *Best Russian Short Stories*
8. KOROLENKO, VLADIMIR, The Old Bell-Ringer, *Russian Short Stories*
9. KUPRIN, ALEXANDER, Cain, *Russian Short Stories*
    —— The Idiot, *A Slav Soul*
    —— The Outrage, *Best Russian Short Stories*
    —— Captain Rybnikoff, *Best Continental Short Stories of 1923–24*
10. PUSHKIN, ALEXANDER, The Shot, *Russian Short Stories*
    —— The Snowstorm, *Pushkin's Tales*
    —— The Queen of Spades, *Short Stories from Russian Authors* (Ev. Lib.)
11. SEMYONOV, S. T., The Servant, *Best Russian Short Stories*
12. SOLOGUB, THEODOR, The White Mother, *Short Stories from Russian Authors* (Ev. Lib.)

13. TOLSTOI, LEO, Master and Man, *Russian Short Stories*
    —— God Sees the Truth but Waits, *Russian Short Stories*
    —— Three Arshins of Land, *Russian Short Stories*
    —— The Prisoner of the Caucasus, *Twenty-three Tales*
14. TURGENEV, IVAN, A Lear of the Steppes, *Russian Short Stories*
    —— Biryuk, *Russian Short Stories*
    —— Mumu, Patten's *Stories by Foreign Authors — Russian*
    —— The District Doctor, *Best Russian Short Stories*

### MISCELLANEOUS SHORT STORIES

1. ALARCÓN, PEDRO (Span.), The Tall Woman, *Stories by Foreign Authors*
2. ANONYMOUS (Arabic), Ali Baba, *Arabian Nights*
   —— Aladdin and His Wonderful Lamp, *Arabian Nights*
   —— Sinbad the Sailor, *Arabian Nights*
3. BECQUER, GUSTAVO (Span.), The Organist, *Becquer's Tales*
   —— The Devil's Cross, *Becquer's Tales*
4. BJÖRNSON, BJÖRNSTJERNE (Norwegian), The Fisher Maiden, (Title Story)
5. CAPEK, KAREL (Czecho-Slovakian), The Imprint, *Best Continental Short Stories of 1923–24*
6. DELEDDA, GRAZIA (Ital.), Two Men and a Woman, Patten's *Stories by Foreign Authors*
7. HEYSE, PAUL (Ger.), L'Arrabiata, Patten's *Stories by Foreign Authors*
8. HOFFMANN, E. T. W. (Ger.), A Cremona Violin, *Stories by Foreign Authors*
9. LAGERLÖF, SELMA (Swedish), *The Girl from the Marsh Croft*, (Title Story)
   —— The Silver Mine, *The Girl from the Marsh Croft*
   —— A Christmas Guest, *Invisible Links*
10. SCHNITZLER, ARTHUR (Austrian), The Fate of Baron von Leisenbohg, *The Best Continental Short Stories of 1923–24*

# BIBLIOGRAPHY

NOTE. — This bibliography is comprehensive but not complete. It lists only such works as are readily obtainable in libraries. Where adequate public library facilities are lacking, schools will find it advisable to secure for their libraries some of the more general works listed below. It should not be forgotten that cyclopedias can be profitably used in short story work, especially in connection with the older writers. The order followed below is that of latest publication.

### HISTORICAL AND CRITICAL

*The Philosophy of the Short-Story,* Brander Matthews, Longmans, Green & Co., 1901.
*The Short Story in English,* Henry Seidel Canby, Henry Holt & Co., 1909.
*Leading American Novelists,* John Erskine, Henry Holt & Co., 1910.
*Some American Story-Tellers,* Frederic T. Cooper, Dodd, Mead & Co., 1911.
*The American Short Story,* Elias Lieberman, James Knapp Reeve, 1912.
*A Study of the Short Story,* Henry Seidel Canby, Henry Holt & Co., 1913.
*American Literature,* Roy Bennett Pace, Allyn & Bacon, 1915.
*The Contemporary Short Story,* Harry T. Baker, D. C. Heath & Co., 1916.
*The Women Who Make Our Novels,* Grant Overton, Moffat, Yard & Co., 1918.
*The Men Who Make Our Novels,* George Gordon, Moffat, Yard & Co., 1919.
*Our Short Story Writers,* Blanche Colton Williams, Moffat, Yard & Co., 1920.
*Contemporary English Literature,* Manly & Rickert, Harcourt, Brace & Co., 1921.
*The American Novel,* Carl Van Doren, The Macmillan Co., 1921.
*Contemporary American Novelists,* Carl Van Doren, The Macmillan Co., 1922.
*Contemporary American Literature,* Manly & Rickert, Harcourt, Brace & Co., 1922.
*Cambridge History of English Literature,* 4 vols., G. P. Putnam's Sons, 1922. (Also a one-volume abridgment.)

*The Development of the American Short Story*, Fred Lewis Pattee, Harper & Brothers, 1923.
*The Advance of the American Short Story*, Edward J. O'Brien, Dodd, Mead & Co., 1923.
*Index to Short Stories*, Ida Ten Eyck Firkins, The H. W. Wilson Co., 1924.
*Authors of Today*, Grant Overton, George H. Doran Co., 1924.
*Cargoes for Crusoes*, Grant Overton, George H. Doran Co., 1924.
*The Short Story's Mutations*, Frances Newman, B. W. Huebsch, 1924.
*The American Short Story*, Alexander Jessup, Allyn & Bacon (in prep.).

## COLLECTIONS OF SHORT STORIES

NOTE. — This list does not include textbooks.
*Stories by American Authors*, 10 vols., Charles Scribner's Sons, 1885.
*Stories by English Authors*, 10 vols., Charles Scribner's Sons, 1896.
*Stories by Foreign Authors*, 10 vols., Charles Scribner's Sons, 1898.
*The World's Greatest Short Stories*, Sherwin Cody, ed., McClurg, 1902.
*The Book of the Short Story*, Jessup & Canby, eds., D. Appleton & Co., 1903.
*Little French Masterpieces*, Alexander Jessup, ed., G. P. Putnam's Sons, 1903.
*Short Story Classics — American*, 5 vols., William Patten, ed., Collier, 1905.
*Short Story Classics — Foreign*, 5 vols., William Patten, ed., P. F. Collier & Son, 1907.
*The Great English Short-Story Writers*, 2 vols., W. J. & C. W. Dawson, eds., Harper & Brothers, 1910.
*International Short Stories*, F. J. Reynolds, ed., P. F. Collier & Son, 1910.
*Short-Story Masterpieces* (Russian and French), J. Berg Esenwein, ed., 4 vols., Home Correspondence School, 1912.
*Selected English Short Stories* (includes American), Oxford University Press, 2 vols., 1914, 1921.
*The Best Short Stories of 1915, 1916*, etc., (an annual selection from American magazines), Edward J. O'Brien, ed., Small, Maynard & Co.
*The Great Modern French Stories*, W. H. Wright, ed., Boni & Liveright, 1917.
*The Best Russian Short Stories*, Thomas Seltzer, ed., Boni & Liveright, 1917.
*French Short Stories*, H. C. Schweikert, ed., Scott, Foresman & Co., 1918.
*Russian Short Stories*, H. C. Schweikert, ed., Scott, Foresman & Co., 1919.
*O. Henry Memorial Award Prize Stories for 1919, 1920*, etc. (an

annual selection from American magazines), Blanche Colton Williams, ed., Doubleday, Page & Co.
*The Best American Humorous Short Stories,* Alexander Jessup, ed., Boni & Liveright, 1920.
*The Great American Short Stories,* William Dean Howells, ed., Boni & Liveright, 1920.
*The Great Modern English Stories,* Edward J. O'Brien, ed., Boni & Liveright, 1920.
*The Best British Stories of 1921, 1922,* etc. (an annual selection from English magazines), Edward J. O'Brien and John Cournos, eds., Small, Maynard & Co.
*Tales from the French,* tr. by Alys Eyre Macklin, Harcourt, Brace & Co., 1922.
*Georgian Stories,* 2 vols., G. P. Putnam's Sons, 1923, 1924.
*Thirty-one Stories by Thirty and One Authors,* D. Appleton & Co., 1923.
*American Short Stories* (74 stories), Alexander Jessup, ed., Allyn & Bacon, 1923.
*Twenty-three Stories,* D. Appleton & Co., 1924.
*Aces* (modern American stories), G. P. Putnam's Sons, 1924.
*Thrice Told Tales,* Blanche Colton Williams, ed., Dodd, Mead & Co., 1924.
*Best Continental Short Stories of 1923–24,* Richard Eaton, ed., Small, Maynard & Co., 1924.
*The Best French Short Stories of 1923–24,* Richard Eaton, ed., Small, Maynard & Co., 1924.
*Short Stories from Russian Authors,* Everyman's Library, E. P. Dutton & Co., 1924.

BOOKS ON SHORT STORY WRITING

*Short-Story Writing,* Charles Raymond Barrett, Doubleday, Page & Co., 1898.
*The Short Story — Its Principles and Structure,* Evelyn May Albright, The Macmillan Co., 1907.
*Writing the Short-Story,* J. Berg Esenwein, Hinds, Hayden & Eldredge, 1909.
*The Art of the Short-Story,* J. Berg Esenwein, Home Correspondence School, 1913.
*The Art of Story-Writing,* Nathaniel C. Fowler, George Sully & Co., 1913.
*The Art of the Short Story,* Carl H. Grabo, Charles Scribner's Sons, 1914.
*The Short Story — A Technical and Critical Study,* Ethan Allen Cross, A. C. McClurg & Co., 1914.

*A Handbook on Story Writing,* Blanche Colton Williams, Dodd, Mead & Co., 1917.
*The Craft of Fiction,* Percy Lubbock, Charles Scribner's Sons, 1921.
*Short Stories in the Making,* Robert W. Neal, Oxford University Press, 1914.
*Materials and Methods of Fiction,* Clayton Hamilton, Doubleday, Page & Co., 1918.
*Plots and Personalities,* Edwin E. Slosson, The Century Co., 1922.
*Today's Short Stories Analyzed,* Robert W. Neal, Oxford University Press, 1918.
*Fundamentals of Fiction Writing,* Arthur Sullivant Hoffman, The Bobbs-Merrill Co., 1922.
*Short Story Writing,* N. Bryllion Fagin, Thomas Seltzer, 1923.
*Fiction Writers on Fiction Writing,* Arthur Sullivant Hoffman, The Bobbs-Merrill Co., 1923.
*How to Write Stories,* Walter B. Pitkin, Harcourt, Brace & Co., 1923.
*Narrative Technique,* Thomas H. Uzzell, Harcourt, Brace & Co., 1923.
*How to Write Short Stories — with Samples,* Ring W. Lardner, Charles Scribner's Sons, 1924.
*A Handbook of Short Story Writing,* John T. Frederick, Alfred A. Knopf, 1924.